WILLIAM S. BECK

MODERN S

NATUR

PELICAN

A 473

# MODERN SCIENCE AND THE NATURE OF LIFE

WILLIAM S. BECK

PENGUIN BOOKS

Penguin Books Ltd, Harmondsworth, Middlesex
AUSTRALIA: Penguin Books Pty Ltd, 762 Whitehorse Road,
Mitcham, Victoria

First published in the U.S.A. by Harcourt, Brace, 1957
First published in Great Britain by Macmillan 1958
Published in Pelican Books 1961

Made and printed in Great Britain
by Cox & Wyman Ltd
London, Reading, and Fakenham

*for*
**TOMMY**
*and*
**PETER**
*and*
**HELENE**

# CONTENTS

7

# Contents

I do not know what I may appear to the world; but to myself I seem to have been only like a boy playing on the seashore, and diverting myself in now and then finding a smoother pebble or a prettier shell than ordinary, whilst the great ocean of truth lay all undiscovered before me.

— ISAAC NEWTON

# FOREWORD

*by Homer W. Smith*

DR BECK mentions me in his manuscript as one of several persons to whose writing he feels some indebtedness. As a matter of fact it is I who am indebted to him.

Recent years have seen the revival of some amazing supernaturalism, not all of it confined to the fundamentalist and revivalist congregations. Many speeches, essays, and books by scientists reveal lack of critical acuity and deficiency in historic and philosophic perspective as the authors seek to escape the impersonality of nature by some speculation which enables them, and encourages others, to extrapolate from the phenomena of human personality to matters transcending the known, and perhaps knowable, cosmos. It is proving harder to stir man's ego out of its rut than it was to get the earth to move.

Such writers, I believe, represent a small minority of our scientific population, but for some reason they are the most vocal and make the best public speakers, essayists, and sometimes even the best university presidents, possibly because it is easier, and more profitable, to sell the public gold bricks than plain bricks, and there is and can be no law against this deception at the level of philosophy. Astronomy, anthropology, and physics have perhaps had the best representation, in both the literary and philosophic sense, before the general public, while biology seems to have had the worst. Astronomy has universal appeal and, despite the transmutation of elements in the sun and stars and some confusing details with respect to 'ultimate particles', it has been ably explained by many writers. Anthropology offers vicarious adventure away from home and *mores* and is readily interpreted at the simply human level. Physics, in consequence of the advent of atomic transformation and the enormous energy content of the nucleus, has forced itself upon the public despite the technical difficulties of popular presentation. It is perhaps not too facetious to remark that if we are all to die, quickly or

13

slowly, from this modern alchemy, informed people would like to know how and why.

But suppose we do not die, suppose that tempers cool off, that the world (despite some other difficulties) continues to be habitable for some centuries or millennia to come – is it not cogent to ask how we are going to live, and even more cogent, why?

Some predict that one day biology will swallow up physics, or that physics will swallow up biology, but for the present we can retain the definition of biology as containing all the sciences dealing with living organisms. The history of biology, thus broadly conceived, can be roughly divided into three phases. The exploratory or taxonomic phase (the designations are mine) covers the period when the biologist was primarily concerned with becoming acquainted with and relating (classifying) the multitudinous members of the vegetable and animal kingdoms. There followed the organic phase in which he was learning anatomy and physiology, the structure and interrelatedness of the organs which comprise plants and animals. Lastly comes the analytic or molecular phase in which the problem of organization is being pursued down to the ultimate molecular level. These overlap to a considerable extent: the first reached its climax with the demonstration a hundred years ago of the reality of organic evolution. We have scarcely yet reached the zenith of the second phase, but we are nonetheless well started into the last, or molecular, phase and with strange consequences. If those who studied biology a generation ago returned to it now they would be surprised to find the subject almost as radically changed as is the physics of the First World War.

Whether life is unique to the earth is at the moment an unanswerable question; it is doubtful if any of the other planets of this solar system have what we would call living organisms on them, but without recourse to science fiction a reasonable guess permits us to think that among the billion stars of our galaxy and the billion galaxies beyond the Milky Way there are probably millions of satellites not too dissimilar to earth on which life could and, given the proper conditions, would have evolved along much the same general lines as here. Then what is life? How does it work? How did it evolve?

Dr Beck has wisely chosen to approach his story by the historical route, selecting only a few of many possible topics for discussion (many volumes would be required to cover the whole of historic and contemporary biology). By way of gross anatomy and microanatomy he comes to the cell theory and evolution. Two books, Charles Darwin's *Origin of Species* (1859) and Thomas Henry Huxley's *Man's Place in Nature* (1863), marked the climax and fruition of this phase.

At this point Dr Beck for a moment turns philosopher: after the demonstration in the eighteenth and nineteenth centuries of the tautological nature of mathematics, philosophy abandoned profitless speculation about the transcendental in favour of the exercise of examining words themselves, searching for the meaning of meaning; and science abandoned the absolute in favour of tentative empirical examination. In tracing this philosophical reconstruction Dr Beck shows us how the new philosophy of science came to influence all thought in the direction of clarity, testability, precision, and objectivity, and how in turn philosophy became more like science in its methodology. He makes it clear that science is not a sealed body of knowledge but a method, a method which is greater than the sum of its results. Philosophers call this method logical empiricism, biologists call it naturalism; nearly a century ago Thomas Henry Huxley called it agnosticism. In his orientation one sees Dr Beck's indebtedness to Hans Reichenbach (who died in 1953), Herbert Feigl, and Ernest Nagel, all in the front rank of contemporary philosophy.

This critique of the scientific method (and of all-too-human scientists) brings us back to firmer ground for the examination of the problem of causality, the Cartesian doctrine of mechanism, and the nature of cells, chromosomes, genes, viruses. The significance of genes he deftly translates in terms of information theory as applied to cellular chemistry, at the heart of which is the master codifying agent of genetics, the complex compound, desoxyribonucleic acid (D N A), now the object of analytical methods which go beyond conventional molecular chemistry as the latter goes beyond the microscope and naked eye, and now on the threshold of laboratory synthesis. And so on to the origin of life, its manifold differentiation in evolution, and its ultimate synthesis, at least in an elementary form. So close are we to this synthesis that when it comes it may be something of an anticlimax, like 'breaking through the sound barrier'. At the other extreme, the biologist – an abstract composite of many interrelated sciences – will begin to make inroads on the problem of consciousness, without resort, this writer thinks, to Cartesian dualism or Berkeleian idealism; and then man, who possesses the most complicated thinking machine in the world, will come of age as a philosopher.

As for the future, and perhaps just over the horizon, is the problem of senescence: 'I can see no reason why death, in the nature of things, need be inevitable ...' but since there is a limit to the materials which conceivably can be turned into food, this, at least, 'would prevent immortality from being widely practised'. And the problem of values: Dr Beck stops short here, wisely I think, but I hope he will agree with me when I say that the assertion, so frequently heard, that science is ethically neutral, that human values must forever remain outside the realm of empirical examination and valuation, is old-fashioned nonsense.

Apart from his historical approach, many of the advances in biology which Dr Beck describes are utterly new and have been made within the last ten years. Biology is exploding with new techniques and discoveries. 'What then, in the name of Miserere, may we expect in the next ten years, in the next century and millennium? ... Our new biology is an infant with a future unimaginable.' So far as we can know at the present time, man is the most magnificent self-ordered creation in this expanding cosmos. He is not, however, quite as magnificent as we think he could be. Somehow or other we must find a way to communicate the essence of today's science – our only reliable corpus of knowledge – to young and old alike; somehow 'thinking must again be made popular, and great thinking synonymous with high adventure.'

I am indebted to Dr Beck because he has written a thoroughly readable book on biology, one that is scientifically accurate, philosophically sound, and fired with humour, imagination, and the spirit of high adventure.

## PREFACE *to the Revised Edition*

LITTLE has happened to change my views in the few turbulent years since this volume first appeared. Drs Ochoa and Kornberg shared the 1959 Nobel Prize in Medicine; and Drs Beadle and Tatum received their Nobel Prize too (conjointly with Joshua Lederberg). So the heroes of Chapter 13 are not mine alone. The pace of work quickens, and my conviction deepens that we stand close to a historic turning point in biological thought. For those who know about these things it is an exciting time to be alive.

WILLIAM S. BECK

*Harvard University*
*Cambridge, Massachusetts*
*June 1960*

# PREFACE

> I've learned one thing about the Universe. There's no
> money in astronomy.
>
> – *New Yorker* cartoon

OF the many charges being flung at scientists these days, one is
that they have failed in their duty to communicate, in a manner
intelligible to non-scientific readers, a sense of what is going on
in science today, where it is heading, where it is not heading, and
why not. I think this charge is a fair one. The book that follows
is an attempt to clear my own conscience on this score.

Scientists sometimes note wistfully that the huge and obvious
reservoir of cordial interest in science among readers of books so
often finds its outlet in science fiction, a genre of writing that is
lately showing alarming signs of taking itself seriously. The pity
of it is that *nothing* in SF – from the Mutants loose among the
galaxies to the trans-Aristotelian world of *Null-A* – nothing in
this ersatz mishmash can stand up next to the truths of real
science, either for human drama and suspense or for intellectual
stimulation and meditation-making. Science is the living dynamic
creature which is feeding the fiction writer; and it is science which
yearns for and deserves the high regard of men.

In this book, I have tried to say something about modern
science as typified by contemporary biology, the background of
ideas, and the men who have helped make it what it is today – an
incredibly exciting adventure story about the human mind and
its subtly powerful enemy, ignorance. In an attempt to convey
some of the sweep and grandeur of this extraordinary chapter of
human history, I have approached the problems of biology, and
science in general, from the point of view of the working scientist,
raising questions more or less in the order he raised them,
wrestling with the obstacles he has encountered and encounters
still. This, it seems to me, is the most meaningful way to think
about science because it makes one literally *feel* the spirit of
scientific inquiry. And it deepens the cultural meaning of science;

21

for it firmly teaches that *all that science has learned, it has learned from hypothesis and experiment.* The scientist learns from evidence, not from innate knowledge, though there have been times when accepted 'evidence' was mere pious wish. The scientist must weigh his evidence, and often he has no way of doing so, possessing neither the tools, the plan, nor the ability to free himself from the preconceptions of his times. It is a fantastic story, filled with pitfalls and portents. It is ours to share.

Throughout the text, I have touched on a good many controversial questions – mostly because this is where the fun is. In all cases, I have taken the stand I believe to be the correct one, and I have tried to defend my positions on their merits. Needless to remark, the basic elements of science and philosophy are inquiry, argument, and evidence. Truth is sought by these means, and if one wishes to dispute another's position, one does so by presenting superior argument or evidence. By this procedure do we hope to arrive at a body of reliable knowledge. If one wishes to reserve judgement, to take a position of scepticism, one may justifiably do so only after examining and rejecting the available evidence. Scepticism then becomes a position in its own right and can be defended by argument. To do otherwise, to reject arbitrarily without examination, to deny the validity of existing thought is emotional behaviour and is out of the realm of philosophical or scientific debate. It is clearly one's privilege to behave this way, but holders of such views have no place in the great search for truth. To these I say good-bye and good luck. Because I am not a philosopher, but a philosophee, I may be proved wrong in my views on philosophical questions. In these cases, I will admit it.

A brief word on the materials upon which I have drawn for this study. A list will be found in the back of the book of the books, articles, and so forth, that are directly cited or quoted in the text. However, this list is not comprehensive, nor would it be possible for me to provide an accounting of the sources I have used. It is too diverse and includes too many books, journals, conversations, meetings, and musings. I have been especially stimulated by the writings of Homer Smith, Herbert Muller,

Lawrence Kubie, and the late Hans Reichenbach – the last of whom gave me needed encouragement in the launching of this project. Knowing him was a very great privilege. I must acknowledge, too, the useful discussions on one topic or another I have held with Severo Ochoa and Robert Yost. To these distinguished individuals and others unmentioned, I am also indebted. But, in the usual phrase, I take little credit for the ideas given here, and full credit for my own interpretations and errors.

To my long-suffering friends Hans Meyerhoff, Norman Simmons, and Lee Pearce go my thanks for support and forbearance above and beyond the call of duty. Gentlemen, I salute you.

Portions of the text – specifically the sections dealing with the cell, the matter of spontaneous generation, and the meaninglessness of 'protoplasm' – were previously together in the form of an essay entitled *The cell: some thoughts on cytology, psychology, and epistemology*, which was awarded the 1954 Wenner-Gren Foundation Honorable Mention Award by the New York Academy of Sciences. Their courtesy is acknowledged in permitting this material to appear here.

WILLIAM S. BECK

*New York City*
*January 1957*

# 1

NATURE, SCIENCE, AND MAN:
HOW THE QUEST BEGAN

# 1

## *The Hall of Mirrors: A Prologue*

I have a toe in the crack of my sepulchral door.
— Homer W. Smith

IT is commonly said that ours is an age in crisis, a time which in a brief span of years has twice witnessed the human race commit mayhem upon itself, which has endured great political, economic, and cultural upheaval. While crisis has been the ever-present human condition through history, from Candide to Mr Antobus, the situation in today's world, its profound depth and immense scale, seems clearly to bespeak the rising tides of change. Our crisis is the crisis of transition between two worlds, the old that is dying and the new that is struggling to be born. Its pain is the pain of uncertainty.

Men have always had to endure misery. The essence of crisis, however, is a disproportionality between the amount of misery men suffer and the potentialities of their culture. It is a disparity between achievement and potentiality, a fettering of potentiality. Its hallmark is wasted and misdirected creative energy and its result is defective growth and conflict.

This book is being written in the belief that science and scientific methods are the best means available to us for solving the problems of our cultural crisis. Science is, beyond question, the outstanding feature of modern civilization. Our world is, to an increasing extent, dominated, if not by pure science itself, then by the conceptions of the general public and its leaders concerning the nature of science. More and more, this idea of science, misunderstood though it is, has gained in influence, and, as its status has changed, great new problems have arisen, many of which have yet even to be identified as problems by the majority of people.

It can be argued, I think, (and I intend to argue) that much of humanity's present difficulty stems from the paradoxically strained relations between science and the other areas of knowledge, and from the surpassing paradoxes within science itself, the very ingredients which make it such a frustrating and delightful mistress to its practitioners. These paradoxes are an important cause of the present crisis; they are its consequences and one of its best examples. For the essence of science is paradox and, in trying to explain science, this is one of the main points I hope to get across.

To the mid-twentieth-century citizen, science is an almost grotesquely ambivalent phenomenon: it is at the same time highly systematic in its approach to the real world, yet it is never complete and never reaches final conclusions. It is the model of certainty in its methodology and logic, yet its driving force is deliberate doubt, and its results are probable, never certain. It requires of its workers absolute discipline, yet it is the fountainhead of exciting new ideas and new ways of thought. Though it may be local in origin, its conclusions are universal. For its creators it is a supreme adventure of the spirit, while at the same time it is the sole basis of endless reams of myth and superstition. It is the healer and builder and the propagator of untold suffering and death. Is it any wonder that science, the strong, the promising, the unforeseeable, the anarchical force in our modern world, should be the cause of acute anxiety.

The remedy is understanding and maturity, and it is my purpose here to contribute what I can to a broader understanding of the essential nature of science, as typified by biology, and of life, as explained by science. What we will find will require a mature viewpoint, for we will learn that wherever we seek certainty, there we will not find it, wherever we establish rigid categories, classes, or concepts, no matter what the reason, these will soon fail us and, like sunken ships, become in time only lumps in the sea bottom. Because science is not an absolutist doctrine, its position is the hardest to defend in the unending battle with absolutism, and its defenders require a maximum of sympathetic understanding. It is their inability to give this

28

understanding, to make the effort it requires, to find contentment in a world in which all questions have not been answered, which has turned men to theism, transcendentalist metaphysics, cynicism, and struggle.

We must recognize for what it is man's predilection for dividing things into tidy categories, irrespective of whether clarity is gained or lost thereby. Learning, thus, is scientific or humanistic. Within science, we have physics/biology/chemistry. We will come to realize that these boundaries have been established by us for our own reasons. They are man-made, and despite their long tradition, despite the problems of university organizers, book classifiers, and curriculum planners, despite the tribal instincts of professional men, fields of learning are ultimately surrounded only by illusory boundaries – like the 'rooms' in a hall of mirrors. It is when the illusion is penetrated that progress takes place. To the cell or the atom, it matters little whether its pursuer is a bio-chemist, philosopher, or diplomat. Likewise, science cannot be regarded as a thing apart, to be studied, admired, or ignored. It is a vital part of our culture, our culture is part of it, it permeates our thinking, and its continued separateness from what is fondly called 'the humanities' is a preposterous practical joke on all thinking men. Science is indeed a hall of mirrors, complex, labyrinthine, glittering, and challenging. What is perhaps more to the point, it shows us what we look like from the side and the rear and this is something worth knowing.

In the pages that follow, we will speak of the nature of science, of the scientist, of ideas, and of life. It is my intention to connect science with the rest of our experience by interweaving the notions of biological thought with aspects of history and the philosophical and cultural climate of each age (including this one), and by showing the scientist to be a human being, not a wizard, demon, or lovable white-haired old man. He is not a caricature or a stereotype but a man who faces difficult problems (for a variety of personal reasons), who succeeds and fails, and who behaves as nobly or erratically as his neighbour – sometimes more so, sometimes less so.

An account of such breadth poses problems for an author who

can say only one thing at a time; thus we will need to plant a number of ideas along the way in order to harvest them in later chapters. Accordingly, the book is divided into four parts. In the first, we will expand on the connexion between science and culture, and we will talk about the nature of science, how it came into being, how biology separated off as a discrete branch of scientific inquiry, and why certainty – despite our dearest wishes – must forever elude us. In Part 2, we will sketch the state of biological thought at the end of its first great modern period, the nineteenth and early twentieth centuries, and we will relive some of the wonderfully acrid controversies which rocked that age. We come then to Part 3 and the great revolution in thought which modern physics brought about. Here we will speak of some of the notions of modern analytical philosophy – the nature of language, models, explanation, causality, information, and the inquiring mind – all of which constitute the basis of the next great movement in biology through which we are living in this hour. These dramatic developments and their implications for the future of man are the subjects of Part 4. Although most people are not aware of it, biology has lurched ahead into a climactic meeting with physics and chemistry and, under the guiding sanity of modern logic and epistemology, incredible new vistas have abruptly opened up for those who will but raise their heads to see them. No longer is biology merely the life and loves of the North American horned grebe. Today it is at one with the totality of human knowledge.

We seem now to be living through a discouraging period of tension and estrangement between intelligent citizens and their science. It is a curious additional paradox that modern man, the unwitting ward and liege of science, should feel ill-informed and little interested in science and its methods. Part of the trouble, no doubt, is related to a breakdown of communication between the specialist and non-specialist. The rapid growth and consequent fragmentation of science decrees that each of us is a non-specialist, whether we be scientist or layman, for we are non-specialists in the other man's area, and a communication failure between scientist and layman is, for all practical purposes, the same as a communication failure between scientist and scientist.

One of the difficulties is what seems to me a failure in the techniques of education. Educationalists have failed to explain science and propagate its broader meanings, and, as has recently been bemoaned by Julian Huxley, particularly is this true for biological science. Not only has this failure been visited upon the average intelligent citizen who may not even realize what he doesn't know, it is partly attributable to those responsible for the training of scientists. Scientists, too, must understand their culture, they must lead their fellow men to the light; for it still takes two to make a conversation.

Unfortunately, the problems of communication are not easily solved. We presume that since a passion for understanding characterizes man, it must exist in some form in all men. The difficulties then would seem to be largely psychological and semantic. In communicating knowledge, all sorts of emotional barriers exist, and if blame is to be assigned to anyone, surely it belongs equally to scientists, laymen, broadcasters, publishers, and editors – for they all have a share of responsibility for the ignorance on the part of the average person of the nature of science, its limitations and potentialities. As for the scientists, many seem to feel they are wasting their time in concocting 'simplifications'. They distrust the public's reaction to the tentative character of science and live in fear of colleagues who will peer down their noses in autocratic disapproval. Earl Ubell, science editor of the New York *Herald Tribune*, once remarked that scientists who get their names in the newspapers inevitably must endure the sneers of their fellows: 'We saw your ad, Joe.' The pressure is there and every scientist knows it is there.

Obviously, the scientist's symbols and vocabulary are partly to blame for that great 'abyss' that isolates the expert. To the uninitiated, symbols are frightening, intrusive, hostile, and discouraging. I am certain, however, that exposition is possible without them. It should be remembered that symbols are simply word or sentence substitutes intended only as time savers. Cordiality follows familiarity, and only occasionally is one hindered by these useful helpers.

## Nature, Science, and Man: How the Quest Began

I have no illusions about the difficulties implicit in trying to reach a non-scientific audience with this sort of an account. A recent editorial in *Endeavour* spoke feelingly of the problems that face scientists who write of science for the general reader, pointing out that 'travellers in foreign countries seem sometimes to believe that they will be perfectly understood if they speak loudly and clearly enough in their own language'. This is true, and it is likewise true, as the editorial contends, that there are certain dangers in believing that all the mysteries of science can be made clear if only the scientist will take the trouble to explain himself in very simple terms. However, I don't think one should underestimate the intelligent citizen. Naturally, he cannot understand the theory of chemical kinetics without the proper background, but he can grasp the notion of biochemical specificity if it is made clear that such specificity means uniqueness and its basis is the same as that of a key or fingerprint. In other words, large and important areas of science are accessible to the uninitiated and much of importance can be said without entering into the nuances, details, and complexities which daily absorb the interest of the scientist. I believe, in fact, that because of his preoccupation with details (I should say *important* details), much can profitably be said about science at large to the scientist himself. We will do our best to stay on the straight and narrow and, if it is possible to do so, to maintain an optimum mixture of rigour and palatability.

We will thus proceed by telling a story of quandary and discovery, of the long years of plodding, often misguided, effort punctuated by electrifying new insights and fructifying ideas. We will talk about the problems involved in arriving at knowledge of living things, and emphasize again and again that our conclusions are tentative because they are based on observations and these are continually subject to refinement and new interpretation. Partly in an effort to counteract the popular simplicities that have been inspired by the complexities of our age, I will try to foster an attitude toward science in general and biology in particular which will induce the reader to distrust the dogmatic statement and to ask always, What is the evidence and how was it obtained? We must educate ourselves to live amidst uncertainty and temporary truth. In probing the magnificent and overwhelming complexities of life, we must proceed humbly and with care.

Science is abstract. Sir William Dampier called it 'the ordered knowledge of natural phenomena and the rational study of the relationship between the concepts in which these phenomena are expressed'. But as the days go by, I am more persuaded that in a way *science is men* – complex men, courageous men, perceptive, vain, anxious, humble, ambitious, brilliant, arrogant, inconsistent, witty, withdrawn, weary, and contented men. Some are like Professor Henry Higgins (who, in his own words, is a 'pensive, forgiving, quiet-living man'). A few are like the giant Prometheus.

The literature of biology abounds in awe-inspiring acts of iridescent genius. And, as we shall see, it contains many an authentic clinical example of extraordinary neuroticism on the part of scientists and public alike. Though emotion in science can be justified in the defence of truth and scientific method, scientists have not infrequently fought obscurantist and emotion-charged opposition with a passionate impatience all their own. In these ironic instances, the cause of science had to lose. As stated above, cool reason is the hardest position to defend on the field of controversy. Regrettably, humanly, entertainingly, *all* parties to many a celebrated dispute ended deep in the muddy water for failing to keep an open mind. Reflecting on this rich past can only strengthen our understanding of man and of truth.

Though a law of nature is phrased in abstract language and is itself devoid of passion and sensibility, the history of its discovery may be an epic worthy of Homer, into whose every page is stamped the personality of a man. We can defend scientific truth by cold logic but we cannot promote its discovery this way. The human factor in the creative equation is an important part of what I want to write about in the following pages. It is a story of irony and paradox and we will find that, in the final analysis, there can be no final analysis.

# 2

## The Coming Reunion of Science and Culture

ANA: But surely there is a great gulf fixed.

THE DEVIL: Dear lady: a parable must not be taken too literally.
. . . There is no physical gulf between the philosopher's class room
and the bull ring; but the bull fighters do not come to the class room
for all that. Have you ever been in the country where I have the
largest following? England. There they have great racecourses, and
also concert rooms where they play [Mozart]. Those who go to the
racecourses can stay away from them and go to the classical concerts
if they like: there is no law against it; for Englishmen never will be
slaves: they are free to do whatever the Government and public
opinion allow them to do. And the classical concert is admitted to be
a higher, more cultivated, poetic, intellectual, ennobling place than
the racecourse. But do the lovers of racing desert their sport and
flock to the concert room? Not they. There is the great gulf of the
parable between the two places . . . [and] the gulf of dislike is
impassable and eternal.

— Bernard Shaw: *Man and Superman*, Act III

THE scientist doesn't just do Science each day. He spends his
hours trying to find answers to specific questions. Thus his first
and most important task is to choose the question he intends to
ask of nature. It is a decision into which many factors must enter.
Among them are considerations of taste, training, the avail-
ability or non-availability of technical facilities, and the prospects
for success in the time available. But even more important in
determining the outcome of this critical decision are factors which
might be termed suprasubjective: the state of science at the
moment, the problems and prospects then causing excitement
along the laboratory circuit, the degree of freedom and per-
missiveness in the institution and the country, the general
intellectual climate of the period.

It is most revealing, for example, to spend an afternoon in the
library paging through the dusty bound journals of former years.

There one can find innumerable papers on topics which somehow were never investigated further despite what looked like promising leads. Likewise, one finds in the published works of different countries curious variations and uniformities in the choice of questions, sometimes to the point of seeming fetishism, which have no clear explanation. The course of our interests through the years is an erratic one, and there are frequently no obvious reasons for the directions it takes. Auspiciously launched investigations sometimes die on the vine, their findings ignored and their conclusions yawned at. Certain topics seem at times actually to be distasteful to the majority of scientists. Other times, dead horses are endlessly beaten upon.

In other words, the scientist in making this first crucial decision is acting under the influence – or tyranny in many cases – of his times. Despite everything, his freedom of action is severely limited. He is, in fact, an individual interacting with his culture, its values and strictures, and what comes out of this interaction is of decisive importance for the course of science. It is as much influenced by the atmosphere of the times as the make-up of the individual scientist. If he is a follower or leader, a novice or seasoned campaigner, a dilettante or zealot, the result will vary accordingly. What we face then, at the very start, is the intriguing question of the scientist and the influence upon him of his age.

## Science and the Temper of the Times

When Huxley published his views on the ancestry of humankind, a century stood aghast at the fancied insult and pious moral men told each other that science had gone too far. Similar events followed the appearance of Freud's scientific conclusions. Yet in the course of time, the theories of evolution and psychoanalysis gained wide acceptance; indeed, both contributions had an incalculably great impact on the culture, religion, art, and everyday thinking of almost all men. This is not to say that opposition to these scientific generalizations has completely disappeared.

It hasn't – partly because some of their problems are yet to be solved (we still don't understand the evolutionary origin of man) and partly because special intricacies in the subject matter of both fields make *proof* extraordinarily difficult. One of the consequences of this difficulty has been the proliferation of countless schools of thought – those opinion-holding factions whose outward appearances in many cases suggest nothing quite so much as a frescoed mural depicting Struggle.

In any event, enlightened men now accept many of the ideas and implications of evolution and psychoanalysis, the ancient pattern having repeated itself, as enlightenment finally came to those who, wrongly as it turned out, considered themselves already enlightened. Even the most superficial backward glance at the history of ideas will reveal the monotonous repetition of this sequence. The daring innovation of an original thinker meets rigid opposition from traditionalists and obscurantists, until at last the pressure of evidence becomes irresistible.

What is not so readily seen, however, is the other side of the coin. There have been times in the past when novel ideas were quite properly opposed by traditional thinkers because the novel idea was either inadequately supported, erratic, or plainly and demonstrably wrong. These occasions, though probably far more numerous than the better-known struggles between genuine scientific evidence and outraged tradition, have tended to escape our notice, possibly because we are less well instructed and entertained not at all by the spectacle of moderate people walking straight roads in erect postures.

But if progress is to continue, and we assume that most men want it to, seemingly wild-eyed or unsupported ideas must be put to the test, and it is perhaps just as well that a touch of inflexibility taints us all. A new idea, particularly one that challenges old and long-held points of view, must endure the battle and win if it is to survive and become a tradition of its own. The battle is necessary, and sometimes it becomes intense.

Interestingly, the battlefield where the innovator struggles with his age is often within the mind of the scientist, and this is another aspect of scientific history that is commonly forgotten. Scientists are men and, like other men, they are brought up to hold the same views that other people hold. The importance of this fact is that the scientist, like everyone else, is a creature of his times, its prejudices, truths, and assumptions, and when the moment comes to make conclusions from the evidence at hand, the scientist may find it impossible even to conjure up, much less believe, a possible explanation for his data that conflicts with things that, consciously or unconsciously, he has always believed. If such a conclusion should seem inescapable, it may still be easier to believe that some error has occurred than that an eternal truth is false.

This is understandable and to some extent desirable. Yet, had such paralysis of the imagination afflicted all men of science, the world would have known no Copernicus, Galileo, Newton, Darwin, or Pasteur. Each of these pulled down an ancient temple of truth because the evidence made it necessary to do so and, in turn, each changed the course of history. How have such men arisen in history? Were they unbalanced geniuses or prodigal titans? Did they happen on their discoveries by chance? Were they so constituted psychologically that *they*, for some reason, could question authority more readily than could their fellow men, all of whom had often seen and satisfactorily understood the rising of the sun, the falling of the apple, and the fermenting of the wine? And one thinks of Darwin, a religious man, whose distress at the implications of his own discovery may have caused him to pass the remainder of his long life in physical pain and anxious retirement.

We wonder about these things because they hold a question for our time. We are the latest modern generation and we know vastly more than those who came before us. Ours is the age of analysis, and we have come to know a great deal about the processes of learning, the psychological pitfalls of prejudice and preconception, and the brute imperatives of logic which, among other things, keep reminding us that *every idea we have might be wrong*. We have brought our research tools to an unprecedented degree of sharpness and have anatomized every last step that falls between observation and conclusion. Not only have we far surpassed the understanding of earlier generations, but we are now doing so at an accelerating rate, a rate whose own speed of acceleration appears to be accelerating.

Why then are there problems that persistently elude the scientist? Obviously, there will always be a supply of unsolved problems, since each new discovery of science uncovers a host of new problems. Physicists, for example, could not now be puzzling over what holds the subatomic particles together in the nucleus if the particles themselves had not already been discovered. But why are we without the answers to a whole hierarchy of old and venerable problems of very long standing? Why, for example, do we know almost nothing about cancer? Is it because insufficient money has been spent in cancer research? Is it because there is a shortage of what the popular press calls 'scientists, engineers, and technicians'?

If the ingrained beliefs and attitudes of the modern world have somehow kept scientists from new and radical approaches to the problem of cancer, then it would follow that what we are waiting for is another Darwin or Pasteur. No doubt it is believed by those who advocate a 'crash programme' in cancer research that larger expenditures of research funds will hasten the day when the lightning strike of genius will flash across the sky. On this day, it is thought, a Darwin or a Pasteur – perhaps yet unborn – will perform the crucial experiment or, in an inexplicable moment of deep insight, he will perceive a fallacy that a generation overlooked.

This sort of thing *is* going on today. Evidence has been presented, for example, that, on the face of it, seems capable of explanation only if mental telepathy or extrasensory perception exists. Most scientists reject this explanation, yet a few daring individuals have concluded that ESP does exist and have accepted all of the implications of this belief, among which is the view that telepathic waves pass between individuals that cannot be obstructed by physical barriers and cannot be detected by any manner of radiation detector. The doubters, recognizing that such a phenomenon is completely incompatible with modern physics and conceding that all of physics just *might* be wrong, nevertheless prefer to believe that the evidence is defective, either through error or through fraud, since to them it seems that, in this neurotic age, there is a higher probability that fraudulent or erroneous evidence has been produced than that all the laws of physics are invalid. And there the question stands, as the world awaits the incontrovertible experiment which will prove that ESP exists.

What then can we say of the age we live in? If this is the most golden of the golden ages of science, why do we not know the nature of matter and the secret of life? Is there a limit to what science can accomplish, beyond which men should ask no more of scientists and scientists no more of themselves? Because science is the mightiest force in the worlds of today and tomorrow, I think these questions are important. And because I see evidence suggesting that non-scientific men are becoming more and more estranged from and unfamiliar with what I believe to be the essential nature of science, I think it important that people look again at the leviathan in their midst, for in certain combinations of light and shadow it appears at times in danger of becoming ice-bound.

It is these questions – in so far as biology may speak for all of science – with which this book is concerned. We will talk about some of the problems of modern biology, the complex changing science of today whose workers are seeking still to understand the nature of life. And in exploring this unending mountainside, we will find, I think, that science is very much more than most of us thought it was, and something rather less than most of us would like it to be.

## Man's Place in Nature and vice versa

Not only is man himself a living organism, he is, as well, surrounded by, dependent on, derived from, progenitor of, inhabited by, threatened by, and – in the inexorable course of time – devoured by an assortment of living organisms other than himself. To put it another way, life is a web of which man is a part and a prisoner. Little need be said, therefore, about the importance of all life to human life.

## Nature, Science, and Man: How the Quest Began

What of man, the organism? What is he? What is his origin, his state, and his destiny? Man, we know, is an animal which, like all animals, seeks food, shelter, and security, mates and reproduces, which fights off the encroachments of a hostile environment until it is possible to fight no longer. Then, like all animals, he dies. But man is unique among animals, for he alone has the ability – and apparently the compulsion – to build cultures. His growth is not completed by reproduction, nor is it fulfilled by death, because the biological pattern of man has made his nature self-surpassing.

*Culture* is that milieu of ideas, myths, and values which only the human animal can exude. It is the result of man's unique ability to create and respond to symbols. 'Without symbols', wrote Lewis Mumford, 'man's life would be one of immediate appetites, immediate sensations; limited to a past shorter than his own lifetime, at the mercy of a future he could never anticipate, never prepare for. In such a world out of hearing would be out of reach, and out of sight would be out of mind.' For these reasons, man needs not only bread, but art, ritual, philosophy, science, myth, religion, dance, and drama. When, by ignorance or adversity, he is barred from these symbols of his culture, man is destitute and, thus malnourished, he languishes.

Presumably, then, a visiting observer from Betelgeuse wishing to sort out the Animal Kingdom would quickly notice the human predilection for culture-building and he might reasonably conclude that here was a reliable, if somewhat roundabout, method of telling men from other beasts. We would then say that the tendency and ability to make cultures is a special property of one group of living things. It is, in fact, a biological phenomenon.

To those members of the species who feel pride in man's capabilities, it must be disconcerting to observe a colt walking away from its birth or a three-month-old puppy performing tricks, while the human infant seems to hold on to its tot-hood as though it were all music and sunshine. Childhood, it then appears, is the prolonged immaturity we *must* have in order to imbibe our culture and learn what went before us, before we can become a part of it in one or another of its many aspects.

Since its beginning, mankind has been interested in the source of its creation, the keys to survival, the pursuit of beauty (and more recently truth), and the secret of everlasting life. Cultural patterns differ widely from people to people, from age to age, and from location to location, the physical environment obviously having an important influence in shaping the ways of men. Eskimos, for example, don't wear grass skirts, and no one could predict a man's cultural behaviour merely by identifying him zoologically as a member of the species *Homo sapiens*. Yet despite these differences, each human culture has concerned itself with these Big Questions and offered up its own answers. Cultures thus contain the truths, biases, *mores*, class distinctions, unconscious assumptions, and motivations of each age, those forces whose powers have led men in their times to defy the more primitive instincts for self-preservation and, instead, to give up worldly goods, to deny the existence of what the senses perceive, and to become martyrs and saints. And as the epochs have faded into the past, each has left its legacy to human experience.

We can say then that culture and biology are intimately interrelated in a number of ways. The creation of culture is a biological imperative and its character is shaped by the needs and limitations of the organism. Moreover, cultures are influenced by man's opinions, whether conscious or unconscious, of what he is and what life is – as was our culture by the impact of Darwinism. And, finally, *to understand culture one must have some understanding of biological thought*. If this book has two themes, surely this is one of them.

Human beings like to classify things on an *either-or* basis. An act is either good or it's evil. An object is animate or inanimate. One is conservative or liberal. And, if we are scholars, we are humanists or scientists – and likewise, if we are scientists, we are physical or biological. These are demonstrably false dichotomies, each of which has been harmful to human progress. When he has argued that scientific education is a critically important part of cultural education, J. Bronowski has often been stopped 'by those whose education and tastes are literary, because they found these claims puzzling. They know what culture is: it is Sophocles

41

and Chaucer and Michelangelo and Mozart and the other figures round the base of the Albert Memorial. And they know what culture is not: it is not laundry lists and sleeping pills and the proved reserves of oil and the *Statistical Digest*. In short, culture is not a body of facts: but what is science but facts? How then, they ask, can science be a part of culture, and why should one learn science to become cultured? There is no scientist in the frieze of the Albert Memorial.'

Well, science is not a set of facts but a way of giving unity and intelligibility to the facts of nature so that nature may be controlled and new facts predicted. I suspect the word *biology* bears a similar taint to most people. It is wriggling earthworms, or paradoxically lifeless portraits in ancient and frayed textbooks of lizards, spiders, and the like; it is a stern, strait-laced teacher and an utterly revolting, never-ending dissection of some lower form of life. We might do something about this now because I intend the word *biology* to have breadth of meaning, encompassing all aspects of the phenomenon of life from the gene to the super-ego, from metabolism to tool-making, from the slime mould to the Irish setter. As for the word *culture*, I use this also in the broadest sense, to refer both to basic and universal human traits such as tool-making, shelter-building, and the wearing of clothing, and to that aspect of the world culture that implies refinement or advancement – art, letters, music, and the like – those things which stand in contrast to Philistinism. In both these senses, the point is clearly valid. Biology and culture are inseparable: they overlap; they are necessary to each other and mutually influence one another to an extent that is quite startling when one begins to think about it. Culture is influenced and conditioned by the facts and phenomena of biology, the needs and limitations of the human organism, just as our art and ideas that men have about themselves and the nature of life. Conversely – and, though less obvious, this part of the inter-relationship is no less important – the state of culture powerfully affects the content and course of scientific thought in biology.

One might cite innumerable examples of this sort of thing. Racial prejudice is one. Many men believe that the white, Nordic, or Anglo-Saxon races are innately superior to other races, many of whose members have pigmented skin and are called coloured. Even those who are not openly committed to this idea are affected by it and, despite professions of tolerance, many are repelled by the thought of racial intermarriage, the ethical teachings of Christianity and the sacred principles of democracy to the contrary notwithstanding. Conversely, it is held by many of those who see evil in these attitudes that there is no such thing as race and there are no biological differences within the human species. It is wrong, of course, to overlook the disinterested conclusions of modern physical anthropology. Human beings *do* differ – in skin colour, hair form, height and physique, and blood groups. There *are* recognizable physical types that are related to some extent to geographical origins and to a lesser extent to cultural and language groups. But there is no evidence to support a doctrine of racial superiority or inferiority. Actually, almost no human types are genetically pure, and all known groups are more or less poorly defined around the edges. It is fair to say that what differences there exist between racial groups are put there by the hostile cultures of men in the grip of cupidity and fear. The lesson of history is clear; all of civilization's golden ages have arisen from mixed races, including that of modern America whose foundations rest solidly on a mongrel antiquity. Yet racial prejudice remains a powerful force in our culture.

Another instructive link between culture and biology is found in modern psychiatry, a metaphorical tree that is growing in the rich ground common to both. Though today's model of the mind resides in the whole organism, the roots of psychiatry push down through the hierarchy of biological organization, past the organ, through the cell, into the sub-cellular level of biochemistry. There is an ancient and honourable tradition of thought – dating at least from the seventeenth century – to the effect that mind and body are separate entities. In 1637, René Descartes declared the absolute separateness of mind and body, and Cartesian dualism has, in varying measure, greatly influenced all subsequent thought – from Spinoza and Leibniz to Mary Baker

Eddy. Certainly the idea makes a modicum of sense – at first glance it is not self-evidently erroneous – but we know now that the mind-body dichotomy is just another example of the human weakness for 'either-or-ism' and, with Ralph Gerard, we must agree that the mind needs the brain and that 'contrary to Alice's experience in Wonderland, the grin cannot remain after the cat is gone'.

When an experience leaves a memory there must be some material imprint in the brain (according to current evidence), since it is clear that brain function at all levels involves, not spectres and poltergeists, but patterns of neuronal discharge. It is not necessary to visualize these material imprints as little scenic bas-reliefs scattered throughout the cranium: the phenomenon bears a closer resemblance perhaps to what happens in the course of magnetic tape recording. Thus memory – and consciousness too – has a physiological basis. At least, so believe many current workers.

It is plain also that the findings of psychoanalysis have strengthened the claim of psychology to stand within the domain of biology. Just as Darwinism challenged mankind to an act of humility, psychoanalysis confronted us with the fact that we are all compelled to live under the influence of powerful unconscious psychological forces having much in common with the emotional patterns and instincts of 'lower' animals. Thereby has psychoanalysis reinforced the unity of biology. Since Freud, the psychiatrist has become the student of all human nature, and this may be regarded as the cultural fruit of our metaphorical tree. The problems of human happiness and discontent, of ethics and moral responsibility, the basic elements, in fact, of all cultures, have ceased to be solely of religious and philosophical concern. They are, we now believe, the subtler manifestations of the unconscious mind which itself stands close to the most primitive and fundamental of life's properties. It is perhaps not too much to hope that a clearer understanding of the mechanism by which normal frustration leads inevitably to discontent will in time free man from the residual hates and lusts of his childhood. This would yield a more productive, less gluttonous culture, free of the envy, rivalry, crime, war, and neurosis of everyday life, whose bitterness is born in the nursery and corrupts to the grave.

As for the reverse phenomenon, the influence of culture upon biological thought, I have already spoken of the importance of his 'point of view' to the scientist who is mulling over his data in search of generalizations, and there will be more about this in a later chapter. But the influence works at many levels and in devious ways. Two examples come to mind which may illuminate the point. One relates to the conflict that rages quietly in the minds of scientists and of those who provide financial support for research over whether the scientist should seek knowledge for its own sake or for the direct purpose of relieving human suffering. It is a fact that much of today's biological research owes its existence to a society interested in the latter goal. National health services and cancer, heart disease, and poliomyelitis foundations want results that are more or less directly related to what must be called an ethical aim: the prevention of disease and the healing of the sick. (Thus is ethics as much cultural as biological, for human benevolence has at least something to do with the instinct for self-preservation.)

On the other hand, it is not historically true that the major developments of science have been due to a specially strong determination to increase man's command over nature. The Greeks were not pre-eminent in technology but in 'useless' abstract thinking such as geometry. Modern science has been more interested in experimental verification, but it has tried to carry on the tradition that valued exploration and understanding above mere usefulness. As we shall presently see, genuine scientific progress in the nature of things cannot take place when science is a wagon hitched to a practical star. And it is time that this realization became a part of our culture. Some hopeful signs suggest that in some quarters this is now happening.

A second example of what culture does to the content of biological thought has to do with the present deplorable state of knowledge concerning the physiology of human sexual intercourse. It is startling to realize how little is known of this fundamental process. The major textbooks of physiology and medical school teaching of today barely mention it. The only imaginable reason for this state of affairs is that no one wants to or feels able to investigate such matters in the laboratory. In other words, an ancient taboo flourishes in the temple of science. How else can one explain the hullabaloo that followed the innocuous publications of Professor Kinsey and his associates a few years ago? A recent occurrence provides an even more vivid illustration. Over two thousand papers were read at the 1956 meeting of a national society for experimental biology. One of these dealt with certain physiological measurements made in the laboratory during human sexual intercourse. It is perhaps not surprising that, in the meagre press coverage of this scientific congress, this modest contribution should have received headline prominence, including a story in a leading news magazine entitled 'Wired for Love'. What was a bit startling, however, was the fact that, among the jaded scientists attending the meeting, this paper caused a minor sensation and was the subject of endless speculation and giggling in the *bistros* and coffee shops. I know because I was there. No wonder nothing is known on the subject.

Culture and biological thought *are* inseparable, and one wonders how they became alienated from one another, for they were not always so estranged.


## The Idea of Biology and Its Fickle Fortunes

For long centuries before the comparatively recent dawn of experimental science, whatever was known about living things was known by all men alike. Somewhat later, biology's interpreters and archivists were the literary men, theologians, and philosophers of each age. In those early germinal years, a single man of learning could know all there was to know throughout the entire province of knowledge. Thus, early speculations on the nature of life were more cultural sophism than science. And as the cultures of the passing eras ebbed and flowed, men's views on life and its place in the scheme of things now followed and now led the capricious parade.

In a way, the purest picture of human life in a biological framework is to be seen in the lives of our nameless prehistoric ancestors. They, by unbelievably arduous effort and ingenuity, made the human race a going concern. They discovered the tool, the seed, and the domesticated animal. They created the marvellous instrument of language by which man discovered and later disguised his humanity. Actually, our 'savage' ancestors are still quite close to us, not only in our abundant talent for savagery, but in the superstitions and fetishes of simple men, as well as in the inner essences of modern respectability, the tabooed word, the national totem, and the ceremonial initiation.

Primitive man, no doubt, began speculating upon the meaning of life when he saw that life must end in death. The phenomenon of disease, of life ebbing from the body, must also have drawn attention to the living state and its vicissitudes. To the primitive mind, sun, wind, fire, and sea were alive and each became, at various times, the object of religious feelings and elaborate mythologies. But like an infant who can cry but who knows nothing of phonation, the knowledge of the times was a superficial practical sort of know-how which was crowded in by the thick mists of magic. The typical primitive man subsisting on his garden would manage it expertly, using well-made rudimentary implements, planting crops by the seasons, selecting soils and seedlings, and knowingly eradicating weeds and pests. For a man to do these things, he must have a strong conviction that they will work and that, barring droughts and locusts, a harvest will come in. Yet with all of this practical knowledge, primitive men performed elaborate sequences of magic rites at every juncture of their agricultural practice, thus revealing a deep division in their attitude toward the living world. On the one hand were the well-known factors governing the growth of plants – water, cultivation, and so forth – and these things one coped with by knowledge and hard work. While on the other hand lay the unknowable, the forces behind pestilence, famine, and drought, and these were staved off by magic.

Perhaps it is improper to speak of the primitive man and his tiny world as the originator of biological thinking. Biology is, after all, a science with the avowed purpose of investigating nature and elucidating general laws. Yet there *were* scientific elements in the culture of primitives, even though this age had no apparent intention to infer the laws of nature for their own sake. The primitive man's power to observe and record was often advanced, but, as we shall see, science is far more than observing and recording. We will agree, therefore, that the savage had no formal science, that although he knew a great deal about living things, he knew nothing about the nature of life and knew not of his ignorance.

Man had to reach a certain level of civilization before he could visualize the world at large, and many civilizations rose and fell before the golden age of Greece. During these years some isolated advances were made: the Babylonians dissected a human body, the Jews somehow decided that they would better prosper by renouncing 'unclean' meat, and the Egyptians learned how to make mummies. And in some Egyptian art, we see the first evidences of racial awareness. For example, we are told that in the reliefs of the royal tombs of the Nineteenth Dynasty (1321–1198 B.C.), a complete classification of the races is found, with Semites painted yellow, Negroes black, Egyptians red, and Northerners or Europeans as white-skinned men with blue eyes. All told, a scanty output from a dozen millennia! It is intriguing to realize how very much more we know of Greek thought than of its antecedents. The history of Greece was unusually well documented by contemporary historians and, perhaps for this reason, has been doted upon by 2,000 years of scholarship. Surely, much that has come down to us from Greek civilization was not originated by the Greeks but transmitted by them from their predecessors, for to the modern Greek student of 400 B.C., ancient history was the history of Egypt.

There is, however, a more substantial reason for the pre-eminence of Greek thought in intellectual history. As pointed out by W. A. Smith, 'The Indians, initially a jolly and extroverted people, early fell under the sway of a sacred literature and a tyrannical priesthood. The Chinese escaped the sacred and the priestly, but succumbed to the past. . . . By way of contrast, the

Greeks had no sacred book, no priestly hierarchy, and no authoritarian tradition to keep them from speculating about the nature of man and the world. Their geniuses were, therefore, relatively free.'

It was a remarkable age, for almost every area of artistic and intellectual experience was entered into and activated by irrepressible innovators. In philosophy, all of the Big Questions were asked: What is the nature of good and beauty? How did the universe begin? What is life and what is the meaning of human life? And, almost to the last *ism*, the age gave forth with the full gamut of answers, from cynicism to idealism. Ignorant of the theological doctrines which were later to remove man from nature, the learned men of Greece in their speculations on life went so far as to postulate the evolution of man from lower animals, though this was pure conjecture devoid of evidence. The point is that nothing in the culture of the age made such a suggestion outrageous.

In reflecting upon another age and in comparing it with our own, most of us make the natural error of overrating the past, by thinking of it only in terms of its symbols, its great monuments and heroic achievements, with no consideration of its everyday life, its meanness, sordidness, mediocrity, and foolishness. The loftiest ideal of a former age becomes its essence in our minds, so that the legacy hides the ancestor. Thus, the classical age of Greece reminds many of us only of Plato and Aristotle, the 'father of science', and Herodotus, the first anthropologist, and a group of handsome masonry pieces in various stages of dilapidation. Greece couldn't have been all Plato because her demagogues led her to ruin, and we wonder what the golden age must have been like to the ordinary people, not all of whom were men of learning. The evidence suggests that the vaunted spirit of enlightenment was experienced only by the educated few. Schooling was meagre, most people were illiterate, and learning was a privilege available only to those who were wealthy enough to journey to the feet of the masters.

As for the masters themselves, some have had no equal in history, if influence be the measure. Of Plato, for example,

Whitehead has remarked, hyperbolically perhaps, that all of Western philosophy since his time has been only a series of footnotes to his writing. It may be that the same can be said of Aristotle with respect to biology, metaphysics, political theory, and law. The gap, however, was very large between the learned few and the ordinary man. It is therefore likely that the biological erudition of the man in the street resembled that of the primitive, while, at the same time, the great minds of the age, flourishing in insular splendour, asked the big biological questions, made beginning attempts at answering them scientifically, and set them down alongside of the major problems of culture and philosophy.

For the ancient and modern worlds to have been peaks, the Middle Ages must then have been a valley, and so it has been judged by most historians from their perches high up on the modern slope. It was a curious age, both for what it was and what it has variously been thought to be by its critics. Depending upon one's point of view, the Middle Ages may be dated from A.D. 500 to 1500, from Augustine to Galileo, from Charlemagne to Columbus, from the fall of Rome to the Renaissance. Literally risen from the ruins of the ancient world, the medieval world was characterized by the emergence of a strong and authoritarian Christian church. Urban life disappeared, to be replaced by a society sharply divided into feudal warrior-chieftains and the peasants and artisans, and, though a major legacy of the Middle Ages was the university, thought and culture declined deplorably during these centuries.

For those who kept alive the flame of learning in monastic centres and isolated universities, the quintessence of knowledge was theology, and the method of scholars was a bizarre hodge-podge of ornate pageantry, recourse to sanctified authority, and undisguised fabrication. Herbert Muller has quoted the following example of the lofty indifference to vulgar fact of a scholarly ninth-century historical biographer, the Bishop of Ravenna, who wrote, 'Where I have not found any history of any of these bishops, and have not been able by conversation with aged men, or inspection of the monuments, or from any other authentic source, to obtain information concerning them, in such a case, in order that there might not be a break in the series, I have composed the life myself, with the help of God and the prayers of the brethren.'

There is little question that the medieval period has been badly treated by Renaissance and modern historians. The burgeoning sixteenth and seventeenth centuries had nothing but contempt for their oppressive parent, and originated the slanderous cliché 'a thousand years without a bath' and the statement that medieval philosophers were concerned primarily with how many angels could stand on the head of a pin. The romantic eighteenth century relented in its judgement because it saw excitement and colour in the style of medieval architecture, calligraphy, chivalry, and the myths of Robin Hood. But the nineteenth-century pendulum swung back again when its historians filed new judgements, and today the period remains poorly understood. A number of recent writers have attempted to 'set the record straight' by pointing out the large number of 'modern' ideas that were articulated in the monasteries and universities of the Middle Ages, as, for example, Grosseteste's work in optics, Jordanus's in mechanics, and the scepticism of William of Occam concerning our ability to attain true knowledge of the 'essences' of things.

For most of us, the Middle Ages is known only by a patchwork of contradictory symbols – knighthood in flower, feudal moated castles, and the burning of Joan of Arc by a sinister Inquisition. Perhaps this is the morning-after that must inevitably follow a historiographic binge. Modern critics do agree, however, that the scientific knowledge of the Middle Ages was meagre, that what little progress had been made by the Ancients in developing the scientific method was allowed to recede into the dishonoured past. Ecclesiastical authority was supreme, and when the High Church theologians who dominated the universities finally recognized what a superb ally they had in the same Aristotle they had earlier denounced as a heathen seer, Aristotelianism became for a thousand years the true scientific basis for the hierarchical aims of the papal power. The Church presumably approved of Aristotle's conception of the earth as the home of all imperfection because this nicely left heaven as the source of salvation. And whatever of Aristotle's writings did not agree with the revealed Word could be easily explained by reference to the author's paganism.

Biology prospered little in these centuries, and the little that was done as a formal pursuit consisted of foolish compilations of ancient writings done in the service of theology and doctrine. Beyond this, the medieval mind was enmeshed in an almost unbelievable tangle of astrology, alchemy, magic, and sorcery. While it has been held that such preoccupations were perfectly reasonable in their time and that alchemy represented an 'advance' over primitive and ancient occultism, it is difficult to acknowledge that science grew out of these intellectual errors, that it owed its existence to them. This would be like assigning parentage of the labour movement to the excesses and cupidity of industrial management. Rather, we would agree with Dampier, who wrote, 'The scattered seedlings of science had to grow in a vast and confused jungle which was always threatening to choke them, and not in the open healthy prairie of ignorance.'

In the next few chapters we will speak of the Renaissance and the modern worlds. For the moment, we will merely note that the dawn of modern science took place in the seventeenth century – a century which Whitehead called 'the century of genius', for, despite the murk of the immediately preceding millennium, it produced Francis Bacon, Harvey, Kepler, Galileo, Descartes, Pascal, Huygens, Boyle, Newton, Locke, Spinoza, Leibniz, and countless others of high distinction. It was the century in which scientific biology had its true beginning.

The Renaissance marked not only the birth of modern science, but a return to respectability of intellectual pursuits. Science had not, by 1700, become the most honoured of occupations, and it remained for some time a gaudy and slightly disreputable parvenu in the academic curriculum. But scientific awareness did begin at last to seep down into the minds of the intelligent public. As we shall presently see, the new enlightenment swept the western world like a wave of fire and shook men's imaginations to their deepest foundations. All that had once been believed was now suspect, and for the first time men challenged the notion that ancient culture must forever symbolize the ultimate in human aspirations. The idea somehow took hold that men were capable of progress! How strange it seems to us, the heirs of that new tradition, to imagine a world not working to improve itself.

Thus, all at once, there arose the great currents of thought which dominate our century: Protestantism, humanism, and—what was a truly dynamic part of the culture of the Enlightenment – modern science. An era had begun in which the intelligent public participated actively in the scientific debates of the day, particularly those marked by sharp controversy. With the forward surges of scientific progress, a watchful public could taste the sweetness of a successful experiment and the gall of contrary evidence, the acquiescence in which, whenever it happened, must surely have been beneficial for the public mental hygiene.

## The Gap on the Albert Memorial

In discussing the theme of the increasing separateness of science in the modern world, J. Robert Oppenheimer wrote, 'We live today in a world in which poets and historians and men of affairs are proud that they wouldn't even begin to consider thinking about learning anything of science, regarding it as the far end of a tunnel too long for any wise man to put his head into.' James Killian expressed it more bluntly by reporting two intelligences that have been making the rounds of the faculty lounges – one the observation that the scientist knows nothing of the liberal arts and regrets it, while the humanist knows nothing of science and is proud of it. The other was an incident said to have occurred at a liberal arts faculty meeting. When a student named Cicero was reported to have failed Latin, everybody laughed, but when a student named Gauss was reported to have failed mathematics, only the science professors laughed.

Since we seem then to be facing a deep, wide gulf between the humanities and science, uncrossed except by an infrequent intellectual frogman, it would be of interest – *scientific* interest

53

actually – to inquire whether or not differences can be found in the character or content of the two domains which might help explain the present situation. And, as it turns out, there are some rather provocative differences.

For one thing, a useful distinction, though not a rigid dichotomy, can be made between two kinds of knowledge: cumulative and non-cumulative knowledge (as pointed out by Crane Brinton in *Ideas and Men*). *Cumulative* knowledge is typified by science, since through the centuries it has been built up by accretions slowly added on to an original hard core of truth. Nothing, for example, has been substituted by modern physics for the truths discovered in ancient Greece by Archimedes, although physics has built upon this solid foundation to achieve its present size and strength. This is not to say that all seminal ideas are necessarily and forever correct. Sciences have been built upon erroneous ideas, and only later was error corrected. We may even assume that certain of today's fundamental truths will in time be proved erroneous. Such is the nature of the great scientific revolutions produced by the work of Copernicus, Einstein, and Darwin, for each of these was such that its reverberations carried back through the entire body of cumulated knowledge to shake the central core itself.

*Non-cumulative* knowledge, on the other hand, is well illustrated by literature. Today's writers deal with questions of right and wrong, beauty and ugliness, human nature, and the universals of life, while the Greek playwrights of over 2,000 years ago wrote on exactly the same themes (as their scientific contemporaries were simultaneously working out the principles of plane geometry). Knowledge in this realm, then, has not, by the process of accumulation, increased in any clear fashion, though perhaps we should say only that the *rate* of accumulation distinguishes science from art, literature, and philosophy. Arnold Toynbee has written, 'Human Affairs are still the Dark Continent of the Universe, compared to the realm of Physical Nature which has been so brilliantly illuminated by the discoveries of modern Western scientists in the course of the last three hundred years. We students of Human Affairs are like those explorers of Tropical

Africa who were pushing their way into the interior from half a dozen different coasts in the middle years of the last century; and, when people are opening up a dark continent by a converging movement, it is a landmark in their progress every time that a Stanley meets his Livingstone.'

We may assume also that these apparent differences (and others) play some role in determining which men and women enter which field. What we have called cumulative or scientific knowledge, for example, is better suited to experimental verification and hence is more clearly true or false. Such fields might be expected to attract the tough-minded, the realist, the sceptic. Non-cumulative knowledge, conversely, is less (or not at all) accessible to clear tests of truth, is less likely therefore to alter the course of human history, and hence might attract the idealist, the dreamer, the artist, and the optimist.

Needless to say, these remarks are superficial. More will be said on this subject later and here I must be hopelessly brief. The literature on this tantalizing subject is massive, ranging from the high plateaux of the psychoanalytic reviews to the trade journals that are wrestling bravely with the 'scientist shortage'. For the time being, we will note only how increasingly difficult it is for a gifted man to play his part in today's society unless he is something of a specialist; and we will concede the existence of deep forces which propel men of learning toward one or the other of the two great continents of knowledge. But let us also remember that the purpose of all scholarship is to project order into the external world and that it is our purpose here to see if somehow we cannot find a continental isthmus across which scientists and humanists might run a little light traffic.

Let us now turn our attention to science itself and see if we cannot learn something of its essential nature.

# 3

## The Nature of Science

The Newtonian having said, That Descartes was an Ignoramus, the Disciple of that Philosopher reply'd in a passion, You Lie.
— D'Argens' Chinese Lett., 1741

CONSIDER the three following case histories.

1. A biologist decides that, since cancer is the scourge of mankind, he will dedicate himself to the task of discovering its cause. He approaches the problem by examining cancer cells carefully and determining their properties in an orderly manner. Upon retiring at the age of sixty-five, he has, in addition to having exhausted himself, demonstrated unequivocally that cancer cells contain 268 of the 302 enzymes that were looked for, that cancer cells can assume over 139 different shapes, and that they have a rather bland taste – all of which are facts not previously known. Unfortunately, this investigation had to end before it was possible to make any conclusions concerning the cause of cancer.

2. A well-known investigator seeks for many years to understand the essential nature of the living organism. He observes the marvellous complexity of the cell, and he is awed by the fact that when a cell divides, its progeny are absolute replicas of itself down to the last detail. He is struck by the 'goal-seeking' properties of living organisms, the metamorphosis of the tadpole, the incredible process by which a single-celled embryo becomes a man, the regeneration of amputated limbs by salamanders, the healing of wounds, the continued vertical growth of a young pine tree even after its trunk has been pulled down and trussed into an unnatural position. In trying to understand these observations, he concludes that the whole organism is very much greater than the sum of its parts and that the complexity of an organism is so unimaginably great there must reside within it some *principle* of life over and above its mere material structure. This principle,

he concludes, is not a physical entity but a vital force that some-how wills or guides the cell toward its goal and the fulfilment of its biological purpose. And it is this force, he logically infers, that must distinguish the living from the inanimate.

3. A small white rat, known in the laboratory as Peter, is placed in a contraption that looks like this:

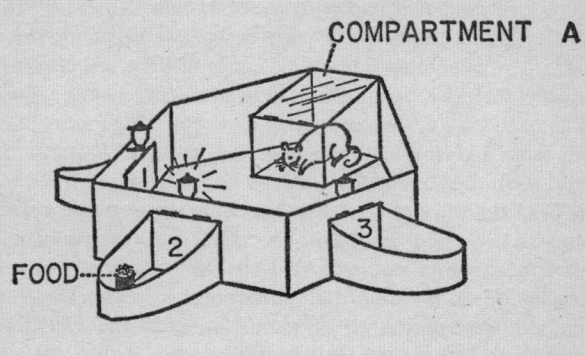

Compartment A is a glass-enclosed observation booth from which Peter may peer out at the three doors which we have labelled 1, 2, and 3. Above each of these is a light bulb but only one door leads to food. Things are arranged for a few weeks so that the food is always behind the one door whose light is on, and, of course, the door is changed from trial to trial. Peter quickly learns this fact, for after some practice he always goes, when released from A, to the lighted door and gratification. Now, however, the procedure is changed. He is detained in A and allowed to watch while the light outside the lunchroom is merely blinked on and off, and he is not released for a fair interval of time. The question then becomes: When released will he find the food, since he cannot now respond to a light that is not on, but only to something in his mind? We watch, Peter is released, he hesitates, makes his decision, and heads for the right door, his problem solved.

It is the purpose of this chapter to help us decide which of these three seekers of truth is using the method of science.

## The Decline and Fall of Speculation

In ordinary conversation, the word *reason* is seldom misunderstood. It means sound thinking, intelligence, sanity, and sense – and, in its various shadings of meaning, we contrast it with emotion, imprudence, and obtuseness. A 'man of reason', in the ordinary phrase, is not a true believer in any absolute dogma.

Despite these commonplace meanings of the word reason, the philosophical position known as *rationalism* (from *ratio*, 'reason') has since the age of Greece represented something quite different from what we now call the scientific method. A paradox, it would seem, but one easily resolved and fascinating for what it tells us of the ways of thought. *Reason*, in the sense we shall use it and as it is used by philosophers, refers to the processes of *logical thought* and not necessarily to the pursuit of truth. For example, if we are told 'all philosophers are immoral' and 'Democritus is a philosopher', we must conclude that Democritus is immoral. The conclusion lies inescapably within the given premises and, by the process of logical proof or *deduction*, we merely unwrap and expose it. Nothing new has been added and thus we see the essential emptiness of deduction. The point to be emphasized, however, is that logical deduction leads to a conclusion *regardless of the truth of the premise*. The above conclusion is logically sound, though the premise is possibly false.

The significance of this fact for the history of thought is very great indeed. What it means is that an internally consistent and logically impeccable system of ideas may be spun out of the reasoning mind whether or not the 'given' or underlying premise is true. Thus did Euclid develop a logically faultless geometry based on an assumption – that parallel lines never meet – which 2,000 years later was found to be unjustified. Mathematics is, in fact, the ideal example of logic at work, for the mathematician proceeds by analysing his given premises for their implicit meanings, and the mathematician's 'truth' has no connexion with the external world.

The difficulty with rationalism arose when men, impressed

and awed by the power of reason, came to believe that all questions, even the Big Questions of philosophy, could be made to yield to the reasoning mind, that the mind, in fact, has access to all of the great and ultimate truths. We may exemplify this point of view by picturing the complete rationalist at work: he is seated in his study, a room without windows, in a deep comfortable chair; his eyes are closed, and his mind is hard at work. The only equipment he could possibly use would be paper, quill, and ink. And we wonder as we view this tableau how, if it is true that the sun always rises in the east, the rationalist could possibly discover it in a study without windows. For here is the crucial defect of rationalism. It needs nothing but mind and a premise and, since it sees nothing of the external world, the truth of its conclusions stands or falls by the truth of the premises. Truth, then, is not the same as logic.

Another point of view that rose to new stature in the seventeenth century held that the mind by itself commands no royal road to truth and that, in the words of John Locke, the mind is a blank page: it is *experience* that writes upon it. This thesis, so indispensable to science, is called *empiricism* (from the Greek words meaning 'experience' and 'trial'). It is the view that says if you wish to understand nature, look at nature, not at Aristotle. We see now why rationalism emerged as a counter-current to science. Though the mother lode of reason, it denied to the mind the harvest of its senses. And it is sense data, what he sees, feels, hears, tastes, and smells, which starts the empiricist on his road to truth.

Rationalism, it should be noted, is not necessarily the same as pure speculation. Neither is it true that rationalism and empiricism were born in the seventeenth century, for both points of view were very much alive in the ancient world. The empirical approach to knowledge is discernible in some of the works of Archimedes, Ptolemy, and Hippocrates, and we know from their technology, their houses, architecture, sailing ships, and, to some extent, their medicine that ancient men learned some of what they knew by reaching out and touching the world. Rationalism prospered too, for the philosophies of Plato and Aristotle were in large part rationalistic, seeking truth by the power of reason alone. But the rationalists of the ancient world gave their brand of thought a stripe of its own. In constructing their world views, they needed a given premise and this they usually obtained by pure and unvarnished speculation. They fabricated the bases upon which whole philosophies rested out of the gossamer of imagination. Hence, through speculation and the fatal fascination it held for them, the ancients were swept into colossal error.

Imagination took over, and huge authoritarian cosmologies arose, packed with exquisitely detailed and utterly false generalizations. While it is true that error is inevitable in an age whose means of acquiring knowledge are primitive or non-existent, and we must not too harshly criticize the ancients from the vantage-point of today, it is still impressive how universal was the willingness to step forward with explanations for observed phenomena in the total absence of knowledge and the reluctance even occasionally to concede ignorance. Reasoning, for example, was based on *analogy* with human behaviour, and conclusions were drawn from the human traits supposedly belonging to inanimate objects. Great forces of nature were embodied in complicated mythologies, phrases were used such as 'planetary attractions' or 'evil humours' which had connotations of humanness or animateness. It was obviously impossible, for example, for Aristotle to have observed microscopic objects such as spermatozoa. It was his view that the female contributed matter to the embryo while the male contributed nothing material, only the principle, soul, power, or – to use a typically Aristotelian concept – form. There can be no reproach for the contemporary ignorance of microscopic life. But surely this unverifiable, speculative statement, scarcely even a hypothesis, represented a misleading error which, because of the stature conferred upon Aristotle by others, doubtless hindered progress for many centuries.

The loose language, the empty verbalisms and doctrines, the intense desire for universal knowledge are all phenomena which are undoubtedly attributable to emotional needs. Psychology explains the universal propensity for myth-making, servility to authority, desire for security, and what we will say of the further progress of thought shows how these ancient errors have at last been recognized and to some extent purged. Only 'to some extent' because modern man is no freer of these psychological impulses than the man of ancient times. Furthermore, having insight into the nature of human compulsions is not quite enough to liberate one from them. (Jules Masserman has referred to the disquieting paradox of people who supposedly have achieved the various brands of self-understanding, yet are unable to apply this vision to the solution to their problems. The condition of those who 'cruise about submerged in oceanic depths of "insight" who are in touch with reality only by a thin throatful of air' he calls *status schnorkelis*.) We still are men, and, in our desire to make the world more like the heaven we wish it, we still must lean toward beliefs and denials which inescapably shape the course of science.

Later rationalism recognized the consequences of a basic premise made of wish and fancy, and the complete and thorough-going new rationalism that emerged in the seventeenth century was obsessed with the importance of finding basic axioms which, though self-evident and therefore knowable without recourse to experience, are nevertheless true and suitable starting points for logical constructions. These would be the *a priori* truths that the rationalist conceived, or better preconceived, us to be born with. In the rationalism of medieval Christianity, God was the basic given truth, and it was held that the human mind without benefit of the senses had the ability to fathom at least in part God's plan for the universe. Not so for the new rationalist. In searching for indubitable basic propositions, he had no need of a supernatural being, nor of ancient authority. He banished God from the processes of truth-seeking in the belief that the mind was all-powerful, and he made as symbols of his century the great rationalistic systems of thought that in their own completeness gave answers to all questions of man and metaphysics.

Here we can but mention in passing a few of the greatest of the rationalistic system builders. Spinoza, for example, the philosopher's philosopher, who devised a system of *ethics* in which mathematical proofs patterned after the geometry of Euclid were used to establish theorems on God and the nature of true goodness. And the brilliant Leibniz, who wrestled earnestly with the nature of the relationship between 'truths of reason' and 'truths of fact' and concluded that harmony between the two depended solely upon pure laws of thought. In his great construction, Leibniz devised a general system outlining all possible forms of thought and the 'universal laws' connecting them. All truths, however complex, could then be extracted from these elements, so it was claimed, by combining them according to the prescriptions of logic.

And there was Descartes, perhaps the greatest of the rationalists – the man many have called the father of modern philosophy. In establishing his method of inquiry, he temporarily became a true sceptic. Believing only in the power of reason and in the idea that he was born to set right the muddled beliefs of his time, Descattes recognized the importance of an unshakable base for a rationalistic philosophy. By systematically doubting, by rejecting, in his words, 'as absolutely false all opinions in regard to which I could suppose the least ground for doubt, in order to ascertain whether after that there remained aught in my belief that was wholly indubitable', he came at last to the proposition that his doubt could not conquer. He could not doubt that he was doubting, and from this came the famous *cogito ergo sum*, I think, therefore I am. This was Descartes' hard-won premise, and upon it, by the power of his logic alone, he proceeded to build a system of thought that went right on up to God. The basic axiom, then, was found by *intuition*, the key feature in the method of Descartes. Unhappily for him, modern logicians have exposed the fallacy in his basic statement and have picked to pieces his logical techniques. The Cartesian system, though powerfully influential upon later generations both for its content and grandeur, is now a shattered hulk, for its basis and structure were in error.

Interestingly, the style of Descartes' life matched his philosophy and probably had a lot to do with the picture we have of the armchair life of the rationalist. His career is filled with charming vignettes of the master at work: in bed, in a warm oven, in a snowbound hut where, alone one day while returning from the coronation of the Holy Roman Emperor, Ferdinand, he had his greatest insights. As a soldier in the Thirty Years' War, he spent most of his time discussing mathematics with the army engineers. When finally he was appointed tutor to the young and romantic Queen Christina of Sweden, the rigours of lecturing on philosophy while horseback riding at sunrise led to his final illness.

The work of Descartes in the seventeenth century and of later philosophers such as the great Immanuel Kant brought rationalism to a high-water mark in its sophistication and in the attractions it held for thinking men. It prospered in an age to which order and system were all important, not only in the pursuit of knowledge but in the political actions of all-powerful princes and the formation at last of stable churches from diverse denominational factions. But rationalism, though it has deductive thinking in common with science, is not science, and in this century the fully developed method of science finally saw the light of day. To understand the nature of science, one must understand why rationalism failed.

## The Rise of Science

It happened quietly, for Europe was being convulsed by religious wars and most people, by and large, are not interested in such things. But a profound revolution was launched when, in the midst of a rationalist ground swell, the first positive and clear statements of the empiricist position began appearing around 1600. The age soon gave way to philosophical struggle, for though at one in their contest with the arid expositors of Aristotle, the fathers of modern science, like many another revolutionary clique, ended their unanimity once they had named a common enemy.

Much of the groundwork for empiricism was laid by the great Galileo, perhaps the most famous of scientific martyrs. A worshipper of facts, Galileo was an ingenious experimenter first and a theoretician second. Clocks were not yet known, yet he discovered two of the laws governing the velocity of falling bodies. To determine time intervals, he used the weight of the water accumulating from a dripping basin. With wily genius, he worked out the mechanical laws governing the motion of objects rolling down inclined planes, so that, centuries later, Bergson wrote, 'The concept of time came down an inclined plane from heaven to the modern world through Galileo.' He enlarged the visible universe by developing better telescopes and, by careful observation of the planets, showed conclusively the error of the astronomy of Ptolemy which was based not on observation but on one man's conception of what the universe ought to look like if it were to be elegant and simple. Galileo's observations bolstered the Copernican theory that the earth revolved about the sun, at a time when the church was committed to the opposite idea, that the earth, the scene of Christ's sacrifice, was the centre of the universe.

Even Galileo had a touch of Cartesian rationalism in him (as do we all), for he must have believed in his deepest mind that the universe is arranged with mathematical precision and that if we could only grasp the true underlying axioms, we might somehow unravel the laws of nature without the need for experiment. He is said to have boasted on occasion that he used experiment only to prove to those less wise than he what he already knew to be true. He was ultimately tried for heresy before the Inquisition and he chose to recant rather than accept its judgement. No one will forget the words Galileo is said to have muttered as he rose from his knees in the chamber of penitence: 'And yet it moves. . . .' If the story is apocryphal, it is history's greatest rumour.

While Galileo was one of the first to practise empiricism, Francis Bacon was its first philosopher, and let no one assume that because a man can do science, he is necessarily able to explain in abstract terms the nature of the scientific method.* Bacon has been a highly controversial figure in the history of

---

* Einstein once remarked, 'If you want to know the essence of scientific method, don't listen to what a scientist may tell you. Watch what he does.' Morris Cohen qualified it, 'Watch what he does when engaged in scientific work, not when he is taking a holiday or is on a picnic, or discoursing on something beyond his competence.' Scientists may or may not clearly grasp the essential nature of the scientific method and still be successful in their scientific activities, as illustrated by the non-scientific character of many of their utterances on non-scientific topics.

ideas. His life had many unsavoury episodes, of which much has been made by latter-day critics under the leadership of Lord Macaulay. But, if a blackguard, he was a brilliant blackguard, for his monumental treatise *Novum Organum* revolutionized thought.

Bacon tells us how, while an undergraduate at Trinity College, Cambridge, he became disgusted with Aristotelianism because, though centuries old, it had yielded not progress but barren dispute. He then and there resolved to establish a new philosophy which would reform all human knowledge and allow man to regain the control of nature he had lost with the fall of Adam. It was a task, however, which he never lived to complete, for it did not begin in earnest until a fantastic political career had climaxed in exile. Although he failed to achieve his goal, his lasting fame was secured by the *method* which he suggested be used in his great crusade. The method was new and the title *Novum Organum*, or *New Method*, was a direct challenge to Aristotle, whose theory of method was titled *Organon*. The work was a magnificently written attack on medieval thought, rationalism, and the defects of Aristotelianism. His rejection of a medieval legacy that argued causes and ignored facts was so vigorous it awoke his contemporaries to high enthusiasm. He bluntly stated that philosophy is not a science of things divine or human, nor is it a search for abstract truth; it is rather a practical seeking to improve our condition of life by increasing our power over nature and forcing her to yield us her fruit. In ringing phrases, he declared that our knowledge of the external world comes only from our sense impressions, and the only way we can discern true knowledge from the flux of sense impressions in which we are swimming is by systematic and orderly observation of nature. We must observe phenomena, record them, and classify them, and, in time, enough knowledge will have been acquired to give us a firm grasp upon nature's laws. Nor should this pursuit of data be left to chance and whim. Societies should be formed, which under competent leadership should send forth armies to win the great battle for knowledge.*

* This proposal to regiment scientists as an army was elaborated in Bacon's philosophical romance *The New Atlantis*.

Could anything be further from rationalism? It was the apotheosis of empiricism – but was Bacon's *novum organum* the method of science? Let us consider the point carefully. In emphasizing the limitations of deductive logic, Bacon stressed the value of *inductive* logic, the difference between the two being the great hinge upon which empiricism hangs. Inductive thinking does not depend upon a given premise but upon observational data, and its conclusion tells us something not implicit in the premise. Therefore, it is something we did not know before, it is new knowledge. Consider the inference 'all cases of Gok's disease *so far observed* have proved fatal, therefore Gok's disease is a fatal disease'. Our inference carries us from the cases we *have* observed to those we *have not* observed. Consequently, the truth of the conclusion cannot be guaranteed, for there is always the possibility that in time we will encounter a non-fatal case. We know now that we should not speak in inductive logic of the truth of a conclusion, but rather of its *probability* of being true. This probability can be high or low. It would be high if our conclusion was based on a wide experience with Gok's disease which had known no exceptions. It would be low if we had made our conclusion after seeing only four cases. For some inductive conclusions, the probability of truth is so high there is practically no chance of future contradiction (though mathematically its probability is never zero). Thus, we are justified in saying the sun will rise tomorrow, not because we are oracles, but because we and others have observed it rise each morning many, many times without exception.

Inductive logic is actually the basis of the many decisions that we constantly make in everyday life. Every hour of every day, whether we realize it or not, we make big and little decisions that are based on short-range predictions having specific probability values. Most of the time, little importance attaches to the success or failure of these low-pitched inductive conclusions. If this morning the sky looks grey and I decide to wear my raincoat, I am basing my decision on some previous observational data to the effect that this sort of sky is usually followed by rain. If today it clears up, I have made an unsuccessful prediction, I have had to carry along a heavy raincoat, and my future reaction to grey skies should lead to an inductive conclusion whose probability rating is one notch poorer. Even in the face of highly improbable outcomes, we like to stay on the safe side when the outcome would be catastrophic should it happen to occur. Thus, we buy insurance though houses rarely burn down, and have bone X-rays taken even though bruises are relatively common and fractures relatively rare.

It was Bacon's merit to have recognized that empiricism leads to new knowledge via the inductive inference. Bacon's failure – and it is a failure only by today's standards – is his belief that empiricism would yield *certain* knowledge. He failed to recognize the probable character of truth as we now know it. Moreover, he believed that his method would provide answers for the Big Questions of philosophy. He advocated making long lists of random facts from which, he felt sure, nature's laws and eternal truth would spring forth when the lists became long enough.

It was Robert Boyle and later Newton and Locke, however, who fostered the marriage of reason and empiricism, whose timely offspring was modern science. Of these three pioneers in the development of the scientific method, chief credit probably belongs to Boyle. Although Boyle was born in 1627 (the year of Bacon's death), Locke in 1632, and Newton in 1642 (the year of Galileo's death), Boyle had established his commanding reputation by the publication of his *Spring and Weight of the Air* in 1660 and *Sceptical Chymist* in 1661, some thirty years before the appearance of Newton's *Principia* and Locke's *Essay Concerning Human Understanding*.

When Boyle returned to London after his service in the continental war, he joined a group of scholars who met weekly to discuss philosophy and further experimental science. Boyle termed this Baconian group 'The Invisible College' and when the war forced them to Oxford, he joined them and there earned his reputation as the final foe of alchemy and the founder of modern chemistry. When the Restoration brought peace in 1660, the Invisible College became the Royal Society, the very society Bacon had urged into existence. In many ways, the founding of this society marks the true beginning of modern science. Its motto, *Nullius in verba*, pledged its Fellows to reject all doctrine in favour of experiment.

As a youth, Boyle was dismayed at the lip service paid to Bacon's method and the meagre effort that went with it. Like Bacon, he resolved to demolish wrongheadedness and, at Oxford, he organized laboratories, secretaries, and all manner of assistants (one of whom was Robert Hooke) into an army of investigators quite in keeping with the Baconian prescription. Between 1660 and 1673, Boyle published fifteen treatises whose success and scope are virtually without parallel in the history of science.

Boyle's contributions to chemistry cannot detain us here. Let us merely make note of the viewpoint which he brought to his investigations as illustrated in *The Sceptical Chymist*. The treatise is a dialogue between an Aristotelian (who believed in four 'elements' – earth, fire, water, and air), a Spagyrist* (who believed in the three 'principles' of Paracelsus – sulphur, mercury, and salt), and the 'sceptical chymist'. The meeting occurs under the chairmanship of Boyle, who early addresses the others: 'I am not a little pleased to find that you are resolved on this occasion to insist rather on experiments than on syllogisms. For I, and no doubt you, have long observed that those dialectical subtleties, that the schoolmen too often employ about physiological mysteries, are wont much more to declare the wit of him that uses them, than increase the knowledge or remove the doubts of sobre lovers of truth.' Boyle died in 1691. The epitaph on his Irish tombstone reads: 'Father of Chemistry and Uncle of the Earl of Cork.'

Boyle had made complete the cleavage between material and spiritual phenomena. There was a God who was creator and ruler, but man, his unique creation, had the power to reason and observe. God created the material world to operate under rigorous mechanical laws that were unaffected by the wishes and

---

* Spagyrism or alchemy was rampant in the century preceding Boyle. A typical example of the sort of thing that went on is a chapter heading in the 1596 edition of *Paracelsus' Experiments & Cures*: 'The Spagericke Antidotarie of the preparation and making of medicines against Goonshot.'

feelings of men. We will come back again to this view of a mechanical world, for it was the hallmark of the natal century of science, it was the necessary precondition for Newton, and it soon settled at the heart of a great question of physics, the nature of causality, and the greatest question of biology, the nature of life. The physical universe was conceived by the natural philosophers of the seventeenth century as a vast machine, a material entity made of atoms possessing mass, position, size, and shape, whose behaviour follows ascertainable laws. The cosmos was autonomous. Being material, it was real and hence offered resistance to the senses. Though Boyle and his contemporaries attributed the mechanistic world to a higher divinity, it is noteworthy that their contributions to knowledge had a mechanistic not a divine derivation.

The thought has been expressed that this world view was far from original, that it had, in fact, begun in ancient Greece with Epicurus, Democritus, and Zeno, and had it not been for barbarian hordes, the collapse of classicism, and a pious, otherworldly, Christian millennium, the flourishing Greek culture would have led to the discovery of the laws of nature so that a later revolution would not have been necessary. But a later revolution was necessary and, with Newton, we reach its climax.

It was said of Newton in the seventeenth century that he was like the River Nile, whose powers were gigantic but whose source was unknown. In the eighteenth century, an age that all but deified Newton, Alexander Pope exclaimed:

> Nature and Nature's laws lay hid in night:
> God said, Let Newton be! and all was light.

And in recent times Newton has been acclaimed, perhaps unwarrantably, as the greatest thinker of all time, whose authority and influence have been paralleled only by Aristotle's. The reason for such encomiums can be easily stated. Newton laid the foundation for three separate fields of inquiry: higher mathematics, celestial mechanics, and physical optics. And what is more fantastic is the fact that these great contributions were all made within a period of eighteen months when Newton was twenty-three years old. It was unquestionably the most fruitful eighteen months in the history of creative imagination. Newton spent the remainder of his scientific career merely elaborating these discoveries. What he accomplished in this period is described in his own words:

In the beginning of the year 1665 I found the method for approximating series and the rule for reducing any dignity [power] of any binomial to such a series [i.e. the binomial theorem]. The same year in May I found the method of tangents of Gregory and Slusius, and in November [discovered] the direct method of Fluxions [i.e. differential calculus], and the next year in January had the Theory of Colours, and in May following I had an entrance into the inverse method of Fluxions [i.e. integral calculus], and in the same year I began to think of gravity extending to the orb of the Moon . . . and having thereby compared the force requisite to keep the Moon in her orb with the force of gravity at the surface of the earth, and found them to answer pretty nearly. . . .

Thus came immortality to a man who, tortured at times with despair and self-doubt, seemed to court controversy and flee adulation; who for some reason preferred not to make public his discoveries; who, convinced that Leibniz had plagiarized the calculus, quarrelled for years with him over the question of priority; who, in a state of collapse after completing the *Principia*, began writing angry denunciatory letters to friends, including John Locke, whom he accused of trying to 'embroil him with women'; and who, as Master of the Mint, was buried in Westminster Abbey not for the *Principia*, which few have read, but rather because he had stabilized the coinage and restored national credit at a time when England was striving to build a vast mercantile empire against Dutch and Portuguese opposition. On Newton's tombstone are the words: 'Mortals, congratulate yourselves that so great a man has lived for the honour of the human race.'

The circumstances leading to the publication of the *Principia* are harrowing to consider. In his first scientific publication, Newton had communicated his theory of light and colour to the Royal Society in 1672. It aroused a storm of criticism, some from men of stature such as Christian Huygens and Robert

Hooke. Of the absurd criticism by a man named Linus, Newton wrote, 'I see I have made myself a slave to philosophy [science], but if I get free of Mr Linus's business I will resolutely bid adieu to it eternally, accepting what I do for my private satisfaction, or leave to come out after me; for I see a man must either resolve to put out nothing new, or become a slave to defend it.' He was already convinced that Leibniz had pilfered his discovery of the calculus.

In 1674, Hooke wrote Newton a pleasant letter soliciting a paper for the Royal Society. In this letter, Hooke casually mentioned thoughts he had been entertaining about a rule of inverse squares. The discussion apparently aroused Newton from his sulks and he began to consider the problem of planetary motion. In 1684, there occurred the famous visit to Newton of the astronomer Halley. Halley asked Newton to describe the orbit of a planet attracted to the sun by a gravitational force obeying an inverse-square rule. Newton immediately replied, 'An ellipse.' Halley asked Newton how he knew that, and Newton replied, 'I have calculated it!' These four words convinced Halley that Newton had worked out the mathematical basis for the law of gravity. Overjoyed and realizing that his own and Hooke's concepts had been no more than intuitive, Halley cajoled Newton into relenting and publishing his work.

Just before publication, however, trouble with Hooke started. Hooke heard that Newton was going to publish the inverse-square law and he concluded that this was the fruit of his earlier letter to Newton. When Newton learned that Hooke wanted to be acknowledged, he exploded, contending that he had developed the theorem long before Hooke had ever mentioned it. Moreover, Hooke had never been able to solve it mathematically. He wrote an angry letter to Halley bitterly attacking Hooke for 'this new provocation' and threatened to suppress the crucial chapters. Somehow Halley mollified him, the classic went to press intact, and Newton retired to have a nervous breakdown. As it later turned out, the book was published largely at Halley's own expense. To the discoverer of Halley's comet, therefore, the world owes eternal gratitude. His vision and self-sacrifice made

71

possible the greatest single monument of human learning, the *Philosophiae naturalis principia mathematica* of Isaac Newton.

What interests us in the achievements of Newton is the fact that his discoveries were made by an unusual method. And it is of some interest again that to discern his method we must examine what he did, not his writings about what he did, for, though his novel method was almost the first and surely the greatest use of the scientific method and though he himself was aware of his remarkable methodological discovery, still his writings did not fully discuss in general terms the method from which resulted his various discoveries.

First Newton made empirical observations in the tradition of Bacon and Boyle. From *observations* of his own and others, one of which, legend insists, was a falling apple, and in the belief that the universe was a mechanism that functioned according to mathematical laws, Newton concluded that some law of nature must govern the phenomena he observed. He formulated a simple mathematical equation (now known as the law of gravity) which would make sense out of the observations at hand by fitting them into a *generalization*. The abstract statement, we must remember, was in Newton's mind, it was not something he saw, nor has anyone ever witnessed an equation at work. It was, in fact, a *hypothesis*. Here we encounter the crucial feature of the method of Newton. If the general hypothesis was correct, he reasoned, it implies what behaviour should be expected in other areas of experience, such as the motion of the moon, whose monthly revolutions should be governed by the hypothetical force. In other words, Newton used deductive logic and reason to extract an implicit conclusion from the tentative premise that was his hypothesis. This part of the procedure could be carried out in his study, for it required only reason, as in the rationalist tradition. Now, to verify and bolster the hypothesis, Newton returned to empirical observations. If the equation carries an implicit prediction of the moon's behaviour, let us look at the moon: *it* cannot be in error. If the moon's behaviour fails to agree with the prediction, it was wrong, the logical correctness of the deduction notwithstanding. For the deduction's premise was wrong as proved by the demonstrable untruth of its conclusion. If, on the other hand, the moon's behaviour has been successfully predicted, the hypothesis gains in strength and will continue to do so with each such successful test.

Interestingly, there was irony in the events that actually took place when Newton looked to the moon to verify the hypothesis of gravity. The observed motion failed to agree with his prediction and, realizing that brute fact must always win over beautiful hypothesis, Newton placed his papers in a drawer where they remained for twenty years. When finally a French expedition had made a more accurate measurement of the circumference of the earth, Newton saw that his original calculation had been based on an erroneous conception of the size of the earth. With the new figures, the old observations of the moon agreed precisely with the theory. Only then did he publish the law of gravity, a law of nature which no Bacon could have extracted from long lists of random observations of the world and which no Descartes could have brought forth by pure reason. We will note, parenthetically, that Newton's curiosity was stimulated not only by a small falling apple, but by the puzzling spectacle of a very large apple, the moon, which for no clearly apparent reason is found hanging in mid-air.

The law of gravity continued successfully to explain and predict the motion of material bodies, achieving its most dramatic success (and thus support) when, in the nineteenth century, astronomers observed certain disturbances in the motion of the planets. It was assumed that *if the law of gravity were valid* these perturbations might be explained by postulating the existence of a large body of matter in a certain spot in the heavens. When the telescopes were fixed on the indicated point, a large new planet was found, exactly according to prediction. Thus was Neptune discovered in 1846.

The scientific method, so beautifully displayed in this discovery of Newton's, *combines* the techniques of empiricism and deduction. Experiments or simple observations lead to individual facts without status as generalizations. The scientist examines these facts and attempts to make sense of them by devising some general explanation to account for them. This is the hypothesis, and if the scientist omits to frame a hypothesis, as did Bacon and the first biologist at the beginning of our chapter, he can proceed no further. For the hypothesis and not random chance should guide the scientist to his next observations. If the hypothesis is true, reasons the scientist hopefully, thus and so should be taking place in the observable world, and the hypothesis can be put to the test. If the predictions are confirmed, a new scientific generalization is on its way into being; if the test fails, the hypothesis needs to be mended or abandoned.

At times in science, as we shall later remark, hypotheses have been formulated that are effectively empty because they are impossible of experimental refutation. For any proposition to embody a possible truth about the world, it must also embody a possible falsehood. Since we proceed by asking nature questions, we learn nothing from her answers if the question is formulated so that the answer must be 'yes'. One example of this sort of thing from psychology is the improper use of the concept of reaction formation. If the observer postulates that an individual has a certain pattern of emotional impulses and then examines him and finds this pattern, all is well and the hypothesis is correct. But if he examines him and does not find the pattern, as often as not it is concluded that the individual does have the pattern but is covering up by reaction formation, so that the hypothesis still remains intact. Employed in this way hypotheses are useless, for they lead to no progress in the acquisition of knowledge. Clearly, this was the error of our second biologist. His hypothesis involved a metaphysical 'principle of life', and no matter what he observed next the hypothesis would endure, for there could be no way of knowing whether the observed phenomena were or were not compatible with the existence of such a principle. We presume that the principle could do anything and hence no event could refute it. This procedure is not science, but, in the phrase of Needham, mere gap-filling after the fashion of Columbus's map-maker who wrote, 'Where Unknown, there place Terrors.'

We are left then with Peter, the rat, as the last defender of the bastion of science. He, it seems, made an observation when he saw the blinking light, and we cannot deny that he formed a hypothesis when he decided that the light meant food. Its confirmation by trial led him to the discovery of a little 'law' of nature. A scientist is rather like a rat in a maze. Both proceed by observation, insight, hypothesis, and trial, and for both, the hypothesis may arise from mere hunch. As we shall see, the invention of hypothesis is the truly creative part of science. It is perhaps this phenomenon that most emphatically distinguishes Peter from Newton.

# 4

## Biology Becomes a Science

> Perish those who said our good things before we did.
> — Aelius Donatus, fourth century A.D.

WITH the Renaissance came a newer closeness to nature. For reasons that continue to intrigue scholars, the new age was marked by a return to classical culture, and a knowledge of classical literature became the mark of an educated gentleman. The culture of the period triumphantly crossed national boundaries and flourished in the exuberance of its freedom, for the new culture was outside and independent of, indeed sometimes hostile to, the Church. The new man was an independent man, an autonomous, versatile, creative man, and, for the first time, his interests turned toward nature, humanism, and art. Painting began to display nature with painstaking and unaccustomed realism, and the observational accuracy of the painter gained new dimensions with the first use of perspective and realistic treatments of light and shadow.

The new interest in nature revealed itself on every side: in the artist's landscapes, his nudes, and in the bawdy tales of Rabelais. And inevitably it became part of the new science as men began to inquire, for the first time in centuries, into the nature of life.

### The Paradox of William Harvey

One of the disquieting things about writing history, especially intellectual history, is the almost universal absence of clear boundaries between periods of darkness and light. Instead, we find in the cases where some individual is considered the 'first' to have expressed a revolutionary idea that more often than not his greatness was conferred upon him by a posterity that could appreciate the achievement in the light of what came after. But in the immediate times of great thought and great works, one often witnesses the puzzling spectacle of an era oblivious to its own innovations or, what is more distracting to those of us who like our heroes unsullied, we find the great men themselves taking inconsistent positions, suggesting that they failed fully to understand the essential meaning of their own contribution. And, of course, we can almost always find, if we look hard enough, intimations of a novel idea in the thought of earlier times, so that we may feel deprived of the high drama which rightly befits the excelsior cry of genius.

Such considerations have particular relevance when we set about attempting to ordain someone the 'father of modern biology'. Usually this designation is given to William Harvey. In the early 1600s, Harvey observed that the beating heart expelled the blood within it. He then reasoned: if the heart contains two ounces of blood and beats sixty-five times each minute, then it must eject into the body over ten pounds of blood per minute. It had previously been thought that blood was derived from the food that is eaten. But one cannot imagine ten pounds of blood being formed anew each minute from the amount of food a man consumes. Reflection on this observation and simple deduction led Harvey to postulate that blood expelled by the heart must circulate through the body whence it returns to the heart. He then performed experiments to investigate the hypothesis. He showed that obstruction of a vein causes pooling of blood on the side of the obstruction away from the heart. He showed that the bleeding arises from the nearest end to the heart of a severed artery and the farthest end of a severed vein. And he demonstrated with elegant simplicity the function of the venous valves, concerning which he wrote that 'so provident a cause as nature had not so plac'd many valves without design'.

Harvey's discovery of the circulation of the blood in man was a monumental and many-sided contribution to science. In the first place, it discredited the beliefs of fourteen centuries that the heart was not a muscular organ and that the blood passed through the septum between the right and left ventricles. In addition, Harvey knowingly or unknowingly utilized the scientific method in almost astoundingly modern fashion; and, finally, he bolstered his already incontrovertible claim to immortality by conceiving the heart as a pump, for in this notion Harvey heralded a new view concerning living organisms – though as we will see he did not appreciate the meaning of his own work on this score. But to his successors his work gave proof to the concept that life, like the rest of the universe, could also be viewed as a material machine. Descartes was quick to praise Harvey for 'having broken the ice in this matter', and in his own discourses he relied heavily on the work of Harvey to illustrate the mechanical nature of living objects. Their only difference from man-made machines, he insisted, was in the degree of complexity. With these assertions, sudden new excitement entered the realm of biological thought. For it now seemed reasonable that if the living organism were a material mechanism then it, too, could be investigated by the new method of science.

The paradox I have referred to arose in the following way. We have noted that antagonism to Aristotelian philosophy was the great common denominator of all the currents and trends of thought which led to the beginnings of modern science in the seventeenth century. Yet despite his weighty achievement and despite the powerful currents in the main stream of thought, Harvey considered himself fundamentally not to have broken with the past. It turns out when we examine his words that he believed himself finally to have proved the main tenets of the physiology of Aristotle:

I begin to think whether there might not be a motion, as it were, in a circle. Now this I afterwards found to be true. . . . Which motion we may be allowed to call circular, in the same way as Aristotle says that air and the rain emulate the circular motion of the superior bodies; for the moist earth, warmed by the sun, evaporates; the vapours drawn upwards are condensed, and descending in the form of rain, moisten the earth again; and by this arrangement are generations of living things produced; and in like manner too are tempests and meteors engendered by the circular motion, and by the approach and recession of the sun.

And so, in all likelihood, does it come to pass in the body, through the motion of the blood; the various parts are nourished, cherished, quickened by the warmer, more perfect, vapourous, spirituous, and, as I may say, alimentive blood; which on the contrary, in contact with these parts becomes cooled, coagulated, and, so to speak, effete; whence it returns to its sovereign the heart, as if to its source, or to the inmost home of the body, there to recover its state of excellence or perfection. Here it resumes its due fluidity and receives an infusion of natural heat – powerful, fervid, a kind of treasury of life, and is impregnated with spirits, and it might be said with balsam; and thence it is again dispersed; and all this depends on the motion and action of the heart. . . .

The heart, consequently, is the beginning of life; the sun of the microcosm, even as the sun in his turn might well be designated the heart of the world for it is the heart . . . which . . . is indeed the foundation of life, the source of all action.

This is florid and fanciful, and one recent writer (Wightman) dismisses this passage with the observation that Harvey was simply a man of his times and did not easily throw off the wordy inanities of scholasticism. But Walter Pagel tells us that in this passage the main thesis of Aristotle's world view is defended: the excellence of the circular motion and the parallelism between the macrocosm and the microcosm, that is, the universe and the living organism.

It thus appears that Harvey not only launched the great biological debate between mechanism and mysticism that rages to the present day, but, grotesquely and paradoxically, he became the leader of both sides of the argument. Descartes, for example, although anxious to avoid offence, for he well knew the fate of Galileo, did nevertheless displease many churchmen by his defence of the mechanistic view implicit in Harvey's work. Samuel Parker, Bishop of Oxford, declared that 'mechanical philosophy is quite unfit for solving the problems of phenomena' and that Descartes along with Gassendi and Hobbes was one of the three most dangerous atheists of the age! Likewise, segments of secular opinion rebelled at the thought of a living machine.

Yet, Harvey himself leaned away from mechanistic ideas toward vitalism. He spoke often of life residing, revealing itself and the soul, in the blood where 'the vital principle itself has its seat'. Just as there exists in the semen, say Harvey, something which makes it generative and exceeds the powers of the elements in building an animal, there dwells in the blood some power which acts beyond the power of the elements. We have already encountered this notion in the thought of Aristotle. The vital principle, says Harvey with Aristotle, is non-material.

Perhaps, then, it is proper that the great Harvey be known as the father of biology, for the paradox he represents has been a leitmotiv behind all that has happened since. Two main currents of biological thought have crossed the centuries: the vitalistic view and the mechanistic. And, though neither originated with Harvey, both received substantial nourishment at his hands. The scientific method attests to the validity of Harvey's brilliant mechanistic discovery. What value we may place upon his non-empirical ideas is another matter. It is difficult to say how one can evaluate any vitalistic conception since no observation that could be made would rule it out. But, as we shall later observe, this has been no bar to believers in vitalism. In thinking of Harvey, one is reminded of the remark that Einstein is said to have made when asked for his opinion of Schrödinger's treatise on wave mechanics, whose conclusions Einstein felt were not justified by the data: 'I enjoyed the data, but I didn't read the novel.'

In any event, Harvey's great discovery did what too long needed doing. It launched biology as a science.

## Corpse Dissection: the Decline and Fall of Galenism

A debate over whether life has a special mystical nature is, in one sense, a debate over whether biology is fundamentally different from physics as a field of inquiry. The physicist looks at the inanimate world and, using the scientific method, elucidates its laws. If there is no difference between the two, the biologist should do likewise and with equal success. With Harvey, he began doing precisely that.

And yet there are differences between biology and physics. Biology faces a more difficult problem, for the complexity of life is built upon the complexity of matter and hence longer years were needed to scrape away the thicker shell of myth to get at the core of valid inquiry. For this reason alone, philosophy in the seventeenth century was dominated by physics, while the science of living organisms has only recently begun to make its impress upon philosophy. Biology offered grave difficulties to the early experimentalists who desired to use the scientific method on the problem of life but who possessed no unifying theories or hypotheses to guide their efforts. For long years, the only generalization that biology could claim was that life existed in many shapes and guises, and it was precisely this meagre conception that dominated most of the early work. Its long early years were devoted to the task of *description*, for, as in all sciences in their formative phase, one must look and examine before seeking explanations.

Description flourished in the first century of scientific biology, and the hallmark of the new awakening became *anatomy*, the very epitome of systematic description – and if we must name a 'father of anatomy' it is the inexhaustible Andreas Vesalius, who lived from 1514 to 1564. The Renaissance was the heir to a medical orthodoxy whose force and supremacy exactly paralleled the phenomenon of Aristotelianism in philosophy. The great physician of antiquity who remained unquestioned for 1,300 years was Galen, who lived from A.D. 130 to 200. A courtier of rank, a fashionable practitioner of imperial Rome, the last great physician of the ancient world, Galen began his career as surgeon to the gladiators and ended it as physician to the Emperor Marcus Aurelius. For thirteen centuries, Galen stood as the final authority on anatomy despite the fact that the nearest creature to man to be dissected by him was the ape, and he was not always careful to avoid drawing conclusions from one to the other despite his warnings to other anatomists of the dangers of such a practice.

## Nature, Science, and Man: How the Quest Began

Why was his influence equalled only by Aristotle's? George Sarton suggests that there were many reasons, most of them irrational. Galen endeared himself to the early religionists, who saw in him an ally who could bolster their theological views with the authority of science. And again, we must remark on the difference between a man and the dogmatism erected in his name. We cannot blame Galen for the idolatrous acceptance of his erroneous views by men who had every opportunity to learn the truth for themselves.

But practically no one thought of doing so until Vesalius. It is a remarkable fact, as Ashley Montagu pointed out, that the two books which most scholars agree mark the end of the Middle Ages were published within one week of each other. The first, *De revolutionibus orbium coelestium* by the Polish canon Copernicus, was published in Nürnberg on 25 May 1543, when the author was seventy years old, while the second, *De humani corporis fabrica libri septem*, was published at Basel on 1 June 1543, when its author, Vesalius, was twenty-eight years old.

It is difficult to fathom the real nature of Vesalius' contribution, for one can scarcely imagine why the world had to wait so long for a man who could write down what his eyes perceived. Vesalius was not the first to dissect the human body. Dissection and the witnessing of surgery became part of the curriculum of the Italian medical schools as early as the eleventh century, and by the middle of the thirteenth century the practice was fairly well organized in the universities of Salerno, Bologna, and Padua. One might suppose that the misleading errors of Galen could have easily been corrected by several hundred years of first-hand dissecting experience. But though the old editions of Galen became encrusted with marginalia, the medieval respect for classical authority knew no limit. Progress, it seems, was not to take place.

One reason for the stalemate should amuse anyone familiar with the inmost secrets of modern medicine, for the situation has not changed very much. It was the antagonism between the physicians and surgeons. In those days, the physicians, having received an essentially literary and philosophical education,

82

looked with contempt upon the surgeons, who were mere technicians. In the dissecting theatre, the surgeon would wield the knife while the professor lectured platitudes and 'demonstrated' items of interest as they were dug up by the surgeon. Occasionally, to the delight of the students, great flatulent professorial debates would arise between visiting philosophical disciples of Aristotle and the medical followers of Galen. And while the discourse ebbed and flowed, the poor surgeon hacked away with his miserable implements, unnoticed except for an occasional epithet hurled from the cathedra. Is there any wonder that anatomy made no progress?

In considering the work of Vesalius, we again encounter the question that was raised in discussing Harvey – about the difficulties surrounding any effort to trace an innovation to its source. In a stimulating essay called 'Vesalius and the Galenists', Ashley Montagu points out that for some reason Vesalius has become the romantic hero of an allegory about good and evil, a knight-errant who with sudden clear-mindedness struck down the living remnants of the Middle Ages who had lingered on into the Renaissance.

The truth is, however, that early sixteenth-century anatomists had already begun drifting toward a reliance upon observations rather than authority. The new spirit was clearly evident in the work of Carpi, Massa, and the brilliantly versatile Leonardo da Vinci, all predecessors of Vesalius who must surely have influenced him. In the *Fabrica*, therefore, Vesalius was, in fact, continuing an existing trend. Nevertheless, the work of Vesalius was prosecuted on a grand scale, and his individual contribution was gigantic.

In the *Fabrica*, Vesalius determined not only to give a systematic and accurate description of all parts of the human body but to present his work in as elegant a setting as graphic art would allow. He fretted over the publication, insisting on the finest engravers, that the paper should be strong and of uniform thickness, that every detail of every picture must be clearly visible. The work was based on the experience of five years' dissections, some of which were performed on decaying corpses taken from the gallows. The volume as published in 1543 contained 663 folio pages, 278 magnificent woodcuts, and numerous decorative historiated initials, one of which depicted a 'resurrection' scene in the dissecting room. Truly, it is one of the great books of the world. Anatomy books to this day stand or fall by the quality of their drawings. From this standpoint, the *Fabrica* remains the most superb anatomical treatise ever to have been published.

Perhaps the tendency of later generations to create legends about Vesalius is an inevitable consequence of his extraordinary bumptiousness and the staggering torrent of controversy engendered by his work and personality. The publication of the *Fabrica* shook the medical world to its foundations. His old teachers, among them Sylvius of Paris (who had been planning an anatomy book of his own) rose up in fury at this mad young usurper who dared challenge not only their own but Galen's authority. Although Vesalius mentioned no names, Sylvius felt the sting of words such as these, wherein Vesalius, speaking of his attempt to make his anatomy complete, writes:

> But this effort could by no manner of means have succeeded if, when I was studying medicine at Paris, I had not myself applied my hand to this business, but had acquiesced in the casual and superficial display to me and my fellow-students by certain barbers of a few organs at one or two public dissections. For in such perfunctory manner was anatomy then treated in the place where we have lived to see medicine happily reborn . . . except for eight muscles of the abdomen, disgracefully mangled and in the wrong order, no one (I speak the simple truth) ever demonstrated to me any single muscle, or any single bone, much less the network of nerves, veins, and arteries.

Of the hysterical and continuing attacks that were launched against Vesalius, Montagu assures us that the resentment was a personal one directed against the objectionable imperiousness and youth of its object. 'It was not a school of thought', says Montagu, 'which through its followers was hostile to Vesalius but frustrated individuals who seized upon Vesalius' criticism of Galen as a peg upon which to hang their abuse of the critic.' The vaunted break with Galenism does not withstand scrutiny. Vesalius, like Harvey, considered himself to have remained in the antiquarian tradition. Though he criticized Galen (sometimes unfairly), he remained a Galenist, and this kinship is clear in Vesalius' work which held continuously to most of Galen's metaphysical ideas.

A first-class historical mystery surrounds the life of Vesalius subsequent to his triumphant publication of the *Fabrica* at the age of twenty-eight, for this event marked the end of his achievement in the history of science. Although anatomy now became Vesalian, Vesalius passed into the background. He left his chair as Professor of Anatomy at Padua and became physician to the Emperor Charles V, an unexplained withdrawal from a brilliant academic life that has caused much conjecture among historians.

Some have suggested that in such an appointment Vesalius hoped to find protection from the persecutions of his enemies. Another theory was that he needed money after the expensive publication of the *Fabrica*. Others have guessed that he feared ecclesiastical retribution as a result of having rifled graves and desecrated bodies. One unsupported story has it that Vesalius, while in the Court of Spain, undertook the dissection of a young woman whom he had attended. When the body was opened, the spectators were horrified to see the heart beating. Following this catastrophe, Vesalius undertook a pilgrimage to the Holy Land in order to avoid the Inquisition, a journey on which he met death at the age of fifty.

The most reasonable speculation seems to be that of O'Malley and Saunders, who consider Vesalius' rejection of his pre-eminent position to be entirely logical behaviour for a man whose world was 'guided by conceptions of a universal order derived from Platonic thinking'. To him, therefore, the ultimate aim of the physician was the perfection of the medical art, attainable only through its practice. To modern physicians who cling to the academy, such an idea may come as an inspirational challenge.

And so, regardless of the identity of its author, a break had now taken place with the meagre but powerful tradition of ancient biological thought. It began when anatomy became a systematic body of observational data upon which the questions of how, why, and whence could be intelligently asked.

## The Microcosm Grows Smaller

There is something magnificently obvious about cutting a man open and peering at his insides. Even a child contemplating his navel might think of trying it. But how could anyone reasonably be expected to assume the existence of a subworld of living creatures too small to be seen by the naked eye? The fact is no one did assume it until long after the lens-grinders and spectacle-makers had placed into the hands of curiosity-mongers powerful magnifying glasses of very short focus.

Although a number of individuals glimpsed at seeds and insects through their new lenses, two men may be singled out as the first to realize the full importance of studying nature with instruments capable of increasing the power of the human senses. One was the brilliant Malpighi of Bologna (1628–94), whose long catalogue of microscopic discoveries included the tiny capillaries – which elegantly completed the circulatory pathway discovered by Harvey – and the fine structure of the kidney. The other was the Englishman Robert Hooke. His point of view was put forth convincingly in a remarkable book published in 1665 under the imprimatur of the Royal Society. We have already encountered Hooke as the assistant of Boyle and a source of irritation to Isaac Newton. Hooke, who lived from 1635 to 1703, had a fascinating career. 'Curator of experiments' for the Royal Society, Hooke was a master mechanic in an age when there were still a few laws left which a mechanic could discover. In the early days of the Royal Society, its meetings were rather like circuses at which the members demonstrated their latest discoveries. Hooke was the fuss-pot who could always be seen tinkering with the equipment and superintending its operation. He became enamoured of metal springs, invented carriage springs and the spiral watch spring, and, by observing that within the limit of elasticity the stretch of a spring is proportional to the stress put upon it, he discovered the law which bears his name. He drollishly published this discovery as an anagram, *ceiiinosssttuu*, and waited two years before disclosing its solution, '*ut tensio sic uis*' ('the power of any spring is in the same proportion with the tension thereof'). It is a manner of scientific communication which never became popular.

The treatise on microscopy was called *The Micrographia; or Some Physiological Descriptions of Minute Bodies Made by Magnifying Glasses and Enquiries Thereupon*. With this work, Hooke launched his study of microscopic anatomy, a purely descriptive voyage through an unknown sea, but one destined in later years to lead to the central discovery of biology, the cell. Upon examining a piece of cork, Hooke perceived it 'to be perforated and porus much like a Honey-comb, but that the pores of it were not regular; yet it was not unlike a Honey-comb in these particulars: first, in that it had a very solid substance, in comparison of the empty cavity that was contained between; next in that these pores, or cells, were not very deep, but consisted of a great many little Boxes, separated out of one continued Long pore, by certain Diaphragms.' He was viewing, of course, only the thickened walls of dead cells, but in later notes he recorded similar divisions in the surfaces of living nettle leaves. Hooke was the first to have described living cells but not the last to fail to understand their true nature. It is, incidentally, often lamented that he termed these structures *cells*. Cell means 'little room' and that is what Hooke thought these spaces were. In the light of later developments, corpuscles – 'little bodies' – would have been more appropriate.

Hooke's contemporaries viewed this new world with considerable excitement, although Samuel Pepys complained that the cost of his microscope, £5 10s., was a 'great price for a curious bauble'. The microscopic century was climaxed by the classic contributions of three great men: Johannes Swammerdam of Amsterdam, who saw the red cells in the blood of a frog; and the London physician Nehemiah Grew, who rediscovered the cells of Hooke, calling them 'utricles' and 'vesicles' but still failed to see the contents of the little rooms. The third was Leeuwenhoek.

Antony van Leeuwenhoek, the lens-grinder of Delft, was as eccentric a character as one is likely to meet in the chronicles of science, although at times I suspect his biographers of making too much of a good thing. That he was garrulous, suspicious, gossipy, and contentious is obvious from his own writings, but as Paul de Kruif depicts him in *Microbe Hunters* his performance borders on the slapstick. This is, of course, far from a scholarly book, but it does seem to have coloured and to have been coloured by the stereotyped image of poor old Leeuwenhoek. It is my impression that his eccentricity vanishes as soon as one ceases making foolish comparisons between this man and his contemporaries of the Royal Society of England, many of whom have passed irretrievably into oblivion. Fortunately, Latinity was not then and is not now a prerequisite for intelligence and skill.

What we do know is that Leeuwenhoek's contributions were monumental. Using lenses of his own making, he patiently examined the microscopic structure of everything he could place his hands on, and, at the request of the newly founded Royal Society, reported his discoveries in a series of communications that went forth without interruption for over fifty years. He found in rain water a subvisible world of swimming creatures and wrote the first description of bacteria. To doubters, he offered affidavits from prominent citizens of Delft who had seen the 'wretched beasties'. He did not, of course, relate them to human disease. He discovered blood cells, and as de Kruif so turgidly put it, 'The most sacred and improper and romantic things in life were only material for the probing, tireless eyes of his lenses. Leeuwenhoek discovered the human sperm, and the cold-blooded science of his searching would have been shocking, if he had not been such a completely innocent man!' At one point, he declared he had seen within a sperm a whole tiny man. In his famous letter of 1674, Leeuwenhoek first described protozoan organisms of pond water. Before dispatching his last communication at the age of ninety-one, he had told the Royal Society of an infinite variety of microscopic life. To the end, he refused to disclose his methods of study.

Curiously, the death of Leeuwenhoek in 1723 ended the first

inquisitive phase of biological microscopy. The age had achieved the pioneer discoveries in a wide range of fields; in general, however, it emphasized what we now call histology rather than cytology. According to Woodruff, the attempt of that time to envisage biological truth from the data at hand was premature because of their superficiality. As Peattie wrote, 'We have the feeling that the men of that age were coasting along golden shores that were hidden from them in thin mists, and that with a little more perseverance, vision, and daring, they would have had a landfall of twentieth-century discovery.' Although cells had been seen, their nature remained unknown until 1838, 173 years after Hooke's examination of a piece of cork.

The power of the past was now broken and the new groundwork laid. With the piling up of triumphs for the scientific method, with the realization that living things were accessible to scientific investigation, with the proliferation of printing, books, and writing, modern biology came at last into its own.

# 5

## The Futile Search for Certainty

> An idealist is one who, on noticing that a rose smells better than a cabbage, concludes it will also make better soup.
>
> – H. L. Mencken

IT has been stated that, compared to the mathematical and physical sciences, biology is an immature youth. Perhaps this is so. But when they start off in search of certain knowledge, biologists and physicists start together and, in the course, of things, they meet the same fate.

### Our Most Cherished Illusion

Can man aspire to certain knowledge? Is there or can there be an ideal of absolute truth? If the universe is a machine, is there a strict plan behind its functioning which will permit certain predictive knowledge, or do parts of the mechanism resemble gambling devices? We must seriously ask these questions because if science is the ascendant force in the modern world, if we are to live with it and by it – or even for it – we must deepen our understanding of what it is and what it is not.

As we view the brilliant successes that science and the scientific method have achieved, are we not entitled to conclude that here is the true pathway to certain knowledge? Sadly, it is not, as all its travellers must inevitably discover. To understand why this is so is to understand science, for, in one sense, the history of science is the history of human opinion on the question of certainty.

It is easy to see how the exuberant age of Newton might have come to believe that nature and reason held the key to certain knowledge. In those years, the air had the tang of the concept of progress and the times were imbued with the exciting new belief that human beings could achieve here on this earth a state of happiness and perfection that previous centuries thought possible only for deceased Christians in a state of grace. Reason – in its ordinary meaning – was the new Nirvana, for it would lead man to an understanding of nature and supreme truth concerning what is good and right. John Locke emerged as a great philosopher of the new method, vigorously (and often uncritically) defending the principles of empiricism and inductive logic. The age idolized Newton and even Locke in his *Essay Concerning Human Understanding* referred to himself beside the 'incomparable Mr Newton, [as] an under-labourer, employed in clearing the ground and removing some of the rubbish that lies in the way of knowledge'. Likewise, the great Laplace remarked that Newton was not only the greatest genius that ever lived, he was also the most fortunate, since there is but one universe and it can therefore be the lot of but one man in history to be the interpreter of its laws.

As the new idea spread through the world of affairs, its impact was felt in every sphere. Free trade replaced protective tariff practices because the way of nature was the way of free and independent competition. Monasticism began to disappear because celibacy made no sense. Men gave up believing that demons caused mental illness and the problem entered the realm of science. Even the high rational standards of the framers of the American Constitution were spiritual exemplars of the Age of Reason. Reason linked with experience was to be the guide to certain truth.

Yet it was not long before a voice of caution was heard in the din. How can one justify the use of inductive logic? asked David Hume, perhaps the greatest of all philosophers who have written in the English language. The answer one thinks of is that it has worked. But, Hume points out, what we are saying is 'induction has so far proved successful, therefore it is justified' and this is itself an inductive inference. This is circular reasoning and the argument breaks down: we cannot justify induction and empiricism by induction and empiricism. And with this declaration, Hume brought to a ruinous end the classical age of empiricism.

It was Hume's steadfast position that none of man's beliefs can be given the stamp of certainty

This onslaught on the inductive inference has been answered by modern philosophy. We need say little on the nature of mathematical truth, for all seem agreed (including Hume) that mathematics in no wise contributes anything to the *content* of our knowledge of the world, but is rather an indispensable and powerful instrument for the validation, understanding, and even linguistic expression of such knowledge. But the defence of induction leaves us a little uneasy if certainty is what we desire. Part of the defence rests on the probable character of knowledge that has been mentioned. However, it is clear that a system which yields probable knowledge is vulnerable to the same critique brought by Hume against a system claiming certainty. Perhaps the clearest account of today's thinking on this question is that of Hans Reichenbach, who wrote:

The man who makes inductive inferences may be compared to a fisherman who casts a net into an unknown part of the ocean – he does not know whether he will catch fish, but he knows that if he wants to catch fish he has to cast his net. Every inductive prediction is like casting a net into the ocean of the happenings of nature; we do not know whether we shall have a good catch, but we try, at least, and try by the help of the best means available.

We try because we want to act – and he who wants to act cannot wait until the future has become observational knowledge. To control the future – to shape future happenings according to a plan – presupposes predictive knowledge of what will happen if certain conditions are realized; and if we do not know the truth about what will happen, we shall employ our best posits in the place of truth. Posits are the instruments of action where truth is not available; the justification of induction is that it is the best instrument of action known to us.*

* This reply of Mr Reichenbach's to Hume's broadside, though it pleases me, has nevertheless failed to please a number of contemporary philosophers. Witness Ernest Nagel's critique of Reichenbach's epistemology in *Sovereign Reason* and, more recently, Roy Harrod's brave attempt in *Foundations of Inductive Logic* to show that there are fully valid inductive arguments that require no support from any presupposition whatever regarding the uniformity of nature.

We begin then to perceive how deep go the reasons which bar us from certainty. But other factors also contribute to the folly of such a quest. We have said that an experiment is an act or procedure carried out for the purpose of establishing knowledge. Consider: What do we do when we conduct an experiment? The key word in the answer to this question is *interaction*. Experiments are procedures deliberately designed to produce the *interaction* of some agency under our control with the system or object we are studying. It is the result of these interactions which we perceive. We seldom or never see (or in any way sense) the thing or event itself, but only the results of our manipulations of it. The reason for this is that our senses are incapable of perceiving the phenomena which illustrate most of the general laws. We can see falling objects and, if we are made of the stuff of Newton, we can suspect a natural law. Much is still being learned in biology by pure observation and brute description. This is the basic technique of the taxonomist, and even he is becoming a meddlesome experimentalist. But we cannot see the amount of acid in a test tube unless we add an indicator which becomes coloured in the presence of acid (and if we wish to be quantitative we can measure the depth of the colour). We cannot see the thyroid gland controlling the body's oxygen consumption unless we intervene and measure the oxygen consumed as we somehow manipulate the thyroid function to make it increase or decrease.

Interaction of some agency with a natural object or system, producing some visible measurable result, is the essence of experiment. It is the implications of *interaction* which spell despair for the one who would seek certain knowledge.

If you look at a cell under the microscope, in most cases you are looking at coloured and easily discernible structures made visible by a process of fixation and staining. The fixative hardens the cell in its natural position at the moment of contact (at least we think it does, but how can we be sure without looking at 'natural' cells and how can we look at them without fixing and staining them?). Stain reacts chemically with certain substances in the cell making their architectural pattern clearly visible in the microscope (that is, we assume the pattern is not disturbed by the stain, but to verify this we would have to compare the arrangement with that of an unstained cell, where, unfortunately, the pattern is only seen with difficulty).

Thus, we have had to infer what is going on in the unmolested system, an inference often difficult or impossible because we do not know to what extent the experimental intervention disturbed the system under study. Nor can we ever know except by further experiment, and this involves a further dislocation of the phenomenon of unknown and unknowable extent. The interactions we are producing are thus *obstacles* in the quest for certainty. This source of uncertainty is of momentous importance in biology.

It is easy to think of examples which make clear the difficulties involved in this situation. How do we know that the removal of blood from a vein for the purpose of counting the blood cells does not alter the blood count? To check this would necessitate doing blood counts in some way which would not require removal of blood from the body, undeniably a formidable task. But let us imagine that someone conceived a way of counting the cells in the blood by passing a beam of light through some blood vessels, say, for example, in the ear or finger, and enumerating the cells as they went by. This would require considerable adroitness because the rate of flow of blood through even the smallest capillaries is known to be rapid and erratic. Now, of course, the problem is one of proving that the light which transilluminates the capillaries either does not disturb the blood count in that area or disturbs it to an extent which is uniformly consistent and proportional to the true count. To prove either of these assertions requires some knowledge of the true count and we are right back where we started.

Instances of this sort occur all through biological science. Every experiment or observation is subject to limitations in interpretation imposed by the inexhaustible sources of uncertainty. It is 'certainly' true in psychiatry that the chief investigative technique of this science, the interviewing or testing of subjects, imposes influences of greater or lesser psychological importance on the subject – what the subject says, it must be remembered, he is saying in a test situation. What we know of his memory is based on what he tells us. He may not tell all. If he is given a drug to rid him of inhibitions, we must consider that the drug may alter either the faculty of memory or the subject's ability to relate the content of his memory. And so on. Yet, despite the unshakable enigma of the inherent uncertainty in all experiments, why do we talk as though a great deal is known with certainty in biology? We do indeed know a very great deal and are learning more each year. The point here is that everything we know has a *probability value*, an attached tag upon which is written the probability or likelihood that this fact is correct. Never is the fact so certain that the probability of its being false is zero. The probability of truth in many cases is great and rests securely on very good observations, repeatedly made in different laboratories by different investigators. Often, similar results come from several experimental approaches permitting us the reasonable inference that if our manipulations are disturbing the experimental object, at least they are doing so to a similar extent in each of the different types of experiments. For example, if no matter which of the many fundamentally different methods we used to determine the molecular weight of some compound we always got the same answer, probably – very probably – the answer is close to the truth.

It is therefore apparent that any conclusions based on 'probably valid' experimental observations will themselves bear the taint. They, too, will have a probability rating, and there is no way in the world of bettering their status except by bettering the data upon which they are based.

A whole new science has arisen to deal with the probability problem: statistical analysis and the science of experimental design. Since the conclusions of scientific research carry an inherent probability rating and are based on experiments that have a certain inherent error, it becomes mandatory to turn to an old reliable helpmate, mathematical analysis, to give us some notion of the value – the degree of probability – of our conclusions. Statistical analysis gives us no new knowledge of the

95

world but it delineates, sometimes in highly quantitative fashion, the *extent of uncertainty* attaching to the knowledge we have elsewhere uncovered. The devices of this type of analysis provide the scientist with accurate statements of the variance of his data, the probability that the results could be attributable to pure chance, clues as to the amount of work or number of experiments he must do in order to make the error of rejecting a correct hypothesis only once, say, in twenty times, an arbitrary decision. (It is surprising how inefficient scientific research can be, unguided by the principles of statistics.) Most important is the direction of the scientist's attention to methods of increasing the sensitivity of succeeding experiments or in some cases to the abandonment of a series of experiments because the factors producing imprecision are clearly beyond control. Finally, statistical methods, generously blended with portions of common sense, are instrumental in determining the design of the experiment.

Experimental design, particularly in a field as complex as biology, is no simple matter. It is essential to the experimental method that every system under study be compared with another system with *all* conditions identical except one. In this way, the role of the one factor may be reflected in the index we have chosen to observe. If we are interested in studying the effect of a certain drug in the treatment of some disease, the proper controls must be rigidly set up. If the disease is like most, it will eventually end in spontaneous recovery. Thus, if our unknown drug is administered to the patient, we will necessarily judge it favourably if no more is done. Presumably, this is the kind of 'proof' behind the therapeutic use of holy oil, amulets, prayer, and the killing of a goat. For scientific evaluation the needed control is a sufficient number of people of the same age with the same malady each given an imitation of the drug (to control the emotional component in drug-induced recovery) followed by careful comparison of the duration of illness and percentage recovery in the treated and untreated groups.

The one factor being evaluated may be very complex, as typified by sociological problems where, for example, one might wish to compare and analyse the political beliefs of Negroes and white men. The individual components of this factor may or may not be accessible to further clarification, hence the unending contemporary debate: Is sociology a science? Such complexity, as we shall presently see, is not unique to sociology.

# 2

## THE FIRST GREAT
## MODERN SYNTHESIS

# 6

## The Unit of Life

> Give me six lines written by the most honourable of men, and I will
> find an excuse in them to hang him.
>
> – Richelieu, 1625

PHYSICS early achieved a sweepingly unifying conception in the
discovery of the indestructibility of energy. And this was precisely what the new biology lacked. Succeeding generations of
biologists sought desperately for some point of view which would
bring uniformity into the welter of data that had begun to ac-
cumulate. Men looked at living organisms, those islands of life
which somehow manage to stay afloat in the great sea of non-
life, and wondered. How did life originate? How did 'simple'
atoms and molecules arrange themselves in elaborate parcels and
then come alive? How did they develop the intricate machinery
for profitably exchanging matter with the inanimate environment,
sucking in food and oxygen, using what is needed and rejecting
what is not? How did they acquire the ability to 'breed true',
men propagating men and microbes microbes while at the same
time evolving into millions of different species? How did they
learn to repair their wounds, to resist stress, to think, feel, and
reason?

We cannot here enter into the details of the history of biology
to which so many have contributed in the years since the
Renaissance. Instead, I should like to sketch the emergence of
what might be called the modern point of view in several
of the key areas of biological thought. The first of these is
the notion that the cell is the unit of life, for this was the
realization that finally brought to biology its long-wished-for
unity.

# The First Great Modern Synthesis

## The Cell Theory is Born

The basic units of matter are atoms, and, true to their etymology, they cannot be split and still retain the attributes of a chemical element. Splitting the atom produces new and incredibly diverse smaller particles, and it is true that some among the subatomic particles do have certain properties in common with intact atoms of elemental matter – mass, for example. But, as we know the elements by their chemical and spectroscopic behaviour, we know also that subatoms are not elemental matter but only parts further divisible perhaps, of enormously more complex wholes. If nothing else, the particles lack the great empty vastnesses of the atom, abysses made of pure vacuum which occupy all but $\dfrac{1}{1,000,000,000,000}$ (or thereabouts) of the atom's volume.

Those basic properties which we ordinarily associate with the phenomenon of life are *all* possessed by nothing less complex than the cell. Many of the components of the living cell, the 'sub-living' systems, may likewise share some of the properties of the living system itself, but the subsystems are not living organisms. The cell is. The biologist's broadening effort to comprehend the cell by intellectually reconstructing it from carefully isolated subsystems and fragments is a major theme of today's biology.

It is generally stated that the cell theory was formulated in 1838 by Schleiden and Schwann; yet the speakers at the 1939 centennial celebration of the cell theory were at great pains to deny that 'the idea sprang Minerva-like, fully formed and original from the substance of their brains'. The biological historians insisted that a closer reading of the literature of the century indicates that these men had many predecessors who had stated, directly or obliquely, that cells were the units of life. 'In spite of all these antecedents,' wrote Professor Conklin, 'one of the most surprising facts in the history of science is that many texts of biology consider Schleiden founder of the cell theory.'

Again we face a familiar question. It is true that by 1835 the cell was beginning to emerge as an entity possessing a life of its own and a complex structure. The time was ripe for a unifying theory stating the cellular nature of all living things – and, as has happened over and over again in science, when times are ripe, realizations come to several individuals simultaneously. If species must evolve then surely so must ideas.

It was in October 1838 that a famous dinner conversation is said to have occurred. Matthias Schleiden was an erratic, volatile character who turned to biology only in 1831 after having already attempted suicide in despondency over his failure as a lawyer. The story is told that shortly after the appearance of his monograph on the microscopic anatomy of plants in *Muller's Archiv*, Schleiden described his work over the coffee cups to Theodor Schwann, the German physiologist who, biographers insist, was a 'simple' man. Schwann recognized the similarity of Schleiden's plant cell nuclei to structures he had seen in animal nerve tissue, and the two went immediately to Schwann's laboratory at the Anatomical Institute. Schleiden, too, recognized the similarities of structure. This, according to the more rhapsodic historians of biology, was the dawn of the cell theory.

Actually, Schleiden, in his famous monograph of 1838 and without acknowledging his indebtedness to his predecessors, proposed three conclusions: (1) that plants are composed entirely of cells which are *units of structure, physiology, and organization*; (2) that cells possess *duality*, that is, they are independent lives within a higher form of life; and (3) the main thesis, that there is a common mechanism of cell formation whereby new cells arise by a process analogous to crystal formation. Professor Karling points out that the last conclusion, Schleiden's false theory on cell origin, was also not original. 'At that time there were two outstanding views as to how cells arise: first, the view that the nucleus and cell develop from an aggregation and confluence of granules of various sorts in the viscid content of the cell; and second, the view that new cells arise by division of a pre-existing cell.' The second view, of course, is the correct one, as we shall mention momentarily. 'How unfortunate', wrote Karling, 'for biological research of that decade and the reputation of Schwann that Schleiden did not choose the alternative and

103

correct view of his contemporary botanists.' Since Schwann agrees with Schleiden on the mechanism of cell formation, he must on this issue stand or fall with Schleiden. As the falsity of the Schleiden and Schwann thesis of cell origin gradually came to light, this part of their work tended to be forgotten and in time their fame was secured by the erroneous belief that they had originated the doctrine of the independence, individuality, and duality of the cell and that it is the fundamental unit of all organisms.

'On the whole', wrote Conklin, 'one gets a very unpleasant picture of Schleiden's relations to his predecessors and contemporaries, and the question forces itself on us, "How did he come to be recognized as the founder of the cell theory?" I once heard a distinguished physiologist say that there are two ways to gain recognition, either brag or fight. It seems to me that Schleiden did both.'

It seems to me regrettable that even in science there exists the need to create heroes where none exist. The compulsion to engraft a man's name on to a vast scientific movement seems to lead only to decades and centuries of quibbling. I strongly doubt that Schleiden and Schwann foresaw that their work would raise this issue and I doubt that they would have claimed paternity to the cell theory. It seems sufficient to say that their work was of value, their theory of cell division reasonable in its time. On that question, they were merely wrong. The detracting tone of the centennial essayists would perhaps have been better directed at the anamnestic errors of Schleiden and Schwann's successors.

It has occurred to me that the cell theory is a curious anomaly in the history of science. At no time in its early years did the theory ever seem a theoretical necessity. Instead, it seemed to wander into being, dawning slowly and simultaneously upon many men's minds, unlike the great discoveries of great individuals. Confronted with brute experimental data, Dalton established the basic laws of modern atomic theory. To explain his observations, Darwin was forced to his theory of natural selection. But the cell theory, which surely ranks beside these two, had no such nativity. As we have noted, cells were seen centuries before they were given special meaning by Hooke and Leeuwenhoek. Surely there was no good reason to suspect *a priori* that life could be divided into unit lives. The atomism of the ancient Greeks had long since gone to the philosophical nether world, and although Democritus had clearly stated that all life and growth and human behaviour arose from 'the conjunctions and dispersions of atoms', he had no good reason to think so. The sixteenth-century physician Fernel, who was brought so vividly to life by Sherrington, wrote that, for his part, divide a bit of muscle and you will merely get smaller muscle. He assumed, in the absence of the microscope, that such subdivision could continue indefinitely – there was no reason to think otherwise. Yet, when the microscope arrived and achieved the discovery that had merely been awaiting its arrival, men's imaginations failed to comprehend these specks of life. Their existence scandalized Buffon. Life seemed degraded if it could exist in such lowliness. It could be argued, I think, that this is yet another example of the conditioning of scientific thought by the philosophical climate and the psychology of an era.

If for no other reason than its heuristic value, the cell theory quickly began to prosper. It was promptly extended to unicellular organisms with the pronouncement of von Siebold in 1845 that protozoa are simply animals consisting of one cell. The majority of observers came to abandon the doctrine of the free formation of cells as expounded by Schleiden and Schwann, and, by mid-century, it was firmly established that cells alone can originate new cells. '*Omnis cellula e cellula,*' intoned Virchow. And, in 1861, simultaneously with the beginning of the great period of histological staining researches, Max Schultze proposed the essence of the modern 'protoplasm theory'. He presumed a fundamental similarity of the basic jelly-like substance of plant and animal cells and, extrapolating to all living forms, concluded that the material called 'protoplasm' is the 'physical basis of all life', differing from species to species only in specific details of structure and composition. To Schultze, we owe the oft-quoted definition of a cell as a 'mass of protoplasm containing a nucleus'. Thomas Huxley's famous Edinburgh lecture of 1868, which was called *On the Physical Basis of Life* (a title destined to become a cliché of biological literature), supported the unifying idea of

105

protoplasm and stressed the universality of its form and function throughout the range of living systems. The concept of the universality of protoplasm became part of the first general synthesis of biological phenomena, and its most penetrating presentation was the 1892 edition of Hertwig's *The Cell and the Tissues*, which brought to a close a fruitful century.

I do not mean to suggest that opposition merely evaporated in the face of these theories. Their abstractions were tenuous and failed to predict or explain a huge number of facts. Many continued to support the idea that there are simpler units of life than cells, and this list included (with their verbal inventions) Haeckel's 'plastidules', Nageli's 'micellae', Darwin's 'gemmules', and Hertwig's 'idioblasts', plus a welter of other conceptions based on the notion of super-fundamental subcellular units of life.

Although much had been learned by direct microscopic examination of living cells, the great bulk of information on cellular structure was collected by painstaking examination of fixed and stained cells. Since fixation means killing and hardening the cell with chemicals, the static quality of this body of knowledge is understandable. Interestingly, the study of cell structure had its golden age in the last half of the nineteenth century in direct consequence of great new discoveries in the theory and technology of dyes. Germany was the centre of activity in the field of dye chemistry, and we find that early cytomorphology was advanced by those biologists who had learned their chemistry well, the Germans. By skilfully applying to the chemically heterogeneous inner structure of fixed cells the principles learned in dyeing and mordanting wool, silk, and cotton fibres, microscopists were able to emblazon individual cell elements in brilliantly contrasting colours. And, in addition to the mere dyeing of non-living tissue elements, cytologists and histologists learned to use colouring agents as a means of identifying specific chemical substances within the cell, as, for example, the recognition of starch by its iodine reaction. In its full flower, this technique came to be known as *histochemistry*. Nineteenth-century workers also learned to render visible certain structures by ingeniously impregnating them with opaque materials, a technique akin to but distinctly

106

different from dyeing. With special care, the most ultrafine structure of the cell could be brought into view by coating it with a delicate film of silver or gold. This technique was brought to its highest art by men like Golgi, Cohnheim, and Cajal.

Of course, like its biological substratum, staining theory was for long years not exactly crystalline in its clarity. Every bottle on the dye chemist's shelf was taken down and tried out as a cell stain, and although there emerged from this zealotry the standard stains of today – carmine, haematoxylin, eosin, and others – most of the early work was exuberantly haphazard. A reviewer in 1902 wrote, 'The method of staining, once having taken root in the animal histologist, grew and grew, till to be an histologist became practically synonymous with being a dyer, with this difference, that the professional dyer knew what he was about, while the histologist with few exceptions did not know, nor does he to the present day.' Even now, fifty years later, we can still complain that much of the literature on staining techniques reads like a witch's *vade mecum*. Long on cook-bookery and short on rationale, many published methods are more easily duplicated than interpreted.

There still persists debate on the question of whether cells are the simplest units of life, some of which retains the flavour of the nineteenth-century word tournaments. In the summer of 1954, there appeared a paper by the well-known Canadian endocrinologist and neologist Hans Selye declaring that the cell theory has become 'too deeply ingrained in the minds of biologists to be displaced by other concepts'. And as an 'other concept', Selye offered a new fundamental element of life – a subcellular unit he calls the 'reacton'. Reactons are defined as the smallest entities capable of 'selective biological reactivity'. The thesis is defended not by data but by verbal analogy and teleological argument, the latter epistemological principle receiving a ringing and entertainingly wayward commendation. Happily, the piece ends by supplying the seeds of its own refutation:

Vagueness of terms and concepts passes unnoticed, as long as there are not sufficient objective observations to which these should refer. Indeed, it would be a futile dialectic exercise to aim at conceptual or

107

terminologic precision in reference to a field which has not been subjected to that degree of laboratory analysis which makes such theoretical precision possible, or even necessary. Yet the theory must always be a little ahead of the facts, otherwise it cannot lead us to them.

Selye, of course, may be right – after all, Democritus was.

## The Matter of Spontaneous Generation

Biology, like physics, now had its atoms. They were the cells, and it became clear that the perpetuation and increase of the living world depends entirely on the production of cells and more cells. But a long and fundamental and rather tedious controversy had to take place before it was possible to state just where cells came from. When they were first recognized, it was evident that many kinds of cells could arise only by division of a parent cell – a case of 'multiplication by division' according to the traditional professorial joke. Yet it was far from clear whether cell division was *the* method or merely *a* method for cell formation. Thus, though it was generally accepted by 1860 that fermentation and putrefaction were caused by living micro-organisms, science still could not decisively answer the question: Where do microbes come from? This is not to say that no one had a hypothesis. Of two obvious possibilities – that like other cells they came from parent microbes identical to themselves or that they arose *de novo* from inanimate matter – for some reason few doubted the truth of the second.

From ancient times, men have believed that, under certain peculiar circumstances, life could arise spontaneously: from the ooze of rivers could come eels and from the entrails of dead bulls, bees; worms from mud, and maggots from dead meat. This belief was held by Aristotle, Newton, and Descartes, among many others, and apparently the great William Harvey too. (Harvey once wrote: '*omne vivum ex vivo*' – all life comes from life – but, in a famous address before the 1870 meeting of the British Association, Thomas Huxley remarked, 'It is commonly counted among the many merits of our great countryman, Harvey, that he was the first to declare the opposition of fact to venerable authority in this, as in other matters; but I can discover no justification for this widespread notion!') The weight of centuries gradually disintegrated men's beliefs in the spontaneous origin of maggots and mice, but the doctrine of spontaneous generation clung tenaciously to the question of bacterial origin.

In association with Buffon, the Irish Jesuit priest John Needham declared that he could bring about at will the creation of living microbes in heat-sterilized broths, and, presumably in propitiation, theorized that God did not create living things directly but bade the earth and water to bring them forth. In his *Dictionnaire philosophique*, Voltaire reflected that it was odd to read of Father Needham's claim while atheists conversely 'should deny a Creator yet attribute to themselves the power of creating eels'. But, wrote Thomas Huxley, 'The great tragedy of science – the slaying of a beautiful hypothesis by an ugly fact – which is so constantly being enacted under the eyes of philosophers, was played, almost immediately, for the benefit of Buffon and Needham.'

The Italian Abbé Spallanzani did an experiment. He showed that a broth *sealed from the air* while boiling never develops bacterial growths and hence never decomposes. To Needham's objection that Spallanzani had ruined his broths and the air above them by excessive boiling, the Abbé replied by breaking the seals of his flasks. Air rushed in and bacterial growth began! But the essential conflict remained. Whatever Spallanzani and his followers did to remove seeds and contaminants was regarded by the spontaneous generationists as damaging to the 'vital force' from whence comes new life.

Thus, doubt remained, and into the controversy came the titanic figure of Louis Pasteur. Believing that a solution to this problem was essential to the development of his theories concerning the role of bacteria in nature, Pasteur freely acknowledged the possibility that living bacteria very well might be arising anew from inanimate matter. To him, the research problem was largely a technical one: to repeat the work of those who had claimed to have observed spontaneous generation but to employ infinite care to discover and exclude every possible concealed portal of bacterial entry. For the one that contended that life did not enter from the outside, the proof had to go to the question of possible contamination. Pasteur worked logically. After prolonged boiling, a broth would ferment only when air was admitted to it. Therefore, either air contained a factor necessary for the spontaneous generation of life *or* viable germs were borne in by the air and seeded in the sterile nutrient broth. Pasteur designed ingenious flasks whose long S-shaped necks could be left open. Air could pass in and out freely but its bacteria-laden dust particles were trapped in the sinuous glass tube. Broths boiled in these flasks remained sterile. When their necks were snapped to admit ordinary air, bacterial growth would then commence – but not in every case. An occasional flask remained sterile presumably because the bacterial population of the air is unevenly distributed. The forces of spontaneous generation would not be so erratic. Continuing scepticism drove Pasteur almost to fanatical efforts to control the ingredients of his experiments to destroy the doubts of the most sceptical. He ranged from the mountain air of Montanvert, which he showed to be almost sterile, to those deep, clear wells whose waters had been rendered germ free by slow filtration through sandy soil. The latter discovery led to the familiar porcelain filters of the bacteriology laboratory. With pores small enough to exlude bacteria, solutions allowed to percolate through them could be reliably sterilized.

The argument raged on and soon spilled beyond the boundaries of science to become a burning religious and philosophical question of the day. For many, Pasteur's conclusions caused conflict because they seemed simultaneously to support the Biblical account of creation while denying a variety of other philosophical systems. The public was soon caught up in the crossfire of a vigorous series of public lectures and demonstrations by leading exponents of both views, novelists, clergymen, their adjuncts and friends. Perhaps the most famous of these evenings in the theatre – competing perhaps with that great debate between Huxley and Bishop Wilberforce for elegance of rhetoric – was Pasteur's public lecture at the Sorbonne on 7 April 1864. Having shown his audience the swan-necked flasks containing sterile broths, he concluded, 'And, therefore, gentlemen, I could point to that liquid and say to you, I have taken my drop of water from the immensity of creation, and I have taken it full of the elements appropriated to the development of inferior beings. And I wait, I watch, I question it! – begging it to recommence for me the beautiful spectacle of the first creation. But it is dumb, dumb since these experiments were begun several years ago; it is dumb because I have kept it from the only thing man does not know how to produce: from the germs that float in the air, from Life, for Life is a germ and a germ is Life. Never will the doctrine of spontaneous generation recover from the mortal blow of this simple experiment.' And it has not. Today these same flasks stand immutable: they are still free of microbial life.

It is an interesting fact that despite the ringing declaration of Pasteur, the issue did not die completely. And although far from healthy, it is not yet dead. In his fascinating biography of Pasteur, René Dubos has traced the later developments which saw new eruptions of the controversy, new technical progress and criticism, and new energetic figures in the breech of the battle such as Bastian, for, and the immortal Tyndall, against, the doctrine of spontaneous generation. There was also new 'sorrow' for Pasteur as he read years later, in 1877, the last jottings of the great physiologist Claude Bernard and saw in them the 'mystical' suggestion that yeast may arise from grape juice. Even at this late date, Pasteur was stirred to new experiments again to prove to the dead Bernard and his followers the correctness of his position.

Dubos wrote:

It is unrewarding for a philosopher to demonstrate his thesis with too much thoroughness and too convincingly. His ideas soon become part of the intellectual household of humanity, and the genius and labours which had to be expended in establishing them either are forgotten, or their memory becomes somewhat boring. For this reason, one often reads and hears that Pasteur and Tyndall wasted much talent and energy in a useless fight, for the belief in spontaneous generation was dying a natural death when they took arms against it. In reality, they had to overcome not only the teachings of the most eminent physiologists of the day, but also the emotional prejudices based on philosophical convictions.

Actually, despite the brilliant work of Pasteur and Tyndall, it has not yet been proved that each claim of its occurrence was scientifically invalidated by experimental error. In the heat of the battle, Pasteur complained that every source of error played into the hands of his opponents. 'For me, affirming as I do that there are no spontaneous fermentations, I am bound to eliminate every cause of error, every perturbing influence. Whereas I can maintain my results only by means of the most irreproachable technique, their claims profit by every inadequate experiment.'

In most accounts of these matters, it seems to me that this one point is often overlooked. The chronicle has become a fable preaching the supremacy of reason over emotion, and, as exponents of reason, reasonable men have always said, as Pasteur did, that spontaneous generation *is* a possibility. With what seems to be the traditional self-contradictoriness of the liberal point of view, many writers, in denouncing the emotional origin of the doctrine, have displayed their own brand of irrational argument. In Castiglione's *History of Medicine*, appears the statement, 'The perennial problem of spontaneous generation, which should have been disposed of by Spallanzani's successful refutation of Needham's contentions a century earlier, re-appeared at this time.' This simply is not so. Spallanzani's work *was* open to legitimate scientific criticism and was therefore unconvincing to perfectly rational sceptics. It seems to me that spontaneous generation is not only a possibility, but a completely reasonable possibility which should never be relinquished from scientific thought. Before men knew of bacteria, they accepted the doctrine of spontaneous generation as the 'only reasonable alternative' to a belief in supernatural creation. But today, as we look with satisfaction at the downfall of the spontaneous generation hypothesis, we must not forget that science has rationally concluded that *life once did originate on earth by spontaneous generation*. It was really Pasteur's evidence against spontaneous generation that for the first time brought the whole difficult question of the origin of life before the scientific world. In the above controversy, what was unreasonable was the parade of men who claimed to have 'proved' or who resolutely 'believed in' spontaneous generation in the face of proof – not that spontaneous generation cannot occur – but that their work was shot through with experimental error. The acceptable evidence also makes it clear that spontaneous generation, if it does occur, must obviously be a highly improbable event under present conditions. Logic tells us that science can only prove an event improbable: it can never prove it impossible – and Gamow has appropriately remarked that nobody is really certain what would happen if a hermetically sealed can were opened after a couple of million years. Modern science agrees that it was highly improbable for life to have arisen in the pre-Cambrian seas, but it concludes, nevertheless, that there it did occur. With this, I think, Pasteur would agree.

Aside from their theoretical implications, these researches had the great practical result of putting bacteriology on a solid footing. It was now clear how precisely careful one had to be to avoid bacterial contamination in the laboratory. We now knew what 'sterile' meant and we knew that there could be no such thing as 'partial sterilization'. The discovery of bacteria high in the upper atmosphere, in the mud of the deep sea bottom, in the waters of hot springs, and in the arctic glaciers established bacterial ubiquity as almost absolute. In recognition of this, Lord Lister introduced aseptic technique into the practice of surgery. It was the revolution in technique alone that made possible modern bacteriology and the subsequent research connecting bacteria to phenomena of human concern, research which today is more prodigious than ever. We are just beginning to understand the relationship of bacteria to certain human diseases, to soil chemistry, nutrition, and the phenomenon of antibiosis, wherein a product of one organism (e.g. penicillin) is detrimental to another.

It is not an exaggeration then to say that the emergence of the cell theory represents biology's most significant and fruitful advance. The realization that all plants and animals are composed of cells which are essentially alike, that cells are all formed by the same fundamental division process, that the total organism is a whole made up of the activities and interrelations of its individual cells, opened up horizons we have not even begun to approach. The cell is the microcosm of life, for in its origin, nature, and continuity resides the entire problem of biology.

# 7

## Life Evolves

> One often hears of writers that rise and swell with their subject,
> though it may seem but an ordinary one. How, then, with me,
> writing of this Leviathan? Unconsciously my chirography expands
> into placard capitals. Give me a condor's quill! Give me Vesuvius'
> crater for an inkstand! Friends, hold my arms!
>
> — Herman Melville: *Moby Dick*

As the primal molecules of the ancient seas wove themselves into
the web of life, so began the slow, pulsing, ceaseless advance of
organism, flowing and fusing across the epochs of time, emerging
hesitantly from the sea, and then thriving, at last, on dry land.
From that time to this, the earth has witnessed the rise of perhaps
many millions of species of living organisms, ranging in size from
the invisible virus to the giant sequoia. Without even counting the
vast numbers of extinct species, there are in the world today over
a million varieties of animals and almost half as many plants. What
explanation can there be for such incredible diversity? What
forces or patterns underlie the bewildering torrent of living forms?

These questions, among the most challenging and incendiary
in the intellectual history of man, have aroused controversy since
the dawn of recorded history. Since the earliest times, there have
been two main streams of thought on these questions: there are
those who believe in the divine Special Creation of fixed and un-
changing species and who, thus, deny the fact of evolution, and
there are those who accept the view that life has evolved and that
species are inconstant. Among the latter, there should be, but
often has not been, a clear distinction between the questions 'Has
evolution occurred?' and 'By what mechanism has it occurred?'
Today, most people in possession of the scientific data (but, as we
shall see, not all) agree to the fact of evolution. On the question of
mechanism there is much disagreement. It was not too far in the

114

past when an advocate of the mere view that some sort of evolution took place was the object of stormy protest and public ridicule.

## Darwinism and Controversy

Nuances of evolutionary ideas are to be found in the earliest writings of philosophers and naturalists in the sixth and seventh centuries B.C., although no doubt it is true that in these great meadows of speculation are to be found the inklings of almost any idea. Thales (640–546 B.C.) believed that life sprang from water, and Heraclitus, a century later, held that all things flow and change, life presumably included. The notion that life arises from non-life, and animals from plants, a clear-cut evolutionary concept, was postulated by Empedocles (495–435 B.C.). While these views were speculative, they may not have been entirely unscientific. It is possible that early thinkers postulated biological evolution – that is, continuous change, step building on step – because they *observed* that indeed all things change in this manner. Clothes, laws, buildings, language, and mountains, all gradually unfold new patterns and yet often retain mute and functionless vestiges of the old, remnants of past form and design. As we shall see later, modern evolutionists think that even the *mechanism of organic evolution* has undergone evolution, modifying and improving itself through the ages.

The erudite Aristotle evolved a theory of descent and skirted close to the doctrine of inheritance of acquired characteristics although he never actually articulated this idea. Though such a view would have been totally erroneous, it would at least have been a bona fide evolutionary concept. Little more was written in this vein for the long duration of the Middle Ages.

The recognition of fossils in the early years of the Renaissance gave rise to a perfectly fascinating series of churchly contortions in defence of the Mosaic account of creation. Each new finding generated its own meticulous explanation in the name of unyielding orthodoxy. These were memorable years in the annals of absurdity. The argument of Leonardo da Vinci that fossils were

115

the actual remains of living organisms embedded in the earth's crust was taken to indicate that these remains must have reached their positions during the great flood because everyone knows that the Creator finished the earth's crust before He made the fishes. The finding of shells on high mountains signified the monstrous proportions of the flood, or, alternatively, they were the fanciful result of God's inscrutable whimsy.

In his remarkable book *Man and His Gods*, Homer Smith wrote:

It was the whimsy view that brought the geologist Johann Beringer to grief. So definitely had this professor in the University of Würzburg committed himself to the theory that fossils are 'stones of a peculiar sort, hidden by the Author of Nature for his own pleasure', that some of his sceptical students determined to give his faith a thorough trial. They prepared and baked a number of sham fossils from clay, depicting reptiles and fish, birds in their nests, and imaginary creatures, and these they buried where Beringer was sure to find them. The Professor was so enthusiastic over his discovery that his tempters elaborated other fossils figuring the sun and moon, as well as Syrian and Babylonian script. With each successive find Beringer was increasingly convinced that he had come upon irrefutable evidence of the hand of God, and he published (1726) his discoveries in a treatise illustrated by twenty-one folio plates, devoting a chapter to the refutation of those among his sceptical colleagues who asserted that the fossils were fakes. Only later, when one of them turned up bearing his own name, was his faith in the divine origin of fossils, and in human nature, shattered.

The probings of the geologists of the eighteenth and early nineteenth centuries, Werner, Hutton, Lyell, and others, forced into consideration the evidence that the earth's history extended back millions and millions of years and not, as Archbishop Ussher had carefully computed, to 4004 B.C., and it was in the eighteenth century that, at last, we find clear, strong statements of evolutionary belief. The inventor of the first satisfactory system for naming plants and animals,* the Swedish professor Linnaeus

---

* The 'two-name' or so-called *binomial* system which gives first the genus and second the species, e.g. *Rana pipiens*, the familiar frog. In the whole animal kingdom, there is only one genus *Rana*, and among its more than two hundred species, only one called *pipiens*. In assembling this catalogue, Linnaeus prepared the first systematic compendium of plants and animals since Aristotle.

(1707–78), although impressed with the likenesses of living things, saw no need to postulate kinship. He was a confirmed believer in Special Creation, and yet there is reason to believe that through caution and prudence his true views were never firmly stated. His early statement that 'there are no new species' is deleted from the 1766 edition of his great book *Systema Naturae*. It appears that Linnaeus arrived at a limited acceptance of evolution.

In eighteenth-century France, the France of Voltaire, a contemporary of Linnaeus, the imaginative Comte de Buffon (1707–88), pruned a few more branches from the tree of Special Creation. He noted that deeply buried fossils bear less resemblance to modern animals than do shallow ones. While believing early in life in divine creation of immutable species and returning approximately to this position in his old age, he detoured for several years through a strong belief in the mutability of species by environment. That his advocacy of this view exposed him to ridicule persisting long after his death is evident in this account of George Bernard Shaw. 'One day,' he wrote, 'early in the eighteen hundred and sixties, I, being then a small boy, was with my nurse, buying something in the shop of a petty newsagent, bookseller, and stationer in Camden Street, Dublin, when there entered an elderly man, weighty and solemn, who advanced to the counter, and said pompously, "Have you the works of the celebrated Buffoon?" . . . The celebrated Buffoon was not a humorist, but the famous naturalist Buffon. Every literate child at that time knew Buffon's *Natural History* as well as Esop's Fables.'

A disciple of Buffon was Cuvier (1769–1832), soon to become a a master anatomist. He obstinately defended Special Creation and, because of his scientific reputation and high rank in the French Academy, was able successfully to belittle and denounce those with opposing views. With remarkable skill, he assembled the fossil bones found by the geologist Smith into reconstructions of the great vertebrates of the past, recognized that they were extinct and yet refused to accept a time scale that differed from that of the good Archbishop Ussher. He reasoned that extinct species had been destroyed by cataclysmic forces and that new species had been created to take their places.

Cuvier is remembered partly for his famous denunciation of an imaginative countryman, Lamarck. Lamarck, in 1814, popularized the doctrine that since certain organs may change as a result of use or disuse, new environmental conditions can place demands on animals such that new organs develop which, in turn, are passed on to the offspring. He chose as an example the giraffe's long neck, which he attributed to its appetite for tender tree-tops. Though grievously in error, these superficially reasonable arguments did much to popularize the idea of progressive change, hence Lamarck's abuse at the hands of Cuvier and the clergy.

Into this arena came the immortal Darwin. It was a time when microscopy was poorly developed, when paleontology, the science of fossils, was in its infancy, and when mathematics had no place in biology. Charles Darwin (1809–82) was the grandson of Erasmus Darwin, a physician, poet, and early evolutionist, whose book *Zoonomia*, published in 1794, obliquely anticipated both the doctrines of inheritance of acquired characteristics of Lamarck and natural selection, later to be formulated by his grandson. The story has often been told of how Charles Darwin's life hinged on the most extraordinary coincidences: his distaste for medicine brought on by the sights of the Edinburgh operating rooms, his transfer to Cambridge to study for the ministry just in time for a fateful meeting with the botanist Henslow, and, of course, the narrow margin by which he almost missed boarding the H.M.S. *Beagle* for the voyage of exploration that now belongs to history.

Darwin seized the opportunity to study the plants and animals of the South American coast, and for five laborious years he made careful notes and gathered priceless specimens. He was overwhelmed by the natural riches of this part of the world, the rivers and layers of sedimentary rocks, the coral reefs and lava beds. On his long field trips, he encountered strange new animals, insects and beetles, lovely orchids, and new grasses and trees. He was like Alice in a strange Wonderland. From this stronghold of life derived his lifelong preoccupation with the problem of species.

Though a confident Creationist upon leaving England, Darwin's doubts grew. His geological findings were incompatible with

118

Archbishop Ussher's date of creation. He was struck by the endless variety of life and pondered its origin. In 1838, he wrote, he read the Malthus essay on population which declared that man's ability to propagate was so great he would eventually outrun his food supply. If he did not check his fecundity, war, pestilence, and famine would do it for him. Here Darwin found the clue to a comprehensive dynamic theory on the riddle of the origin of species.

The tale of Darwin's discovery is classical to those interested in the ways of genius. A mighty creative intelligence turned from the accumulation of data to the formulation of theory, and there occurred a great moment in the history of thought. In attempting to see a solution to the species problem he decided to explore the field completely. He wrote in his *Autobiography*:

By collecting all facts which bore in any way on the variation of animals and plants under domestication and nature, some light might perhaps be thrown on the whole subject. My first notebook was opened on July 1837. I worked on true Baconian principles, and without any theory collected facts on a wholesale scale, more especially with respect to domesticated productions, by printed enquiries, by conversations with skilful breeders and gardeners, and by extensive reading. ... I soon perceived that selection was the keystone of man's success in making useful races of animals and plants. But how selection could be applied to organisms living in a state of nature, remained for some time a mystery to me.

How could selection operate in nature? The Malthus essay gave the clue. Darwin wrote:

Being well prepared to appreciate the struggle for existence which everywhere goes on from long-cultivated observation of the habits of animals and plants, it at once struck me that under these circumstances favourable variations would tend to be preserved, and unfavourable ones to be destroyed. The result of this would be the formation of a new species. Here then I had at last got a theory by which to work.

Although this decisive idea came to Darwin in 1838, he remained to the end his own severest critic. He waited almost four years to draft a first sketch of his theory and did not publish the *Origin of Species* until 1859, almost twenty years later. The kernel of Darwinism is simplicity itself:

1. The reproductive power of animals is much greater than is necessary to maintain their numbers. Only if a very large part of the offspring is destroyed will the numbers remain constant.

2. There must be, therefore, a 'struggle for existence' between members of a species and between the different species in the case that several species have the same habitat and food supply.

3. Animals vary widely – and, presumably, such variation is inherited.

4. In the struggle for existence, favourable variations have survival value. Unfavourable variations will lead to extermination. This is *natural selection*, the selection of the favoured by nature. By accumulation of favourable variations, natural selection leads to gradual change in animals tending toward better and better adaptation and thus to evolution.

Here we have a remarkable example of the fruitful interplay of induction (reasoning from observation with deference to the law of probability) and deduction (reasoning by logic). The argument went something like this: first observation: some animals vary; first inductive conclusion: all animals probably vary; first logical deduction: variations must be inherited. Second observation: some species overproduce; second inductive conclusion: all species probably overproduce; second logical deduction: there must be a struggle for existence. And from the two logical deductions comes the third deduction, the major one: natural selection.

No account of this era can pass over the hullabaloo that followed the publication of the *Origin of Species*. Ecclesiastical critics, members of Parliament, fellow scientists descended upon Darwin. The disingenuous Bishop Wilberforce, widely known as an orator, condemned the book outright and, at a memorable meeting of the British Association in 1860, engaged in debate with 'Darwin's Bulldog', Thomas Huxley.

'In conclusion,' said Bishop Wilberforce, 'I should like to ask my honourable opponent whether he considers himself descended from a monkey on his grandmother's side or his grandfather's.' Huxley, white with anger, rose to reply. 'A man', said he, 'has no reason to be ashamed of having an ape for his grandfather. If there were an ancestor whom I should feel shame in recalling, it would be a *man*, a man of restless and versatile intellect, who, not content with an equivocal success in his own sphere of activity, plunges into scientific questions with which he has no real acquaintance, only to obscure them by an aimless rhetoric, and distract the attention of his hearers from the real point at issue by eloquent digressions, and skilled appeals to religious prejudice.'*

With the publication of *Man's Place in Nature* in 1863, Thomas Huxley became the true author of 'Darwinism' and its central figure. For here interest was focused from first to last upon *man*, as Huxley proclaimed in exciting phrases and compelling arguments the descent of man from ape, while pleading with his doubting generation to abandon its vanity. Though Darwin had been timid, Huxley did not falter and, by placing man firmly within the evolutionary scheme, he fashioned a movement which extended far beyond the range of Darwin's immediate personal interests.

The impact of evolutionary ideas on the intellectual world was monumental. In the sixth edition of the *Origin of Species*, Darwin gave his scientific theory connotations of human progress and goodness, suggesting that evolution is pointed toward an ultimate perfection. This line of thought passed rapidly into the cultural stream where it has since modified every minor current.

Evolutionary ideas swept into explorations of human life and values, social institutions, religion, and morality. Great debates started which in many cases have still not quieted. It was a half-century of great writings bearing the evolutionary stamp: Spencer's works on sociology and ethics, Frazer's *Golden Bough* which traced the evolution of religious rite, Westermarck's *Origin and Development of Moral Ideas*. The trend was toward explaining the higher as evolving from the lower, mind from life and life from matter. On these questions, on the question whether the evolu-

---

* This story, always quoted for its entertainment value in accounts of this era, may be apocryphal. According to a recently unearthed letter, Huxley once wrote: 'I said my say with perfect good temper and politeness — I assure you of this because all sorts of reports have been spread about, e.g. that I had said I would rather be an ape than a bishop, etc.'

tionary drive was necessarily toward perfection, there were grave disagreements. Surely the evidence of history on mental and moral evolution helped to divorce the concepts of evolution and progress. The 'naturalistic' movement in moral philosophy soon became divided. One faction courageously supported the reducibility of mind and morals to the organic level and eventually formed the vanguard of modern materialism. The other, led by men like William James and John Dewey, insisted on the reality and separateness of moral ideas, but accepted their natural conditioning. This doctrine wove itself into the great American philosophical movement of pragmatism, which in its various forms has so profoundly affected education, law, and human life in general.

As for the response of the Church to the onward surge of evolutionary thinking, this varied with the various formulations of Christian doctrine. The Protestants, committed to the literal interpretation of the Bible, found Darwinism in flat disagreement with the Biblical account of creation. Following the famous Scopes trial in Tennessee in 1925, several American states tried to legislate evolution out of existence by forbidding its teaching in public schools. Catholicism earnestly tried to make fine distinctions between evolution as applied to animals and as applied to man and between theistically oriented evolution and that based on materialism and atheism, the general position being that science, properly interpreted, does not conflict with sacred dogma. A splinter movement from Catholicism, which became known as Modernism, attempted to reformulate Christian doctrine in the light of new knowledge, but this uprising was terminated in 1907 by papal encyclical implemented by a certain number of excommunications. The movement has since been confined to the Protestant Church. As recently as 1953, His Holiness Pius XII, addressing a scientific audience at Castel Gandolfo, took an ultra-conservative view toward evolution, admitting it only as a possibility, a hypothesis yet to be verified, an opinion of some scientists and not others. To this, the eminent geneticist T. Dobzhansky replied, '[The statement] does not hold evolution to be contrary to or incompatible with Divine Revelation. But regrettably, it does not show evidence of being well advised concerning the actual state of knowledge in biological science. . . . This is injurious both to science and religion, keeping up several centuries of misunderstanding.'

It was in biology, however, that the great transformation took place. The field was galvanized by its sudden conversion from a static classificatory discipline to a dynamic, integrated, autonomous science with its own philosophical understructure. The changes that occurred in physiology, psychology, and biochemistry were tremendous. There arose the new science of ecology. It should be remembered that Darwin did not originate the idea of evolution. His work, however, made it reasonable and provided a starting point from which science could proceed to further inquiry. In the scientific controversies which raged and spumed, there was frequent confusion between the fact of evolution and natural selection, its postulated mechanism. Darwin quickly attracted a small cordon of staunch defenders, Huxley and Hooker in England, Asa Gray in America, and the brilliant German Ernst Haeckel. There were also articulate opponents, notably von Kölliker, Richard Owen, and the Swiss-American Louis Agassiz (who, it is said, embraced evolutionism on his death-bed), and these objected variously to evolution, natural selection, or both.

A number of modifications of the natural selection idea did appear in later decades. At the turn of the century, strong reaction against the theory almost drove it into disesteem but it staged a vigorous recovery and is today, at least among geneticists, almost universally accepted. These later developments in evolutionary theory overlap and are intimately bound up with the science of genetics.

## The Modern Point of View

Evolution is a *process*, a scheme of events occurring in time, and because of its indolent tempo is itself invisible to the human eye. We know of it through indirect evidence, the results of its workings that remain available to us for examination, and we are precluded from manipulating it experimentally. There is ample experimental evidence bearing on the mechanism of evolution, largely from genetics, but we will defer this until after we have had our formal introduction to the gene. Here let us sketch in the evidence for evolution, those empirical observations that demand a theory of evolution as their only plausible explanation.

There are several main types. First, there is the pattern of order that runs through the diversities in living things. Despite the vast array of differences between organisms, there are unmistakable

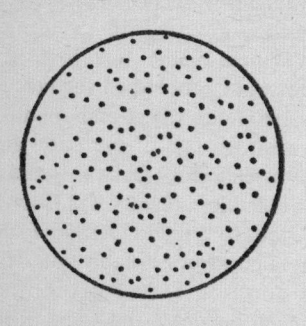

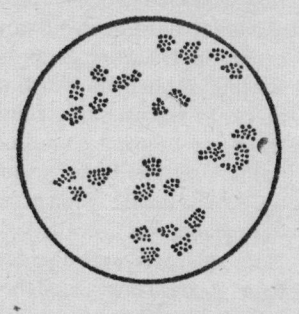

Random distribution of shot on a target

Grouping of shot on a target which indicates some connexion between the separate shots.

groupings of similar types. Shull has shown the following diagrams to illustrate the differences between utter randomness of events and a pattern that implies some connexion between individual events.*

Some sort of theory of evolution is immediately suggested as a possible explanation for these groupings. Close examination of these patterns reveals that there are higher and higher categories, larger and larger groups which are made up of smaller groups. In the living world, the individual on the lowest classification is a member of a *species* and may differ from members of other species only in minor ways such as colour of fur or shape of wings. When

* Figures are redrawn from A. Shull, *Evolution*, 2nd ed., McGraw-Hill, 1951, and Remington Arms Co., by permission.

several species have strong resemblances to one another which distinguish them from another cluster of similar species, we have two higher groups, each a *genus*. The same is true for genera and up the scale through *family, order class*, and *phylum*. Thus taxonomy has given us a table of organization that looks something like this:

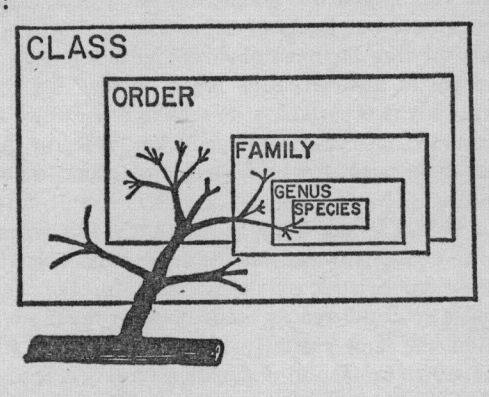

The big animal phyla, of which there are over a dozen, include the worms, the insects, jellyfishes, single-celled organisms, and backboned animals, the last including man. The plant kingdom has a similar taxonomic scheme.

Classification is a complex undertaking. First of all, let us agree that it is probably necessary: to be understood, all variable phenomena must be sorted into categories wherever it is possible to do so. In any system of classification, there are two steps: first, defining and describing the units to be classified and analysing for their diagnostic differences, and, second, arranging the units into a classificatory scheme, a hierarchy of ever-larger groups. In biology, as elsewhere, we use names as recognition symbols. At first, names like 'skunk' or 'catfish' were entirely adequate, but the establishment of the biological classification of Linnaeus introduced the binomial system of nomenclature according to which the second word of the name indicates species or *distinctness* and the first word indicates genus or *relationship*. Clearly, such a system must be based on a sound knowledge of the items being named and classified. The better our knowledge, the more meaningful the classification.

Classification was long based on the most obvious characteristic of the organism, structure – how the animal is built and what he looks like. This approach is plainly full of hazards. Appearance and structure are but facets of a much larger picture, though admittedly they are the most obvious and first looked for. But what happens to a classification based on structure when two organisms – say two bacteria – look alike physically but one is sensitive and the other resistant to penicillin? It is true that many functional characteristics are reflected in structure: for example, the salt-water fish whose kidney must conserve water, not salt, has a different kind of kidney from the fresh-water fish whose kidney must conserve salt, not water. But the newer science clearly shows that on the deeper levels of cellular structure, function, and chemistry, fundamental differences occur between organisms (sometimes within the same species) which have no gross structural counterpart. Are we then to designate several new species?

This should make it evident that species, the lowest common denominator of classification, cannot be simply defined. Even if structural similarity were the sole criterion, there has to be some decision on how rigid one wants to be. As it is, no two living beings are exactly alike. And so we are left with a concept of species that lacks preciseness. Species, the books tell us (and the vague words are italicized), are made up of *similar* individuals, *differing* from other species, which breed *mostly* among themselves, are *quite* permanent and yet are *flexible* and *plastic*, tending to change in the course of many generations. What we can unhesitatingly accept is that there are likenesses among living beings, and from this we infer kinship.

There are likenesses, too, between genera and classes. Much study has been devoted to anatomical analogies between the different types of living things: the ear of the frog and the ear of the dog, the human arm and the bird's wing. Many organisms possess vestigial remnants, such as the human ear-moving muscles, present but functionless, and these hint at remote consanguinity with present-day ear-moving animals. Impressed by the resemblance of the early mammalian embryo successively to a single-celled organism, a hydra, and a fish, Ernst Haeckel outlined what he called the 'biogenetic law', according to which each individual in his own development recapitulates all the stages through which the entire race has passed. The validity of the 'biogenetic law' is open to doubt* but the data which it seeks to explain show clearly that embryos possess what must be 'inheritances from the past'. This is evidence of common ancestry and, together with the grouping into species and genera, is evidence that somewhere along the line of descent, change took place. *Common ancestry plus change equals evolution*. The deduction cannot be avoided.

If species arose by evolution, they did so in a world that was itself evolving. In the course of geological time, continents have heaved up and subsided while the land bridges between them have often come and often gone. The peculiar distribution of certain species throughout the world is good evidence that evolution took place. This is illustrated by the striking differences between the large mammals of North and South America. Geological evidence indicates that at one time Panama was submerged so that no exchange of species could take place between the two continents. By the time the land bridge was established, mammalian evolution had reached an advanced stage. Remote islands such as the Galapagos, which Darwin visited in 1835, have species of insects, birds, and reptiles that are to be found nowhere else. The distribution of life in the world indicates that species must have originated everywhere and on many occasions. This in turn substantiates the fact of evolution.

Perhaps the most impressive evidence for evolution is the fossil record. Paleontologists have been probing around in caves and potholes for over two centuries and have assembled a remarkable collection of fossilized remains of extinct species. From these, they have made deductions about the course of evolution. For certain

* It is currently believed that the individual does not pass through the *adult* stages of its evolutionary ancestors but through their *developmental* or embryonic stages. Thus, the gill clefts of the human embryo more resemble those of the fish embryo than they do the gill slits of the adult fish.

species, the lines of descent are very well known from direct fossil evidence. But, interestingly, paleontology has its methodological problems too. It is at its best in the fortunate circumstance when it has uncovered a *series* of fossils, neatly laid down in successive, uninterrupted geological strata, giving a strong probability commendation to the inference that C evolved from B and B from A. As it happens, findings of this type are rare and few have been extensive enough to show more than the appearance of new species. For the formation of new genera, families, and classes, the major changes of evolution involving true novelty, such series provide no evidence.

In the usual case, the paleontologist is forced to deal with isolated fossils from widely separated geographical locations and geological eras. He can do no more than deduce the nature of intermediate forms. In addition, he must wrestle with other problems connected with fossils: they derive mainly from animals with hard shells and skeletons; because they have been embalmed in the earth in somewhat random fashion, they reflect chiefly the dominant species of an era and not the rarer forms whose recognition is highly important to an evolutionary theorist; and, of course, they can be formed only where sedimentation is taking place, such as sea bottoms and coastal areas. This is not to mention the technical difficulties in piecing together fossils that have been broken, baked, or squashed by the weight of time. These problems, however, should not discountenance the positive evidence of paleontology. Nor should any theory of evolution conflict with it, for this evidence is direct.

Paleontology has perhaps made its greatest contribution to our knowledge of the phylogeny* of vertebrates, the subphylum of backboned animals of which man is a prominent if not always chauvinistic member. The fossil record suggests that the vertebrates have been the most successful of animals and hence have evolved the most rapidly, extending their dominance over the widest range. By assembling the fragments, we can picture the emergence of the earliest known vertebrates following the Cambrian Revolution some four or five hundred million years ago.

* Phylogeny means development of race (genesis of phylum).

These were the heavily armoured, bottom-living, jawless fishes of the fresh, continental lakes. In turn came actively swimming fish, the 'cartilaginous' fishes, whose modern descendants are the sharks, and the 'bony' fishes who were the ancestors of most modern fishes. Events had by then established the survival value of the segmented, flexible backbone, the power of fast swimming, and the location of major sense organs at the head end of the body.

But times changed and the heaving earth brought invasions of salt water into the continental areas. Inland fresh-water fish were forced to choose between an alien salt-water habitat and a shrinking fresh-water pool. Some took to the sea, and those who remained behind had to modify themselves in order to survive. Thus came the dawn of the age of air breathing and the prologue to the lung-possessing, terrestrial vertebrates.

Evolution was also advancing among plants and insects, and the world was entering the coal ages. Under the pelting rain and blazing sun, the lowlands became stretching green seas of vegetation, populated with spiders, snails, and scorpions and, at last, the vertebrate amphibians who lived half on land and half in water.

Soon came the glaciers and the careening, expanding earth grew cold and dry. Amphibians passed slowly into landlocked reptiles who, via stages of unsurpassed grotesquerie, evolved into the great dinosaurs. At about the time of the formation of the Rocky Mountains, a hundred million years ago, the age of the reptile came to an abrupt end. Up to this time, birds and mammals had remained in the background. They may have been evolving in small local groups and hence failing to represent themselves adequately in the fossil record. But whether the dwindling of the reptiles was caused by the prosperity of the mammals or vice versa remains an open question.

In any case, the mammals arrived, furry and warm-blooded to resist the cold and capable of nursing their young to protect them from egg-hungry predators. They grew better teeth and larger heads and in due time gave rise to upright, walking forms, the primates. Not until fifty million years later, a mere million years ago, is there any sign of man. The few available fossils of early transitional man have been widely publicized and, of course, dis-

as to find no parallel in the history of paleontological discovery.'
The identification of the villain will be a nice conundrum for a new
generation of scholars.

Following this announcement, the anthropologists of the world
devoted a number of special meetings to the Piltdown hoax, and
the published accounts of their proceedings communicate equal
parts of consternation and relief. At least the evolution of man
now seemed slightly less cryptic. To quote Straus:

> The Piltdown story is a significant one in the history of ideas, more
> particularly as it bears on the concept of the precise course of human
> evolution. For, if man's biological history be likened to a book, it is
> seen to be composed of both blank and written pages and, by those who
> note them carefully, many if not most of the written ones will be seen
> to be in the nature of palimpsests – pages that have been rewritten after
> their original writing has been rubbed out. Of this, the Piltdown affair is
> a striking demonstration. It is a demonstration, furthermore, that the
> palimpsest nature of the pages of man's history is not always due
> directly to new fossil discoveries but can also result from changes in the
> philosophical climate of the science. That this phenomenon is peculiar
> to anthropology, however, is seriously to be doubted.

Thus the likelihood of evolution is great. Save for a few shrill
dissenters, all accept this fact. And there *are* dissenters, although
few can be taken seriously. A Dutchman named van Houwensfelt
published a book in 1931 called *Darwinism Has Deceived Humanity* in which he violently repudiated the scientific argument for
evolution. His chapters, one of which is decisively titled *Scholars
Have No Proof of Darwinism and Their Theories Are Wrong*!, are
so acrid with contempt, they make amusing reading. Between
salvos, things are kept lively with sly anecdotes such as the one
about the International Zoological Congress of 1895 in Leiden
where scholars had gathered to view the bones of the *Pithecan-
throp-'s erectus*. 'At this congress the learned Rudolph von Virchow was so excited when he took the femur (thigh-bone) of the
*Pithecanthropus* in his hands, that he flourished it about like a
madman, and Dubois, who had become famous through its discovery, was frightened to death lest all at once the prehistoric
bone should fall to the ground in pieces.'

132

In a more recent and much more temperate book called *Is Evolution Proved?*, Arnold Lunn wrote:

Influenced as I am by the mental fashion of the day my bias is in favour of evolution and I should accept evolution as proved but for the following facts: (*a*) the difficulty of reconciling the suddenness with which new types appear in the geological record with any theory of slow mindless evolution, (*b*) the impossibility of tracing any family into another family by means of true lineage series of fossils, (*c*) the impossibility of reconciling the alleged imperfection of the geological record with ... statistics which suggest that most genera are represented in that record, and, finally, (*d*) the fact that no evolutionist had produced a plausible *guess*, much less a theory supported by evidence, to suggest how a purely natural process could have evolved from the mud, sand, mists and seas of the primeval planet the brain that conceived Beethoven's Ninth Symphony and the reactions to the beauty of music, of art, and of nature.

It seems that the argument against evolution is pure metaphysical brocade, artfully draped so as to obscure the cogent evidence of science. Evolution like everything else is not a certainty. But in the present state of knowledge, it must be regarded as proved beyond reasonable doubt. The consequences of the general acceptance of the doctrine of evolution were utterly typical of all such sophistical arguments when at last they fizzle out. With the collapse of explanation by unknowable unknowns, *scientific questions were asked that would not otherwise have been dreamed of*. The door swung open wide on a whole world of new and pressing problems of direct importance to biology: What is the mechanism of evolution? What forces shape the course of evolution? What does it all mean? Many of these questions are at the centres of actively raging, latter-day controversies, some between science and the regrouped forces of the supernaturalist legions.

We cannot explore here all the byways of evolutionary theory. This has been done masterfully by a leading student of the subject, Julian Huxley, in his book *Evolution: The Modern Synthesis*. Some of these subsidiary ideas will emerge in subsequent chapters. But because it is directly pertinent to our later discussions, let us dwell a moment on one vital concept which has crystallized from evolutionary thinking, the notion of *adaptation*.

## The First Great Modern Synthesis

Since men first began to think charitably about evolution, they have been impressed and awed by the conception of marvellously integrated men arising from lowly forms of life. To many, this signified that evolution was *creative* or possessed some sort of *orientation*. It was denied that evolutionary change was entirely random, for, if it was, how could one explain the magnificent inter-relationship between structure, function, and environment as found, for example, in the protective coloration of butterflies or in the design of the human hand? Some insisted that the evolutionary process proceeded in straight lines, transformations building upon each other undeviatingly and inexorably. Thinkers of this persuasion (the concept has been called *orthogenesis*) usually point to the ancient, tiny eohippus who by gradual and stepwise change evolved into the modern horse.

G. G. Simpson presented a very instructive lesson on the psychological pitfalls in interpreting data in problems of this sort. He suggested a hypothetical case wherein a fossil collection had been assembled and some feature such as leg length was plotted on a graph against the time of origin of the fossil. The individual observations would look like this:*

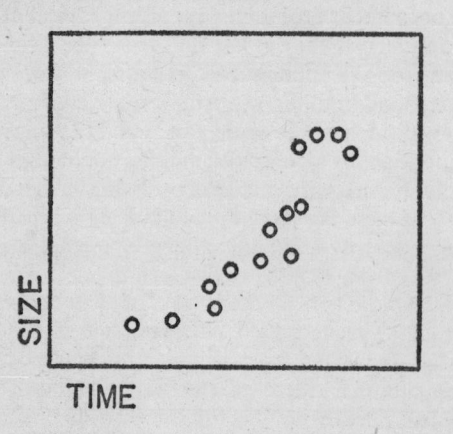

* Figures are redrawn from G. G. Simpson, *The Meaning of Evolution*, Yale University Press, 1949, by permission.

A Student A, desiring to find evidence of separate orthogenetic series, might interpret these data in this way:

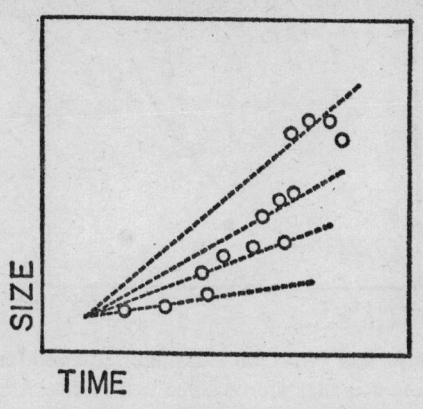

Student B, who basically believes that evolution occurs in a sequence of stages each arising by a major leap without passing through transition forms, will visualize the findings differently:

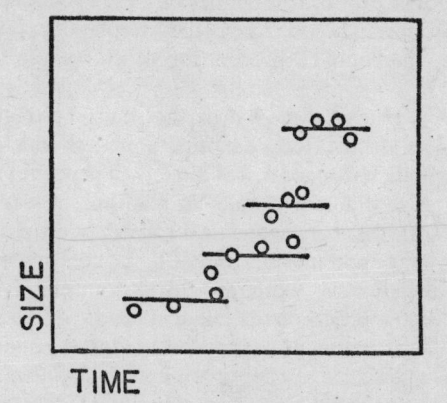

And, finally, Student C may see the findings as evidence for a single, continuous, *oriented*, but not necessarily orthogenetic, process:

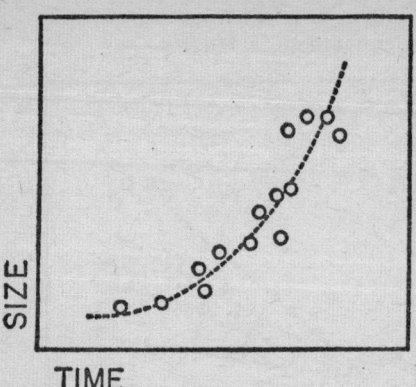

We must agree that evolution is not entirely random. The environment does, after all, impose some limitations. An organism has only a restricted number of available environments, and each imposes its own terms for survival. And yet it appears that the *direction of evolution* cannot be attributed solely to something within the evolving form. It is neither of these two alone but, instead, the relationship between them, the interplay of organism and environment, the complex process for which we use the term *adaptation*.

*Adaptation* is one of those words that must be treated very carefully. As an abstract term denoting a process which may or may not be wholly understood, it is directly in danger of meaning different things to different people. In addition, as was pointed out by Medawar, there are syntactical hazards in its use. Unlike the combinations 'mutant and mutation', 'concept and conception', 'adaptation' is both gerund and substantive noun: 'adaptation' is the process and 'the adaptation' is the result of the process. What is true of adaptation used in the substantival sense may be quite false of adaptation used in its other sense.

The omnipresent process of adaptation has produced numberless instances of the harmonious fitting of the organism to its environment, some of the utmost delicacy, and many, no doubt, so subtle as to have so far escaped discovery. One could fill a book with examples: the parasite and the host, muscles and the skeleton, enzymes and substrates, the humming-bird and flowers, the stable, mild alkalinity of the blood in the face of varying diet, the nervous system and exasperation. A microcosm of fitness can be seen on every level of integration in the living organism, from molecules to societies. The existence of the adaptive process has actually been denied by some biologists, but to the biological fieldworker, long schooled in the lore of the sea urchin and the shrike, this position is ludicrous. 'Adaptation', wrote Huxley, 'cannot but be universal among organisms, and every organism cannot be other than a bundle of adaptations, more or less detailed and efficient, coordinated in greater or lesser degree.'

A variety of themes has developed around the central idea of adaptation. *Preadaptation* refers to changes in an organism that do not necessarily suit him for his own environment but do fit him for some other environment available to him. Preadapted organisms who are near a new, and now suitable, niche are likely to immigrate into it and to do so successfully. Here further adaptation occurs and the original preadapted level of fitness is improved upon. Goldschmidt gives as an example of preadaptation the case of cave-dwelling animals, who have a highly developed sense of touch but lack eyes. They are eyeless not because they are in caves but, conversely, for one of two other reasons: (1) only animals who already prefer darkness will survive the ever-possible loss of eyes by chance variation (mutation), and (2) animals who by chance develop a superior tactile sense are then preadapted to enter caves where they can thrive despite the chance loss of eyes.

By such mechanisms, evolution has succeeded in filling with life every corner of the vast world. With the emergence of land animals, a whole category of new environments became available, waiting only for the process of adaptation to provide tenants: the soil, the branches of trees, the air, the caves, the deserts, and the sides of steep mountains. This process, called *adaptive radiation*, gets very complicated because before new environmental niches can be filled they must offer food. No animal could live on land until there were plants, and when herbivorous animals did become established there were now attractive prospects for carnivores and intestinal parasites.

Simpson quoted the analogy, first proposed by T. Huxley, for the filling of the earth with life.

He likens it to the filling of a barrel with apples until they heap over the brim. Still there is space into which quantities of pebbles fit before they overflow. Again sand is added, and much of it packs down between the apples and the pebbles. The barrel is not yet full and quarts of water may be poured in before at last the barrel can hold no more.

There is a duality in the adaptedness of any organism to its environment. Since no two organisms experience exactly the same trials and tribulations, there is a limit to the consonance of evolutionary predesign. Weiss wrote: '. . . what an organism is pre-fitted for by its evolutionary endowment is merely a statistical norm of conditions, the standard range which is relatively constant, the individual manifestations of which, however, vary at random from case to case.' Thus we find that evolution provides an approximate sort of fitness which is elaborated by mechanisms for on-the-spot adjustments elicited by random need. If one were never wounded, one's blood would never clot and yet one would always have in reserve the clotting mechanism. The same is true for innumerable mechanisms, neurological, skeletal, endocrine, which are available to restore tranquillity should the need arise. Of these we shall hear more in later chapters.

It should be noted that evolutionary adaptations can be detrimental. Why, it might be asked, if adaptation brings specialization and successful adjustment, do races become extinct? The answer probably lies in the sluggishness that often accompanies prosperity. When a race has filled its environmental range and all opportunities have been seized, the ability to adapt diminishes. While better and better adaptations to the specific environment may be accumulating, the species becomes more and more inflexible to change in the environment. Should conditions suddenly be altered, a whole race of lazy, specialized organisms, whose avenues of possible change are limited, may be wiped out. Should environmental change come gradually, the group will wane and, as it grows smaller, reach a point where deleterious inbreeding occurs with consequent accentuation of undesirable family traits. The appearance of freakish, 'unadapted' forms heralds extinction as it did with the dinosaurs. This seems to be the price of over-specialization and, no doubt, points a moral.

The world contains some species that seem immortal. The shark, the oyster, the opossum, are almost unchanged from their ancient ancestors low on the evolutionary ladder. These are perhaps best explained by their small size, modest requirements, and general lack of fastidiousness. The environment which permitted their early survival has never drastically changed and so they continue on – not an immortal species, because all life on earth will one day end, but close to it.

Occasionally, a species long believed to be extinct, turns up alive in a remote corner of the modern world and presents the evolutionary theorist with an indescribably valuable link with the past. Perhaps the most exciting example of this kind of discovery was the recent appearance of a coelacanth on a baited hook in the Indian Ocean off Madagascar. It was previously thought that a very early type of fish had, 350 million years ago, evolved into three different forms: the lungfish which still lives today; the amphibians, progenitors of today's land-living vertebrates; and the coelacanths which for some reason died out seventy-five million years ago. But in 1938, a living coelacanth was pulled out of the water off South Africa. The icthyologist J. L. B. Smith hurried to the scene, but, to his and biology's great disappointment, the creature had decayed and only its skeleton and occasional pieces of skin remained. The announcement of the find, however, stunned the scientific world.

Smith began the quest for a second specimen and systematically distributed thousands of leaflets to native fishermen asking their help. The campaign succeeded when in December 1952 a fisherman recognized a five-foot, 100-pound coelacanth in a Madagascan village market. Smith obtained a special aircraft from the prime minister of South Africa and flew 3,000 miles to the specimen. Though its odour was strong, its head slightly bashed in, and its body partially cut, the find was largely intact. It is said that Smith broke down and wept.

He excitedly reported his discovery in *Nature* and concluded preliminarily that the species is indeed alive though in 300 million years it has changed very little. The discovery was hailed as the 'greatest of the century', and detailed researches on the grotesque carcass were launched immediately. In the meantime, the channels of Mozambique have been watched for new specimens, and, according to recent word, nine living coelacanths have been captured, all in good condition. The discovery of these specimens has magnificently confirmed theoretical predictions made by the paleontologists about the origin of vertebrates from the indirect evidence of fossils. We now have a 'living fossil', and it is an impressive testimonial to the sophistication of modern paleontological theory. For once, a deduction made from fossils has received confirmation.

Because this is not a textbook on evolution, I will not undertake to discuss some of the more technical questions in evolution, as, for example, the microevolution-macroevolution theory* which (in a word) distinguishes between the mechanism of evolutionary change within a species and that which, by large steps, creates new species and genera. The burden of this book is to throw light on the workings of living organisms, the fruit of millennia of evolution and adaptation. Adaptation would be the leitmotiv behind everything one could say about organism. In considering organism, we are considering nothing more than 'bundles of adaptations' each carried down as an historic response to the challenge of environment.

* The author of this controversial view was Goldschmidt, the late distinguished professor of zoology at the University of California. He held that 'large mutations' give rise to 'hopeful monsters' which may serve as the starting points for new evolutionary trends. This theory has been recently and effectively disputed by G. G. Simpson in his excellent book *The Major Features of Evolution*.

# 8

## The Nature of Life

The ass went seeking for horns and lost its ears.
— Proverb

SEVERAL years ago, I was present at a meeting of one of the most distinguished of biochemistry departments. We were having tea. Members of the group were then following up a recent discovery made by one of them relating to the chemical mechanism by which the cell synthesized nucleic acid, the substance of which the genes are made. The discussion was interrupted by a message from a local philosophical society asking if the department would provide a speaker to participate in a forthcoming symposium on the nature of life. Everyone was filled with dismay. All assembled understood biochemistry and heredity and genes and enzymes, but no one felt he had anything to say about life. The request was politely declined.

One of the remarkable and frustrating aspects of modern biology is the fact that the roaring tide of specialization has left no one who feels qualified to hold forth on the problem of life itself. Biology has its taxonomists, botanists, bacteriologists, and biochemists, each an expert in his own domain, but no one wants to tackle the single overriding question common to all. Much has been written on the subject but, happily or unhappily, little by working biologists, who are chained to empiricism and not to speculation. The bulk of such literature has, therefore, appeared in philosophical journals and in books written for general readers.

Linus Pauling recently remarked on the difference in viewpoint between the working physicist and biologist: 'The physicist says "what can I say about the world that these data will not rule out?" while the biologist says "what is it that these experiments force us to believe about nature?"' Unfortunately, nothing has

141

been observed empirically that forces us to believe any one thing about the basic nature of life. Of the several hypotheses that have been offered, none has been capable of definite testing. We cannot yet do what we would like to do with a hypothesis: designate it true or false. At the moment, the most we can say of such notions is that they are useful or useless in leading us to new experiments. Actually, experimental data can at best contribute only indirectly to this problem. No one can enter a laboratory as Sigmund tried to do and undertake to study Life. We study examples of life, in specific areas of inquiry, by asking discrete questions of limited scope. The answers when taken together may provide a basis for generalization by whose reflected light we hope to illuminate the biggest question of them all.

In this chapter I will say something about the development of the point of view that most biologists now hold about the nature of life. It is a question which, in my opinion and in the light of what is now going on in science and philosophy of science, is capable of an answer right now. We will return to it later. It is not a very satisfying answer, for it suggests that the question is meaningless.

## Living Systems: Are They Machines?

When men became aware that they were somehow different from sod, they began a polemical sword dance which is today not yet ended. A fatal fascination lay in the question of whether the riddle of life could be explained by sophisticated combinations of physical and chemical laws or, alternatively, by the workings of some extramaterial agency which alone gives life its anima. (It is, of course, fallacious to reason that this question admits of only two possible solutions. As Bertrand Russell has remarked, 'When you meet a stranger, there are exactly two possibilities: on the one hand he may be called Ebenezer Wilkes Smith, on the other hand he may not.') From the Age of Greece to the Age of Biochemistry, the battle has shuffled back and forth across traditional disciplinary boundaries, into and out of biology, physics, and chemistry, back through theology, up and down the long, draughty corridors of metaphysics. Here, as perhaps in no other field of inquiry, can be seen the crazy quilt of frank speculation, honest application of scientific method, the paternity of wish to thought, the ceaseless kneading of modest but partial evidence into exorbitant theory. The old maxim 'Who is to decide when doctors disagree?' did not here apply. All men seemed to have an answer to this question. And so, in true philosophical tradition, the issue comes richly garnished with a fretwork of 'isms' – a little something for everyone. I have no intention of discussing all of these, but instead propose to sketch in briefly the past and present thinking on this question, take a tentative position, and then, because this is the central issue of theoretical biology, return to the problem in a later chapter.

It is obvious to all that living things are physical objects. They have weight and solidity and exist in a physical matrix. No one has reliably experienced disembodied life. The materials which make up the organism are known to every chemist. We know how some of these substances are put together but we are far from knowing all there is to know on the subject. We know also that all living things die and, after death, retain, at least momentarily, their same structure, weight, and physical continuity. These two general assertions are perhaps indisputable. The question is: What accounts for the difference between living and non-living physical objects, between the animate body and its corpse?

The *something* that transforms matter into life has been many things to many men. To the ancients, it was the psyche, the life principle, or the soul. To Aristotle, it was three souls. To the early atomist Democritus, it was something made of atoms as were all things. Because soul atoms were conceded to be of a finer and more mobile texture than ordinary ones, this theory gave nourishment to the universal belief in ghosts, shades, wraiths, and other such discarnate post-mortem phenomena. But to the later atomists Epicurus and Lucretius, the particulate nature of the soul implied that the soul could not survive the death of the body, therefore death and ghosts were not to be feared. Descartes, early in the seventeenth century, made his famous distinction between mind and matter wherein a dualistic world was pictured whose material half was strictly mechanistic. Mind did not occupy space and was characterizable only by its function: it did the thinking. To Descartes, the non-material part of the world was chiefly concerned with intellectual matters, thinking, reasoning, and feeling. And, though the 'rational soul' did directly act upon the material body somewhere in the valve manifold of the pineal gland, the remainder of life's functions all had a material basis. Thus, Descartes gave such great impetus to mechanistic biology many began to urge that the soul was merely a superfluous hypothesis.

Biology, however, was not purged of animal spirits. Frank spookism did give way to more scientific-sounding concepts embodying the idea of *vital force*, a term which was perhaps less objectionable because it better passed the meaninglessness test. Obviously it explained nothing, serving only as a verbal symbol of the answer still being sought. Vitalism became a diluted animism and today includes a whole catalogue of non-materialistic points of view.

Progressivism in the vitalist camp plus excessivism in materialist interpretation soon started the pendulum swinging convulsively. The entrance of rigid mechanical explanation into psychology and the resulting conclusion that human morals and judgement are merely the automatic products of mechanical processes almost by itself brought on a revolt against mechanism. Perhaps the most instructive case history was that of Thomas Huxley himself. According to McDougall,

Huxley, the most effective champion of Darwinism ... the most positive of the positives, who had eloquently celebrated the iconoclastic thrusts of mechanistic biology, in his famous Romanes Lecture (*Evolution and Ethics*) delivered at Oxford near the end of his life, revoked the main feature of his earlier teaching and called upon mankind to defy the laws of mechanical nature which throughout his life he had so effectively expounded as all-sufficient. . . . Huxley seems to have been moved to his revulsion by pondering upon the intolerable implications for human life of the mechanical biology.

The turn of the twentieth century is remembered as an era of truculent debate and experimental derring-do. Prior to this period, discussion hinged chiefly on how best to interpret the everyday facts of life. Argument was more dialectical than scientific. How can one explain human action, development, and memory? The gifted and beguiling Henri Bergson, using a curious methodological combination of intuition and fragmentary (and selected) scientific evidence, argued that memory has no material basis. To the principle that does guide such functions, he gave the name *élan vital*. Again and again, science stubbed its toes on the point that organic evolution, especially as advocated by the extremist neo-Darwinians, had failed miserably to explain the enigma of human consciousness. Vitalist arguments of this type took on new weight with the emergence of seemingly corroborative *experimental data*. Wilhelm Roux dramatically reported in 1888 that he had taken a frog's egg, allowed it to undergo its first cell division, and then killed one of its two cells. The results were a half-embryo and an enthusiastic renaissance of the science of experimental morphology.

Because this experiment suggested that something invisible and very complex resided in the egg and controlled its future destiny, there was launched a whole string of audacious, if somewhat macabre, experimental manipulations of the growing embryo. The German biologist and philosopher Hans Driesch commenced the work which made him probably the greatest of all the champions of vitalism. He tried to repeat Roux's experiments using the sea urchin egg. After destroying half of a two-celled embryo, he obtained, not a half-embryo, but an embryo normal in every detail except size: it was half the nominal size. Roux's findings in the frog were controverted in the sea urchin and it looked very much as though the first cell division of an egg did not result in two dissimilar halves. Driesch went on to produce perfect miniature embryos from partially destroyed larger embryos and from small bits removed from embryos. He demonstrated in newts the most astonishing restitutions of whole limbs following the amputation of a leg. From all of this, he concluded that life must be a 'harmonious equipotential' system and in each organism must reside a vital *entelechy* which somehow keeps track of the blueprints for the whole adult form. (Driesch resurrected the term entelechy from Aristotle, who used it to mean a potentiality which has become an actuality.) He argued that no conception which views life as a machine, however far pushed, can account for the origin of a whole organism from a single cell. Something else must explain it, and this something *per exclusionem* is the entelechy.

In response to the challenging fire of Driesch and the experimental morphologists, men of biology dispersed themselves along a broad spectrum of opinion ranging from thoroughgoing, hard-boiled materialism on one end to idealistic metaphysics (which held that the world of matter is pure illusion) on the other. The dispute, while still fundamentally between mechanism and vitalism, took on a more subtle character as interpretations developed finer shadings. By hindsight, much of this conversation has a distinct flavour of carping, as men fought to introduce new names for old ideas.

The vitalist cause was carried forward into the new century by an impressive array of natural scientists. By knitting together the diverse threads that dangled from the separate fields of biology, philosophy, and psychology, these men were able to fabricate what could be called the doctrine of modern vitalism. We might quickly sift through these arguments and identify their advocates. They break down roughly into two categories of inexplicability: life and mind. We have already referred to the claims of non-materialists on the origin of life and to the jaw-breaking theories of Driesch, whose operating procedure, we recall, was first peering at a regenerating newt leg, failing utterly to understand it, and then concluding that this wonderful event can be explained only by the entelechy. A group led by E. S. Russell and W. E. Ritter emphasized that organisms depend for their autonomy on their *wholeness* and their marvellous integration. This position, sometimes called *organicism* or *bolism*, is, in essence, not particularly unpalatable to materialists. To say that life depends upon the complex organization of its material parts is perfectly compatible with good mechanism, which will agree cheerfully that there are no pieces of living matter, but only living organisms. It is when certain organicists start talking of purpose and denying even the possibility of a physicochemical explanation of the integration of organism that mechanists politely demur. This more rigorously vitalistic faction of the organicist group included J. S. Haldane,* father of the resolutely materialistic J. B. S. Haldane, General Jan Smuts, the late South African statesman and philosopher, and A. N. Whitehead, the profound and erudite philosopher of Cambridge. These men held firmly to teleological views and to theories that spoke of organismic 'wholes' and which, paradoxically, often professed to be non-vitalistic. They merged imperceptibly with the views of the last vitalistic sect we will mention, the one which arose chiefly because of the apparent impossibility of accounting for psychic phenomena and religious experience. So much for vitalism.

As these positions were taken, mechanists did not remain silent. Lancelot Hogben, in his book *The Nature of Living Matter*, dismissed Bergson, Whitehead, and Haldane as introspective philosophers and stood strongly and squarely on the empiricist position claiming that non-verifiable ideas of vital forces were pure nonsense. The vitalistic psychologist McDougall angrily accused Hogben of conducting his case according to the good old legal maxim 'When you have no case, abuse the other party's attorney.'† Joseph Needham in 1936 published *Order and Life*,

---

* Haldane *père* provides us with a good example of conceptual myopia. When it was discovered how to measure the energy going into and out of an organism, mechanists pointed to the fact that *everything* that went in could be accounted for. No energy, they said, was converted into vital forces. Haldane replied that this was no argument at all against vitalism. 'One might as well try to prove from measurement of the intake and output of energy by a locomotive that the driver does not exist.' If the driver is intended to be analogous to the vital force, this is a poor analogy indeed. It ignores the fact that locomotive drivers also have energy requirements and, in this example, the driver is an integral part of the whole system. Of the energy put into the locomotive *system*, some would clearly go to the driver.

† McDougall also declared Hogben's position to be far to the right. 'I say "right" because, although Hogben no doubt considers himself to be far out on the left wing, that is, I think, only one more misunderstanding on his part.'

the Terry Lectures of that year and, as an experimental embryologist, spoke out for mechanism and against the views of Driesch. He closed the volume by saying:

In conclusion, I would refer to the perplexities of Driesch, at the beginning of the century. . . . A great deal of water has flowed under the bridges since then. We no longer feel the necessity which we felt to place the 'intensive manifoldness' of the egg outside space-time. In 1895 very little was known of the complexities of the colloidal state, next to nothing about molecular orientation at interfaces, and nothing at all about the biological significance of paracrystals. . . . The potentialities of the protein chain, and the phenomena of molecular deformability and contractility were unguessed at, and there was no hint of the exploration of solid bodies by X-ray analysis. These many and great advances give us every promise of a profounder insight into the nature of organic form. To abandon the quest at this stage would surely be the height of folly.

This argument might be made even more strongly today.

It would be pointless to try to give notice to all the leading spokesmen for the mechanistic view, now so widely held. Instead let us look into the merits of the case.

## Frogs, Clocks, Flames, and Crystals

The fact of the matter is that extravagant and implausible vitalism of the variety of Hans Driesch is all but a dead issue in biology today. As we have already mentioned, vitalism leads to no progress since it addresses no questions to nature and, as a matter of course, receives no answers. Whatever happens, it is the principle at work, all-knowing and inscrutable. To the mechanist, all biological events require explanation in physical and chemical terms, and hence *everything* arouses surprise and interest. Probing questions are asked, nothing is taken for granted, and the result is progress. The vitalist is left in his armchair, contentedly pondering the occult.

Still, despite the fact that 'flagrant' vitalism is dead, neither is strict and rigid mechanism universally accepted by biologists today. The organicists survive and hold on to the view that biology is irreducible to physics. To them, the biological structure and method is intrinsically autonomous. Were they maintaining merely that much of biology has *not yet* been reduced to physico-chemical explanation, their position would be unassailable. But they say much more than this. They hold that *in principle* such explanation is not possible and that such explanation should not be the goal of biological research. How valid is this view?

In the first place, nothing so far discovered warrants the view that biological events will *never* be totally explained in physico-chemical terms. That is only for further research to say. According to the philosopher Ernest Nagel (with whose position I agree entirely), there are two problems: *defining* biological laws in physicochemical terms and *deriving* biological laws from physical and chemical laws. Certainly the realization of the former is frequently possible (for example, the connexion between the amount of blood ejected from the heart and the rate of the heart-beat) whereas the satisfaction of the latter is not as often possible (as, for example, the lack of a clear physicochemical explanation for cell division). But what is there to indicate that such explanation will not one day be possible? There is no reason to abandon this as our goal.

Organicists talk about the 'wholeness' of organisms, their unifiedness, integrity, and oneness. They claim that we are dealing with a sum which is greater than the sum of its parts. From the complex integration of parts emerges something bigger and better than a mere sum – an organism! They decry the mechanist who studies the parts separately under the delusion that these results will in any way increase our understanding of the total organism. Nagel makes a vigorous and long overdue attack on the verbal reefs which surround the word 'sum'. He acknowledges the familiar use of 'sum' in expressions such as 'the sum of 2 + 2' or the 'sum of forces'. But what is meant when someone says 'the function of the kidney is more than the sum of the functions of its cells, blood vessels, tissues, etc.'? The answer does or should depend on the body of theory underlying one's concepts. Using a purely mechanistic theory, the behaviour of a clock is easily explained as the sum of the behaviour of its cogs, wheels, and pendulums. But, says Nagel,

Though the thermal behaviour of solids is not the sum of its parts relative to the classical kinetic theory of matter, *it is such a sum relative to modern quantum mechanics*. To say, therefore, that the behaviour of an organism is not the sum of the behaviour of its parts, and that its total behaviour cannot be understood adequately in physicochemical terms even though the behaviour of each of its parts is explicable mechanistically, can only mean that *no body of general theory is now available* from which statements about the total behaviour of the organism are derivable. The assertion, even if true, does *not* mean that it is *in principle* impossible to explain such total behaviour mechanistically, and it supplies no competent evidence for such a claim! *

Organicists point to living *form* and *reproduction*. But does not the flame have form which restores itself after distortion by wind or motion? And cannot flame produce numberless other flames by mere contact? We can explain the flame mechanistically and do not postulate a 'spirit of flame' or a flame principle – although, interestingly, ancient peoples did think flame was alive. Crystals reproduce and grow, and recent years have seen new machines with memories.

In defence of organicism, much has been said on the subject of the laboratory synthesis of life. The organicist pointedly claims that this can never come about. Perhaps this is true and perhaps it is not. Our materialistic account of life is still quite sketchy. Possibly, even in the future, such a synthesis might still elude us. But what bearing does this have on the issue? We can now give an adequate materialistic explanation of the solar system but the day is far away indeed when we will be able to make one.

For the practising biologist, for the man who every day enters the laboratory to perform his experiments, organicism means little and contributes less. Thousands of biological scientists the world over, whether explicitly or not, have rejected this outlook and are proceeding upon mechanistic suppositions. The measure of their success is the growing profundity of their insight and the

* Italics added.

thickness of each year's periodical lists, both of which seem to be increasing exponentially.

With progress occurring at such an incredible rate, who is to say what will happen in another hundred or thousand years? What can justify the solemn pronouncement that this or that will never happen? The answer is nothing. This is not to argue that we will one day possess the 'secret of life', whatever that phrase may mean. Because of the indeterminateness of the small events which go to make up the big event, the organism, because of the probability aspect of all scientific propositions, because every new truth is joined indivisibly to its *bête noire*, new ignorance – for these reasons, we shall *probably* never know all there is to know about the living organism. But, decidedly, this is not the same as saying that an adequate explanation of life in the language of physics and chemistry is not possible. As we shall momentarily see, it may be close at hand.

# 3

## TWENTIETH CENTURY, THE AGE OF ANALYSIS

# 9

## The Latest Revolution

> We have found a strange footprint on the shores of the unknown.
> We have devised profound theories, one after another, to account
> for its origin. At last, we have succeeded in reconstructing the
> creature that made the footprint. And lo! it is our own.
>
> – A. S. Eddington

ABOUT 2,500 years ago, a Greek named Zeno confounded his contemporaries by proving that the fleet Achilles could not possibly overtake a tortoise who had been given a head start. The proof was elegantly simple: the pursuer must always come first to the point from which the pursued has just departed. When Achilles arrives at the tortoise's starting line, the tortoise will have moved a little way beyond this line to a new point of advantage. If Achilles takes any time at all to nullify this new lead, he gives the tortoise time to creep ahead to still another, if progressively smaller, advantage. Achilles thus can never defeat his rival.

This paradox of Zeno had a profound effect upon the history of logic and mathematics, for it instilled in the Greek mind a *horror infiniti* – which paralysed the creative imaginations of the classical geniuses of mathematics. Yet the concept of infinity and the infinitesimal is the cornerstone of modern mathematics. By abhorring it, as Dantzig has observed, Greek mathematics stopped short of algebra in spite of a Diophantus, stopped short of an analytic geometry in spite of an Apollonius, and stopped short of an infinitesimal theory in spite of an Archimedes. Modern calculus is nothing more than a theory of infinite processes. But today we realize that in the very act of moving, Achilles is traversing a continuum and not an infinite set of discrete discontinuous points – or, in the words of Grünbaum, his motion is *legato* not *staccato*. His course, then, is more like a series of whole numbers than of points in space, since for every whole number, there exists a next number, but with any two points in a continuum, another point can always be squeezed between them. An infinite number of non-vanishing distances converging to zero can have a finite sum and can be traversed in a finite time. And so, in the view of modern science, Achilles could have overtaken the tortoise after all!

What is extraordinarily interesting, therefore, about the paradox of Zeno is the fact that Zeno always knew that Achilles could outrun a turtle. Everyone knows that. Yet, in the light of his proof, Zeno reached a metaphysical conclusion: that change and the testimony of the senses are illusory and that time is unreal. He could have chosen the alternative course by concluding that his proof might be faulty – but he did not, presumably because he didn't want to. The lesson of this parable is significant. It is at the heart of the great revolution that the twentieth century brought about in science and philosophy.

In the next four chapters, we will consider in outline some of the ideas brought forth in this era: ideas which, as we shall later show, have profoundly influenced the course of biological thought.

## The Decline and Fall of the Absolute

The issue at stake in this ideological revolution concerns the relationship between the real world itself (if such there be) and our knowledge of the world, as set forth in what we think of it and can meaningfully say about it. The point is nicely illustrated by the case history of Euclidean geometry. Although ancient geometry probably arose out of mere practical necessity, Euclid gave it its organization and rigorous deductive character. Through deductive logic, all of the theorems of geometry could be proved true, or at least as true as the few necessary basic axioms upon which every deductive system must rest. But these were easily available to the ancient Greeks. There were, everyone agreed, a number of self-evident truths that are so obvious they could be accepted without proof, for example, the statement that 'only one straight line can be drawn between two points'. Another such axiom was that 'through a given point, one and only one straight line can be drawn parallel to another given line'. This, too, seemed self-evident to Euclid as it also does to us.

Yet there was something disturbing about the 'parallel postulate'. Euclid himself must have thought so for he avoided using it in his first twenty-eight propositions. And other mathematicians disliked it, too, feeling uneasy about employing it as a basic axiom upon which the validity of the remainder of geometry would depend. For twenty centuries, unimaginably vast efforts were expended in an attempt to convert the axiom into a proved theorem derived from *other* axioms. All efforts had failed when, in the nineteenth century, a number of mathematicians almost simultaneously brought forth the same new idea. Although the geometry of Euclid clearly corresponds with our everyday world of moderate dimensions, what is there to indicate that Euclidean geometry remains valid in the vast expanses of celestial space? It is true that the sum of the three angles of a triangle is 180°. But this is a triangle small enough to be measured in our laboratory. What of a triangle in space at whose corners are the sun and the two most distant nebulae? Need the sum of *these* three angles equal 180°, and how could we verify our answer? It is clear that there exists no logical necessity for believing that Euclidean geometry is valid in the reaches of astronomical space, which, after all, may have bizarre properties affecting the measurement of size and distance. These considerations gave rise to a variety of *non-Euclidean* geometries in which the parallel postulate was arbitrarily denied. If this is done, geometries emerge which are perfectly consistent internally but which merely conflict with our 'natural' and visualizable picture of the world. The question now arises, if there is a multiplicity of geometries, which one corresponds with physical reality – both in terrestrial and celestial space?

This was a dilemma that caused Newton no serious difficulty. In his time, the universe was a visualizable machine, whose geometry was Euclidean and whose space and time were absolute. Thus, Newton denied absolute motion, the movement of bodies which bore no relation to any external object. This concept is usually illustrated by picturing a laboratory aboard a moving train. As long as there is no acceleration, the passengers would have no way of discovering evidence of their motion by experiments done exclusively with equipment belonging to the laboratory. (Needless to say, the earth is such a vehicle.) Interestingly, as Mach has pointed out, Newton violated his own expressed intention to investigate only *facts* when he spoke of things like absolute space and absolute motion, for these are purely constructions of the mind that cannot be observed empirically.

It was another such construct of the Newtonian era that began to cause trouble. Although somewhat non-committal in his views on the nature of light, Newton criticized the wave theory, whose founder had been Huygens. And the Newtonian school, interpreting the master's views perhaps more narrowly than he had intended, developed a corpuscular theory of light which pictured light as particles streaming from a luminous body. But the followers of Huygens insisted that light was a wave-like phenomenon. Moreover, it was argued, if light is a wave motion and the world is a material mechanism, light must do its waving in a material medium just as the waves of the sea exist in water. This function they assigned to an unobserved entity, a substance first described in detail by Descartes – the ether. It was a curious substance, imponderable, ubiquitous, space-filling, and capable of vibrating. The fact of the matter is that the ether was an elusive phantom which Newton himself sometimes referred to as a 'spirit'. Clearly, its main property was to serve as the carefully fabricated final piece in a huge jigsaw puzzle which fit because it was cut to fit. But, as the late Lord Salisbury put it, the ether amounted to little more than the 'subject of the verb "to undulate"'. Its saving grace was that the theory in which it played a part continued to be phenomenally successful in predicting many natural events.

The ether's days were numbered, however. Firstly, the ether had been visualized as an 'elastic solid' for the simple reason that the properties assigned to it by the needs of theory were similar to the properties of ordinary elastic solids which were already understood and mathematically formulated. In other words, the unobservable entity whose invention was a theoretical necessity was thought of as something analogous to a well-understood observable entity. It did not take long for scientists to recognize the trap: merely because two separate physical phenomena are described by almost identical mathematical formulas, one cannot justifiably conclude that one of these phenomena is the ultimate reality in terms of which the other is to be explained. One might as well say that since gasoline flows like water, it may also be used to put out fires.

Secondly, there is a considerable difference between concocting a physically unobservable entity (such as the ether), which successfully enables us to predict the behaviour of observables (such as light), and the question of whether such unobservables really exist. In 1881, Michelson and Morley asked whether the ether really existed by performing an ingenious experiment, one that could not have been done earlier because of its reliance on the new skills of optical instrument makers. These workers reasoned that if the earth is careening through the stationary ether and if light is a wave motion that advances through the ether at a fixed rate, then it must follow that if a light beam is split by mirrors so that one half goes a certain distance and is reflected back again, while the other half is projected the same distance and back again but at right angles to the first beam, then the reunited rays should produce an interference pattern, since the two half-beams will now have been altered by the differences in their path lengths through the ether. It would be similar to what would occur if the path lengths were measured of two swimmers swimming equal distances in a swift current, one downstream and back and the other across and back. The experiment, repeated many times since, flatly contradicted the view that the earth is moving through a stationary ether. For if it is, the results of this experiment should have revealed it.

It was clear then that our ideas of space and time had been superficial, and the stage was now set for the work of Einstein. Einstein recognized that uncritical assumptions were being made in the merest act of measuring distance and time. To eliminate confusion, he postulated the radical-seeming view that things look different to different observers at different places and different times, while the velocity of light must appear the same to all observers no matter what their position or motion may be. To illustrate, length is usually measured by laying a measuring rod alongside the distance to be measured. We have measured an object and find it is one yard long. We wish to compare its length with another object in another city. We take our yardstick with us and perform the second measurement. They are the same. But how do we know that by moving the ruler we have not altered its length? One way to find out might be to use a second ruler to measure the first since length can be gauged only by the use of rulers. But the same question crops up again. We may *observe* that the two rods are equal and congruent when they are next to each other, but when they are apart, we cannot establish their equality by direct observation. Likewise, to establish the simultaneity of events in distantly separated places, we must rely on synchronous clocks, that is, clocks whose minute to minute intervals are the same in terms of time elapsed. But how can we establish that two distant clocks are synchronous? If the clocks are 'stationary', one could send light signals from one to the other. If the light took the same number of seconds on the two clocks to traverse the same interval, we would say that time was being reckoned the same on both clocks. Now, however, let us compare several clocks located in various points in space, one of which is 'stationary' while the others are all moving at the same rate of speed and in the same direction. We could easily synchronize the moving clocks with each other by the same method of light signals we used to synchronize two stationary clocks. But if the moving clocks are synchronized with respect to one another, they cannot be demonstrably synchronous with the stationary clock since the criterion of its synchronousness – the time it takes for a light signal sent by someone sitting on the travelling clock to reach an observer on the stationary clock – will be changing as the position of the moving clock changes. Thus, if we wish to establish the simultaneity of two events, one of which is occurring in the vicinity of the moving clock and the other near the stationary clock, the result of our determination depends entirely upon which clocks we employ as our standard.

We see then that *simultaneity* and *length* are relative concepts which depend upon the position and state of motion of an observer. It follows from this that we can make no more than a relative statement about whether the geometry of the universe is Euclidean or non-Euclidean. Just as the statement 'MacDougall Street is to the left of Sixth Avenue' depends for its objective truth upon an additional statement telling whether we are looking north or south, all statements about which geometry corresponds to the physical world depend on a number of separate considerations. As Reichenbach has pointed out, we cannot say 'the two rods located at different places *are* equal' but only 'we will *call* them equal'. In making such a statement, we are not stating a truth but a definition. By this definition, which implicitly accepts a solid rod as a standard, the world's geometry is plainly Euclidean. In a different part of the universe where we cannot use yardsticks, the geometry appears to be non-Euclidean. And thus we must qualify every statement and measurement with detailed addenda containing definitions and the positions of observers. The basic dilemma remains unresolved but we must agree that the realization of its unsolvability is a discovery of the first importance.

It would be difficult to exaggerate the importance of this discovery upon the philosophical basis of science and on all thought. The essence of Einstein's critique of classical mechanics, and this is the kernel of his brilliant insight, is the idea of construing scientific notions in terms of the actual operations or measurements upon which they rest. This concept, to which P. W. Bridgman has contributed so much, has been called *operational analysis*. We may illustrate it by quoting an example cited by Carl Hempel. How can we think meaningfully of the concept 'harder than'? 'This rock is harder than that one' – the answer is simple if we define 'harder than' operationally. Rock A is harder than rock B if upon drawing a sharp point of A across B, a scratch appears in B. As a methodological precept, operationism has had a profound influence upon modern physics.

What kind of connexion can there be then between human knowledge and the physical world now that Einstein has told us to beware of physical statements that contain no terms capable of operational application and to reconcile ourselves to the fact that in making theories we must first make apparently arbitrary decisions between alternative geometries, chronometries, and benevolence knows what else? With some exuberance, A. N. Whitehead wrote:

The new situation in the thought of today arises from the fact that scientific theory is outrunning common sense. The settlement as inherited by the eighteenth century was a triumph of organized common sense. It grounded itself upon what every plain man could see with his own eyes, or with a microscope of moderate power. It measured the obvious things to be measured, and it generalized the obvious things to be generalized. The eighteenth century opened with the quiet confidence that at last nonsense had been got rid of. Today we are at the opposite pole of thought. Heaven knows what seeming nonsense may not tomorrow be demonstrated truth. The reason why we are on a higher imaginative level is not because we have finer imaginations, but because we have better instruments.

To the weary travellers of the centuries, these developments variously appeared. To the young in heart, the new tidings were joyous and exciting, and vigorous new movements in logic and philosophy promptly took shape. To the backward-looking and tender-minded, the new world view was little short of catastrophic. It meant that an opaque curtain had once and for all descended between science and philosophy, behind which neo-Thomists, neo-Kantians, and neo-Aristotelians could carry on their traditions in peace and quiet. To biologists, there appeared only an illegible scrawl on a dimly seen wall. And it should be noted, perhaps, that to most people the work of Einstein meant nothing.

## Words, Conceptions, Models, and Meanings

Of the suitable topics for long evenings of pleasant but inconclusive conversation, a perennial favourite is the question of whether progress in science follows after advances in philosophy or whether it is the philosophers who do the following, devising new views of the world when events force them to it. Did the political philosophy of Rousseau lead to the French Revolution or did the philosopher's insights follow upon the cataclysm? It is an intriguing question which historians still debate, and it is clear that there can be no simple answer. As we have already noted, science and progress are intimately involved with the beliefs, philosophical assumptions, and traditions of each age. I mention this here, however, to point up an instance about which there can be little doubt as to who followed whom, the scientist or the philosopher. For the potent province of modern analytic philosophy owes its existence to the Einsteinian revolution in physics. Only later did the sequence reverse. As we shall presently see, the precepts of today's philosophy have reached out to influence and unify all manner of intellectual currents. Not the least of these is our conception of the nature of life.

Einstein pointed out that the statement 'two events some distance apart occur simultaneously' cannot be used to derive any observable fact. Here was the impetus to a new philosophy whose chief preoccupation has been with the meaning of language. Since all knowledge must be set forth in language, it is the meaning we give to language which confers upon knowledge its weight and ambiguity. What Einstein was saying was simply that if one wished to understand the Michelson-Morley experiment, one had to commit oneself to the view that the meaning of a statement is strictly related to its verifiability. This conception of the meaning of language had already been voiced by other physicists before Einstein, but it was the monumental work of Einstein that gave these gropings their vast significance for all thought.

Let us consider this question of meaning. I have already mentioned that the great difference between men and beasts is the power to use symbols. Language, of course, is a system of symbols, and it is language, both for its ability to represent ideas and to aid in their development, that largely accounts for the intellectual superiority of men over animals. What is curious is the fact that we look so seldom at the phenomenon of language, whose role in the world of affairs has no parallel. Fortunately, students of language are doing it for us, and what they have told us about this mighty commonplace is fascinating and disquieting.

For example, we recognize that our language is made up of a large number of individual words. Let us suppose that someone tried to improve the language by increasing its richness indefinitely, that is, by inventing a horde of new words to designate more and more subtle and complex concepts. From an alphabet of twenty-six letters, we could concoct, say, $8^{26}$ or about 300 sextillion eight-letter words, more than enough to replace each whole sentence that has ever been written by a different printed word, which could then serve to represent the meaning of the whole sentence. It is apparent that such enrichment of a language would destroy it, since nobody could remember so many words and since the manifestation of meaning for a word depends upon its repeated use. Thus, a child, having seen the word 'naughty' used repeatedly, comes to associate it with a common and recurrent feature in a collection of otherwise differing situations. Since nothing in the world is ever *exactly* repeated, our word carries with it a range of applicability which more or less determines how much variation can be tolerated before the word becomes inappropriate. The word then is a generalization which selects and labels a feature or class of features from the welter of irrelevant features.

If our language was so rich that each word would be used only rarely, words would lose their meanings, because the essential ingredient for a process of generalization, repetition, would disappear. This is evident in the difficulties experienced by children in learning a language. Their main trouble is that they have had too little experience with a word to have grasped that feature of experience which the word designates. That is why a two-year-old will point to a glowing street lamp and say 'moon' or to an ape in the zoo and say 'Daddy!'

Now the meanings of words are attached to them by human decisions. There is no physical or biological necessity that connects a word with the thing it denotes. These connexions are definitions, and in the understanding of definitions lie some great issues. There are several ways of defining words. We may define them ostensively, that is, by saying the word and then pointing the finger. For example, 'building' is defined:

But we cannot define every word by pointing; some we must define explicitly. Thus, 'Profit is the excess of returns over expenditure.' This is the meaning we decided to give to the word 'profit'. We could just as easily have said, 'Profit is a place where limestone is quarried.' But we didn't.

Part of the power of words lies in the fact that they aid us in recognizing instances of things for which a word exists. That is, we *use* definitions as diagnostic formulas for the recognition of phenomena or objects. Here is the kernel of a practical problem. It is our daily need for recognition criteria, our absolute dependence upon identification methods based on observed correspondences with our man-made criteria, the necessary preliminary act to drinking water, to selecting the toothpaste from the cabinet, to commenting on the weather, to everything we do. In most cases, we are caused little inconvenience by such problems. If we are asked for a dime, we have no difficulty selecting a coin from the many in our pocket that agrees with the definition of the word 'dime'. But the difficulties in this area can plague and frustrate the scientist. If one wished to study the properties of the amoeba and were handed a small blob of jelly-like material, a preliminary question would need to be answered: Was it an amoeba? Did it possess those characteristics which by definition are designated by the word 'amoeba'? If one wanted some sodium chloride and someone handed him a bottle of white powder. Was it sodium chloride? It is apparent that in most cases of this kind, we tend to rely upon the label on the bottle for assurances as to what the bottle contains, thereby transferring to another the responsibility for having verified the correspondence between the contents and the properties attached to the word on the label. As every bio-chemist knows, however, there are too many bottles whose contents have nothing to do with the words on the label.

Even this problem is simple compared to the difficulties in establishing the applicability of those many words in our language which are vague in that there are borderline cases in which it is impossible to say whether the word should or should not be applied. I shall speak of this later, though the reader is correct in suspecting that I consider 'life' to be such a word.

We have spoken so far only of words and their meanings. But language is more than mere words: it is also statements. Pro-positions or statements are the fundamental units of language which possess actual meaning and truth value. In this sense, an isolated word has no meaning, for the logicians point out that unless it stands for a sentence, a word by itself has no meaning. Thus, 'table' has no meaning unless one points, physically or mentally, to a table indicating that he means 'that is a table'. The sentence has meaning. And, of course, meaning and truth value are confined to language and do not apply to the physical things themselves which are denoted by language.

The abstract truths of science are propositions containing the words and symbols of science. This is interesting to consider in view of the hectic rate of expansion of the scientific vocabulary. The truths that we seek today may find expression tomorrow in sentences containing words that are unknown today. Is not our seemingly limitless present vocabulary adequate to cope with any conceptual eventuality? I think the answer to this lies in the realization that the vocabulary of science represents a symbol-ization of the scientist's intellectual models, and as his models change, his vocabulary expands.

But what are models? This important and tantalizing concept demands our attention. We have already mentioned that science consists of a sequence of oscillations between abstraction and experiment. Good scientists are therefore constantly ambulating back and forth between armchair and laboratory. Experimental data suggests theories and theories suggest new experiments designed either to help confirm or effectively contradict theory. A well-confirmed abstraction thus becomes a highly probable parcel of knowledge.

Abstractions can exist at every level of complexity, as pointed out by Rosenblueth and Wiener and many others. Those low on the ladder of complexity are directly open to experimental verification. If I say the drug colchicine stops the division of cells in a growing onion root tip, I have only to test this experimentally to justify the abstraction (and give it a certain probability). If I next attempt to say that *all* drugs that generally resemble colchicine inhibit the division of *all* cells, the abstraction is of a much higher order of complexity and enormously more difficult to test experimentally.

Because of the complexity of higher abstractions and because of the desirability of establishing such higher generalizations, scientists are forced to devise *models* of nature, simplifications achieved by eliminating irrelevant detail, from which higher abstractions can be more easily derived. It happens that most attempts to explain the meaning of models break up in hopeless confusion, yet the idea is simplicity itself. To most of us, 'model' suggests small aeroplanes or sailing ships inexplicably moored within whisky bottles. But in science, the word 'model' means a construction, real or imaginary, in which something complex is rendered understandable – or, as is usually the case, simpler. Their purpose is only to help us formulate our ideas the better to evolve new ones.

The validity of this procedure is as good as the exactitude with which the crucial actuality of nature is embodied in the model, the best model of nature obviously being nature itself. The model is intended to incorporate in workable form the *essential* features of the natural system under examination. Models may be intellectual or material, the former being abstract statements in words or symbols of an idealized simplified situation. Their language may be informal, as, for example, 'all stress stimulates the adrenal gland', or the statement may be formal, symbolic, and mathematical. Material models are simplified material representations of a complex system (such as electronic computer and brain) selected on the supposition that some essential aspect of the complex system may thereby be singled out for study.

Obviously, much of the inevitable uncertainty of science lurks in the question of the admissibility and appropriateness of the chosen model. Should my chosen model be too simple or actually irrelevant, I am predestined to failure. Many chosen models are, by hindsight, astonishingly unsuitable. Other dubious-seeming models have turned out to be the inspirations of genius. Unfortunately, we cannot know the propriety of our models, intellectual or material, except from the retrospective vantage point of future success or failure. Recently, I heard a lecturer describe his researches in sociology in which he used as his model the ultimate particles of physics. Their clinging together as atoms and molecules suggested to him the essences of society and he termed the phenomenon *proto-society*. Here we will have to await confirmation or denial of our present scepticism about the suitability of the chosen model.

Clearly, there are dangers involved in using material models. The elastic-solid model of the 'luminiferous ether' which we have discussed suffices to illustrate this danger. The error lurking in material models far different in size scale from that of nature is amply illustrated by the mechanical model of the universe propounded in the Newtonian era. This structure, embodying Euclidean geometry, seemed correct and logical because it was most easy to visualize conceptually. But the geometry of celestial and subatomic space turned out to be non-Euclidean, far more difficult to visualize mechanically in the mind's eye and hence untranslatable into handy material models. Here, contemporary models eventually retarded progress.

In biology, models of every level of complexity are used, and because of the nature of the scientific problem they can be helpful and treacherous. Some appear outwardly more 'mechanical' than others. There has been great enthusiasm lately for 'mathematization' in biology, and frequently this has had amusing consequences as pointed out by J. A. Rafferty. It leads sometimes to *circularism*.

The biologist builds an elaborate and intricate theory in vernacular.

The mathematician simplifies the theory and describes it in mathematical symbols. He then deduces consequences which are already evident from the verbal reasoning of the biologist. He 'puts into numbers what everybody knows in words.' Or he arrives at consequences which are fictions of his simplifications in devising a neat mathematical model. The mathematician may have enjoyed his mathematical exercise, but science is none the better for it. Biomathematicians working *in biologica vacuo* are particularly susceptible to the insidious circularity of modelling by description.

Models in biology consist chiefly of substitutes for the total organism which are variably reduced in complexity. We may use a smaller animal to study psychology because this animal has a seemingly simpler social integration. We use fruit flies to study genetics because they enter a new generation every twelve days, a notable change in the time scale when it comes to comparisons with some other organisms. We use bacteria to study intermediary metabolism because they are single-celled organisms and can be grown on simple media of known composition. We constantly compare the thermodynamics of the organism to that of the engine and teach our classes that metabolizing food is like burning coal. Purified enzymes are used to eliminate the complexities of cell membrane permeability and structural organization. Each of these models represents a different level of complexity. Each has only a limited contribution to make to the highest abstractions, those of universal applicability.

Thus we see the connexion between a scientist's mental models and his vocabulary. In an essay called 'Language and Science', Stanley Gerr clearly showed how scientific terms (and non-scientific terms for that matter) are evolved. They may arise from a crystallization of phrases and groups of words into fixed expressions which are used over and over again as symbols of an intellectual model. An example is 'the specific dynamic action of proteins', an expression which refers to the observation that, following a protein meal, the heat production of the body increases. This heat is essentially wasted and has been called, in another expression representing another abstract concept, 'the cost of digestion'. In using these terms, we seldom think of the

169

intimate events of metabolism which are proceeding in blissful unawareness of our discursive ruminations. We don't even think of the scientist sitting by his calorimeter watching its dials. We think instead of the intellectual model embodied in the expression 'cost of digestion'. This functional sense of language is reflected also in terms like 'spectrophotometric methods', 'depolymerization', 'electrify'. These terms are the linguistic evidences of the progress of science.

In the early stages of knowledge of a subject, when little is known, our inadequate conceptions force us, as Gerr states, to use linguistic props, metaphors, crude similes, and elaborate descriptions which endow our first fragile models with structural rigidity. But as knowledge grows, language is formulated and entities and relations emerge as *conceptual units*. Thus concept and language are correlates. In the early days of biology, the basis of heredity was completely unknown. When Morgan postulated the gene as a particulate bearer of hereditary characteristics, an extremely useful model was elaborated. In recent years, more subtle and precise experiments have shown several possible shortcomings in the gene theory and our language is now changing to include words like 'locus' which correspond to newer intellectual models.

And so it appears that the nature of truth is intimately bound up with semantics. The philosopher Tarski, in a brilliant analysis of this question, ended with the definition, 'A sentence is true if it is satisfied by all objects and false otherwise.' For example, 'The sentence "the snow is white" is true if, and only if, snow is white.' The degrees of correspondence between abstract statement and model and model and nature are the degrees of truth of a scientific statement. In both areas, there is ample room for fallibility.

Modern logic has asked the question, 'When is a proposition meaningful?' and after much polemical controversy has proposed as an answer the *verifiability theory of meaning* which, stated simply, holds that a proposition is meaningful only if it is, in principle, verifiable as true or false. (We would be more explicit if we said confirmable as more or less probable.) It should be kept

170

in mind that meaning here refers to cognitive meaning. *Meaningless* means factually meaningless and has no reference to psychological, emotional, or aesthetic meaning. Despite all that has been said for or against this view, it has given a powerful tool to science. One recalls the famous interchange of published remarks of C. I. Lewis and M. Schlick on the merits of this theory of meaning. Lewis argued, for example, that the concept of immortality is unverifiable and yet meaningful. Schlick answered that indirect phenomena may, *in principle*, justify a hypothesis of survival after death. To this verifiability, the hypothesis of immortality owes its meaning; beyond the possibility of verification it has no meaning. A sentence whose probability of truth cannot be determined or altered from possible observations then is meaningless: *here is a cornerstone of modern science*.

Schlick wrote:

If we utter a sentence without meaning it is always our own fault. The tremendous philosophic importance of this remark will be realized when we consider that what we said about the meaning of assertions applies also to the meaning of questions. There are many questions which can never be answered by human beings. But the impossibility of finding the answer may be of two different kinds. ... If it is due to chance circumstances to which our human existence is confined, there may be reason to lament our fate and the weakness of our physical and mental powers, but the problem could never be said to be absolutely insoluble, and there would always be some hope, at least for future generations. ... But what about those problems for which it is *logically* impossible to find an answer? Such problems would remain insoluble under all imaginable circumstances ... this calamity could happen only if the question itself had no meaning. It would not be a genuine question at all, but a mere row of words with a question-mark at the end.

The history of science and particularly biology abounds with examples of meaningless questions or pseudo problems. How was matter generated from nothing? Do organisms contain vital forces? What was the cause of the universe? (If there were a first event in the universe, it could not have a cause.) What is the purpose of human life? What is the nature of nothing? And so on and so on. When we can set aside such questions as being outside the realm of possible empirical verification, we have arrived at the view that the logic of language determines the limits and structure of meaningful discourse.

Let it be said in ending this discussion that the problems of language are among the deepest questions that men have essayed to answer, and they are merely mentioned here, not delved into. Philosophers continue to debate the questions of meaning and language, and the quality of this dialogue remains vigorous, particularly since certain formulations of the verifiability criterion of meaning have turned out to have a number of unwelcome logical consequences. Although the empirical and analytic trend in philosophy represents a major turning point in the history of critical thought, no one need fear that speculative and intuitive philosophy has passed into the beyond. It remains alive and presumably always will as long as there are people whose views of the world are basically rooted in emotion, hope, and fear. Certainly, many a distinguished present-day philosopher still considers speculative philosophy worth doing. As might be expected, one of the problems in the growth and consolidation of logical empiricism seems to have been the over-aggressive use of the theory of meaning by what Feigl has called 'young iconoclasts'. The temptation is strong to sweep aside difficult problems by declaring them meaningless, and this has happened too often. This criticism is easy to make, but it, too, is shaky because it implies the desirability of absolute criteria of meaningfulness against which we can measure whether young iconoclasts have indeed gone too far. Unfortunately, there are no such criteria, and here is where the question stands in the philosophy seminars of today.

Nevertheless, the analytic view has made monumental contributions to our thinking in science and biology. Before we discuss them, however, let us say a word about some of the other notions that have sprung up in the fertile soil of modern philosophy and science.

# 10

## *Explanation in Science*

SHEMIN: I think —'s theories are infantile.
RACKER: We don't care if they're infantile, David, just as long as
they're correct.
— Overheard at the Enzyme Club, 1956

AT a recent international meeting of Nobel Prize winners in physics, something of a furore was created by statements made by two of the world's greatest nuclear physicists, Werner Heisenberg of Germany and Hideki Yukawa of Japan. What caused the excitement was a declaration of dissatisfaction with the two theories which are the keystones of contemporary thought in nuclear physics – the theory of relativity, which seeks to explain the universe at large, and the quantum theory, which deals with the forces within the atom. Science, they said, must now seek a new explanation for the structure and properties of the elementary particles of physics, for neither the relativity theory nor the quantum theory adequately explains some of the revolutionary discoveries that have been made in recent years.

Heisenberg said, 'Existing theories at best serve to give a semiphenomenological explanation for the qualities of elementary particles, but they fail to explain their existence convincingly.' And Yukawa said, 'Granted that the existing theories have something essentially correct, our further step must be to have a deeper insight so that we can approach nearer to a unified theory of elementary particles.'

We can learn much from this episode, for just as great dramas draw upon the emotions shared by all men, what we are witnessing here is a great scientific drama whose theme is a commonplace of everyday life: the search for explanations. The physicists are telling us that discoveries have been made which are not yet explainable. They now seek the answer to the question 'why?' having already answered the question 'what?' We recognize in

173

this quest the essential purpose of all scientific inquiry, going beyond mere description by providing explanation. No one could reasonably disagree with this assertion. It is worth noting, therefore, that there is continuing and often hectic disagreement among philosophers about aspects of the nature of explanation. If we are to enter the catacomb of science – and particularly biology, where the gloom has been thickest – we should really look in on this wrangle. Some of it is uncommonly interesting.

## The Nature of Explanation

Some have held that there is no real difference between *description* and *explanation*. Others have taken the position that all scientific explanation is *circular* and can ultimately be boiled down to statements like the famous one of Calvin Coolidge, 'When many people are out of work, unemployment results' or 'He takes eight baths a day because he is compulsive.' We will recognize that if 'compulsiveness' were diagnosed on the basis of the eight baths a day, the statement is circular and adds nothing to our understanding.

Still another conception holds that explanation consists in the systematic reduction of the unfamiliar to the familiar. But this view makes us uneasy: falling apples are familiar but what is familiar about the law of gravity?

Let us consider these points. There are, of course, differences between description and explanation. A descriptive generalization simply formulates in some manner the results of many observations. Usually, in the history of science, description precedes explanation and, in fact, makes it possible. Suppose, for example, we observe the motion of a particle, making observations at successive intervals and recording its position at those times. To answer the question 'Where was the particle at such and such a time?' we have only to look at our descriptive table. Even if we find it possible to express the motion of the particle in a simple mathematical formula, we have still done no more than describe its movement.

Similarly, to invent a biological example, suppose we are concerned with the colour of animal fur. We might set up a table in which we list down in one column the names of various animals with their coat colours in another column. If now we list the predominant colour of the customary habitat and then declare that animals tend to have the coloration of their environment, have we achieved an explanation? No, because the generalization is still purely descriptive. It is 'what' and not 'why'.

Turning to the circular view of explanation, here is treacherous terrain. We know where we stand in the simple case of the physician who says, 'You have a headache because you have cephalalgia.' Although this type of explanation is common in medicine, it consists of nothing more than translation into Greek. But in the history of biology, a number of crucial developments have rested solely upon such flimsy supports. An example occurs to me which I have not seen discussed previously. It will be recalled that one of the widely applauded developments of nineteenth-century biology was the theory that *protoplasm* is the universal stuff of life. This theory is still being taught as a fundamental principle of biology. Yet in reading the literature of that period, an odd thought arises about the theory and its status as a scientific generalization, for it contains a paradox, and I believe one can show that the discovery of protoplasm both aided and hindered the cause of science. When it emerged ,'the brotherhood of protoplasm' seemed to be a potent concept that threw new light on a variety of scientific questions. But the protoplasm idea had another aspect: it was logically empty and colossally vague. The ground stuff of life? What does it mean?

Let's take a moment to analyse this point briefly. Formal logic tells us that a statement is a tautology that is empty of empirical content and necessarily true. The facts of the world can never falsify it. The statement 'If my mistress were named Penelope, her name would start with "P"' is true whether or not my mistress's name is, in fact, Penelope, and, happily, nothing in the sentence informs us what her name might actually be. As a source of empirical truth, the sentence is empty; that is why logical relations are empty or tautological. Science is filled with unchallengeable tautologies. But when the same statements are phrased in terms open to empirical verification they may be true and they may be false. Thus, if 'east' is defined as that point on the horizon which is 90° to the right as one faces north, the statement 'The sun rises in the east' may or may not be true and can easily be tested experimentally. Here, the word 'east' had a meaning before we brought the sun into it. But, if we define 'east' as the place where the sun rises, the same statement becomes a tautology, empty of empirical meaning. Under these circumstances, the sun can rise nowhere else.

The question then becomes: Did 'protoplasm' have a meaning before the theorists decided that all living substance is made of it? From the evidence I have seen, the answer is no. Certainly, it was not a new word in the nineteenth century. According to Cameron, the phrase '*De parentis protoplasti*' appeared in a sixth-century hymn that was sung during Passiontide. Purkinje, before 1840, used the word protoplasm to refer to the living substance of plant and animal cells – what he said was that cells *consist of* protoplasm – but I see no indication that he defined it by any special physical, chemical, or biological properties. If he had and *then* it was pronounced the universal substance of life, the 'protoplasm theory' would be an induction based on experimental data. What happened, I think, was the exact reverse. The theory was stated as a tautology, 'All life is protoplasm,' which inescapably means 'That which lives we shall call protoplasm.' *Then*, in time its physical properties *were* gradually defined, and the word took on a new significance in the light of later empirical experience. In any case, we eventually found that what we have known as protoplasm is an elaborate organization which is dissectable into a hierarchy of parts. Although one is never justified in criticizing the techniques of discovery – an important discovery would remain important though its discoverer stumbled over it in a dark alley – this concept, by its nature and its era, could only have been an intuitive decision on an essentially verbal level.

I raise the point about the protoplasm theory, because, suspecting it of being a tautological definition, I further suspect it of being a definition that implied different things to different people.

Did it mean a physical entity or a class of entities? One is reminded of the beginning of Woodger's tale of the land Naamba.

Once upon a time, long long ago, there dwelt in a village which later was called Naamba (the precise geographical location of which need not detain us) a people endowed with the power of recognition and speech but, to begin with, a very limited vocabulary. They had demonstrative pronouns and made great use of gestures. But they had no proper names, nouns, or adjectives. The results of acts of recognition they expressed in the form 'here is another of those.' Finding this highly inconvenient one of these people – a man of great originality – invented proper names. This man, whenever he recognized his pet dog, said, 'here is Fido again,' and whenever he recognized another object which was more like Fido than anything else, but at the same time obviously *not* Fido again he said, 'here is *another* Fido.' But this also proved to be inconvenient and insufficient, because another inhabitant, copying the first, had decided to call his dog 'Dido.' So instead of one saying 'here is another Fido' and the other saying 'here is another Dido' they agreed each to keep his own name for his pet, but both to say, 'here is another bobo,' when they recognized Fido-like *or* Dido-like objects.

In other words, the question was: Is protoplasm a Fido, Dido, or bobo? If we mean it as a class of objects rather than an object of the class and merely explain away its almost infinite variations with the epigram, 'All flesh is not the same flesh for there is one kind of flesh of men and another of beasts', then we are again opening the door to conceptual trouble. Empiricists most willing to subordinate hypothesis to fact hardly knew where to go to 'confirm' the theory of protoplasmic universality. But to some of the metaphysically inclined (and this raises another point), protoplasm was made to order: it had wonderful overtones of mystical music of the spheres and conveyed poetic images of quivering disembodied life, flowing and swirling in a cloud of unknown unknowables. For those who wished to see it that way, I suspect that the protoplasm theory may have heaped extra fuel on the fires of vitalism by implying anew a degree of complexity that only vitalism could account for while simultaneously arousing fervent opposition to this new outrage of materialistic science.

I only suspect that the first happened, but I know that the second did. In a pungent essay written by Thomas Henry Huxley

177

in 1871, one finds the following passage referring to his earlier lecture *On the Physical Basis of Life*:

In it there was nothing new; and, as I hope, nothing that the present state of knowledge does not justify us in believing to be true. Under these circumstances, my surprise may be imagined, when I found, that the mere statement of facts and of views, long familiar to me as part of the common scientific property of continental workers, raised a sort of storm in this country, not only by exciting the wrath of unscientific persons whose pet prejudices they seemed to touch, but by giving rise to quite superfluous explosions on the part of some who should have been better informed.

Dr Stirling, for example, made my essay the subject of a special critical lecture, which I have read with much interest, though, I confess, the meaning of much of it remains as dark to me as does the 'Secret of Hegel' after Dr Stirling's elaborate revelation of it. . . . A most amusing example of this fashion of dealing with scientific statements is furnished by Dr Stirling's remarks upon my account of the protoplasm of the nettle hair. That account was drawn up from careful and often-repeated observations of the facts. Dr Stirling thinks he is offering a valid criticism, when he says that my valued friend Professor Stricker gives a somewhat different statement about protoplasm. But why in the world did not this distinguished Hegelian look at a nettle hair for himself, before venturing to speak about the matter at all? Why trouble himself about what either Stricker or I say, when any tyro can see the facts for himself, if he is provided with those not rare articles, a nettle and a microscope? But I suppose this would have been *Aufklärung* – a recurrence to the base common-sense philosophy of the eighteenth century, which like to see before it believed, and to understand before it criticized. Dr Stirling winds up his paper with the following: 'In short, the whole position of Mr Huxley, (1) that all organisms consist alike of the same life-matter, (2) which life-matter is, for its part, due only to chemistry, must be pronounced untenable – not less untenable, (3) the materialism he would found on it.'

In the furnace glare of today's biology, the word protoplasm has a somewhat old-fashioned look. The analytical movement has bitten deep into the complexities of living substance and has yielded a more concrete, if not 'ultimate', vocabulary. Today, we speak of protoplasm in its latter-day context, wherein it is defined in chemical, physical, and biological terms. We *now* have enough empirical evidence to agree enthusiastically that there *is* fundamental similarity between the protoplasm of all living things and that, no doubt, protoplasm is 'the ground stuff of life'. This, however, is a very different thing, in fact the very opposite, of stating as a principle that protoplasm is the substance of life because that which lives is protoplasm.

We achieve explanation when we relate our specific observations to a separate verifiable generalization or law which is outside of them and from which they could potentially have been predicted. We did not explain our moving particle merely by describing its motion mathematically, but we would explain it if we showed that the motion is under the influence of a nearby magnet, for the law of magnetic fields would permit us in principle to predict the particle's movement. Similarly, we did not explain the colour of animal fur merely by pointing out its resemblance to the background. It is by connecting coat colour with the idea of visibility and the concept of protection from predatory animals that permits us to say the polar bear is white because white fur enhances his chances of survival. By going behind what is observable, we have explained his colour. And likewise, if 'compulsiveness' were an independently ascertainable empirical quality, we could use it to explain the behaviour of a man who took eight baths a day.

We do *not* achieve explanation when we refer our observations to an analogy or to some appealing metaphor – as, for example, the attempt to clarify biological parasitism on the basis of what we know of human political systems. Just such an explanatory view was recently set forth in the scientific literature by H. W. Stunkard, who, among other things, wrote that the honeybee is *in reality* '. . . a most pathetic little creature . . . a martyr, and a victim of the "welfare state"'. The hazards of such an analogy need no comment. It clearly does not bring together a set of observations with a general law under which they may be subsumed. It, therefore, is not a valid explanation.

I regret to say that the very laws upon which explanations must rest are themselves the subject of fretful discussion. We all understand intuitively what a law is: it is a generalization about the

179

world for which considerable evidence has been gathered. But philosophers are troubled by the borderline cases in which it is difficult to say whether a statement is a law or something else. These are intricate questions of logic and we will not presume to enter them here. It does not seem to me that great importance attaches to the precise limits which are set to the application of the word 'law'. For our discussion, our rough definition should suffice.

Interestingly, Haldane has even complained about the use of the word 'law' in this context. He prefers to speak of the 'uniformities of nature' and do away with the possible implication of a lawgiver or a legislative body of atoms. 'If a piece of matter does not obey a law of nature it is not punished. On the contrary, we say that the law has been incorrectly stated. It is quite probable that every law of Nature so far stated has been stated incorrectly.' Several views have been held on the nature of these laws. There is the older view that laws are absolute, and the extreme, recent positivistic view that we can only say that phenomena occur *as if* certain laws held. The British physicist Jeffreys wrote, 'A well-verified hypothesis will probably continue to lead to correct inferences even if it is wrong.' He comments that 'laws' which ultimately turn out to be inexact have often been remarkably more exact than the data on which they were first formulated.* 'When Einstein's modification [of the law of gravitation] was adopted, the agreement of observation with Newton's law was

---

* We have recently witnessed a dramatic instance of a law of physics – one which had successfully predicted natural phenomena since its innovation thirty years ago – abruptly shattering before our eyes. The so-called law of parity held that two sets of phenomena, one of which is a mirror image of the other, behave in an identical fashion except for the mirror image effect. According to this law, were we in communication with beings on another planet, we would have no way of telling whether they meant the same thing by 'right' and 'left' as we do. But in early 1957, brilliantly conceived experiments were reported that invalidate the law of parity, for they proved that among the particles of physics right-handedness of spin is crucially and discernibly different from left-handedness, thus permitting an absolute identification of right and left in all possible worlds. It would be difficult to overestimate the importance of this discovery.

three hundred times as good as Newton ever knew.' There appears to be no reason for saying there are no regularities in nature to which our statements of natural law correspond. 'One might as well say,' wrote Haldane, 'that because no maps of England give its shape exactly, it has no shape.'

When all is said and done there seems to be evidence that even the 'laws of nature' are changing. Modern physics suggests the possibility that changes are taking place in the speed of light and the rates of chemical reactions. The universe may be changing, and it becomes hazardous to attempt calculations concerning the very remote past and future. It appears that eternal natural stability is as improbable as its psychological corollary, eternal truth. This should worry no one except the seeker of eternal certainty. It may turn out that fundamental change and uncertainty are the nearest things we have to eternal principles.

Frequently, we seem to content ourselves with descriptive generalizations without seeking to reach the explanatory plane. Worse, sometimes we confuse the two. The error is serious simply because descriptive generalizations preclude reliable predictions. Of course, we do often predict on this basis, but with scanty justification. Without an outside connexion, we have little real basis to assume that A5 will necessarily follow A1, A2, A3, A4. If the series is not explained, we do not understand the thread connecting the terms and we can never know when the series is long enough to permit valid prediction. For example, would 4 or 12 be more likely to come next in the series 18, 57, 42, 91, 72, . . .? Only after it is recognized that when the numbers are written out as words (eighteen, fifty-seven, forty-two, ninety-one, seventy-two) they are arranged alphabetically as in a dictionary, is the series explained. The answer is obviously 'twelve'.

There are a number of things that we as authors of biological explanation aspire to and take for granted but rarely discuss. For one thing, we assume that there is order in the universe and that nature is intelligible. We assume that inductive reasoning is safe. We also tend to stick close to the 'simplicity postulate', a rule of cerebral economy that can be traced back to the medieval thinker William of Occam. His rule, often called Occam's razor, read *Entia non sunt multiplicanda praeter necessitatem* – entities shall not be multiplied beyond necessity – a sane preachment that has greatly influenced thought. Restated by Bertrand Russell, it says that 'if everything in some science can be interpreted without assuming this or that hypothetical entity, there is no ground for assuming it.' We are, thereby, admonished against inventing unnecessary entities, dominions, powers, rules, causes, and connexions. What we must bear in mind, however, is that there is no proven necessity for this rule of thought, for though logic may tell us not to invent unnecessary symbols, logic cannot tell us not to multiply entities. As we have seen, the course of biological science raises substantial doubts as to the equivalence of simplicity and validity. As Woodger has aptly written: 'The biologist especially, faced with the unutterable complexity of living things, cannot but feel that the apparent successes of the simplicity postulate are liable to be achieved by throwing some of the main cargo overboard under the mistaken impression that it is merely ballast.' This warning presumably goes to young and old iconoclasts alike.

## Looking Backward for Causes and Forward for Goals

The story is told that a citizen of the town in which Democritus lived was killed one day by a tortoise that fell from the sky upon his head. The people were shocked and wondered what explanation there could be for such an extraordinary event. Suddenly someone recalled that an eagle had been observed circling around directly above the scene of the tragedy. Things then began to make sense. The eagle was the bird of Zeus and it had dropped the tortoise on the victim's head. Why would Zeus have sponsored such an occurrence? There could be only one reason – to punish a man who must have been guilty of some grave crime. And, with this, the people began to probe into the man's past for the scandal they knew they would find.

Democritus watched these events and shrugged. If they find their scandal, he thought, they will think they have proved the operation of divine vengeance. But why need these events have occurred to serve a purpose? And so Democritus confronted his neighbours with some irrefutable facts. True, eagles are fond of tortoise meat. It is also true, they agreed, that in order to break the hard shell of the tortoise, the eagle must drop the tortoise from a goodly height on to a suitable rock. 'Therefore,' said Democritus pointing to the victim's bald head, 'why can't we simply assume that the eagle mistook this shining pate for a rock fit to break a tortoise on?' And the people conceded that it was just as reasonable to imagine a near-sighted eagle as an impetuous and wrathful king of the gods.

We have spoken of explanation but have said nothing of causality. Yet in ordinary life, the usual method of explaining an event is to state its cause. I was sick because I ate a green apple. The stock market collapsed because the President was sick. Poliomyelitis is disappearing because of a powerful new vaccine. There is the cause, then the effect – what could be simpler? Unfortunately, almost anything could be simpler, for the concept of causality has long been a troublesome one. A large part of this difficulty is traceable to the ineradicable idea that everything that happens happens for a purpose.

Man is a vain creature. All through history he has enthroned himself at the centre of the universe, indisputable emperor of all he surveys. He has traditionally ignored or uneasily repressed the conclusions of geology and astronomy, that man is but a brief interlude, having existed during less than a hundredth of a per cent of the history of a tiny speck of cosmic dust, the earth. Instead, he has often seen himself as the object and goal of the whole cosmic enterprise.

Philosophers call this attitude *anthropomorphism*: it has led people to grave and often fatal error. Historically, this point of view has taken many forms: the *a priori* assumption that the sun rotates around the earth, the ancient and modern gods who look like men and share their foibles, the reluctance to believe that man descended from apes, the strident contention that living and non-living matter are necessarily fundamentally different, the attribution to evolution of some great and awesome purpose.

That the world has purpose, the view called *teleological*, is believed by a large number of people. The teleologist's arguments are many. He says that the world has a pattern and must therefore have a purpose, that man is too intricate and complex to have just happened. He points to evolution (now that he has been forced to accept the fact of evolution) as a cogent argument for world purpose: life is becoming more complex and it is evolving toward a goal of perfection. Furthermore, argues the teleologist, if the world had no purpose, why else would it have been created? Humans can have purpose, why can't the world have it? Most people believe in it, and it says so in the Bible.

If we are to discuss the living organism, this issue requires some consideration. Refutation of most of these arguments is not difficult; a few, however, do not yield so easily. Furthermore, refuting an opponent's case is not the same as establishing your own. Modern philosophy, moving both in the *avant-garde* and in the rear encampments of modern science, has given careful attention to the debate between explainers-by-cause and explainers-by-purpose, and it presents us with a parcel of rejoinders whose conspicuous unwrapping would be most instructive. As we shall see, the modern view of causality – which has profound significance for biology – is still another outgrowth of the new physics.

As was evident in the town of Democritus, the attitudes of the ancient Greeks toward physical occurrences were somewhat divided. The early discoverers of mathematical regularities in the movement of the stars believed that a strict and inexorable order characterized these events: they were attributable to blind, causal laws, or to what is called *causal determinism*. All the events of the world were the results of other events; nothing was arbitrary or accidental. But for the majority of the ancients, the apparatus of causation was viewed through anthropomorphic glasses. *Fatalism* was the accepted basis of natural events. Just as men controlled physical objects, the gods controlled men, each of whom was impelled toward his inescapable destiny according to a heavenly plan.

But the success of mathematical formulation could not be ignored. Using mathematical relationships, a Galileo could predict the outcome of a physical event, such as the position and velocity at any given moment of a ball rolling down an inclined plane. The unequivocal success of such predictions soon spread to the domains of light, heat, and electricity. With complete knowledge of the initial state of a system, mathematical analysis permitted rigorous prediction of the future state of the system. Of course, in most cases, one was unable to determine the *exact* state of affairs in a physical system but this was one's own fault. Human imperfection, it was generally agreed, would eventually be got around when better instruments of observation became available.

Causal determinism was given its most trenchant affirmation by the brilliant mathematician Laplace, who declared that were there a superhuman intelligence capable of knowing the position and momentum of every atom in the universe and of solving all the mathematical equations, it could, with precision, state the minutest detail of every event whether it be thousands of years in the future or as remote in the past. This strict view of physical determinism was the direct outgrowth of Newtonian physics which viewed the world as a huge machine whose mode of operation would be completely described if our knowledge of physics were perfect. Nor was its universal acceptance to be wondered at. Not only was its power of prediction demonstrably uncanny but there was the captivating spectacle of progressively improving agreement between observation and equation following directly upon every refinement in technical accuracy.

Causal determinism is distinctly different from fate. 'It is blind,' wrote Reichenbach, 'not planning; it does not favour or hate men; it is a determinism not in terms of future aims but of past facts, a determinism not in terms of a supernatural command but of a physical law. But it is as strict and exceptionless as the determinism of fate. It makes the physical world comparable to a wound clock that goes automatically through its stages.'

But the mid-nineteenth-century discovery of the laws of gas behaviour hinted that all was not well with rigidly interpreted causal determinism. Gases are swirling collections of *individual* molecules whose agitated movements appear completely random,

185

senseless, and, of course, quite unpredictable. And yet the gases themselves, in the whole, nicely follow the mathematical laws of pressure and temperature and conform admirably to classical deterministic science. Thus the experimenter was confronted with a *large and rigorously predictable* event which was the resultant of an enormous number of *small and totally unpredictable* events! This is not to say that the movement of each tiny particle is not governed completely by the laws of classical mechanics. It well may be. The unpredictability of its path means that, for one reason or another, *no human observer* could make the prediction. Recognition of this paradox forced him to the conclusion that the seemingly predictable behaviour of gases was, in fact, nothing more than the very high probability that the average result of many small seemingly random events would be something corresponding to mathematical expectation, the replacement, really, of causal law by probability law.

The question remained whether or not determinism was operating on the micro-level. Does not causal law determine the zigzag path of each individual particle? It soon became apparent that there simply was no way of knowing by observation the behaviour of the individual particles, especially those particles which make up the atom. And there would be no way until the unlikely day when measuring instruments could be made which approached in size and energy the particles being measured, for these are particles which are joggled around merely by being looked at. Although many wished to believe that the tiny elusive particles moved deterministically and there was no absolute proof that this was not the case, *there was no experimental evidence for believing that it was* and no reason or need for continuing to do so except habit. We seem to be living in a world which looks, and for practical purposes is, deterministic and yet which deeper down contains a shadow world of cryptically indeterminate micro-events whose causal basis, quantum theory tells us, is fundamentally and intrinsically undemonstrable.

Such notions are familiar in daily life. In America each year about 40,000 people are killed in automobile accidents. This number is so remarkably constant it is predictable, that is, it is predictable with a high probability of accuracy. And yet, despite the intransigent protests of modern-day fatalists, each individual accident is clearly the result of a certain constellation of circumstances: error, weather, position, and so forth. Even though each individual accident is causally determined, we as observers lack the means to predict these circumstances with enough accuracy to enable us to predict which individual will have a fatal accident in a given year. As far as we are concerned, his fate is indeterminate, but in a population of 160 million individuals, the prediction of the number of accident victims can be made within a few per cent. This, then, is not true determinism, but statistical probability. It is not impossible that some year, under identical conditions (newfangled crash preventers would disqualify the argument), this number will be much smaller or perhaps larger. It is highly unlikely, however.

Probability operates in another way in this situation. It could be argued convincingly, I think, that there is nothing in principle that prevents us from improving our prediction of the annual accident rate to the point of almost absolute accuracy. What would be necessary would be complete information on the weather throughout the country, the detailed driving plans of each individual, the mechanical condition of every automobile at every minute, and so forth. This information is only technically unattainable; in theory it could be obtained. We then could sit down and by massive calculation and analysis successfully predict the occurrence of accidents. Why then would this not give us *absolute* accuracy? For if it does, we have a causal law that is strictly deterministic. The answer is: because we have forgotten to obtain complete data on the position of meteors, since it is clearly possible that one of them could upset our predictions by landing on someone's car. With this possibility accounted for, who can say what others may have been overlooked? We begin to see that we can never formulate absolute laws. Our laws are high probability statements, and this is true also of the laws of classical physics which deal not with gases and particles but the simple mechanics of the inclined plane. If they were not probability statements, laws would have to contain the phrase, 'This law will operate successfully as long as nothing happens to prevent it from working.' If laws were written that way, they would lose their meaning.

Since we have said that explaining an event consists in relating it to some outside law, what do we mean when we explain it by pointing to its cause? The answer to this lies in the fact that *causes* are events which are connected by little causal laws to other events. Here we encounter one of the most crucial questions in science. We all speak of causes and we know what we mean when we say 'A causes B'. But it is often overlooked that no one ever observed the phenomenon of anything causing anything else: *what is observed is a temporal sequence of spatially contiguous events, not causation.* One can observe that B follows A. When one observes that *whenever A occurs, B occurs*, he may be in a position to declare that he has found the cause of B. The repetition of the observation is essential, because we are surrounded by a stream of miscellaneous events occurring in temporal sequence, one after the other. But because these are not regular occurrences, we do not infer causality. If they were regular occurrences, we would assume causality, or, in more precise language, we would say, 'If A occurs, it is highly probable that B will occur.' This, in fact, is a causal law. And it is a law to say, 'If I eat a green apple, I will get sick,' for this is the law by which I explain my sickness, and eating a green apple is its cause.

There is one further question about causality. A regularly preceding causal event may be difficult to identify. Is the five o'clock whistle, which is regularly followed by an exodus of workmen from the factory, the cause of their departure? If A, in a black mood, calls B a numbskull, and B takes a gun and shoots A dead, what is *the cause* of A's extinction? Is it the bullet? Is it the hole in A's head? Is it A's ill temper or perhaps an event in his childhood? Is it B's volatile nature, or does it have to do with some chemical occurrence in his hindbrain? It is apparent that danger lurks in using the word *cause* in its substantival sense – *the cause* of something. In a dynamic stream of events occurring in space and in time, it may be impossible to pin down *a cause*. We must fall back on the intuition of the scientist and hope, with

Woodger, that he does not 'sharpen his demands too much and unconsciously turn his causal postulate into an absolute metaphysical principle.'

The theory of evolution burst forth in an era when causal determinism was at its zenith. The process of evolution was readily assumed to be subject, like other natural phenomena, to absolute laws. Biologists, as we have seen, were, as usual, divided into two camps: the *mechanists*, who, as we recall, see no difference between living and non-living matter and who assume that both are subject to the same laws of physics and chemistry, and the *vitalists*, who believe that life is a singularity not open to final analysis in physicochemical terms. Many vitalists are *finalists*, holding the teleological view that the universe is purposeful, evolution has a goal, and that all life has been a means to some end, persuasions which are clearly on the fringes of theology. Interestingly, as was pointed out by Simpson, there was a curious reversing of roles by vitalists and mechanists on the subject of evolutionary determinism. In physics, materialism or mechanism was traditionally associated with strict adherence to causal determinism. But in evolutionary theory, we find the staunch advocates of a material basis of evolution gravitating toward the view that randomness and apparent indeterminism characterize the overall process, while the vitalists, conversely, were strongly deterministic.

It should be noted that determinism in evolution can have gradations of meaning. The strict Laplacian view that all evolution is implicit in some event of the remote past represents an extreme position. Conceivably, the course of evolution could be determined by material means and yet not be destined by fate or any other external influence to follow a set course.

Darwin and the so-called neo-Darwinians (known to some as the 'muscular' Darwinians) stressed as all-important the role of hereditary variation (mutation) which many assumed to be *wholly random* and thus beyond the pale of a mechanistic observer. The lineal descendants of Buffon and Lamarck, the early evolutionary vitalists, deny a final material basis for life but nevertheless invoke a theory of predetermination to explain the supposed tendency

189

of evolution to follow straight and fixed pathways toward some finalist goal. Actually, no one denies that there is direction in evolution. The question is: Why need direction involve purpose? Anything going anywhere has direction but need this be called purposiveness?

Simpson, the brilliant American paleontologist, holds that evolution is in part demonstrably deterministic and aptly points out that evolutionary sequence is historical in nature.

In any truly historical process, the determining conditions are far from simple and are not immediate or repetitive. Historical cause embraces the *totality* of preceding events. Such a cause can never be repeated, and it changes from instant to instant. Repetition of some factors still would not be repetition of historical causation.

This view, it seems to me, best accords with the facts as we know them. We cannot infer even apparent causal laws because we are not in a position to observe repeatedly the clear and unentangled process of temporal sequence as it occurs in evolution. The situation is always too complex to be repeatable and our evidence is necessarily indirect. In other words, we are unable to carry out *experiments* on the process about which we are making hypotheses.* If determinism does, to a limited extent, play a part in evolution, it is far from predictive and, by every predilection of science and logic, totally devoid of purpose.

The arguments against teleology seem decisive. One who infers a master purposeful design from the complexity of life should remember that complexity is a relative term. In a world with almost infinite time and material at its disposal, the number and complexity of possible combinations is almost infinite. If complexity presupposes purpose, then it must presuppose complexity of purpose. Surely this is an unnecessary burden on one's already overstrained wits. To the argument that as long as mechanistic determinism is unprovable, teleology is reasonable, there is the obvious and equally inconclusive retort that as long as teleology is unprovable, mechanistic determinism is much more

* Though an exception to this statement will be mentioned in Chapter 13. It has recently been possible to simulate bacterial evolution in the laboratory.

reasonable. Some contend that because 'the world has a design' – a hideously vague statement – like a watch it must have a designer. To this Bahm answered, 'The argument from purposiveness of parts of the world to purposiveness of the whole world involves what logicians call the "fallacy of composition". The fallacy in the argument, "This is a bunch of large apples, therefore this is a large bunch of apples," and the fallacy in the argument, "This world is made up of purposive beings, therefore this world is purposively made up," is the same.'

Harold Blum suggested what I think is a very good argument by analogy. He recalled the striking evolution in French cathedral architecture which occurred within a few medieval centuries. 'Starting with the round-arched Romanesque style, which could only build stone vaults over small squarish areas, developing through the Norman, was reached the Gothic, which flung its stone vaults high into the air to the joy of men's hearts and the greater glory of Mary the Virgin.' Although by hindsight it looks very much as though the ultimate goal of this evolution was the vaulting with stone of areas large enough to accommodate large hordes of worshippers, can it be argued that the early architects foresaw this achievement or the means of its accomplishment? Clearly they did not and clearly the analogous position with regard to evolution is untenable.

## The Decline of 'Either' and the Fall of 'Or'

From time to time in these pages, we have had a harsh word for that habit of thought which contentedly reduces all questions down to a tidy set of alternatives: pleasure-pain, scientist-humanist, mechanism-vitalism, animate-inanimate. Undeniably, such a pattern of thinking arises naturally, for we are surrounded by clear-cut examples of dichotomies at work. A light switch is either on or off. A doorbell is either ringing or silent. A problem in long division is solved correctly or incorrectly. In these clear cases, we have opposites standing in absolute conflict with one another. There is no overlap; the middle ground is excluded.

191

The trouble begins when we set up our alternatives in areas that either need not or cannot be so treated. Order and chaos; hot and cold – these are not opposites but relative positions on a continuous scale of values. There is a middle ground that is thoroughly respectable, for it is as much on the scale as the more remote positions. Another kind of difficulty occurs which can be illustrated with an example. Suppose we examined ten thousand houses in succession and found that half were made of wood and half were made of stone. We would then conclude, with some justification, that the next house we see will quite probably be stone or wood. And if we are correct and our experience continues to show no exceptions, we may begin to believe that houses are made of stone or wood, that they *can be* only stone or wood. If someone then told us of a house that wasn't stone, we would logically conclude that it then must be made of wood. Here is a different kind of dichotomy. We haven't said that wood is the opposite of stone, nor that wood and stone are at different ends of a spectrum of values. Neither is the statement 'houses are wood or stone' the same as the statement 'houses are wood or not wood', for the latter is necessarily true and would not require us to have examined ten thousand houses.

The point of these remarks is simply this. Biology, as perhaps no other field, is rooted in an apparent antithesis: life versus non-life. And dangling from its branches are hordes of similar conceptions that through the years have been supposed to facilitate thinking: body and mind, structure and function, organism and environment. In view of the fact that the great 'antitheses of biology' and their use in explanation have had such a hoary tradition, it is quite necessary to say a brief word about them, for I believe we have here another kind of trap in need of being closed.

We have spoken of four kinds of antitheses: the on-off kind, the hot-cold kind, the stone-wood kind, and the structure-function kind. The first is, implicitly, a yes-no situation. An event occurs or it does not occur. There is the thing and its negation, and, in most cases, we have contributed little to the advance of knowledge if we declare that something either will or won't happen. We are necessarily right about such predictions. Our chief concern should be to restrict such statements to those situations that are open to a yes or no interpretation. When we do, we can then relax for we know that to accept A is to reject B and that nowhere in the universe is there a third possibility.

Hot-cold, as was pointed out, is not a yes-no dichotomy, but a pair of positions on a scale. We must never forget the in-between positions. As for stone and wood, these are not opposites at all, though they are in danger of appearing to be, since our experience seems to tell us that they are the only available alternatives. The hazard here is a psychological one against which we must guard ourselves. The next house may be made of gingerbread.

We come then to structure and function, perhaps the most puzzling of the four. It need hardly be pointed out that these are not antitheses, contrasts, or gradations. They are two aspects of a thing, two ways of looking at it, which have no business appearing in the guise of an antithesis. Their equivalents in society are anatomists and physiologists, and though they are often found quarrelling, they are not the antithesis of each other.

With the ultimate recognition of the needless confusion in such usages, some interesting ideas emerged about different ways of looking at things. When confronted with the fact that certain physical phenomena could be equally well explained by postulating a particle or a wave, and no possible way of determining experimentally which was the case, Niels Bohr developed what was called the *principle of complementarity*, according to which both interpretations were accepted as two ways of looking at the same thing. They are complementary, not contradictory, and we are urged to accept the fact that two different mutually exclusive but equally truthful observations may be made of the same phenomenon.

This notion, which has the appearance of good sense, spread rapidly into other areas that had long been knotted up in similar dilemmas. In studying the brain, for example, should one employ the method of psychology, which considers the mind, or the method of biochemistry and physiology, which studies neural transmission and metabolism? Complementarity says both are necessary aspects of the picture, though they are operationally mutually exclusive, for no one can manipulate a brain in a test tube and interview it at the same time.

From here, the great leap was easy. The discoveries of science and the dogma of religion were quickly set forth as complementary descriptions of the world. Here we must be sceptical. Religion and science are not competing descriptions of the world with an equal claim on truth. For religion, *by definition*, is inaccessible to science, and the facts and 'evidence' upon which it rests are unacceptable to science. And because scepticism seems wise here, one feels like taking another look at the principle of complementarity in its original physical context. It does, in fact, do nothing to resolve the impasse, but substitutes instead a different word for the Heisenberg principle of indeterminacy. It conceals the fact without helping us to understand that we are trying to say *both* that the two descriptions – religious-scientific, mental-mechanical, wave-particle – are about the same thing *and* that they are about different things. This would, it seems to me, discourage further inquiry into difficult problems by generating an illusion.

The key question then is: What sort of a pair is life and non-life? On the face of it, the question is one that could scarcely be answered without observational data. What do biologists, the collectors of data, have to say on the subject? Regrettably, it is rather difficult to find out.

In 1937, N. W. Pirie published an essay called 'The Meaninglessness of the Terms Life and Living', and in 1953 in an article called 'The Origin of Life' he said essentially the same thing. Pirie is an excellent writer and the arguments were convincing. He pointed out that 'life' and 'living' are words that the scientist has borrowed from the layman who has always regarded life as a metaphysical entity. But now we have entered a zone where these words serve us no longer.

There is little point in entering all the evidence on this question. The matter comes down to this: whatever quality one would like to consider as a minimal requirement or a diagnostic trait of life, that quality can be found present in objects that we all agree are not living and absent in objects that everyone knows are living. This is true of movement, reproduction, metabolism, and so on, although authors have insisted at various times that one or another of these traits, self-replication or autoregulation, was the *sine qua non* of life.

I tend to agree with Pirie though not with everything he says, and, interestingly, I find neither does he. One of the difficulties is the circular conflict: 'This definition of life is no good because it includes some non-living things.' Clearly, the statement implies a prior accepted definition of life. Pirie, too, despite his rigorous style and aggressive technique of scientific debate, discusses the 'origin of life' and, while stating, 'Life is not a thing or philosophical entity: it is an attitude of mind toward what is being observed,' simultaneously he uses the term he denies, e.g. 'No other place and time seem more suitable for the appearance of life than here and now.'

In addition, he stands in a variety of combative postures upon a stage whose very boards are the presupposition that 'life' has a meaning. For example, there is his published comment concerning the views of his physicist friend J. D. Bernal, 'He does not know enough to contribute usefully. This criticism may be looked on as a simple example of the old injunction to the cobbler to stick to his last.' One feels like asking Professor Pirie exactly what last a cobbler would have to be familiar with to be qualified to discuss the origin of life. Physics? No, Pirie seems to say: Bernal is a physicist. Furthermore, we are interested in life, not matter (though at other times we deem the distinction meaningless). Biology? No, we are dealing with a phenomenon of inanimate molecules. At the witching hour of the 'origin' are we to trot out the physicists and trot in the biologists? Who precisely is qualified to consider and speculate upon the origin of life? As far as I am concerned, until we have learned very much more, the answer is *everyone*, including the feuding luminaries, Pirie and Bernal.

This sort of double-think is not easily avoided. Most of us feel we know the difference between life and non-life and life and death. With some self-discipline we can accept the view that there is no rigid boundary between the two, but only a zone, a spectrum shading from the obvious to the obvious. In this area so far, we can only describe, and we gain little from pontificating on whether an object lives or lives not. We realize, in candour, that nothing is added to our understanding if to accommodate the entity we mould our definition.

But let us not forget that if a zone of ambiguity exists, it exists where we put it. We control the verbal stratum of our science, and I see no reason why the zone of ambiguity could not exist elsewhere, say between plants and animals. Though absurd by our present conceptions (whether or not they are explicit), is there any compelling reason why our 'instinctive recognition' of life should not fade into uncertainty at the point where movement ceases? There is none. To argue that there is, one must maintain that plants *are* living though they don't move, and to do this, one must have already formulated a definition of life which includes plants. As perceptual objects, plants are plants whether we call them living or not: 'life' is a conceptual object. In other words, Pirie is correct: 'life' is beyond rigorous definition – but he, I, we will speak of life because we all know what it means in the large area of non-ambiguity. The errors to be avoided are compulsive rigidity and failure to be happy in the company of uncertainty. When asked what viruses are and what they do, we can answer. When asked, what is life, we must reply with no more or no less than an enigmatic smile.

At the moment, I am having difficulty thinking of any use to which a definition of life could be put – *other* than to the everyday problem of recognizing death. When a scientist manipulates a living system, it is occasionally useful to him to know if it has died. If the system is a horse, there would seem to be few problems. But we quickly discover that the ambiguity of 'life' affects 'death' in reverse. If it is a bacterium, a seed, or a spore, the problems may be insurmountable, and in practice we usually establish an arbitrary end point at which death, by decision, is recognized to have occurred. Quiescence and death can look very much alike and their distinction brings us straight back to the bar of verbal decisions.

I think we will agree, a chapter or two hence, when we have seen some of the recent evidence and the direction it is taking, that 'life' and 'non-life' are words like 'hot' and 'cold'. They are ends of a spectrum whose graded quantity is complexity: life is on the complex end, non-life on the simple. Between the two is a middle ground which is neither one nor the other. It is, one might say, what it is. . . .

# 11

## Instrumentation, Information, and Long Distance

> Writing is practised either by means of the common alphabet . . . or of a secret and private one, agreed upon betwixt particular persons, and called by the name of cipher.
>
> – Francis Bacon (1605)

LET us imagine that we are scientists working in a laboratory where we have at our disposal all of the techniques and measuring instruments of physics and chemistry. We can measure physical dimensions such as weight and length with enormous precision and can analyse the chemical composition of an unknown object down to the last impurity. We have the conviction that under these circumstances we could completely characterize any physical object and, with accuracy, state whether two given objects are the same or different.

A sceptical friend decides to put us to the test. He arrives with two bundles and requests us to say in concrete terms whether their contents are the same or different, and, if different, what the differences are. We open the package and find that one contains the Sunday edition of the New York *Times* and the other contains an equal weight of blank newsprint in the middle of which is a large, messy blot of printer's ink. We start to work. Both specimens contain the same weight of paper and the same number of particles of whatever it is ink is made of. Both have the same musty odour. Both serve equally well as seat pads in a sports' stadium. We know there must be a difference since the circulation of the New York *Times* is extremely large, but would no doubt be nil if people found on their doorsteps only paper containing an ink blot. With our backs to the wall we concede that the only *physical* difference is in the *spatial arrangement* of the ink with respect to the paper. In one case, the ink is arrayed in neat rows

198

of discrete curlicues and lines; in the other, the ink is in one large puddle. The difference, then, is a question of the *order* and *arrangement* of particles of matter.

Here is another of those conceptions which, we suddenly recognize, has an absolute significance for every phase of our existence. The idea of order! Let us examine this notion, for it is a pillar of contemporary thought and only recently have men awakened to it.

## *The True Nature of Noise, Dirt, Stuttering, and Poison*

Let us consider a more familiar situation. A man is sitting at home waiting for an important telephone call. His children are in the next room re-enacting the French and Indian War, down to the last screams of the dying. The phone rings but, in the din of battle, our man does not hear it and he misses his call.

The phone bell in our little story was a signal which was being sought and, in the presence of a high noise level, the signal was lost. What could have been done to prevent this loss? If the man moved out into the garden to escape the noise, he would also have eluded the signal. If he put on a hearing aid to amplify the signal, he simultaneously would have amplified the noise. Thus, the *signal-to-noise ratio* was too unfavourable and unless it could be changed – by selectively amplifying the signal, silencing the children, or both – the difficulty would continue.

The same would be true if one were searching for a house number from the front seat of an automobile. All would be well in the clear light of day. But, in a fog, the light rays passing from the sign to the eye would be chaotically scattered by droplets of water in the air. The result would be a blurring of the physical shapes being sought, which, if severe enough, would prevent their detection. These situations are commonplace. In everything we do, there is a background of distracting phenomena which becomes disturbing whenever its intensity level is high enough. The static on the radio, the light seeping into a sealed packet of film, the commercial advertisements we must endure on television – in each of these cases, we must successfully minimize the unwanted background if we are to receive the signal with clarity.

Aside from their simple appropriateness, there is another good reason why we use the terms 'signal' and 'noise' in this general way. Although the crucial importance of the signal-to-noise ratio has long been understood intuitively, its formal analysis and introduction into the world of great ideas were the achievements of communication engineers working in the Bell Telephone Laboratories. (And here, in my opinion, is a magnificent illustration of the power of abstract thinking.) These workers became concerned with the following practical problem: An individual wishes to send the message 'I love you' to an acquaintance in a distant city. He is aware that there are several technical systems for sending such a message, all of which are essentially mechanisms designed to reproduce this sequence of words at a distance. The sender is of a pedantic turn of mind and has determined that his message shall go forth via the quickest, cheapest, and most accurate of the available communication systems. He will, of course, be dissatisfied if his message becomes scrambled, whether into something incomprehensible like 'T kolg yom' or into something comprehensible but different in meaning like 'A live cow'. The communication engineer, on the other hand, has the job of satisfying his customer while making his service economically competitive against all others.

Assume that a new telegraph company decides to bid for the contract. How should it transmit the message? It might, for example, devise a code wherein a telegraph key is held down one second for the letter 'a', two seconds for 'b', and so on, with one-second waits between each letter. By this method, it would take 131 seconds to transmit the message. The wastefulness of this is apparent, and because of it the Morse code was invented. In this system, three signals appear in different combinations: a long pulse, a short pulse, and a short silence. By arranging the code so as to give those letters most frequently used the briefest code symbols (the letter 'e' is a short pulse or dot, the letter 't' a long pulse or dash), our message now can go forth in 67 seconds. Even this isn't very good, and the next obvious step is the invention of short code units for whole words or common phrases. But when we start doing this, some new problems arise. For one thing, the saving in transmission time should not be squandered in accuracy, for it is obvious that economy in time can often be achieved by permitting some deterioration in the final replication of the message. Communication engineers have intentionally promoted a certain amount of deterioration because they have recognized that the English language contains many redundancies. The letter 'u' after 'q' is always redundant, the 'h' after 'w' often is, and many double letters are too. By cutting these out in their coding practice – so that any transmitted message is already 'deteriorated' – a moderate increase in efficiency can be made.

But a major problem arises when deterioration occurs unintentionally. Since the message is transmitted by physical means, via electrical impulses in a wire, it is subject to the distortion inherent in all such processes which originates from the constant random motion of all molecules, the so-called thermal noise. The behaviour of the electrical circuit is always the statistical average of the behaviour of innumerable individual electrons. If the noise level goes up, the signal may become garbled. Likewise, if the code becomes too efficient (say, one very brief dot means 'I love you'), the signal, in effect, becomes weak, and the message may again be lost in the noise. To offset this a certain amount of redundancy in the form of repetition may be desirable. That is why telegraph companies always repeat numbers and names in sending telegrams. But if the code is so subtle or the signal so weak, no amount of repetition will guarantee that each feeble blip is not just part of the noise. Such subtlety becomes secrecy.

The implications of this are very great indeed, for our message has two aspects to it. It is first a set of words selected out of all others, to convey some information, and it is second a physical phenomenon in a wire that can be interpreted as an orderly orientation of electrons in contrast to a thoroughly random arrangement, which incidentally conveys no information. From here, it is an easy step to the realization that the degree of order is a measurable quantity with a profound meaning. The relative rarity of the ordered arrangement of the code symbols when compared to the number of possible arrangements gives a measure of the information in the message. This is not as difficult as it sounds. If our wire could transmit no more than 1,000 different arrangements of code symbols, the ones that were used most infrequently would contain the most information. Their rarity implies their improbability and unexpectedness. When they finally do occur they convey much information. Thus, the combination of three letters 'the' would be used frequently, would be never unexpected, and would add little to the total of information. The three letters 'SOS' are a much rarer combination and convey a great deal of highly specific information. A printed page of the New York *Times* is obviously a rare arrangement of ink marks compared to all the possible ways of applying ink to the paper. The New York *Times*, then, contains a much higher level of information than a random collection of letters or an ink blot.

The concept of information content applies in many situations. Suppose the busy desk clerk of a large hotel was handed an unmarked key by a mysterious stranger who would say only that a valuable necklace was hidden in a room that this key would open. He could extract the desired information – which room should be searched for the necklace – without too much difficulty, *if* the key contained that much information. In other words, if the key's structure was unusual enough to open only one door, the correct one, he should have to search only that room. The information would reside in the rarity of the pattern of grooves and notches. If, however, it was a master key capable of opening all the doors, it would contain no information, and he would then have to search all of the rooms. The same considerations apply to the use of fingerprints.

What is so interesting is the fact that the mathematical expression for the content of information in a system is precisely the same as that for the *negative entropy* of a system. As we may or may not recall, the second law of thermodynamics states that the negative entropy of a system, which is, among other things, a measure of its degree of molecular order, is always moving in the direction of chaos, and, in any self-contained corner of the universe, order may be restored only by putting energy into the system. To anyone with a formal garden, these physical terms are unnecessary. If the garden is planted in a highly ordered arrangement of rows and designs, energy must be expended constantly to prevent a drift toward disorder in the form of weeds, ragged growth, and desiccation. Likewise, energy in the form of thinking, writing, and linotype-operating must be expended to create the ordered rows of ink that are the New York *Times*. It is just as unlikely that the New York *Times* would appear if the ink were just thrown at the paper as that the garden would maintain itself through the summer if untouched by gardener's hands.

The significance of these concepts for biology is fundamental. As we shall presently see, the organism is a highly unlikely arrangement for a group of molecules to find themselves in. Yet this almost incredible complexity is all provided for in a blueprint carried within a single fertilized egg cell. The hereditary code is carried in the genes, structures almost too small to be seen in the microscope. This is extraordinary! When biologists realized that the gene's enormous information content must reside in a highly specific arrangement of the matter within it, as in a key or phonograph record, the greatest biological question of them all was joined. It is the problem of determining how physical aggregations of matter become twisted and bent into complex arrangements in space, whose information content is so phenomenally high they become little oligarchies capable of directing their own reproduction, of accumulating other matter into their orbit, and of occasionally coming up with something like the Theory of Relativity. In Chapter 13, I shall elaborate on what biologists now believe is going on here. But first, a bit more information.

## Scientific Instruments and their Limitations

I should like to say a brief word about scientific instruments, the very symbols by which modern science is known. And well they might be symbolic of science, for progress in instrumentation is a necessary condition for the progress of science. The instruments and machines of science are essentially devices for extending the limited powers of our own bodies. Our telescopes, microscopes, and spectrophotometers are strong new eyes; electric motors and nuclear reactors are extra muscles; and the UNIVACS, MANIACS, and assorted other -ACS are our extra intelligences. We will speak of 'electronic brains' in a later chapter. Here I want only to make the point that the laboratory instruments we use in our experiments are basically communication systems for the transfer of information. And, as a message can 'deteriorate' in a telegraph wire, it can surely do the same in a laboratory instrument, no matter how elegant its control panel. If the results of an experiment depend on a reliable message, here is a place to tread carefully. The importance of instrumental accuracy in hypothesis construction is perfectly illustrated by the story of the fat lady who tried to weigh herself on a defective penny scale. A passing inebriate, noticing that the dial read twenty pounds, muttered, 'She mush be hollow!'

In Chapter 5, it was observed that the essential feature of a scientific experiment is an intentional interaction with the object under study that can be controlled and manipulated by the experimenter. It is the purpose of such interactions to produce some *signal* discernible to the senses. Where the scientist is interested only in establishing the existence or non-existence of some entity or occurrence, he will be satisfied merely to note the presence or absence of the signal resulting from his intervention. This would be a *qualitative* experiment involving a 'yes-no decision'. For example, if we wished to know if a test tube contains iron, the simple addition of a substance which interacts with iron to produce a blue colour would provide this information.

Experiments become *quantitative* when a measurement is made of the extent of the perceived interaction. Measurement implies comparison with some appropriate yardstick. The yardstick here would be a similar chemical reaction, but one conducted with accurately known quantities. The measurement consists in comparing the extent of the reaction of the unknown with that of the known. Thus, if we wish to learn how much iron is in the tube, the blue colour must be compared with blue colours produced with carefully weighed amounts of pure iron. If the colour is found to be identical with the colour obtained with one milligram of pure iron, we conclude that the unknown contains one milligram of iron. This is measurement. Measurement is comparison.

All quantitative measurements in science are conducted in this way. The establishment of a measuring scale by alignment with known standards is called *calibration*. If someone is presented with a kitchen scale which for some reason lacks a dial, his predicament is not entirely absurd. He has only to obtain a good set of weights (which were themselves carefully calibrated with other weights) and, one at a time, place them on the scale, marking the dial where the needle comes to rest. Actually only two points need to be marked, since Hooke's law states that the deflection of a spring is proportional to its load. Thus, one could establish the one-pound mark and the ten-pound mark with weights; the locations of all intervening marks could be simply computed. Presumably, the manufacturer of a scale which comes equipped with its dial has already gone through these manoeuvres. Often, however, he has done so with only one scale and has copied the dial face on to all the other similar scales. The error of this practice may be of little consequence in the case of scales used in fish markets. Clearly, the weighing instruments intended for delicate scientific measurement must be accurately and individually calibrated.

In many instances, measuring instruments are easily calibrated against certain natural 'constants' instead of other calibrated standards. In these situations the unit of measure may be defined by the natural phenomenon. For example, 0° Centigrade is defined as the freezing point of water under certain conditions; 100° C. is the boiling point. Given a blank thermometer we can calibrate it either by immersing it in freezing water, marking the mercury level, then boiling water, marking it again, and dividing the space between the two marks into a hundred equal intervals (each a degree) *or* we can place it in contact with an already calibrated thermometer, transfer the reading on to the unknown scale, change the temperature, and do it again. Then by simple arithmetic the interval of a single degree can be computed and scratched carefully into the glass.

There is a strong inclination among physicists to define as many units of measurement as possible in terms of accurately reproducible natural constants. The advantages of such standards are obvious. The metre unit of length was devised in 1790 to represent one ten-millionth of the earth's quadrant (the distance from the North Pole to the equator). Speculation arose as to whether the metre could be reproduced if the earth were changed, say by collision with a comet, and so a natural standard independent of terrestrial form was sought. Various proposals were made but it now appears that the ultimate standard of length has been found in a wave length of radiation emitted by mercury 198, an isotope transmuted from gold by neutron bombardment. The spectacular accuracy, reproducibility, and presumed immutability of this standard of length will, no doubt, survive world catastrophes and planetary collisions. This should be comforting to all who make measurements.

So much for the measuring scale of the instruments. The uncertainties of calibration contribute importantly to the danger of message deterioration. But they are not the only danger source. First the instrument acts as a detector. Its photo-cell 'sees' the ultraviolet light we cannot see, its sensitive antennas 'hear' the distant radio stars we cannot hear. Then with the message plucked out of the universe, the instrument communicates it to its other side. It now is an indicator. A dial registers, a column of fluid rises, a moving pen makes a tracing on the long roll of graph paper being driven past it by a clock motor: the length and intricacy of this pathway of communication is often incredible – from the phenomenon to the detector to the communication circuit to the indicator to the eye and then the mind of the observer. It is a long dangerous journey and, at every step of the way, including the last one, the noise must be kept down and the signal up. When that is done, and the calibration is reasonably good, an instrument can sometimes be used with profit.

# 12

## The Technique of Discovery

Seated one day at the Organ,
    I was weary and ill at ease,
And my fingers wandered idly
    Over the noisy keys.

I do not know what I was playing,
    Or what I was dreaming then;
But I struck one chord of music,
Like the sound of a great Amen.
                    – Adelaide Anne Procter

HAVING explored the nature of language, the scientific method, and truth, having purged ourselves of the taint of non-empirical, non-logical, non-acceptable thinking, we come to that enigmatic something which, to me, gives science its riotous excitement and rugged, romantic beauty – those non-utilitarian qualities for which adequate allowance is never made in the syllabus of method. It is the *mind of the scientist*, the meat that gives body to the meal and the cognac that makes it memorable.

Most of what we have said on the principles of logic and the analysis of language tells us only how scientific truth may be defended. But we have learned nothing of the mechanisms of its discovery. We lightly repeat in discussions of this sort that knowledge derives from the sequence: experiment, hypothesis, deduction, test experiments, inductive generalization. But the ground that must be crossed in order to move through these stages is mountainous, misty, and unmapped, as only those who have dared it can know.

We have done our experiment and recorded its results in a black notebook. We recognize the uncertainties built into the data but can only estimate their extent. *What do we do now?* The book says invent a hypothesis that will 'explain' the results. We have come face to face with the mystique of the creative mind.

## The Creative Act

I have thought about the nature of the creative process and have reached a somewhat aberrant conclusion. I don't understand it and I don't think anyone else does either. From what has been written, the main approach to the problem seems to have come from introspective psychology, the autobiographical accounts of great creative thinkers which try to tell how they did it. In a recent book, one finds such statements by thirty-eight individuals,* ranging from Einstein to Mozart, Spencer to Spender, and though the material is extremely interesting, it is clear beyond all doubt that no man has the capacity alone to raise to the surface all the underwater currents and rip tides of his own consciousness.

In any event, all tell different stories, often in wonderfully vague phrases. For example, the poet Spender spoke of 'a dim cloud of an idea which I feel must be condensed into a shower of words'; Whitehead: 'the state of imaginative muddled suspense which precedes successful inductive generalization'; Chekov: 'If an artist boasted to me of having written a story without a previously settled design, but by inspiration, I should call him a lunatic'; and Poincaré, whose statements on this problem are classical: 'Ideas rose in crowds; I felt them collide until pairs interlocked, so to speak, making a stable combination. By the next morning I had established the existence of [new truth].' The only obvious common prescriptions are hard work, self-discipline, and thorough educational preparation. And all seem to agree that the moment of achievement is a moment of delight and satisfaction reminiscent of Spinoza's definition of pleasure: 'the passion by which the mind passes to a higher state of perfection.' In the words of Agnes Arber, 'This emotional element in discovery is perhaps the factor which makes it so elusive, and so refractory to organized control.' Machines cannot control it, 'Marches of Dimes' will not promote it, and we, apparently, cannot explain it.

* B. Ghiselin's book *The Creative Process*.

The reason is, I think, that the creative process is so closely tied in with the emotional structure of an individual, it is a poor subject for generalization. All sorts of factors are at work and no analysis can avoid over-simplification. Ideas come by day, by night, by chance, by work, and by play. They come in dreams, in hallucinations, in seminars and saloons. Most are quite bad and are seldom voiced, suppressed by their authors' critical faculties. Some are good; a few are brilliant. Since we seem not to know how they arise, we might reasonably inquire from whence they arise.

Professor Boring of Harvard has offered an impressive answer to this question. He points out that 'in each age there are covert influences that make up what has been called the climate of opinion, and by Goethe the *Zeitgeist* – the conventions of thought and the unquestioned assumptions that are implicit in the culture in general and science in particular. . . . They constrain originality and reinforce tradition, as well as limiting the irresponsibility of the cranks who, excelling in originality, are deficient in critical wisdom.' Apparently, we all feed on the *Zeitgeist*, unconsciously directing our interests to the issues of the day, formulating our thoughts in the linguistic clichés of the day, employing the established techniques of the day. The result is eternal frustration for the historian of science who would trace out the 'influences' acting upon any given scientist. Did Newton's teachers shape his development or was it the *Zeitgeist* of his century? Who knows? Wrote Boring, 'Again and again scientific progress halts because the correct next step contravenes some firmly rooted theory or belief.' How true this is we have already seen in some of our historical reflections.

We must recognize, therefore, what Bacon and Descartes failed to recognize. Science is a truly creative enterprise. Though the logic of its method can be described with rigour, the successful *use* of the method requires an act of intuition by the creative mind. Science, then, is an art. For the method of the artist is also well understood. All he does is dip his brush in paint and apply it to the canvas in the proper places. It is knowing which are the proper places, however, that distinguishes a Cézanne.

## *The Beast Within: Its Nature and Nurture*

All of which brings up a matter too rarely discussed. What about the scientist as a creature of emotion and human fallibility? The temper of our times has generated widening gulfs of alienation and distrust between scientists and other people and, in the spirit of scientific inquiry, those of us who are dedicated to it begin looking at ourselves to learn what we are and if the blame is ours. We see some interesting things.

At first glance, scientists may appear to be different. A well-done study of the outstanding young men of American science was recently published in *Fortune* magazine (and, in my opinion, its subjects were indeed outstanding). The survey clearly showed them to be mavericks, differing from the majority of society in endowment, desire, and belief. Among other things, most were well aware of their so-called alienation from society, were politically liberal, and, interestingly, were hard-headed hedonists who found pleasure in the thrill of discovery and generally doubted the view that scientists tended to be nervous wrecks.

But these were the *successful* men of their generation and, though many seek it, not all gain success. What of the rest of us? Here we encounter the disturbing conclusion of Lawrence Kubie, who has delved into the emotional problems connected with the scientific career. His argument is based on psychoanalytic experience with individuals, but no scientist reading it will fail to discern in part the outlines of his own reflection. Kubie tells us that the young scientist often reaches maturity after the abnormal childhood of precocity – overly bookish, unathletic, socially withdrawn, sexually immature. He may choose a career in science under the influence of highly complex and unnoticed symbolisms, as, for example, the aspiration to medical careers by those filled with guilt-laden curiosity about the body. Since no youth can know in advance the joys and sorrows of his chosen field, his choice must be based upon outward appearances, dramatizations, and fantasies.

Each successive step in the method of science calls forth a greater emotional investment and adds to the difficulties of remaining objective. When the ego is involved, self-criticism may come hard. (Who ever heard of two scientists battling to prove the other right?) One has always a vested interest in the successful outcome and, whether we enjoy admitting it or not, each of us feels the pressure to succeed, to blaze 'new trails' perhaps before we have mastered the old, to remain productive and therefore admired, to embark obsessively (as did Sigmund) upon a romantic crusade towards epic truth. It is apparent, therefore, how latent neurotic tendencies may impinge upon and distort the clear mandates of scientific method and may generate error, unrealistic values, anxiety, and – let's face it, since science is done behind closed doors – dishonesty. Because scientists are human and science is not, as in all fields the thin thread of integrity is sometimes strained to break.

The idea of dishonesty in science is a hard one to swallow, for it is as difficult to understand as it is shocking. Yet the history of science is studded with tales of fraud and grand larceny, some of which have an ill-boding Old Testament flavour. For example, a recent note in *Science* recalled the case of one of biology's more notorious mountebanks, Paul Kammerer, a Viennese zoologist, who claimed in 1924 to have proved that acquired characters are inherited with experiments done on spotted salamanders. The great William Bateson challenged Kammerer, and the acrimonious debate that followed found many eminent biologists on both sides of the argument. Bateson demanded to see Kammerer's specimens but Kammerer demurred. No matter where Bateson went in pursuit, Kammerer always managed to elude him. The chase finally ended in 1926 with the examination of the specimens by G. K. Noble of the American Museum of Natural History and Hans Przibram, director of the institute where Kammerer worked. The sensational findings were promptly reported in *Nature*. The genetically transmitted salamander spots turned out to be made of India ink. A short time later, Kammerer committed suicide.

What dishonesty exists among scientists is rarely on such a grand scale. It is subtle and, no doubt, frequently unconscious behaviour. The experiments that 'work' are reported with no mention of those that failed. The data that support the hypothesis are seized upon; the rest are explained away or forgotten. In today's hectic world of publicity and promotion, the spreading practice of granting academic advancement to those who have made 'important' scientific contributions has added fuel to many a latent fire. In a highly complex field, published scientific work cannot be quickly confirmed or denied, nor do most scientists care to spend their time verifying or challenging what other scientists have claimed. In any case, university trustees are not likely to go to the laboratory for guidance in making staff promotions.

Many scientists, similarly, find themselves in a breathless race for priority – for the glory of being first to make some discovery and report it. While there is nothing dishonest about that, its effect can be disturbing upon sociological conditions within the scientific community. Moreover, it breeds dishonesty, for in its wake comes the disingenuous double-talk we normally associate with advertising and politics. Perhaps such competitiveness has one useful function: it is an inexhaustible source of reliable lunch-room conversation, for the gossip of scientists is eternally concerned with the latest bulletins on who is 'scooping' whom. I'm reminded, however, of the plight of a former colleague who, at the proud completion of a job of scientific work, found that he'd been scooped in 1891.

The balancing factor in this situation is the honesty, wisdom, and intuitive good sense of the large majority of scientists and scientific editors. Dubious work should not be published; but dishonest work often has the appearance of solidity. And yet, when it reaches a journal, as often as not, it meets a proper scepticism – partly because the work somehow does not 'sound right', and partly because every scientist knows in his heart that this sort of thing goes on in the world. It's uncommon, it's difficult to talk about, it's sad, but it's true. It is equally true that honest work may not 'sound right' for reasons of novelty. Scientists realize this too: that is why their darkest suspicions are practically never made audible.

Kubie gives us some haunting case histories: a scientist so anxious to bolster an already proved theory, he falsified data; a sarcastic professor perennially vituperating against his colleagues from the security of the lectern; an acclaimed scientist who finds no joy in success. The portraits are familiar and the conclusions sobering. One thinks of these things on one's daily rounds, as one views the contemporary scene, as one reads statements to the effect that scientists should not enter debates upon morality, art, and politics (those areas beyond the ken of scientific inquiry) – and depending on one's fibre, one may feel naked, perplexed, resentful, or gratified that these insights are at last being achieved.

The conceptions of Kubie are not an indictment of scientists: they are descriptions and attempted explanations of some of them (and, in saying this, I wish to disavow any sense of mysticism I may have invoked about the scientific mind. At the moment, it seems mysterious, but I do not doubt that it is, in principle, explainable). No more do these ideas detract from the status of science than did Darwin's dyspepsia from the greatness of his thought. Whether or not they are valid, only time will tell. But we cannot deny that we have made progress if we recognize with Kubie that 'the idyllic picture of the innocent, child-like scientist who lives a life of simple, secure, peaceful, dignified contemplation has become unreal fantasy'. We see that science is not a thing apart and there should be no moat of isolation. This viewpoint, it seems to me, enlivens the spectacle of modern science and endows it a little with some of those universals that are the essences of great literature and drama.

Regrettably, then we have had nothing to say on the technique of making discoveries.

# 4

## CONTEMPORARY BIOLOGY,
## ITS PROBLEMS AND PROSPECTS

# 13

## The Living Organism Today

> Life is not a tale told by an idiot, because no idiot is sufficiently
> irrational to think up such a tale.
>
> – Herman Betz

IN the preceding four chapters, we took notice of certain recent intellectual currents that, together, may be loosely referred to as the analytical movement in thought. It is the turning upon itself of the quest for knowledge, wherein every instrument of thought is held up to the light. Language, logic, models, meaning, information, intuition – each has been put to the test and all have emerged as creatures of human dimensions. We have seen that, to a large extent, the spearhead of this intellectual dragonnade was the great new revolution in physics. We now turn our attention to the arena of biology. How has modern thought influenced our inquiry into the nature of organism – if indeed it has influenced it at all? What is the condition of biology today?

In 1929, a book was published called *The Science of Life*. Its eminent authors were H. G. Wells, Julian Huxley, and G. P. Wells. It was a massive treatise over 1,500 pages long, purporting to set before a general audience a summary of the state of biology at the time of writing. We would be unfair were we to regard it as the definitive word on this subject, for the book was not intended as a scholar's encyclopaedia. Yet, we may consider it a reasonable statement of the biologist's frame of mind a short generation ago – despite the occasional reviewer or two who complained at the invasion by Wells and Huxley into territories not technically their own. As we turn through its pages, we find discussions of the various forms of life from flatworms to sea serpents, the theory of evolution, blood and breathing, heredity, vitamins, disease, emotions, and very much more. What is missing, however, in this meadow of material is a sense of structure or direction, a clearly defined centre of intellectual gravity, around which all other ideas may be balanced. This is no criticism of the skill of the authors, for they accurately divined the temper of their subject. That was the condition of biology then. Needless to remark, each of the topics mentioned is of exceedingly great importance. Later work has expanded these areas into even larger, more impressive domains, no one of which may be overlooked.

But a discourse on the fundamental nature of bricks need not linger long over houses and walls. The intervening years have clearly revealed that there is one question in biology that transcends all others – a question that science needed insight to ask and that now it may soon be ready to answer. It is the question of the gene.

## What is a Gene?

Living organisms *reproduce* themselves and *regulate* themselves. All of their other properties – growth, motion, adaptation, irritability, metabolism – are but specifications of these two broad functions. Autoregulation, the self-perpetuation of functional stability and structural integrity, confers upon an otherwise highly unprepossessing blob of jelly and its gritty little inclusions of solid matter the ability to maintain itself in the face of a universe of destructive forces. But the property of self-duplication is more mysterious still.

To say that a cell reproduces itself is to say a very great deal. It implies that every one of its whirling atoms and molecules, every biochemical system and self-regulating mechanism, every ingredient we have yet to discover is somehow reduplicated in ultimate detail. It implies that the cell will be of the species of its parent: an amoeba will not produce a paramecium. This is an astonishing state of affairs. Given the particles of life, the proteins and sugars, the enzymes and small organoids that must float in the protoplasm, the surface membranes and nucleus, how would one arrange them, if one had to, so that they would do this for themselves? The question recalls the image of Sisyphus.

Deep within the flux of cellular reproduction lies the dominion of heredity, where time past and time future are joined in physical dimensions. Because all living systems, from microbes to men, are born of their kind and bear their kind in perpetuating the breed, they must somehow transmit to their offspring their own distinctive traits. Stating it another way, they pass on to the next generation its membership in the species – which, we may recall, is roughly defined as a distinctive, interbreeding, constellation of traits and characters. Clearly, the number of individual *traits* that a living organism can possess is limited only by the number we can make out. Men have always distinguished each other by skin colour and physiognomy, but who would have imagined a century ago that humans could be classified by blood groups? Yet blood groups were found to be heritable according to strict laws once they were discovered, and the same is true for countless other traits which in contrast to structure and outward appearance are equally less conspicuous. As techniques of observation improve, the list of observable traits grows larger. Hence, we cannot yet classify an organism *completely* because we have yet to discover its every trait.

All traits are not heritable anyway. Many of the characteristics of an organism belong to it alone and are not transmitted to the offspring. When it goes, the traits go. Goldschmidt makes clear the difference between hereditary and non-hereditary traits in his instructive example of the beans. If an experienced bean farmer finds he has three seed varieties which reliably give good harvests of small, medium, and large beans (say ten, fifteen, and twenty millimetres in diameter), we would assume that he has three hereditarily different strains. (Beans are useful for this example because they breed by self-fertilization. Interbreeding thus will not confuse the argument.)

If 1,000 beans are harvested from the crop of each strain, it is readily seen that within each harvest the beans are not all identical.

We find in each group a certain number of beans above and below the average size. The crop, laid out in rows, looks like this:*

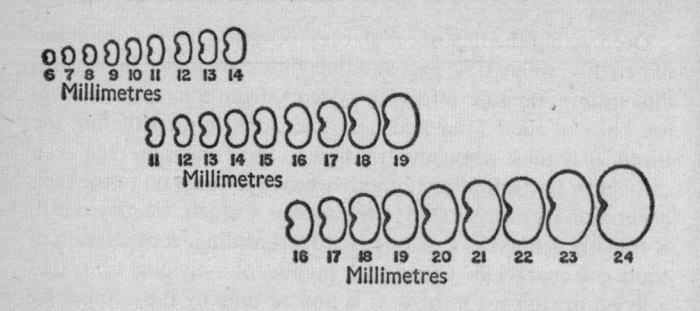

It would seem that the pure strain does not yield pure offspring but that individual differences still exist. These are called *variations* and they represent chance deviations from the 'pure' trait, which, strictly speaking, is the recurring average trait of large numbers of progeny in many generations. From this it is clear that unless we were told its plot of origin there would be no way of telling whether a randomly selected thirteen-millimetre bean was in fact a large ten-millimetre bean or a small fifteen-millimetre bean – so that the bean's size, even though easily observable, would not necessarily reveal its hereditary constitution.

How then do we distinguish the hereditary strain? Goldschmidt's farmer plants his unknown thirteen-millimetre beans and at harvest time brings in a crop of beans varying from six to fourteen millimetres in length but averaging ten millimetres. The origin of the unknown parent bean is now clear. Heredity has delivered a generation whose *average* size equals the perennial average, although the parent was a variant which in its own generation contributed to the normal average. Geneticists call this kind of analysis the test of progeny.

* Figure is redrawn from R. Goldschmidt, *Understanding Heredity*, Wiley, New York, 1952, by permission.

To be valid, the test requires a constant environment. If two fifteen-millimetre beans of the same strain were planted, but one received more than enough sun, food, and water, one might yield an eighteen- to twenty-two-millimetre crop averaging twenty millimetres and the other a four- to twelve-millimetre crop averaging eight millimetres. It is seen that the 'hereditary size' of fifteen millimetres is meaningful only if the environmental circumstances are carefully specified. Thus from the parable of the beans, we can deduce two great facts about heredity: (1) differences in *actual hereditary type* (which are called genotypes) can be masked by the appearance of the visible externals, and (2) the progeny of a single hereditary constitution are importantly influenced by environment so that the outwardly visible traits (phenotype) of offspring result both from heredity and environment or, as is often said, from nature and nurture. Thus a moderate-sized organism might actually be one of three things: a moderate-sized genotype in a normal or average environment, a hereditarily large genotype whose growth is stunted, or a hereditarily small genotype which is overly well-nourished. If either of the last two, the trait has been acquired and will not breed into the next generation.

We know this from everyday life. One sees the tall, healthy American-born children of foreign immigrants, who physically and mentally have come to resemble other American children, acquiring the language and culture of their environment. Despite the familiarity of such phenomena, exceedingly strange circumstances surrounded the development of our understanding of heredity. Even though science was a going concern in the mid nineteenth century and there existed great contemporary interest in biology, when the portals were at last opened to an understanding of heredity by the Moravian monk Gregor Mendel, it took almost half a century for his work to be 'discovered', though it had been duly published before the scientific community. In seeking to explain this major riddle of scientific history, Bentley Glass suggested that, in Mendel's time, thought had been so obsessed by the question of origin of species, that is, with hybridization *between* species, it had no interest in crosses *within* species.

Glass recalls how tantalizingly close some contemporary writers seemed to come to understanding Mendel's work. In his book on hybridization, Focke referred to Mendel's work fifteen times and even quoted him, but with no understanding. The great theoretical biologist Nägeli corresponded actively with Mendel for years, exchanging reprints and experimental plant material, but because of Nägeli's preoccupation with his own theories on the nature of life, he failed completely to comprehend the work of Mendel. In time, says Glass, he came to despise it. H. J. Muller says of Mendel's neglect, he was 'ahead of his time', uniquely perceiving both the nature of the problem of hereditary mechanism and the means by which it might be solved. Perhaps this is so, though it is ironic that this catachresis of history found the Genetics Society of America celebrating in 1950 not the eighty-fifth anniversary of Mendel's discoveries, but the fiftieth anniversary of the discovery of Mendel! This was entirely appropriate because genetics, the science of hereditary mechanisms, did not get into gear and drive away until Mendel's work had been disinterred.

Like all great scientific theories, Mendel's work knitted together in one magnificent idea an enormous collection of 'useless' facts. First Mendel made the simple observation that sometimes a plant or animal has variations which differ in some characteristic such as colour or size. But if an animal arises from a single sperm and a single ovum – as does a plant from a single pollen grain and ovum – does the appearance of two kinds of offspring mean that there are two kinds of germ cells? This was a question for nature to answer. Mendel went to his garden and selected some pea plants – a species whose pollen can fertilize its own egg cells – and after demonstrating in the chosen plants that, self-pollinated, they breed true for many generations with no diversity in the character of the offspring, he crossed two varieties which differed in size. The seeds that resulted, of course, had to be planted before the consequences of the cross could be known. And the new generation, as it unexpectedly turned out, were all the same, resembling one parent. In this case, tall plants crossed with dwarfs gave only tall offspring.

Now Mendel self-fertilized these offspring – their own pollen with their own eggs. In the next generation, however, there were talls *and* dwarfs, a result likely to turn men of lesser stature to other pursuits. How could this be explained? Mendel then did the simple thing which made him immortal. He *counted* the percentages of talls and dwarfs in this generation, perhaps the first use of a mathematical approach in the history of biology. The results were impressive: in a large number of trials, this generation contained three talls for every one dwarf. In subsequent breedings, the dwarfs breeded true, yielding only dwarfs. But the talls continued to yield mixed populations. Such results, Mendel concluded, point to a separateness or 'atomicity' of the heritable traits and suggests the following hypothesis: hereditary characteristics are due to something that *determines* these traits; this something is actually transmitted from parent to offspring; these hereditary determinants must be *physical particles* which retain their identity and integrity during the process of fertilization. The fact that in the first mixed generation, the trait of dwarfness disappears altogether while it reappears in the next generation *in a definite quantitative proportion* proves that it was 'there' all the time. In the course of its assortment (or recombination as it is called), it had merely been masked in one generation by the factor for tallness. And although these plants were outwardly, or phenotypically, tall, their true nature or genotype was hybrid as shown by the test of progeny. In brief, then, the core of the theory is the notion that heredity depends on a mosaic of separate and discrete physical particles with a continuing existence in time. The great Danish botanist Wilhelm Johannsen christened them *genes* in 1909.

The theory was soon brilliantly confirmed with only minor ⸻ⁿs in other plants and certain insects. It became clear, ⸻ we cannot enter into here, that the hypothetical ⸻ⁿayed in a linear arrangement along the stringy little structures called chromosomes that microscopists had long been observing in the cell nucleus. Textbook writers promptly seized upon the obvious model: the chromosome was a string and the genes were beads. And many microscopists looking at

223

the chromosomes, or more precisely their stained formaldehyde-treated remains, felt sure they could see little bulges along the edges of the chromosome. These, they wrongly concluded, must be the genes.

We cannot here follow the details of the work that soon poured forth. Suffice it to say that the idea of a *physical* basis for heredity galvanized the field of biology. There were great difficulties, of course. No one could examine a naked gene, for its properties were assayable only by genetic analysis of the progeny. It itself remained an inferred entity and a thoroughly remarkable one, for its small size and durability suggested that its material construction must be startlingly complex in detail. If a single gene were made of many small molecules, it was reasoned, it would be difficult to imagine how such structural complexity could be maintained since in these circumstances its properties would depend on the average behaviour of many small molecules. The alternative view, according to theorists like Schrödinger and Delbrück, would be to picture the substance that makes up the gene, whatever it might be, as an enormous single molecule rather than a collection of small molecules. In this way, its stability, order, and permanence would be uniquely determined. They would not then be the consequences of statistical laws.

But how to get at the gene? If an experiment requires that we tamper with our object, how are we to experiment with the gene other than by simple crossbreeding? The answer to this question was provided in the late 1920s by H. J. Muller. Mendel's theory viewed the genes of each strain and species as permanent and unvarying. But this concept fails to explain how different strains and species arose in the first place. The theory of evolution, of course, rests squarely on the proposition that species som... do vary – although Darwin knew nothing of M... cautious and confused attempts to explain v... *of Species* revealed a lingering faith in t... characteristics. How, then, can ge... variation be reconciled? The an... alteration of the gene itself.

When a gene mutates it is p... ly altered. The offspring

receive the mutant gene and transmit it to all subsequent generations. The three main reasons why the incidence of mutations might appear to be lower than it actually is are, first, that many mutations are lethal in that they prevent reproduction and, thus, extinguish themselves; second, many mutant genes are recessive and, hence, do not express themselves phenotypically; and, third, the visible results of many non-lethal mutations are so subtle they are lost in the welter of non-hereditary variations. Nevertheless, they do occur and studies on the genetics of corn showed that each gene has its own characteristic frequency of spontaneous mutation. This means that in every 100,000 seeds, for example, there will be one in which a given gene has mutated. Muller's contribution was the discovery that the incidence of mutations can be artificially increased by exposing the egg cells or spermatozoa to X-ray irradiation; the higher the dose the greater the frequency of induced mutations. Here was the tool genetics was waiting for! It was now possible to tinker with the gene on a wholesale basis.

One of the consequences of this work was the ultimate realization that it is the rare spontaneous mutation – whose cause is probably a stray bolt of the background radiation that is always present in the physical environment – which is the operating factor in evolution. This can be demonstrated in a nice experiment which, incidentally, also demonstrates the role that bacteria have come to play in modern theoretical biology. In bacteria, we can now observe evolution. We spoke of the burden that the historical nature of evolution places on the theorist. If evolution happened, it happened only once. With natural evolution, we can observe and cerebrate but not experiment, because evolution proceeds too slowly. We now recognize that a laboratory bacterium can pass through more generations in two years than has man in a million years. Bacterial evolution, therefore, can be studied by subjecting a pure culture of organisms to drastically unfavourable environmental conditions. As in the evolution of all life, only the fittest survive. In the experiments, 'nature selects' only those individuals who may be resistant to such adversity. If for example, an antibiotic is added to a culture plate, most (or all)

T – H

of the organisms will be killed. Should survivors remain, they will grow and reproduce on fresh plates containing the antibiotic, revealing that the property of resistance is heritable. By such experiments, calculations can be made of the frequency with which the bacterial 'antibiotic-resistance gene' spontaneously appears.

Although the antibiotic experiment could not have been described by Wells and Huxley – because antibiotics had not yet been discovered – they could have, in 1929, pointed to a similar experiment in radiated fruit flies subjected to unfavourable environments (they could have but they didn't). In any case, we have drawn even with the understanding of their decade. In broad outline, we see the gene as a hypothetical physical particle whose ordinarily stable complex organization can be disrupted by X-irradiation and whose properties can be known only by the consequences of its actions. As did Wells and Huxley, let us leave the gene here. We will rejoin it momentarily, but first let us enter another domain and speak of viruses. As we shall see, they will lead us back to the gene, though we may have trouble recognizing it this time around.

## How the Virus Makes the Cell Make Virus

What are viruses and what do they have to tell us about the nature of life?

Having argued that spontaneous generation had to be unequivocally demonstrated to be believed, Pasteur must have needed courage to declare that certain human diseases were caused by microbes which he could neither see in the microscope nor grow in the culture plate. But in those diseases that are caused by viruses, this is the case, and several of these engaged the attention of the great Pasteur. Several clear-cut facts were then known concerning ordinary pathogenic bacteria: they were microscopically visible, they could be cultivated on lifeless laboratory media, and they caused certain recognizable diseases. Pasteur knew only that he could neither see nor grow a causative agent in rabies.

For a time, he suspected that these agents must be smaller than bacteria.

Pasteur's recognition of the role of viruses in infection strikes me as one of the larger scientific insights of all time. To appreciate it fully, we must recall the contemporary state of knowledge. The germ theory of disease was very new and still on shaky ground. To the medical mind, the whole abhorrent idea had long seemed ridiculous. But its successes could not be ignored, and by 1875 the theory enjoyed fairly wide acceptance. Germs caused disease, and the scientist's problem boiled down to proving that an individual organism caused an individual disease. It was a simple matter to find bacteria in the diseased body: the difficult part was to prove causation. The brilliant Robert Koch attacked this problem in 1876 while studying anthrax, a vexing disease of farm animals. As a result of his experiments, he proposed a set of criteria to aid in the establishment of a bacterial cause for a specific disease. These are the famous 'postulates of Koch', which state (1) a specific organism must always be associated with a disease, (2) it must be isolated in pure culture, (3) when inoculated into a healthy susceptible animal it must always produce the disease, and (4) it must again be obtained in pure culture from the test animal. These rigid standards codified the problem of causal proof and guided the massive researches of the next few decades. The dawn of 'pathogenic bacteriology' can perhaps be dated back to these classic studies on anthrax.

The germ theory, therefore, rested fairly securely at this point. Biologists had wrestled with the concept of bacterial life and, by struggle and creative genius, had established that the 'infinitely small' play an 'infinitely great' role in the economy of nature. It had been 'proved' that spontaneous generation does not occur and that microbes arise only from parent microbes. It was established that bacterial species are real and stable, yet these theories were but ill conceived, and barely tested, when Pasteur failed utterly. It was dependable in its mode of action. Yet these theories were real and stable.

visible organism from a rabid dog.

It was known that rabies was transmitted to man by the bite of a rabid dog, and Pasteur had little difficulty demonstrating that

227

the saliva of an infected child when injected into a rabbit produced a fatal disease, readily transmissible from rabbit to rabbit. But repeated attempts to culture saliva failed to reveal the cause of rabies. At this point, the germ theory was clearly at the crossroads.

It is something of a cliché to say that Pasteur was a great scientist. For those who may have wondered why, here is one of the reasons. Believing that rabies was an infectious disease, yet confronted with the frustrating failure of the cultures (a technique with whose success he must certainly have been involved emotionally), Pasteur probed the deep canyons of his mind and came up with an exciting new idea. He abandoned the culture technique and conceived the notion of using the susceptible tissues of experimental animals to cultivate the causative agent instead of sterile nutrient broths. By inoculating a patient's saliva directly into the brain of a healthy dog, it became possible to induce rabies in the dog after an incubation period of fourteen days. As Dubos wrote:

Thus was discovered a technique for the cultivation of an unknown infectious agent in the receptive tissues of a susceptible animal. This technique has permitted the study of those agents of disease which are not cultivable in lifeless media, and has brought them within the fold of the germ theory of disease. The Koch postulates in their original form could not be applied to the study of filtrable viruses and it is one of the most telling examples of Pasteur's genius that he did not hesitate to free himself of their requirements as soon as they proved unadapted to the solution of his problem. For him, doctrines and techniques were tools to be used only as long as they lent themselves to the formulation and performance of meaningful experiments.

It was soon recognized th... ...acteria have one other property not shared by viruses ...ain filter, but in 1892, Ivanowski, a small pores of ...ed that the agent responsible for mosaic Russian bo...ose pores were ...would pass through the same filters. What disease ...n seeds of a great ...were the 'filtrable viruses'. They were ...alize the importance ...new enigma. Actually, Ivanowski of his experiment. Doubting his own data, he still believed mosaic disease to be bacterial in origin, and the world had to wait seven years until Beijerink rediscovered the phenomenon and enunciated the theory of 'living infectious fluid' (*contagium vivum fluidum*). In short order, a viral cause was established for a large number of animal and plant diseases, including many a plague of ancient infamy.

The demonstration that invisible viruses could be cultivated as readily as bacteria *if grown in the animal body* had enormous theoretical implications for biology. If the virus was a living unit, why could it survive only within a living cell? If it can survive only inside a living cell, we are compelled, whether we enjoy it or not, to ask, 'Is virus a living organism?' Not even a half-hearted attempt could be made to answer these questions for many decades following the initial discovery of virus and its curious, rather dimly comprehended properties. The concept of virus emerged in a single context and no other, the power to produce disease. It was quickly recognized that different viruses can infect cells of all types, be they animal, plant, or bacterial. By residing in them they came to destroy them (and for our discussion this will pass as a definition of disease). This remained the only property which labelled the virus and hence the only means of its identification. This is, as a matter of fact, still true today.

For years, the question of whether viruses are living units has been begged by a variety of verbal devices. Since they were too small to be seen, it was not possible to say whether they had a nucleus or some other interior organization. In recognition of the single behavioural trait by which we can recognize viruses, they have (or it has) been referred to as 'a factor' or 'an agent' in careful stead of 'an organism'. To appreciate the scientific drudgery connected with any investigation of this question, it must be understood how severely the scientist was handicapped by the technical difficulties involved in merely deciding when he did and when he didn't have a virus before him. Each virus is absurdly fastidious and will grow only in a specific cell, frequently of only a single species. To survive, it must have its own kind of cell. The virus of rabies, for example, flourishes only in certain cells of the brain, that of mosaic disease of tobacco plants will live only in their leaves and no other. What this means is that the virologist confronted with a tube containing a drop of turbid fluid, which may or may not contain tobacco mosaic virus, must rub some fluid on to the leaves of the tobacco plant growing in his window box and then wait patiently. The appearance or non-appearance of the pathological symptoms of mosaic disease tells him yes or no. Actually, this isn't too bad. What of the encephalitis virus? These demand the brain cells of humans or near-humans, and encephalitis is fatal. Using one's laboratory assistants for such identification tests would only revive that anti-scientific slogan of another decade, 'They would boil their mothers in oil just to see what temperatures they died at' – so it became laboriously and tediously necessary to inject unknown samples into susceptible monkeys. If, in a month, the wretched beasts developed encephalitis, without first biting the investigator or coming down with something else, it would appear that the tube had contained virus – that is, if the anthropoid hadn't already been incubating a case of encephalitis on his own initiative.

The inconvenience and expense of such techniques requires no comment. For these reasons, certain areas of virus research could be explored only in the larger, better equipped laboratories of the world, to the great detriment of rapid progress. And for the same reasons, it is clear why much of the fundamental work on the nature of virus – as contrasted to the medical or applied problems – has been done on the viral enemies of plants and bacteria: they are simply easier to recognize.

Scientists did in time pull themselves together and, resignedly using these techniques, began to cut their way through the underbrush. If a porcelain filter passes the virus, will a filter with smaller holes exclude it? In other words, does the word 'filtrable' imply an absolute or relative characteristic? Collodion membranes of graded porosity answered this question by showing that viruses are particles of widely differing sizes, ranging from three hundred down to ten millimicrons. (A millimicron is a millionth of a millimetre.) The difficulties in measuring the virus by the size of the hole which will just fail to pass it are obvious. (It is also obvious that the term 'filtrable' became obsolete when smaller filters were used.) Any inference of size from filter methods presupposes that the virus is a spherical particle. If it were a rod, passage through the pores would be much more difficult because of jamming and blocking of the type that occurs among logs floating down a narrow stream. Another great technical problem was the preparation of collodion membranes whose pore size was both uniform and reliably known. This was no easy matter. Not until 1927 was it possible for Elford to prepare collodion membranes with graded pore sizes such that the ratio of the largest pore diameter to the average pore diameter was no more than two. Elford's ingenious membranes greatly lowered the error inherent in such measurements but far from eradicated it. A third difficulty – one which we will better appreciate later – was simply the migrainous necessity of having to assume that a particle only ten millimicrons in diameter, smaller in fact than certain protein molecules, could possess attributes of life such as reproduction.

The collodion membrane work which in 1930 disclosed the diminutiveness of viruses was the first departure of virology away from the classical narrows of medicine and clinically oriented immunology, the first look at *virus* as contrasted with *virus disease*. The reward was a first-class conundrum which a generation of biologists has been trying to solve.

Interestingly, an entirely different approach to the question of size took form during the 1930s with the invention of the ultra-centrifuge. The great centrifugal force developed by the instrument threw down the viral particles in their spinning tube at a rate mathematically related to their size. All one had to do was follow a moving boundary by suitable optical devices. Unfortunately, here there were difficulties too. The mathematical laws governing sedimentation behaviour required an accurate fore-knowledge of the density of the settling particles. Such data are extremely difficult to obtain in viruses. Also, since virus is usually available in only meagre quantities, it was often impossible to see the moving boundary of the virus column. Its position would then have to be located by tedious exploratory measurements of 'infectivity' at various levels in the tube, to the great detriment of experimental accuracy.

Because virus particles are in a size range too small for microscopic visualization and too large for chemical investigation, a number of years passed before the picture of virus came into sharper focus. In time, a variety of increasingly sophisticated physicochemical techniques converged on the problem of shape and size. The rod or sphere hypothesis received support from X-ray diffraction studies, and when the electron microscope finally crossed the barrier of optical microscopy, it became possible for the first time to measure viruses directly. Viruses were at last *visible* – little rods or spheres amazingly similar in size and shape to the models inferred from indirect measurements. To look at viruses in the electron microscope is pure fascination. There they are: shadowy and opaque, uniform and cleanly sculptured, inscrutably devoid of internal structure. One instantly feels the great appeal of such visual evidence and must warily guard against it. At the 1953 Cold Spring Harbour virus meeting, Robley Williams was moved to remark:

The very directness of such evidence brings with it considerable hazard of misinterpretation, inasmuch as the temptation to accept visual evidence is great indeed, particularly when this evidence is in conformity with previously established notions. Lately, however, there has come a realization that the appearance of viruses, as discerned directly through the electron microscope, almost without exception fails to portray the shape and size of the virus particles as they exist in aqueous suspensions. It now appears that many of our morphological notions, derived from electron microscopy, are due for considerable revision.

The future of this problem is difficult to foresee. One gazes at these structures and recalls a prickly fact: they reproduce themselves *but only inside certain living cells* – and to each his own! What does it mean? The question may be asked two ways: What does virus reproduction mean and what does 'virus reproduction' mean? We have already defined 'virus', but what about 'reproduction'? Here one must be careful. Since we recognize virus only by its infectivity, observing virus reproduction actually means observing an increase in virus activity *together with* an increase in the number of certain particles in the field of the electron microscope. The question arises again as to how one might be certain that the particles before one's eyes are the virulent agents causing the observable lesions in the host organism. It is the question that Koch tried to answer for bacteria, and to this day we must be satisfied with partial evidence yielding a measure of probability to the identity of physical particle and biological agent. For example, we can show that they have similar chemical and physical properties (but this clearly does not prove their identity); we can show that formaldehyde combines with virus substance *and* alters virus activity (but we can also show that other substances combine with virus particles without altering virus activity and still others destroy virus activity without combining in a manner accessible to chemical analysis). Uncertainty remains, though in many circumstances it has shrunken small. It is hard to doubt the identity of a particle under study to the bearer of virus activity when the particle sediments in the ultracentrifuge at exactly the same rate as the infectious principle, the particle migrates in an electric field at the same rate as the principle, and the particle has the same diffusion constant and filtration end point as the infectious principle.

Luria has emphasized the importance of recognizing the difference between *reproduction* and *replication*. The point is subtle but keenly important. When we think of reproduction, we think of an organism growing in size and then dividing. Let us remember that this sequence of events *must* be a mere outward manifestation – an epiphenomenon, if you like – of some critical event in the inner workings of reproduction in which *some elementary structure responsible for transmitting the hereditary code* from generation to generation is duplicated or replicated point by point. This inner event happens – replication occurs – and *then* reproduction can take place. The existence of this time sequence would seem to be a matter of logical necessity. If the reader finds the logic muddy, will he mentally tread water until we return to this crucial thought in another context?

Saying it in another way, (1) cells grow and divide, (2) cell

233

growth and division is controlled by some inner mechanism carrying coded information, therefore (3) this mechanism must somehow be duplicated, and *duplication* may have nothing to do with *division*. In the rigorous language of Luria, 'all growth and reproduction should ultimately be traceable to *replication of specific chemical configurations by an essentially discontinuous appearance of discrete replicas*'. It is an abstraction of gigantic power. As we shall see, the study of virus reproduction is one of the most rewarding approaches to bridging the gap between growth and replication.

What apparently happens is this: the virus attaches itself to the surface of a cell of its choice; it (or part of it) enters the cell and literally disappears; the virologist looks and sees no trace of the virus; if he grinds up the cell, he fails to liberate a demonstrably infective agent; he watches; twenty-four minutes later the cell bursts releasing two hundred new fully formed virus particles ready to infect new cells; the host cell is dead, drained, and broken. Since these are the things we observe, we are clearly un-justified in stating that viruses grow and reproduce: we know only that they replicate. The burning question which is baking today's best brains is simply: What happens inside the host cell during those twenty-four minutes?

Considerably more information has been gathered on this question from the study of bacterial viruses than plant or animal viruses. It is interesting to note that the students of each of the three kinds of virus were for long years quite remote from each other. Thoroughly preoccupied with the practical problems resulting from virus activity, they communicated little on general questions concerning the nature of virus and inevitably they built up large semantic and methodological barriers between them-selves. Only since 1950 have the three groups begun talking to each other earnestly and constructively. Books are now appearing on 'general virology' and cross-fertilization between fields is slowly commencing. It is reasonable to guard against the *a priori* assump-tion that what is true for one virus is true for another; but it is unreasonable to contend that each virus is a distinct entity and that nothing learned on one is valid for another. The bacterial viruses more or less gained the upper hand for obvious reasons. These viruses cause bacterial dissolution or lysis. 'There are few biological phenomena', wrote Evans, 'that are as dramatic as this. When one adds a small amount of bacterial virus to a vigorously growing bacterial culture, nothing occurs immediately. Then, suddenly, the suspension begins to foam, as materials inside the bacterial cell are liberated into the medium, and within a short time the heavy mass of growing bacteria has been replaced by floating shreds of debris that settle slowly to the bottom of the containing vessel. The clear bluish supernatant liquid now contains a hundred-fold multiplication of the original virus inoculum.'

Thus, bacterial viruses have the technical advantage of easy detectability. They can be found simply by looking for clearing spots in a bacterial culture plate. It was the chance observation of such a clear zone that led to the original discovery of bacterial viruses. The early workers hoped that bacterial viruses (which they named bacteriophage or 'phage' in laboratory jargon) would kill the bacteria in infectious diseases and thus prove useful therapeutically. There is hardly a bacteria known for which there is not a corresponding bacteriophage. Such hopes were overly optimistic, however, because phages like all other viruses turned out to be too narrowly specific in their attack on bacteria. Phage resistance would result from the first mutation toward resistance in a susceptible bacterial strain. Phage made its contribution in another way. It became the fruit fly of virology, the great model system that almost alone integrated virology into a unified science.

Actually, plant viruses, particularly the tobacco mosaic virus (known in the laboratory as T M V), had held the centre of the stage for over twenty years in all matters of physico-chemical characterization. The difficulties in their bioassay unfortunately make them not inaccurate but quite inefficient study systems. In recent years, a number of technical developments have emerged which may have greatly simplified the propagation and assay-ability of certain animal viruses. It is now possible to cultivate the poliomyelitis virus in living chick embryos rather than in the central nervous systems of apes and men, and it has been discovered that certain viruses such as the influenza virus cause red blood cells to clump together, the degree of clumping being proportional to the amount of virus present. A basis for an assay procedure is readily apparent. Interestingly, this phenomenon has provided an important theoretical clue to the mechanism by which a virus makes contact with the cell it is going to infect. The red blood cell is not penetrated by the influenza virus but its surface seems to have the same mosaic of chemical components as the cells lining the nasal passages. The red cell may prove to be an excellent model for the study of virus-cell interaction.

Faced with a bewildering array of viruses, each possibly unique and maddeningly fastidious, biologists made a decision calculated to expedite work, facilitate communication, and save wasted effort. A single strain of a common bacterium was elected – *E. coli*, strain B – an organism known to extend its hospitality to seven distinct bacteriophages. These were separated, characterized and named T1, T2, T3, T4, T5, T6, and T7. The plan was to concentrate study on these seven 'coliphages', five of which turned out to look like tiny tadpoles in the electron microscope. T3 and T7 were small spheres. A large number of other traits of each of the seven phages were delineated, for example, their individual sedimentation behaviour, diffusion rates, immunological specificity, etc. (Here again are traits whose recognition had to await technological developments. In the age when virus was no more than an invisible infectious agent, one might reasonably have wondered what traits a virus could have!) I emphasize the matter of coliphage traits in order to point out a series of hugely exciting discoveries made possible by their recognition. For one thing, when a bacterial cell is simultaneously infected by two closely related but different phage types, the progeny include both types in proportions similar to the infecting mixture. This may not sound especially startling but it could not, of course, have been predicted. During the 'eclipse' referred to above, the period between the disappearance of the infecting particles and the appearance of new ones, particles and infective activity are both temporarily out of sight. Presumably the substance of virus becomes mixed in with the substance of host cell. In a double infection, however, everything seems to straighten itself out before the deadline and from temporary 'disorder' reappears high order. A mixed infection with unrelated types yields a pure brood of one type only. The infecting particle of the other type is lost.

But when certain pairs of phages are used to produce a mixed infection in a host bacterium, a startling thing happens. The off-spring include *new* types resulting from a recombination of the traits of the parental types. This fundamental result means that genetic mechanisms, genetic recombination, occur in viruses! As is true in the genetic processes of higher living forms, recom-bination of parental traits in the offspring requires the formal conclusion that somewhere, somehow there must exist a number of *discrete recombinable genetic units*, vehicles by which a parent contributes its share to the traits of the offspring. These would be genes. We dimly sense that behind the twenty-four-minute eclipse lies an ancient and utter secret, perhaps the broad design by which life emerged in a frigid, star-pocked universe.

We know that virus replication occurs only if the metabolism of the host cell is proceeding actively – and if the environment provides adequate nutrition. It is clear that virus reproduction depends upon the metabolic machinery and food supply of the *host cell*, the virus particle apparently taking charge and turning all cell processes to its own purposes. What confronts us then is the supremely challenging spectacle of two separate viruses – structures not only lacking chromosomes but themselves far smaller than chromosomes in many cases – entering a host cell, fading from view for a brief interval during which the cell is forced to make new viruses according to instructions it has never seen before, and, finally, the emergence from the broken host cell of a large litter of new viruses, some of which bear the traits of both parent particles. This is mating and genetic recombina-tion among otherwise inert particles! Before inquiring what significance this startling fact may hold for our concept of the gene, let us consider some observations that are even more astonishing.

## The Meeting of Virus, Gene, Information, and Chemistry

At the time that *The Science of Life* was written, one could truthfully say that the problem of heredity had been solved. It was known how the genes were sorted out to the off-spring, and the concept of spontaneous mutation was firmly established. As far as the fact of heredity was concerned, it was explained by these mechanisms. What was not known, however, was *how* the gene does its work, how it influences the new organism to develop this or that trait. If the gene is pictured as a blueprint, how does it communicate with the builder? Some new approaches would now be timely.

The ingenious work of the California investigators Beadle and Tatum soon provided an important clue. To pea plants, fruit flies, and bacteriophages, these workers added a red mould of bread as a classical object of genetic investigation. So that we can clearly understand their experiment, let us consider some preliminary facts. Once the living organism has been conceived and its future traits determined, it becomes essentially a metabolic machine whose primary activity is the chemical conversion of nutrient materials to other compounds needed by the organism as structural elements or energy sources. We may illustrate the essential character of metabolism quite simply:

$$A \to B \to C \to D \to E \to F.$$

A is an ingredient of the diet; F is a compound that the organism needs. The intermediate compounds are merely products and precursors in an orderly sequence of stepwise chemical reactions, each of which is made possible by a specific *enzyme* within the cell. Catalysing and controlling these reactions is the only function of enzymes and, as we recall, enzymes are specialized protein molecules. For almost every one of the huge number of chemical reactions in the organism, there is one enzyme 'in charge' of it. Without its specific enzyme, the corresponding reaction would not occur. There is evidence indicating that the high specificity of each enzyme is the result of the unique and intricate structure of its surface. It will, in fact, 'fit' only one reaction. From information theory, however, we might have predicted such a physical basis for specificity.

We may, therefore, regard all biological traits as visible results of the functioning of one or another such sequence of enzymatic reactions. For example, brown eyes are brown because a brown compound has been chemically synthesized by a collection of enzymes in the cells of the iris, starting from some simpler compound obtained from the diet. Red hair, too, is a consequence of the enzyme-directed synthesis of a red pigment in hair. The same is true of height, blood group, shape, and all other traits. In other words, the presence or absence of specific enzymes determines the appearances which we call traits. Here we may have achieved a simplification, since it is surely easier to imagine a palpable relationship between a gene and an enzyme than between a gene and a pair of brown eyes.

Beadle and Tatum took a sample of mould that could successfully make F from A. (F could be any number of essential compounds such as tryptophan or pantothenic acid, but for the sake of clarity, let us stick with the letters.) The mould needed F for growth and reproduction, but if grown on a medium containing only A, it flourished since it possessed the enzymatic machinery to convert A to F. They found then that if they irradiated the mould, many offspring appeared which could no longer grow on a medium containing only A, but could grow if F were added to the culture. In other words, the F requirement for growth was unchanged, but the mould had lost the ability to convert A to F. By closer analysis, they could demonstrate that this radiation-induced loss occurred in just *one* of the steps, that is, the organism could not now convert C to D (for example), while the other steps remained intact. This could be shown in two ways: by demonstrating normal growth on a medium containing only D (proving that $D \to E \to F$ is intact); and by showing a large pile-up of C when the medium contains only A (showing that A is still going to C, although C is not being removed). These

239

results suggest that X-irradiation of the mould caused its off-spring to lose a single enzyme. When an actual search was made for the 'C → D enzyme', it was indeed found missing. Further-more, if the mould was sustained by artificially providing it with the product of the missing reaction, it reproduced normally, and all subsequent generations were without the same enzyme and, hence, in need of a special diet of D.

The implications of this classical experiment are evident. A mutation, induced by radiation, results in a new strain lacking one enzyme. Beadle and Tatum, therefore, postulated that for each enzyme, there is one gene – the 'one gene-one enzyme hypo-thesis'. If the enzyme is a workman, in this view, it has its own gene as a personal executive.

This work, in addition, clarifies several outstanding mysteries. For example, the red mould uses vitamin $B_1$ just as we do; but *it* can make $B_1$ from simpler compounds and we cannot. When Beadle and Tatum produced a mutant that could no longer make its own $B_1$, the compound – or an immediate precursor – had to be provided artificially. Since we must have our $B_1$ ready made, $B_1$ is a vitamin for us, because by definition a vitamin is a neces-sary substance that the organism cannot make for itself. That is why it is essential in the diet. To the normal mould, $B_1$ is not a vitamin. We may reasonably speculate that in the course of evolution, our ancestors once could make $B_1$ but through a mutation such as Beadle inflicted on his moulds the enzymatic machinery necessary for its synthesis was lost forever. Had there been no creatures in our environment who could make it for us, like the bread mould, wheat plant, or whatever else passes under the name of 'food', we might have perished then and there.

The question now comes down to the nature of the relation-ship between the gene and those protein molecules which are enzymes. Conceivably, the gene is some kind of master pattern which is copied physically in the manufacture of specific enzyme molecules. Since such high specificity is conveyed from the gene to the enzyme, we cannot avoid visualizing some sort of physical relationship such as occurs in printing. Thus, the gene might be an intricate template for stamping the specificity into its enzyme.

If the gene were physically damaged, the resulting enzyme would be imperfect – and since an enzyme will not function at all even if only slightly imperfect, the consequence of mutation may not necessarily be a missing enzyme but an imperfect one which, lacking the ability to function, might just as well be missing.

This 'printing' or 'stamping' motion is compelling because it is a physical model, and it is clear that we are being pressed toward an examination of the physical nature of what biologists have been calling the gene. Some method had to be devised to permit such a frontal assault, for the analysis of the gene through its genetic consequences had now entered turbulent, dilemma-infested waters. The geneticists were reaching that inevitable point in their science where suddenly old and trusted words began defaulting. For example, it was discovered in a number of cases that certain factors outside the nucleus (which we will not dwell on here) can affect heredity. Since an alteration in a gene can be recognized only by its genetic effects, how can one distinguish between the effects of mutation and those of extranuclear hereditary determinants? This must mean that those observable genetic phenomena which we normally called mutations, should not be so readily labelled, since the word 'mutation' implies a specific mechanism for the phenomenon. In other words, geneticists awoke to the fact that they were trying to argue that X-rays produce a gene mutation because the mutants induced satisfy the accepted criteria for gene mutations, and that these mutants were due to an alteration in a specific gene because that is what we mean by gene mutation!

Likewise, it was pointed out that the fundamental idea of gene stability rests on experimental evidence obtained in 'good' genes that behave 'properly'. A flock of elaborate explanations are available to account for the bad genes that behave improperly, but the fundamental problem remains. Genes, in fact, may always be stable and the explanations may, therefore, be unnecessary. Thus, we have another instance of data interpreted so as to insure conformity with a prevailing idea. This agonizing reappraisal within the field of genetics is quite analogous to that which occurred in physics with the theory of relativity. For we are here

241

forced into a completely operational point of view. We must not only prevent ourselves from assuming any properties for the gene that are beyond verification, we must, in fact, define the gene in terms of the actual operations that are performed in dealing with it. Operationally, then, we can now say no more about the gene than that it is the smallest segment in the string of genetic material that can regularly be associated with some genetic effect. As we consider this meagre statement, we again feel the necessity of tearing into the gene's substance. What is this stuff anyhow? Is it a thing? Is it a molecule? Is it a phantom?

The new approach began as a simple question: What is the gene made of chemically – or, more precisely, what is the chromosome made of, since genes are worrisome postulations and chromosomes are visible structures? It had been known for years that a peculiar substance could be extracted from the cell nucleus which, being acidic, was ingeniously named *nucleic acid*. It was then discovered that there are two kinds of nucleic acid which differ slightly in chemical composition and source: the kind that was found only in the nucleus was desoxyribonucleic acid or DNA and the kind that may be outside the nucleus, ribonucleic acid or RNA. The molecules of nucleic acid were found to be extraordinarily large, especially that of DNA. They were long thin chainlike structures made up of a large number, possibly thousands, of smaller units called *nucleotides*. These were the links in the chain. The nucleotides themselves were quite complicated, each containing four different kinds of substances called nitrogenous bases. For convenience, we may refer to these as 1, 2, 3, and 4. Thus, chemically speaking, DNA appeared to be long chain of repeating units, each of which contained the same four bases, more or less like this:

$$\ldots - (1\text{-}2\text{-}3\text{-}4) - (1\text{-}2\text{-}3\text{-}4) - (1\text{-}2\text{-}3\text{-}4) - (1\text{-}2\text{-}3\text{-}4) - \ldots$$

No one knew, of course, whether the chain was as shown or of a random configuration such as this:

$$\ldots - (3\text{-}2\text{-}1\text{-}4) - (1\text{-}4\text{-}3\text{-}2) - (2\text{-}4\text{-}1\text{-}3) - (4\text{-}3\text{-}1\text{-}2) - \ldots$$

And for many years, no one much cared. The tedious chemical

facts we have recited were eked out in the early part of this century and, shortly thereafter, nucleic acid was placed on the shelf to gather dust, a curious, gummy sort of white powder of unknown significance. Wells and Huxley didn't even mention it, for if it belonged to anyone in 1929 it was to the biochemists, not the biologists.

In the course of time, however, nucleic acid reappeared on the scene in several unexpected places. Wendell Stanley, for example, showed that the tobacco mosaic virus contained nothing but RNA and protein; and later workers found that the bacteriophages consisted entirely of a particle of DNA surrounded by a protein coating. When the virus workers managed to incorporate radioactive 'labels' into the protein and DNA, they found to their surprise that when a virus enters a cell, the protein remains outside while the nucleic acid enters – as though the protein were a syringe which gave the cell an injection of nucleic acid. This was a stirring observation, for it suggested that it is nucleic acid alone – the same material biochemists had long ago put into bottles – which inside the host cell stimulates the production of two hundred replicas of itself plus, of course, two hundred protein overcoats like the one left outside. According to these results the power of virus reproduction resides somehow within the virus's nucleic acid. Since it alone can instruct a cell to begin turning out new viruses, it alone must carry the hereditary information which guarantees that the new virus will be a replica of its parent.

While biology was trying to swallow this fundamental development, still another emerged from the bacteriology laboratories. The following simple phenomenon was observed: Two cultures of the same species of bacteria were grown up which differed only in that one had trait $x$ while the other did not. (We are using $x$ for convenience. It could be any one of several hereditary traits – penicillin resistance, for example. Thus $x$ bacteria would be penicillin resistant; non-$x$ bacteria penicillin sensitive.) An extract of the $x$ bacteria was prepared which was demonstrably free of whole bacteria, particles, or other debris. The extract was then added to the growing culture of non-$x$ bacteria. The results were quite startling, for the treated culture developed many colonies of *x* bacteria as a result of having been exposed to a mere fluid extract of the *x* bacteria. Moreover, the new *x* bugs bred true, showing that their newly acquired trait was hereditary. This phenomenon was called *transformation*, and the active ingredient in the extract was called the *transforming principle* or TP. As the reader has undoubtedly predicted, it was promptly shown that TP was, in fact, the DNA of the *x* bacteria. And again, DNA turns up as a carrier of genetic information.

An avalanche of questions followed these discoveries. Is DNA the substance of which genes are made? If so, is 'a gene' one molecule of DNA or several – or, conversely, is a single molecule of DNA one gene or several? Where does DNA fit into the chromosome? Does DNA carry the information of heredity? If so, how, since no *chemical* difference can be detected between the constituents of the DNA of horses and bacteria? If a cell makes its own DNA in the course of reproducing itself, what insures that the new DNA will carry forward the hereditary code? How, for that matter, does a *molecule* duplicate itself? The only thing that could not be questioned was the dramatic fact that, at last, the fateful meeting had occurred between biology, chemistry, and physics. For DNA is a *chemical* compound carrying *genetic* information somewhere within its *physical* structure. The die was now cast for a unified attack on one of the greatest enigmas of science.

We cannot, of course, enter into the details of this work. Nor would it be possible to, since these are the questions that science is investigating in the hour of this writing. It is worth noting perhaps that almost all of the great developments mentioned above have taken place since 1950. And today, 1950 seems like the Middle Ages, for the situation is moving more rapidly than ever. Tantalizing developments are literally tumbling from the laboratories, in a manner which clearly suggests that possessing knowledge is not half as much fun as discovering it.

Thus, for example, in 1953 Watson and Crick examined a preparation of isolated DNA by the method of X-ray diffraction, a technique so brilliantly applied by Linus Pauling to the study of the structure of proteins and other giant molecules. It was found that the long DNA molecule is not a mere string of nucleotides but a highly organized structure shaped like a spring or helix. The exciting part of their discovery, however, was that the winding of the spring involved two strands, not one. In other words, two parallel nucleotide chains were together wound around an empty cylindrical space. It was also concluded that any given order of nitrogenous bases in one strand determined the order in the other strand, since the limited space available in the tightly joined structure meant that only certain pairs of bases could exist side by side.

Here then was a picture of the DNA molecule which could explain a great deal. The presence of a double set of strands at once suggests a self-duplicating mechanism. The two chains could separate, then each could serve as a template for the formation of its partner strand, particularly since each base in the chain would attract the correct complementary base. The daughter DNA would then be similarly double-stranded while the order of the bases would be kept undisturbed. The preservation of the *order* of the bases is a crucial feature of this discovery, for every finger points to this order as the code in which all of heredity is written. Theorists were quick to point out that if the DNA chain contained only one hundred nucleotides with four bases each (it actually contains thousands), the number of possible arrangement of these bases would be $4^{100}$, a number one thousand times larger than the number of atoms in the solar system. Here would be more than enough room for specificity in the synthesis of enzyme proteins, and one can imagine these bases in the act of assembling the different amino acids which make up protein in a *specific order*. Since all of the many varieties of enzymes contain the same kinds of amino acids, their specificity too lies in the order of their subunits.

In the current view, DNA does not directly preside over protein synthesis of specific enzyme proteins. This scheme would be analogous to the manufacture of phonograph records for commercial distribution. First, the artist makes a master. In order to duplicate the master, a negative pressing is made, and this in turn may be used repeatedly to press out new positives. Here the master is the DNA, the negative which transfers the information is the RNA, and the soft shellac which is stamped with a specific high-fidelity pattern is the protein or its precursor which becomes an enzyme. Or, as it was phrased at a recent scientific meeting, DNA is the Father, RNA the Son, and protein the Holy Ghost.

The two most recent developments in this field must be mentioned, for they typify the experimentalists' efforts to give meaning to the implications of the Watson–Crick hypothesis. In 1955, a bacterial enzyme was discovered in the laboratory of Severo Ochoa which, when placed in a test tube with some free nucleotides, links them together to form a giant molecule chemically indistinguishable from RNA. A similar enzyme for 'synthetic' DNA was discovered a year later by Arthur Kornberg. And, in 1956, Schramm, in Tübingen, and Fraenkel-Conrat, working in Berkeley, discovered that free RNA, isolated from tobacco mosaic virus, could alone infect tobacco leaves, showing that the protein component of the virus was not essential for replication. Now capable of synthesizing an RNA-like molecule which lacks only a specific base order and is thus non-infective, the biochemist stands ready to join the virologist, whose specific RNA-replicating system provides a means of testing the success of attempts to bring order into the present disorder of the synthetic nucleotide chain. Although the random arrangement of bases in synthetic nucleic acid appears disordered to a tobacco leaf cell which rejects its instructions, one might reasonably suppose that some cell in the living world, past, present, or future, might find this arrangement the precisely correct one to effect its own duplication *in that cell*. This can be illustrated by supposing that we have drawn thirteen cards from an ordinary deck which, for the game of contract bridge, constitutes a miserable hand. We can, however, imagine the existence of another game of cards in which this same hand would be a winner. Thus, the 'disordered' synthetic RNA may actually be a hopeful virus in search of a willing host cell. Unfortunately, the biochemist hasn't the time to test his product for infectivity in every existing cell type, for this would take an eternity. Rather, he will attempt somehow to achieve the specific order necessary for reproduction within a given cell. He will play contract bridge and try for a good hand, instead of taking any hand and searching for a game he can win with it.

One might call this an attempt to create life, but such a statement adds very little to our understanding of what has been done and what remains to be done. These are physical phenomena entirely accessible to our comprehension and, in this light, the word 'life' has an anaemic appearance. As for the gene, it, too, remains nebulous. At the moment, it is a property of a portion of a molecule and not a 'thing' at all.

## Current Views on the Origin of Life

Having cut down the problem of the nature of life to molecular dimensions, having considered the question of how a collection of atoms might arrange themselves into a self-duplicating key, we are in as good a position as we will ever be to inquire how life began in the first place. It must have had a beginning since we know that the earth did not once exist. It is now well established that the earth was born of the sun. Modern theory concerning what Gamow calls 'the blessed event' holds that very long ago, probably three to five billion years ago, the incredibly large mass of flaming matter which is our sun threw off portions of itself – possibly under the gravitational influence of a passing star. The solar tidal wave of hot gas cast off into space and broke up into separate portions which arrayed themselves in orbits about the sun, trapped by its gravitational field. Soon these gas balls began to cool and solidify, until hard crusts had formed. It was upon the outer crust of one of these planets that life, like a thin film of rust eventually appeared.

There is an intriguing aspect to the history of scientific interest in this question. As we have already observed, the problem needed no answer as long as men believed that life could arise spontaneously on every side. Only when Pasteur showed that life must come from life did the problem of life's origin loom into view. And at the other end of the story, the most recent phase, it is abundantly clear that, during the years since Pasteur, speculation on the problem was almost doomed to meaninglessness by the lack of understanding of the nature of genetic material and the physical basis for the self-duplication of nucleic acid. Only the recent insights into information theory, specificity, and order, and the new work on nucleic acid and virus have brought perspective into this inquiry.

Thus, in the thinking of a decade ago, there seemed to be a logically reasonable way of picturing the origin of life. But it quickly ran into trouble. In this view, simple chemical molecules by a process of evolution gradually became more complex until finally, by chance or whatever, a combination occurred which, like DNA, could effect its own reduplication. The trouble with this is that DNA, as we know it today, can duplicate itself only when the catalytic machinery of a fully formed cell is available to provide the building blocks for the daughter DNA. The first DNA-like molecule would have no such servants, since enzymes and cells are of biological origin and we are speaking here of the *first* organism. Let us see how current thinking is attempting to 'get rid' of this difficulty.

First of all, it is generally agreed that the events we are talking about took place between one and two billion years ago! Among other things, this means (1) that we do not know for certain what the earth was like at that time, (2) that we are constructing hypotheses that cannot be directly verified, (3) that their chief claim to truth must rest on their reasonableness, and (4) there is a great difference between stating what might have happened and what did happen. For in these 'simple difficulties' begin the perennial arguments such as the one between Pirie and Bernal. According to Bernal, Pirie is saying we must remain silent until everything is known, and, according to Pirie, Bernal rushes into print with dangerous over-simplifications every time an astronomer or geochemist offers a new description of the infant earth. These are the occupational hazards that surround this question. In an attempt to avoid them, let us quickly try to outline the area of agreement.

The earth *was* created, and as the process of cooling took place, great quantities of heat were given off. But soon the earth's surface reached a temperature that was largely determined by the sunlight that fell upon it. During the early millennia of the cooling period, rain began to fall – steaming, warm, drenching rain. It fell ceaselessly and formed at last the seas of the earth.

In the beginning of terrestrial time, the waters of the vast oceans were fresh, containing no salt. The salinity of the sea resulted from the steady erosion of land by 'fresh water' rivers which poured endlessly into the sea. Over the long stretches of geological time, billions and billions of tons of salt and other minerals have been carried into the oceans so that the sea water of the modern world has a salt content of about three per cent.

It is fascinating to try to imagine what the world must have been like on its one-millionth birthday. We must visualize a scene of incredible desolation, no living thing, no trees, no fish in the sea, no sounds except the sounds of the waves and the wind. The land masses were surfaced with jagged, unweathered rocks and had no true soil, since soil is largely a by-product of bacterial activity. It is almost impossible to comprehend the amount of time that passed while the earth held no life.

Of this era, science has little specific knowledge. The strata, rocks, and sediments of this period in the earth's history, the period known as pre-Cambrian, which are the usual types of geological evidence, are deeply buried, hidden by the crushing weight of later volcanic ages, continental periods, and glacial revolutions. A few exceptional sectors of today's earth have been discovered which are the result of very early geological transformation. One of these, the Laurentian mountain range of eastern Canada, is the remnant of probably the first extensive crumbling of the earth's crust, the so-called Laurentian revolution. But the main clues upon which geologists have had to rely have been indirect. What we know of the early world was learned with difficulty, by ingeniously gathered evidence and shrewd deduction.

In the great pre-Cambrian seas, where life did not exist, a different sort of evolution was taking place, the evolution of chemical molecules. We can say with some assurance that the infant world had its full complement of elements, its hydrogen, its phosphorous, its carbon, all the substances which are now so intricately woven into the fabric of life. But these elements, we must assume, then existed in a simple form. In considering the situation of that time, one naturally conjures up a model, a huge watery solution of chemical substances floating about and interacting. We have at our disposal a body of modern theory, both in thermodynamics and chemical kinetics, which gives us strong hints as to the probable mechanisms by which simple molecules evolved into complex ones. Suffice it to say that in a chemical system such as the one of our model, the events and interactions that take place are not governed *purely* by chance, but by chance functioning within the laws of chemical reactions, equilibriums, entropy, and free energy. We find that certain chemical substances such as carbon, which is so important to the living organism, have properties which predispose them to form long, complex molecular chains, especially when exposed to the powerful energy of sunlight. As Beutner aptly remarked, 'Life is just one of the countless properties of carbon.'

We have now arrived at the point where most arguments begin. The advance of chemical evolution has produced oceans of what Haldane has happily called 'dilute warm soup', and we may reasonably suppose that in this soup is a large variety of randomly distributed chemical compounds, continuously building up and breaking down. We must now produce a hypothesis which will explain how a pattern of order could emerge from this disorder. Many suggestions have been made: molecules collected at air-water interfaces, on clay surfaces, in the oceanic depths, and gradually there developed a molecular chain whose growth and splitting was catalysed by itself or by simpler molecules in the vicinity. It now appears that there is no logical necessity for assuming that protein catalysts are *essential* for the assembly of a replicating chain: they are only the best, not the only, way of doing it.

The difficulties caused by the assumption that enzymes had to assist in the origin of life call to mind the contention of a century ago that inorganic compounds differed from organic in that the latter could be made only by living organisms. This distinction appeared to break down when Wöhler artificially synthesized urea. However, as George Wald remarked, '. . . it showed nothing of the kind. Organic chemists are alive; Wöhler merely showed that they can make organic compounds externally as well as internally. It is still true that with almost negligible exceptions all the organic matter is the product of living organism.' But it is the exceptions that interest us, because the origin of life was an exceptional occurrence.

The most recent theory to explain the spontaneous appearance of molecular order is that of Melvin Calvin. He points out that certain kinds of organic substances combine together by 'piling up face to face or plane to plane', not as true crystallization, which would require concentrated warm soup, but as a kind of incipient crystallization that could occur in dilute warm soup. Calvin points out that DNA is precisely the kind of molecule that might form this way. And once formed, its ordered structure would influence the order in which a neighbouring collection of molecules would orient themselves.

If such events led to the first nucleic acid, it is evident that there was no specific moment when life began. Had we been present as observers at that time, we could have wasted a great deal of time waiting for the first amoeba, for it is doubtful if one could have recognized the origin of life while it was taking place. In this view, we are relieved of the notion that life began in a cataclysmic instant as a result of a chance collision of the 'right' molecules. This concept has always been hard to swallow. When one reflects on the stupendous complexity of the living organism, it is entirely reasonable to doubt that it could have arisen as the result of a chance event completely physical in character. And this has been the argument of writers like Du Noüy who interpret the extreme improbability of this event to mean that life was created by some extraphysical agency. One is not forced to this conclusion, however. While the probability is very low, particularly as viewed by the scale and context of human experience, it is not zero, and if the probability of an event is not zero, it can be expected that in a period of a few billion years, in a milieu as vast as the primeval oceans, the event may have occurred at least once and probably more than once. When the time scale is long enough, the improbable becomes the inevitable. But we need not postulate an event as unlikely as a cataclysmic collision. No individual element of a theory such as Calvin's is improbable; the measure of the improbability of all the elements occurring in proper sequence is the billion years or two it took to happen. That is why one should doubt – to quote Calvin – 'that we will ever be able to put all the chemicals in a pot and place it in a radiation field and go away and leave it for a while and come back and find nucleic acids.'

One of the problems in deciphering the origin of life is simply this: if chance could make a living system could not chance destroy it? Were not the forces of dissolution which surround all living systems powerful enough to destroy the first feeble slime of life? The answer lies in understanding the ultimate nature of the destructive forces of the environment. Essentially, they are two: oxidation and decay. We find, however, that chemical attack by oxygen could not have occurred to the first organism because the earth's atmosphere at the time contained no oxygen. It was not oxidative but reducing. It was, in fact, the organisms of the earth that themselves placed the oxygen in its atmosphere and produced its oxidative character. With the evolution of plant chlorophyll, photo-synthesis commenced and the plant kingdom flourished, sucking in sunlight and dumping out oxygen. Today it is estimated that every molecule of oxygen in the earth's atmosphere has arisen from a plant at some time in the last two thousand years.

As for decay, we must recall that decay depends upon bacterial action and bacteria did not exist in the desolate world of the first citizen. Though a weakling, he was unthreatened; though easy prey, he met no enemy. For all we know, life is originating anew in our own times, but *today* it is quickly eaten by those creatures who, unknowing, are preparing themselves to be eaten. Such is the world of life.

One might make some deductions as to *when* life originated. Since life as we know it can exist only in a cool, solid-liquid world, the origin of life must have been delayed till the earth had a cool crust. Some actual evidence is available on the approximate time of the origin of life. Fossils have been found that can be dated back to the Cambrian period some five hundred million years ago, but these were already advanced in evolution, including the basic invertebrate animals and the beginnings of vertebrates. The fossil record before the Cambrian record is very unsatisfactory. The world's oldest sedimentary rocks do not contain fossils because the earliest living forms did not have the skeletons or hard bodies necessary for fossil formation. There have been some reports of algae fossils, 'worms', and sponges in late pre-Cambrian rocks, but, according to various authorities, these are open to question. Recent studies on the dating of rocks by their isotope and radioactivity content have permitted geologists to establish that certain early pre-Cambrian rocks are two billion years old. Some of these contained materials that could possibly be organic in origin, so that life's beginning must be placed between the origin of the Earth, three billion years ago, and the oldest known sedimentary rocks of two billion years ago. It is clear that this still leaves enough time for some highly improbable goings on.

It is often asked whether life does or could exist on other planets. There is surely nothing to suggest *a priori* that our planet stands uniquely alone in the universe. Wald says, 'Life is a cosmic event . . . it has come many times, in many places – places closed off from us by impenetrable distances, probably never to be crossed even with a signal.' Urey believes that other planets, such as Mars and Venus, have histories similar to that of Earth with similar transformations of the atmosphere induced by the energy of solar radiation. But because of the lower gravitational field of Mars, its oxygen probably escaped completely from its atmosphere much as helium in time escaped from the atmosphere of Earth. The atmosphere of Venus is almost pure carbon dioxide with a total absence of water. Saturn apparently still has an atmosphere of hydrogen and methane, suggesting that it is a fossil planet. If, indeed, ultraviolet solar radiation is responsible for the oxidizing character of the atmosphere, it is easy to understand the situation on Saturn, which is so far from the sun it receives only one per cent as much solar radiation as the Earth. It appears that conditions satisfactory for life as it exists on Earth probably do not occur on the other planets of our system. This is not to say that some other sort of organism could not be thriving under these seemingly alien conditions. It just seems unlikely. And, of course, we are not speaking of numberless other solar systems.

One entertaining theory of the origin of life had it that life was seeded on the earth by little living particles brought through space from other planets. Arrhenius believed that these particles were propelled by radiation energy, literally by the power of starlight. We now know that the ultraviolet light of stars is destructive to life, and, for the purpose of our discussion, the pushing of the problem to another planet does not help us answer the question as to how life began. The event, say, on Pluto, inaccessible though it is, would still have to be explained.

In considering these problems, it is quite likely that we are ignorant of the extent of our ignorance. Further progress in this area must await a solidification of our ideas in other areas, from geochemistry to biochemistry, from genetics to physics. But we have a start and, as Bernal has said, 'After all, biochemical evolution cannot be more complex than the organic evolution to which it gave rise.'


## Organism: the Elusive Hierarchy

Living organisms are *not* nucleic acid, however, and we must make a real effort to bear this in mind. Though we have spoken chiefly of the gene and the enzyme, it is the organism that lives in the world, that walks and grows and writes books on biology. What is the nature of this complexity that knows so many forms, but fails to hide their brotherhood? What is there about the organism that has made poets sing and scientists despair?

The essence of organism is at once subtle and irresistibly fascinating. The secret is in its name. The organism is an *organization* of materials and functions that are dedicated to the preservation of itself and its species. The allure of this concept, however, stems from the intricate system of *levels* of organization, a pattern which characterizes all living things. Thus, the cell is an organized entity at one level of complexity. It lives in a community of other cells, joining them in certain projects, competing with them for food, and either dying or dividing to form new offspring. Yet these cells may be part of a higher organization, the brain, which is a whole made up of the sum of its parts. Here is a structure on a more complex level of organization, existing and interacting in a community of other organs, not cells. Likewise, the whole man is still higher on the scale of organization, and men talk to other men, not brains or cells. We may also start with the cell and go down the ladder, for within the cell are self-concerned substructures, like the nucleus, the particles within the nucleus, and the particles within those particles – until we reach the level of the molecule and atom. It is this rising table of organization that is characteristic of organism, the elusive hierarchy that makes of thin voices mighty antiphonal choirs.

It is in the organism, the creature wrapped round the genes, that the property of self-regulation resides. Here is the machinery for coping with an environment that behaves as though it were eternally hostile and conspiratorially dedicated to life's disruption, fighting and prodding it at every moment of its existence and, inexorably, defeating it and reclaiming its stilled and functionless substance. The power to resist these forces of decay gives its possessor a unique, if temporary, autonomy which manifests itself in a bewildering number of ways.

For example, the living system exposed to cold generates heat in the furnaces of its own metabolism, using for fuel special chemicals stored within its structure. Depletion of stored fuels generates hunger and repletion. Wounds, both to the body of the multicellular organisms and to the subcellular structures of the cell, are repaired by processes of invisible weaving that still far outrun our understanding. Invasion by foreign matter is resisted: bacteria are eaten by blood-borne structures (themselves living systems but also components of larger forms of life) or they are inactivated by antibodies, humours that are produced by life but are not themselves living. Poisons are neutralized by chemical attack; foreign bodies are walled off. External danger is thwarted

255

either by physical movement – voluntary, as in flight, or involuntary in the reflex action of rapid recoil – or by a whole dramaturgy of unbelievable weapons, including eel electricity, serpent poison, thorns, claws, stench, and teeth. All factors, internal and external, tending to disturb the repose of the organism, however subtly or obscurely, are resisted by equally subtle systems that are triggered by the insult via its effect, say on membrane permeability, thermodynamic equilibrium, viscosity, or whatever. The physiological axiom seems reasonable that says every manifestation of life is not an action but a reaction restoring the *status quo*. That is why Homer Smith called the cell 'a self-centred comfort machine'.

The exquisite precision of life's mechanisms of self-regulation has impressed and inspired biologists for centuries. The ancient symbol of organism was the burning bush – all afire but never consumed. Life's defences against 'time's arrow', the second law of thermodynamics which decrees their need, were called mechanisms of *homeostasis* by Walter Cannon. They are the means whereby stimulus begets reaction to restore equilibrium. Cannon recognized that the homeostatic state, whose existence we can empirically observe, is itself *prima facie* evidence that certain agencies must be acting to maintain it, whether we can observe them or not. And he pointed out that these controls were largely automatic. To him, this was 'the wisdom of the body'.

One can fit into the framework of self-regulation every function of the organism. The ingestion of food maintains energy reservoirs for other activities. The wheelworks of metabolism convert assorted nutriments into available energy or building blocks suitable for the manufacture of whatever staples or other concoctions the organism may call forth – from antibodies to offspring, from coconut milk to squid ink. Excretory organs eliminate the unwanted by-products of organismic chemistry and, in addition, do one other thing. As brilliantly demonstrated by Smith, they are important not only for what they eliminate, but for what they keep – a property of immense importance for internal constancy. The *status quo* must be preserved, and especially is this true for the chemical composition of living systems. Homeostatic mechanisms somehow must retain the power of choice over what goes and what stays.

Homeostasis, being an observable reality, can have been actually observed in only a relatively small number of species and in a limited number of spheres. But it is so close to a tautology to say that life is characterized by self-regulation, it seems reasonable to extend the concept to all living forms. It then follows that a failure of self-regulation means death, and it is curious that death is so much easier than life to characterize – and define. In death, the mechanisms of resistance have been overstressed and can respond no longer. Apparently, therefore, death and even senescence are not necessities or inevitable consequences and, thus, attributes of life. It should be remembered that single cells and single-celled organisms like the amoeba do not ordinarily die but divide down the middle to form new offspring, leaving behind no mother, no father, no corpse, and no reality except an amoebic equivalent of the smile of the Cheshire cat. In a sense, this is immortality. Of course, single cells do die when their homeostatic defences have been crushed, but with good fortune this need not be. Immortality, in another sense, exists in higher forms in the descent of the germ plasm, but in this arrangement there do remain mothers, fathers, and corpses.

Homeostasis is, therefore, one of the great central ideas of biology, for it interlaces every aspect of biological organization. It is homeostasis – the effort of the organismic machine to restore its equilibrium whenever disturbed – that gives the organism an appearance of purposive behaviour, since these activities seem directed toward a future steady state. In contrast to the problems of heredity and reproduction, those in this area of biological science are the subject matter of such familiar fields as endocrinology, physiology, immunology, biochemistry, neurophysiology, and so on. Each of these is concerned with the mechanisms of self-regulation at one or another level of organization, and each still harbours great unsolved problems – for example, it is not known how hormones control metabolism or how antibody specificity is achieved. But the inescapable common denominator in all of these problems is the phenomenon of *control*.

Just as with the concept of information, the basic nature control processes has been examined in recent years under the leadership of Norbert Wiener. What interests us in this body of ideas is the universal pattern of effect acting back upon cause to provide information on the consequence of its previous action, thereby determining its future behaviour. The usual illustration is the ordinary room thermostat which turns the heat off when the rising air temperature tells it to. Or the steersman of a boat: when he sees his vessel moving too far to the leeward, he acts by swinging the rudder to the windward. Thus, the controlling function of the steersman (or the thermostat) consists in holding the course (or the temperature) by swinging the rudder (or the heater) in a direction that will offset any deviation from that course. This is called *negative feedback*. In both cases, we will observe that a mechanism or system is essential. It is the whole, the dovetailed integration of coordinated processes, that seems greater than the sum of its parts. Control then requires organization.

With this in mind, we may cast another glance at evolution, this time viewing it, not as a means of explaining the origin of snails and chickens, but in more abstract terms – as a process whereby complexity was added to patterns of biological organization. For example, it is interesting to consider how single-celled organisms which reproduce by fission evolved into highly organized many-celled organisms which reproduce sexually, irrespective of the particular species. Reproduction seems tidy and forthright as it is transacted by individual cells. In dividing by mere fission, they give the whole affair an elegant, if deceptive, simplicity. Life did not evolve far, however, before the reproductive process took on a new dimension. It may have taken a long time to emerge, but sexual reproduction, once elaborated, was the basis for rapid upward surges in evolutionary progress. For the first time, substance from *two* living systems joined to create the primordial cell of a third. When one considers the difference in complexity between single cells and multicellular organisms, it is apparent that until some sort of fusion could occur evolution could not move far beyond the single cell.

The first step toward sexuality was fusion or conjugation, the precise opposite of fission. In this curious process, which originated in the larger, more complicated unicellular forms, two cells that normally multiplied by fission joined together, internally exchanged parts of their anatomy, and then fused into one. After a period of rest, multiplication by fission resumed just as before. Biologists have long recognized that, after many generations of multiplication by fission, cells will often show decreasing vigour and increasing somnolence. In time, they may seem near death. If at this point, conjugation can occur between two such cells, the resulting organism has great new vigour and proceeds to subdivide by fission for many generations. Why does conjugation invigorate? The answer is that through mating, an organism, weakened by the prolonged reinforcement of its own weakest 'family' genes, now receives a therapeutic transfusion of strengthening new dominant genes. This explains the vigour of hybrids.

The next evolutionary step toward greater complexity of form was the establishment by individual cells of cell colonies. While clearly not multicellular organism, the colonies were considerably more than casual get-togethers of random cells. Although the first such grouping probably happened by chance, its survival value for the participants quickly gave significance to the arrangement, thus converting a chance distribution into one of meaningful order. The problem was: If a group of cells should discover each other and find that living together is exceedingly beneficial for one and all, how would it be possible to transmit this confidential information to the offspring so long as each member cell continues to multiply by solitary fission. There could be no way except to appoint a keeper of the plan, a specialized cell that could somehow retain within its structure the coded pattern of colony structure.

When the designation was made, the precedent was set for specialization within the community. The cell-elect became a productively active member of the colony and, as was 'hoped', gave rise exclusively to cells with an inborn predilection for colony life. It could reasonably be asked in this borderline situation: Which was the individual, the cell or the colony? All such questions, of course, evaporate the instant the associations of cells developed shadings of cellular specialization and interdependence. At that point, the individual cells had cast their lots; thenceforth they could live better lives, but only if they lived with each other. For the community to become a perpetuating entity however, the process of reproduction would have to yield *new communities*, not merely new gregarious individual cells. Within the community, cells could still divide as individuals but, as individuals, they could not be responsible for perpetuating the whole. And, for the first time, reproduction of cells was to occur within a framework of higher integration.

As a means of accomplishing this, conjugation of whole multicellular organisms was clearly an awkward idea. Reproduction of higher organisms, it turned out, would require an improvement of the device developed in colony life, the designation of certain cells as reproductive specialists. By having the cell-designates of one organism fuse with the equivalent cells of another, species could propagate and retain to itself all the advantages of specialization, interdependence, growth by fission, and reproduction (and continuing invigoration) by fusion. Life divided into animal and plant kingdoms long before the appearance of the more complex single-celled organisms, and it is suggested that both branches of life probably evolved the cell fusion method of reproduction independently. It was, apparently, the only way.

The ultimate importance to the species of designation of the germ cell is illustrated by the following. In the very early course of differentiation and morphogenesis of the embryo a remarkable thing occurs. At perhaps the eight- or sixteen-cell stage, one cell becomes visibly different from the rest, and as the others writhe in metamorphosis, changing and evolving into new shapes and functions, this cell remains unchanged, primitive, and mute. It is this cell, still unspecialized and uncommitted, that in the midst of its immensely specialized and otherwise preoccupied siblings, becomes the vault of the germ plasm, the sperm or egg of the future being. The earliest of all differentiations is the one that ensures the continuity of the species.

Evolution has kept these basic devices and elaborated them

into a variegated universe of detail and invention. The means and mechanisms that evolved to foster the sexual union of two individuals (only later identifiable as male and female) are almost as varied as life itself. With the sharp differentiation of sex cells into ova and sperm, evolution unveiled a number of basic techniques of accomplishing their union. Among primitive sponges, worms, and corals, sexual reproduction depended upon chance collisions between eggs and sperm which had been merely ejected into the water. When a whole population of sea urchins, for example, discharged eggs and sperm over a wide area, the probability of such a collision could be quite high. Advanced forms soon developed special organs with duct systems for the production and delivery of the germ cells, although the union of germ cells took place outside the body until the great evolutionary development of internal fertilization. Reproduction also acquired cyclical patterns in time and rhythmic periodicity. For certain species, sexual development could occur only as a consequence of sexual stimulation, or puberty, or special foods (for example, the famous blood meal of the Diptera). In others, sexual activity was limited to certain times of the year by the seasonal growth and recession of the sexual organs and the oestrous cycle. In all cases, life evolved elaborate inventions to make sexual union a reliably likely occurrence. When the advent of sense organs and nervous systems made cooperation between the sexes a prerequisite for fertilization, there emerged the phenomenon of courtship, a phenomenon we will not enter into here.

Biologists today are deeply involved in investigating the detailed nature of the mechanisms of control at every level of organization. Yet, interestingly, there are at least two zones of inquiry in the domain of organism in which little has been learned despite their supreme importance. We will speak of them briefly in closing our sketch of the organism.

The first has to do with the process of *differentiation*, a truly astonishing feature of higher organic life. It is the problem posed by the emergence of an organism from its embryo. In differentiating, *single fertilized egg cells*, the progenitors of the adult multicellular organism, not only must undergo division to produce the new cells that growth requires, but somehow must be trans-figured in the course of time from the general to the specific. The progeny of this 'first cell', though remaining true to species, must nevertheless acquire new forms and function as liver cells, nerve cells, and blood cells appear in the course of embryonic development.

'The process of differentiation', wrote C. H. Waddington, 'has always seemed particularly mysterious because there are so few phenomena in the non-living world that might give us clues as to how it takes place. In the inanimate realm we do not often come across a situation in which parts of a single mass of material gradually diverge from one another and become completely distinct in character.' Thus, the problem of cellular differentiation is a classic example of the biologist's dilemma, having led him into logical fallacies and methodological dead-ends by the dozen. How can a single, amorphous, nondescript 'precursor cell' give rise to innumerable offspring, not only infinite in variety but also rigidly on schedule? Chrysanthemum seeds contain plans for autumn, not spring, blossoms, and a single sperm-fertilized human ovum carries on its schedule one set of teeth that in six years and nine months will be replaced. Since the fourth century B.C., this problem has been debated by the advocates of two theories. One group held that the 'precursor cell', the fertilized egg, contained all parts of the future organism in miniature and given time these would grow to adult size. The human egg, in this view, contained a tiny, dwarf-like homunculus in the shape of a man but greatly abridged in size. (This is the little man that Leeuwenhoek thought he saw within the sperm cell.) The other theory, the one held by Aristotle, stated that organs and parts arose by gradual interaction of the simpler constituents of the egg.

In this view, we are confronted with a single cell, a precursor of precursors, containing in addition to its normal inclusions nothing more than the genic blueprints and time-tables and per-haps a few bricks and mortar for the big construction job ahead. We can see nothing more in the small space. It is true that newer techniques of visual examination – electron microscopes and such

– may improve the power of our vision, but, in the words of Weiss, 'we are still essentially concerned with tracing "products" rather than the production processes that lie behind. Once we can detect the "product", most of the story of its production is over and we have certainly missed its essential beginnings. It looks as if the analytical methods at hand are of no avail.'

What solution there is for this dilemma has come from the experimental embryologist using 'behavioural' rather than 'analytic' tests upon his material. His premise is that if you watch two systems under identical conditions, cells or organisms and they behave identically, they *are* identical and if they behave differently, they are and must have been different from the very beginning. Failure to detect differences in the appearance of two seeds, for example, means nothing if, when planted side by side, one yielded marigolds and one poppies. If two cells thus judged to be different can be shown to arise from the same precursor cell, they must then have *become* different (i.e., differentiated), identical external appearances to the contrary notwithstanding. In a sense, it is the test of progeny all over again.

Let us state once more, for the purpose of emphasis, what is meant by differentiation: though we have marvelled at the process of reproduction wherein a cell *duplicates* itself in every detail of form, function, and species, cells that are *differentiating* are becoming something quite new in form and function, though they do remain of the species. The problem confronting the biologist wishing to study this phenomenon is quite simple in its hulking, immense way. He cannot get his hands on experimental material. Since differentiation occurs chiefly during embryonic life, studying it means more or less ending it. In grappling with this dilemma, experimental embryologists may have come up with a fascinating solution to their technical problem. First, the simple observation was made that when the gullet end of a single-celled protozoon is cut off with a tiny needle, a complete new one grows back in the course of several hours. It seems reasonable to suppose that this process of regeneration is one of cell differentiation completely analogous or identical to the process occurring in embryonic cells. In acquiring a new gullet, the protozoon cell changed

263

its character before the investigator's eyes, thus providing a whole new experimental object. Among other things, the technique has disclosed intriguing relationships between the regenerative or differentiative process and the internal architecture of the cell. Somewhere geometry must be involved. Why else would the cell grow a new gullet and not a tail?

The second virgin corner in the science of organism needs only to be mentioned, for we alluded to it earlier in remarking that biologists today feel unqualified to discuss life. It is the problem of grappling, once and for all, with the problems of organism and organization. For years, the 'purposiveness of life' has been a topic for philosophers and wise men. Now it is time for the scientist to take over. Recent work, such as that by Sommerhoff, shows beyond any question that the total organism – as distinct from isolated physical or chemical systems – can be treated with a mathematical rigour completely devoid of vagueness, ambiguity inconclusiveness, and spirits. Goal-directed behaviour has nothing mystical about it; it is a property of material systems that is susceptible to analysis. When this begins in earnest, the science of organism will come into its own.

This then – in a word – is the living organism today.

# 14

## *The Taste of Frustration: Some Unsolved Problems*

KLÜVER: What about the relationship between humour and irony?

BATESON: Do you mean irony in the classical sense, such as occurs in Greek tragedy . . . ? Or do you mean irony in the sense of saying the opposite of what is meant?

TEUBER: One would be the irony of the situation of Oedipus who does not know what everybody else knows, and the other would be the Socratic irony. Socrates insists he doesn't know what everybody else presumes to know. . . .

MEAD: Just a moment. Why are we getting so literary?

PITTS: Well, who started it?

MEAD: I'm just raising it as a question. Why this outcrop of literary-historical erudition here?

GERARD: Maybe we haven't anything constructive to say.

– From the *Transactions of the 9th Macy
Conference on Cybernetics*

WE have now painted a somewhat impressionistic landscape of the great rolling hills and cultivated plains of contemporary biological thought. And we have seen how the flowering of these fields has been aided and enriched by the fertile humus of modern philosophy and physical science. For those who believe and hope that science will again find the basic unity it lost in the avalanches of complexity and specialization – and of segregative rather than integrative writers like Du Noüy, who wrote in *Human Destiny*, '. . . it is *totally impossible* to account scientifically for all phenomena pertaining to Life' – there is much satisfaction in witnessing this trend in biological thinking. At last, it would seem, is the road staked out that will lead us to the future.

Unfortunately, this rosy picture has a less optimistic side, for there is an inescapable implication within our new-found sophistication. It is that the problems we have so far failed to solve must, therefore, be more sophisticated than we are. This is sobering and, hence, worth reflecting upon. There are, of course, many questions that science has not answered because the questions themselves have not yet been discovered. New discoveries raise new questions and we cannot anticipate what these will be. But there are also many questions that have been before us for years and that science, despite a massive attack, has so far failed to answer. There is much to be learned in considering these areas of frustration. For one thing, we may see how the sharp cutting edge of contemporary analytic thought planes away at flimsy constructions, by recognizing no question incapable of answer and no answer incapable of proof. Moreover, we may witness again what frustration can do to its victims. Since many of these problems are in areas affecting human welfare – the nature of cancer, and other diseases – because men *want* these questions answered and scientists want to answer them, an atmosphere of pressure can sometimes build up which may generate exceedingly strange behaviour.

It is not difficult to understand why men would want science to lift their burden and relieve their suffering. It is also understandable that the scientist is almost never subjected to external pressure for the solution of abstract problems which have no visible connexion with human welfare. However, since no one knows in advance which 'useless' scientific inquiry will ultimately benefit mankind, there is some irony in the drum-beating surrounding 'cancer research' when it is entirely reasonable to suppose that the cause of malignant growth may some day be found by a seaweed physiologist.

No one is at fault, of course, in failing to solve a scientific problem. But when failure occurs, it is useful to ask why it occurred. In an age when science can 'do anything', why are there areas in which it has done nothing? And – perhaps of equal interest – why are men outside of the scientific community often led to believe that the answers are 'just around the corner' when, in some cases, the fact is that science hasn't even found the street of this mythical corner?

We have already mentioned a number of basic biological problems that are yet to be solved – the basis of the ordered arrangement of DNA, the explanation of organismic architecture, the

266

nature of differentiation. Somewhere in these puzzles may be the answers to the two biological problems I propose to discuss in this chapter – the nature of cancer and the nature of mind – both enigmas whose solutions now seem far away despite sanguinary popular accounts. It is always interesting to try to locate the dividing line between knowledge and ignorance. But our effort here is also directed at exploring the possible reasons for our ignorance and at arousing a genuine respect for these difficulties. In no case is one justified in assuming such problems to be either 'almost solved' or impossible of solution. We can say only that they are difficult problems whose solution will require time and intelligence. For the working scientist who has so far failed, no further excuses are required; for the public to whom he looks for support, no cajolery should be necessary beyond this statement.

## The Great Cancer Mystery

The trouble starts with the word 'cancer'. The biological phenomenon to which we refer in speaking of cancer has a single characteristic by which we recognize its existence. It is a pattern of growth behaviour exhibited by certain cells within a larger community of cells. Usually, this behaviour is described by an analogy. The cancer cells are outlaws who show contempt for the welfare and orderly life of the community at large – that is, the whole organism – recklessly plundering and aggressively invading in a thoroughly non-altruistic manner. As of this moment, we are able to recognize cancer cells *only* by this behaviour pattern. If a cancer cell has been removed from the organism and successfully grown in a culture plate, we could identify it as a cancer cell only by transplanting it back into the organism and observing its growth pattern.

This problem of *recognizing* a cancer cell is a singularly slippery one. As we remarked in speaking of the definitions of words, a clear understanding of the zone of applicability of a word such as 'cancer' is an absolute prerequisite to knowing what one is talking about. The question is really one of taxonomy, that old and

267

honoured subdivision of biology which is concerned with the accurate identification of organisms. It is the taxonomist's problem, for example, to decide whether the frog before him is or is not *Rana pipiens*. As we mentioned earlier, biologists have long worried over whether there really exists such a thing as species, for the overlap and variability of many living organisms make it difficult to define the word 'species'. No matter what the definition, many creatures refuse to be 'either' or 'or' and at least one taxonomist has defined species as an assemblage of animals recognized as a species by a competent taxonomist. This is not entirely facetious, for it implies that the most important purpose of the species concept is to facilitate thinking and communication. This definition recognizes that when one biologist says 'rabbit' to another biologist they will understand each other; the odd cases will remain odd cases despite our concern. Thus, to whatever extent the dilemma has been resolved, its solution has rested on a now familiar proposition: Our definition of species is bound up with the phenomena we see and the operations we go through in seeing them. It is not related to our ideas of what ought to be seen.

These considerations are particularly relevant to the cancer problem. For in trying to establish some agency as the cause of cancer, we are obliged to find it operating in cancer cells and absent or inactive in non-cancer cells. In other words, as scientists, our problem is the problem of proof. If there are varieties of 'in-between' cells – as there appear to be – the problem of proof is made that much more difficult.

Another hazard in the word 'cancer' is the hidden implication that all cells which exhibit this behaviour pattern do so for the same reason. A wildly proliferating cell in the human stomach or breast as much deserves to be called a cancer cell as a similar type of growth in a plant. It is perfectly reasonable to use a single word in referring to such growth behaviour wherever it may be found. It is fallacious, however, to assume uncritically that one instance has the same cause as the other, even in cases of cancers of the same cell type. In other words, it is true that they *may* but false that they *must* have the same cause. One might reasonably argue that an ordered and controlled growth pattern is quite probably a delicately adjusted mechanism, somewhat like a smiling baby. And as a shrieking infant may have many 'causes', any one of a large number of things could disturb a cell's growth-controlling mechanism. In the absence of control, it does the only thing there is left to do (if it is to grow at all): it grows without control. Presumably, if we could demonstrate one reliable instance in which two similar-appearing cancers had clearly different causes, we might then be encouraged to look more closely for the relevant differences in the cancers that must surely be there. In such a case, we would be reminded again of the superficiality of 'appearances' as criteria of identity.

A second difficulty, then, is our ignorance of whether cancer has one or many causes. Scientists trying to resolve this question have naturally looked into all types of cancerous growths in search of a common denominator which would simplify the inquiry. The search has been a long and arduous attempt to discover some other property – chemical, physical, or whatever – which is *universally* present and hence will serve both as an aid in its taxonomic recognition or diagnosis and as a clue to the events underlying disordered growth. Scientists are still deeply involved in this search and large volumes can be filled with the data so far accumulated. Here we encounter another great difficulty, for a number of differences *have* been found between normal and cancer cells in addition to their differences in growth behaviour. For example, there are certain chemical differences between normal white blood cells and the cells of leukemia: there is a typical pattern of sugar metabolism in almost all cancer cells wherein larger quantities of lactic acid are formed than in the normal cell. These are exciting findings and, in the vernacular of the headline writer, may be 'a clue' to the cause of cancer. Unfortunately, no shred of evidence is so far available to tell us whether such abnormalities are *causes* or *consequences* of the cancer with which they are associated.

An extremely thorny problem faces the scientist who would explain the behaviour of the cancer cell by some property he has observed *in that cell*. As we agreed in speaking of causality in an earlier chapter, the most that can ever be said in proving that A causes B is that A regularly and necessarily *precedes* B. For the scientist, this means that all chemical or physical abnormalities must not only be unique to the cancer cell, they must be discernible prior to the appearance of abnormal growth if they are to be considered as possible causes or links in the causal chain. In seeking the events that regularly *precede* the malignant state, we are often hard put to find experimental material whose destiny we can be sure is to undergo malignant transformation. To some extent, this obstacle can be circumvented by the use of animal strains with a known high incidence of spontaneous cancer, or of tissues exposed to certain chemical compounds that have been shown to produce malignant growth.

The observation that cancer cells have an abnormally high rate of lactic acid production has an interesting and illuminating place in the history of this search. This discovery was made in the 1920s by Otto Warburg, the great German biochemist whose many other contributions helped make biochemistry what it is today. At the time, this observation was hailed as one of the greatest possible discoveries. Here at last was a deeper point of difference between normal and cancer cells. But its discoverer had no hesitation in declaring that this unique property of cancer cells was the cause of cancer. As the years went by, however, 'abnormal' rates of lactic acid production were found in certain rapidly proliferating normal cells, such as the white blood cell, and it began to appear that a high rate of lactic acid production was not the cause of cancer but a consequence of rapid growth (or something else), whether normal or abnormal. Warburg attempted to dismiss these findings by stating that injured tissues may show such a pattern, and it is common knowledge that the white cell is easily injured. It was suggested that white-cell injury in the course of experimental manipulation was responsible for this result. Whether or not this is true remains controversial. In any case, Warburg stuck to his guns and as recently as 1956 published an article called 'On the Origin of Cancer Cells' in the journal *Science* – an article which, as might be expected from its title and distinguished authorship, was widely reported in the press. In it, Warburg said, 'What was formerly only qualitative has now become quantitative. What was formerly only probable has now become certain.' No one today will deny that Warburg's metabolic pattern *may* be involved in the causation of cancer. Whether it is or not, however, can be ascertained only from airtight evidence. Most biochemists would agree, I feel sure, that such evidence has not yet been produced.

Many stories of this kind could be told. In 1926, the Nobel Prize was awarded to a man named Fibiger for 'proving' that cancer was caused by certain small worms. Over the years scientists have implicated bacteria, moulds, viruses, emotions, and in each case a nebulous association evaporated under rigorous examination. Within recent years, however, the frustration has deepened because a body of work has begun to emerge that permits some imaginative speculation within the framework of solid evidence. The result has been a number of tantalizing hypotheses on the origin of cancer cells whose only difficulties are the traditional ones, the problem of proof. Behind this thinking lies a number of well-established experimental facts. It is known, for example, that the incidence of cancer in men and animals can be greatly increased by exposure to radiation, the same agency which is known to cause mutations. In addition, a large number of chemical compounds have been discovered – chiefly in tar – which induce cancer in experimental animals. Some of these compounds have been found in the tars of cigarette smoke. In each case, the cancer-producing compounds can be shown by appropriate methods to be capable of inducing mutations. It would appear, then, that the cancer cell may be a *mutant*, characterized by a deficient ability to mature and grow in an orderly manner. In this view, we might imagine that cancer originates from the chance encounter of a normal cell with some mutagenic agent in its environment – a molecule of coal-tar derivative or a stray bolt of radiation. Surely the chances of such an encounter are as good as the chances of any given cell becoming malignant, for cancer remains an exceedingly rare event when one considers the large number of cells in the body, the duration of human life, the rarity of two separate cancers in a single individual, and the known incidence of cancer in the human race.

There is another exciting view about the origin of cancer. Several recent workers have isolated a filtrable virus-like agent which transmits cancer from one animal to another. In the light of newer developments in our understanding of the virus and the gene, the hypothesis that cancer is caused by a virus may still be reconciled with the view that it results from mutation. In the last chapter, we spoke of the transforming principle, a fragment of genetic material (now known to be DNA) which was capable of transforming another strain of bacteria in a manner which otherwise would have indicated that it had undergone mutation. It is now known that a similar transformation may be caused in bacteria as a result of their invasion by certain bacteriophages. In these cases, the bacterial host does not immediately break open to yield a new generation of phages. Instead, the phage becomes part of the genetic material of the host cell where it remains quietly. When the host bacterium reproduces by division, the passenger phage particle does likewise so that both offspring bacteria carry within their chromosomes a latent bacteriophage. This may be carried down for many generations and, in a sense, the host cell may now be considered not only to be infected but also to have acquired a new gene – and it is interesting that to whatever extent the acquisition of new genic material is the same as infection, fertilization itself of egg by sperm may be termed an infection. In this case, however, the dormant phage particle retains its potential ability to start reproducing itself in the traditional style of viruses, and this can be brought on experimentally by some external insult such as *radiation*. We may readily imagine, however, that such phage particles could lose their ability to exist separately and may continue as part of the host chromosome for the rest of biological time. Conversely, many existing cells may be carrying such passengers, whose ancestors 'came aboard' millions of years ago. Some of these may still be capable of activation by radiation; some may not.

Conceivably such a 'virus-gene' could convert its host into a cancer cell – or when set free could do the same to neighbouring cells. In any case, we begin to see the dim outlines of a theory that will explain the known facts about cancer, particularly its resemblance to mutation, its apparent transmissibility in certain animals, its high incidence following radiation, and its heritability in certain animal strains. In the search for the cause of cancer, this work is clearly the bellwether of the future.

Frustration would reach its zenith, no doubt, if such events were proved to be the cause of cancer. For then we would know all there was to know about cancer except how to prevent it or cure it. Yet these are the aspects of the cancer problem that touch upon human welfare. If cancer should be shown to results from some mutagen, such as radiation, the most we could accomplish toward prevention would be to advise radiologists to be diligent in their safety precautions and to minimize those chemical compounds in our environment – such as cigarette smoke if current evidence is substantiated – which predispose cells to malignant transformation. As for the problem of cure, here would be the greatest irony of all, for knowing the cause would net us nothing in our search for a cure. Despite the great and continuing search for a successful therapeutic agent in cancer, we know of no method to convert a cancer cell into a normal one. The only successful treatment to date depends upon total extermination of the cancer cell by radical excision or massive radiation. Much of the investigation into the metabolism of cancer cells has not only been aimed at revealing the cause of cancer, it has also sought to characterize and describe the metabolic processes of these cells, for their own sake, in hopes of locating points of vulnerability, areas of metabolism upon which the cell's existence depends, particularly if these 'lifelines' are different in quantity or quality from those of normal cells. If such were discovered, we might then have some rational point of attack in planning a drug that will reliably kill the cancer cell while sparing the normal. To date, no such drug has been found. Many have been turned up which will eradicate cancer cells by blocking their metabolism, but in all cases these ultimately affect normal cells too – and this is like trying to starve the criminals out of a community by cutting off the food supply for the whole town. Moreover, even those drugs which seem to affect cancer cells preferentially have failed in their intended purpose, because, in almost every case, one or more of

273

the cancer cells develop resistance to the drug, by a process of mutation. Then when all susceptible cells have been killed off, only the resistant ones remain to produce a whole new generation of drug-resistant offspring.

Because of its transcending importance, a number of laboratories throughout the world are engaged in 'screening' chemical compounds of all descriptions in the hope of finding one that will be efficacious in the treatment of cancer. In the rare instance when one seems to be promising in experimental animal tumours, it is given a more detailed examination and, if warranted, is tried in human cancer. There has been much debate over the merits of such an approach. Its defenders, some of whom are quite vociferous, point out that pure luck led to the discovery of penicillin, morphine, digitalis, and quinine, and that a number of useful agents have already come out of these screening programmes that are helpful, if not decisive, in the treatment of cancer. Its detractors claim it is a wasteful approach, a mere gathering of data in the fashion of Bacon which is almost foredoomed to failure. Each year a thick publication appears containing the negative data that have accumulated in this search. It is difficult to take sides in this controversy. Everyone agrees that the cure of a disease may be found long before its cause is known. Smallpox vaccination was discovered years before the word virus had been spoken. Surely no stone should be left unturned in our efforts to relieve man of the scourge of cancer. Unfortunately, any search for a drug that is unguided by rational considerations is almost certainly bound to fail. It is argued that similar points were raised concerning the drug treatment of bacterial infection prior to the discovery of antibiotics. This is no defence, since there were then no good reasons for making such a statement, but there are many reasons for making it about cancer. We have evidence now to support our discouragement. No matter what we say, however, and despite our solidly rooted belief in its unsoundness, perhaps it is just as well that this work continues. We may just possibly be wrong. What would be highly desirable, however, would be a period of lessened loquacity from the workers in this field and their spokesmen until they have something to tell us.

And so the problem of cancer stands unsolved. This is the frustrating truth behind the barrage of half-truths to which the public is subjected. It is not wholly true, as was stated in a recent publication, that 'steady progress continues in our understanding of the manner in which cancer-producing substances act.' It is not true, despite the wide publicity given to its announcement, that a blood test is known that will reveal the presence of cancer. There are many available blood tests but they are not any good. It is not true that early and repeated medical examination can be reliably depended upon to 'discover cancer while it is still curable' – though there is obviously a better chance of exterminating it surgically or radiologically while it is small and localized. But a negative medical examination does not rule out the presence of cancer, as much as we would like it to.

The problem of cancer remains a Gargantuan challenge to the science of biology. Some day it may yield, but until it does, biologists have their work cut out for them. Nothing substantial is yet known about normal growth! Why, when a wound heals, do the regenerating skin cells cease growing at the proper moment? How is it that most organisms reach a size limit which they rarely exceed, although limitation in size is not a universal phenomenon? Why do some living systems (trees, certain fishes, etc.) continue to grow as long as they live? The complexity of growth regulation is also evidenced by its periodicity – typified by seasonal growth, whose traces are the growth rings of cut wood, the stripes of feathers, and the markings of sea-shells – and by the great rarity of freaks, giants, and dwarfs, whose growth has been quantitatively peculiar. It is interesting, too, that abnormal growth is so much rarer in large multicellular organisms than it is among the less complex organisms.

The answers to many of these questions will ultimately come from the new frontiers that are advancing into the problems of gene, virus, and organism. But it is difficult to know whether optimism or pessimism is presently called for. One may look at our present state of knowledge in two lights: we may feel proud at the great accomplishments science has achieved or we may bemoan the fact that we have gone no further than we have, that we wasted a millennium in the Middle Ages, that we have allowed wars and fear to hold us back. We may also lament one other phenomenon in our midst. It is the scientists who evoke optimism or despair with no justifiable reason. A book was published recently which illustrates the point – *The Biology of the Spirit* by Edmund W. Sinnott, Dean of the Graduate School at Yale University. In this puzzling volume, the author presents 'scientific' evidence for the existence of the soul and a personal God. His argument is based on his inability to comprehend life's complexity and its apparent pursuit of goals. Caught in a blizzard of uncertainty between science and mysticism, he finally throws his hands up and joins the mystics. As was pointed out by Martin Grant, Professor Sinnott, in one quotation, 'begins with a case of reasoning-by-analogy, which is followed by a mixture of three unsupported assumptions and three non-sequiturs'. This from within our scientific ranks. This in a discussion of the very subject upon which our ultimate understanding of cancer must depend, the nature of organism.

In this light, I believe we might say that cancer research has a very long road to travel, longer perhaps than it ought to have.


## The Mind As an Object of Biological Interest

We now enter biology's Grand Guignol. No question in the whole of scientific history has proved more deceptive, exciting, frustrating, and elusive. In considering the mind, biology meets its greatest challenge, for in no other area of inquiry are there richer opportunities for self-delusion and verbal sophistry, and in no other are the implications of success greater. Every facet of human life, every issue of science and philosophy, every question of truth, memory, reality, belief, and ethics rests within the structure of the mind. Repeatedly in these pages, we have noted the peculiar role that man's conception of mind has played in the evolution of his ideas. As we mentioned earlier, Descartes was one of the first to state formally a point of view which had been implicit for centuries in mankind's mythological, animistic, and theological beliefs. It was the 'common-sense' view that matter is one thing and mind is another. Matter occupies space; mind does not. They are different existences, different categories of being, and are therefore incapable of interacting. As C. E. M. Joad put it, 'A paving-stone can crush an egg because an egg belongs to the same order of being as the stone. But how can the paving-stone crush a wish, or be affected by a thought?'

It has also been held that the principle of complementarity must be invoked to resolve the 'psychophysical' dilemma. This is the principle, we will recall, that holds that mind and matter are merely different, though fully autonomous and complete descriptions of the same thing. It is typified, according to D. M. MacKay, by the following two descriptions of the same encounter with a friend. We may say, '"He rises to his feet wreathed in smiles and greets us heartily," *or* "A mass of pink protoplasm rises to a height of five feet and begins to pucker and wobble up and down noisily."' Both descriptions are correct, but in one context one is appropriate, in another the other is.

To the thoughtful scientist, such pronouncements contain little nourishment, even though scientists have originated many of them. To maintain that the mind and brain do or do not 'interact' seems to suggest that they are separate entities which impinge upon one another through *physical* interaction. What entity would a brain be impinging upon in these circumstances? This would be like arguing that the Beethoven Violin Concerto 'interacts' physically with what William James called the rasping of hairs from a horse's tail on the intestines of a cat. What we can say from the elementary evidence is that so-called mental activity *accompanies* somatic activity – whether its mechanism be dualism, interactionism, parallelism, or whatever. *Causal* interaction may thus be postulated to exist between psychic and somatic activities: as when shame produces blushing and Benzedrine, elation. And yet, even here we encounter difficulty, since we are usually incapable of observing the temporal priority of the mental event over the somatic event or vice versa – and, in looking for temporal sequence, we are in danger of assuming a separateness of mind and body, thus prejudging the issue. Our problem then should

277

presumably be 'what do we mean by mental activity?' Can the phenomena of mentality be causally explained by physical and chemical events within the brain and, if so, how?

Unfortunately, we are almost as much in the dark on this question as we were a century ago. To explain the physical causes of mental activity, we need empirical data on both brain and mind from which we have so far been barred by methodological difficulties. Moreover, we have here entered an area that is conceptually hazardous. How, indeed, could a feeling of indignation be one and the same as some observable neurophysiological event? How, in fact, may we convert into a scientific datum an introspective account of what is going on in our own heads, if, indeed, it is possible to introspect the relevant things that go on in our heads? These are as much problems in logic as biology, and logicians have had considerable to say on the subject. The logical positivist H. Feigl has contended that there is an absolute identity between the corresponding introspective, behavioural, and physiological events, and he dismisses the 'mind-body problem' as a relic of the Stone Age. For one thing, introspective observations are *private* facts in contrast to the public nature of ordinary scientific data. Thus, there are profound differences between the two in terms of the accessibility of data and the ways in which such facts are known. The only way in which we could establish a correlation between private introspective facts and public neurophysiological facts would be to perform both observations within our own brains.

Because this has not yet been really feasible (notwithstanding Penfield's experiences in interviewing subjects while probing their brains with energized surgical needles), a school of psychological thought was developed in the early part of the twentieth century which is known as *behaviourism*. This view accepts the impossibility of ascertaining private facts in other minds, or in the minds of experimental animals, and instead sticks only to what can be observed, external behaviour. Here is a remarkable thesis! In its strict form, behaviourism tells us that what we observe are not mental processes but various bodily actions. To the behaviourist, the act of thinking or perceiving is equated with a certain pattern of bodily behaviour. The introduction of this sweeping concept as an alternative to introspective psychology set off one of biology's most intemperate tong wars. The cry went round that behaviourism seeks to get rid of the mind completely. Writings appeared such as the following by J. W. N. Sullivan:

We do not think; we make incipient speech movements. We do not perceive anything; we adjust our eyeballs. It would certainly seem to be a waste of time to discuss this theory were it not for the fact that there are a fair number of people who profess to believe it, as well as a large number of people who, for one emotional reason or another, would like to believe it.

We will not presume to enter into this controversy. It is still claimed by more sober critics that strictly interpreted behaviourism leads to trouble. Much of their criticism goes to the point that behaviourists deny introspection and the 'inner life'. This, of course, is not so. Behaviourism merely affirms that, as a science, psychology cannot make use of the private data of introspection. But even this is not as simple as it sounds. Observations may be open to the public, but *making* the observation is, in one sense, itself a private experience. The behaviourist does not record how far a needle moves, he records how far *it seemed to him* to have moved.

The fact remains, however, that we may have made real progress in turning our backs at last on 'the mind' as a separate metaphysical abstraction. Again we must witness the downfall of such a verbal abstraction. As Sherrington pointed out, the 'mind' is utterly dependent upon the detailed architecture and function of the brain. Later workers have preferred to speak of consciousness instead of mind. Here perhaps is an observable state of the organism which is carefully defined by the physiologist Homer Smith as an 'awareness of environment and of self, revealed objectively by self-serving, neuromuscular activity which exhibits choice between alternative actions and simultaneously relates past experience to anticipated future'. In this view we may have the makings of a new way of visualizing mental activity, for this

279

definition is closely tied to the physiological and anatomical aspects of neural activity, those phenomena to which we must ultimately look for an explanation of conscious experience.

Here, too, we are in deep trouble. Neurophysiology has yet been unable to provide any description of the events taking place in the neural unit during the simplest possible forms of mental activity. It seems clear, however, that all hopes of progress lay in deepening our understanding of the neural organization of the brain itself. Just as our description of the action of muscle depends on knowledge of the structure of muscle, we must eventually comprehend both the individual neural units of the brain and their patterns of higher organization if we are to fathom the connexion between brain and consciousness. What, in other words, can we point to in the neuron as a correlate of conscious experience?

While there is no answer to this question at the present time, it is extremely interesting to note how the problem is being attacked by contemporary biology. For one thing, the brain itself has been carefully examined from a number of different angles. Structurally, it is an unbelievably complex knot of nerve cells and fibres, which, though characteristic in their basic arrangement, vary in detail from individual to individual. It was early observed that weak electrical emanations which could be readily picked up and recorded accompanied brain function. The observed patterns of these 'brain waves' could soon be correlated empirically with a number of functional states of the brain – such as sleep, active thinking, and certain abnormal conditions such as epilepsy – though again there was no way of knowing whether these electrical patterns were causes or consequences of the functional states in which they appeared.

In time, it became clear that each nerve cell and its fibre, that is, each neural unit, were parts of a complex *network* which trans-' mits (or 'intentionally' fails to transmit) electrical impulses throughout the brain. It is now recognized that the patterns of movement of these excitation waves – their rhythm, arrangement, timing, and spatial distribution – are the phenomena which somehow we must learn to correlate with consciousness. Thus, for example, *memory* could conceivably be explained as a property of a circular network. If a number of neurons were arranged in a ring, an impulse introduced into the circle could circulate indefinitely as long as energy remained available to maintain electrical activity. Patterns of impulses could thus be stored in the brain in the form of permanent reverberating circuits.

It also became apparent that the possible number of patterns of electrical behaviour is as staggeringly great as the possible dimensions of mental experience. Hence, the attempt to correlate the two is virtually doomed before it starts. We therefore reach the point where evidence fades into speculation. Many speculative theories have been advanced to 'help' the neurophysiologist in his dilemma. For example, it is suggested that when we perceive a triangle, a little triangle is projected in the brain in electrical form. This *isomorphic* theory could not be supported, however, nor was it felt that such a neural copying process would gain us very much in terms of understanding. And yet, the neurophysiologist has been unable to eliminate from his thinking the necessity for some sort of *code* in the patterns of neural excitation. From information theory, we would expect that the physical arrangement of neural impulses must in some manner account for the content of mental activity. It was this realization that started the communication engineers trooping to neurophysiology seminars and the 'information theorists' off into gleeful calculations of what the brain code 'has' to be like, speculative abstractions which many physiologists look upon with jaundiced eye.

Nevertheless, if the brain is an electrical network whose connexions work on an all-or-none basis (that is, they pass an impulse or they don't), then we have before us an elaborate communication system for sending coded messages from one place to another. It is, in fact, a great calculating machine which affords us the most exciting possible opportunity to make progress in this field. The 'electronic brains' that have arisen in our midst are, in fact, engineers' copies of the functioning brain. They are also *models* of unprecedented usefulness in advancing our understanding of the brain. As noted by W. Grey Walter, 'A model or analogue of this sort is, in fact, a crystallized hypothesis; it should be clear and brittle. When it breaks down, as all working hypotheses must, its failure must be obvious and explicit.' The giant computing machines have served this purpose well. In addition to revealing how an unvarnished mechanism can perform all the operations of memory, choice, logic, learning, satiety, 'neurosis', recognition, and prediction, it has forcefully set before us a number of difficult verbal issues. How do we now define feeling, perception, and thinking? Perhaps the answer ultimately lies in circuitry. Since it is as foolish to argue that machines can think as it is to maintain that they cannot think, we have found our way home again to the quicksand of words.

Warren McCulloch recently put it this way: 'To the theoretical question, Can you design a machine to do whatever a brain can do? the answer is this: If you will specify in a finite and unambiguous way what you think a brain does do with information, then we can design a machine to do it. Pitts and I have proved this constructively. But can you say what you think brains do?'

We hope Dr McCulloch isn't looking at us.

# 15

## The Boy on the Seashore

God has given the earth to the faithful, and the sea to the infidels.
                                                              – Proverb

A YOUNGISH man has moved to the speaker's rostrum, across whose front are the words Hotel Statler. He peers into the gloom and, for a brief moment, examines his audience. Though strewn through the hall in no sensible pattern, they have for some reason left the first three rows vacant. It is a curious miscellany of people, and in the span of faces can be seen many things. Some show expectant interest, others boredom. Some seem lost in thought, others cruelly beset by the penalties of diversion. Over to one side are two well-known investigators in earnest conversation. From their expressions, it is clear that delectable morsels are being exchanged. A small group of wanderers enter through ornate French doors and, to the man, they trip noisily over the skein of wires on the floor leading to a lantern slide projector. In the last row, a pair of glazed eyes has finally closed.

The chairman rises. 'Each speaker will have exactly ten minutes. When the alarm clock rings, please have the courtesy to conclude your remarks.' And the first paper begins. All that can now be seen in the dimly reflected light of the lantern slides is a sea of inscrutable faces. The speaker reads on, the bell rings, and as the chairman menacingly comes to his feet, a concluding paragraph is hurriedly launched. 'Thank you,' says the chairman. 'There will be five minutes for discussion.'

The audience stirs itself in momentary hesitation. Several tentative arms go up. One of the elders rises. 'I just want to congratulate the speaker on a piece of work well done.' Suddenly the room comes alive, engulfing the elder, who makes for his seat. Questions crackle forth, counter-evidence is unsheathed.

The speaker handles himself well, though he acknowledges that much work remains to be done. 'Have you tried this experiment in chickens?' someone calls out. 'No,' replies the speaker, 'I haven't tried this experiment in chickens.' An ancient enemy comes to his feet to fulfil a fancied obligation: under no circumstances must a traditional vendetta be allowed to 'just end'. Among the younger members of the audience, few can summon the courage to speak. Of the two who do, one is brash, the other is brilliant.

The audience, this time, has been deeply stimulated and there are murmurs of protest when the chairman terminates the discussion. 'I'm sure the speaker will be glad to continue this privately. We must get on to the next paper.' The audience looks at its programmes, and in the babble of voices is heard the sound of intellectual peristalsis. Several individuals shuffle out; new-comers arrive, each tripping over the wires. Over on one side, the well-known investigators are deep in the same conversation. The fact of the matter is that it had never really stopped.

Though it was a brief quarter of an hour, in it we have seen re-enacted a drama as old as human intelligence. If there be any sacred rite in science, this must surely be it.

## The Pursuit of Science

The meeting – local, national, international – is an indispensable institution in the pursuit of science. It is here that each man is given his hearing, his opportunity to communicate to his scientific peers the results of his own observations of nature. It is his opportunity to hear the criticism of his fellows and their leavening suggestions, as his ideas are given their intense moment of cool imaginative attention. It is, moreover, his hour of glory, the recognition from his colleagues for which the scientist works, and which, in many ways, is his only tangible reward.

Science today is a very large enterprise. It has proliferated throughout the world into an almost unmanageable giant. The number of scientific journals is constantly increasing, while each journal's backlog of papers awaiting publication, is increasing too. Great new problems have arisen around the mere matter of recording and communicating new scientific information as it appears. To avoid duplication of work, scientists must be aware of what other scientists are doing, but in today's rising mountain of scientific literature, a real crisis confronts the documentation experts who must make the contents of the archives conveniently accessible to its users.

We find ourselves afloat in a surging sea of new researches and new ideas. The contemporary biological scene is alive with activity. Every innovation both converges toward and diverges from new insights. Traditional interdisciplinary barriers are all but gone: all science is now biology. Regardless of our own scientific latitudes, we are each interested in the same thing – the living organism. And yet new barriers keep arising. The field of learning is deeply scored and broken into fragments of specialism, pieces and corners each the size of a man's mind. Fortunately or unfortunately, no one knows where the next advance will take place. The new biology is being spoken everywhere and by everyone. The living organism today has as many profiles as viewers, as many dimensions as measuring rods. Its image is an image of adventure.

Perhaps, youth's alienation from science is a problem for science itself. Surely some explanation may be found in the socio-psychological area for the recent discovery that no one likes mathematics any more, for the fear that seems to pervade our high schools that science is 'hard'. Perhaps some of the antagonism arises from the feeling that modern science is too materialistic and opposed to humanism. If so, we have returned to home base, for we are back to the problem with which we started this book. Can this gap be bridged between science and humanism? Can science, and particularly biology, make a meaningful contribution to culture? To a large extent, these are questions for the future. Let us look then at our science of biology and see if we can divine where it is destined to lead us. What will be biology's contribution to the future community of men?

## To the Future, Where Science and Mankind Must Meet

In attempting to speculate on the future course of biological thought, one is suddenly struck with the almost incredible fact that modern biology has been a going concern for only about a hundred years. And what we have called 'the new biology', the vigorous and dynamic science of today, has actually come into being only since the Second World War. In this brief decade, we have witnessed: the demonstration of genetic recombination in viruses; the first synthesis of a hormone; the discovery of co-enzyme A, the key to the processes by which biological compounds are synthesized; the synthesis of artificial RNA; the demonstration that virus nucleic acid by itself is infective; the production of the giant electronic computers; the development of modern information and communication theory – all of this in the last ten or twelve years. What then, in the name of Miserere, may we expect in the next ten years, in the next century and millennium? For the world has this and much more to look forward to. Our new biology is an infant with a future unimaginable.

We will only mention in passing the more obvious inevitabilities of biological progress: birth control, food production, medical progress, domestication of animals (it has already been suggested that we train monkeys to pick crops). These will be the by-products of increasing knowledge and must surely lie ahead.

One of the great concerns of the biology of the future will be with the problem of ageing. As we gradually prolong human life, we must simultaneously make old age more than mere dilapidated despair. In time, human life may go on indefinitely, for I can see no reason why death, in the nature of things, need be inevitable. The great complexity of living systems numerically increases their areas of vulnerability, increasing also the probability that time and circumstance will eventually overthrow the balance at one point or another. In multicellular organisms, where all cells live by a measure of mutual dependence, the smallest break in the dyke upsets the community equilibrium causing death or a state of senescence, that unravelling which is ultimately destined to exceed the tolerable limits within which life can exist. Could this probability be lowered, life would be lengthened, persisting on until it ended on the shoals of the next probability metric. Medicine has done just this for man. Free of the diseases of childhood, he now lives to die of something else. Freed of today's diseases of old age, man might live as long as the giant sequoias. Were all disease and want eliminated, life expectancy would depend almost entirely on the accident (or suicide) rate. In principle, the probability of fatal adversity could be almost zero (that is, if we restrict the scope of the future to our own neighbourhood in the time scale – say, the next $10^{12}$ years). In reality, it could never be exactly zero. Among other things, there is a limit in the supply of food and the materials which conceivably could be turned into food. This would, at least, prevent immortality from being widely practised.

As might be anticipated, scientific thought about senescence has been so laden down with metaphysical and verbal confusion, the area will serve as yet another illustration of how intellectual slums develop. Despite the theoretical and practical importance of understanding senescence, almost no work has been done in the field for twenty years. Alex Comfort lamented this situation in a recent review and commented on the close connexion of ageing with human fears and aspirations, all of which is reflected in theories that attempt to invoke a 'general principle of senescence' for all living organisms and use phrases like 'ageing is the price of multicellular existence' and 'it results from the exhaustion induced by reproduction'. Such views are all mixed in with philosophical meditations on the necessity and meaning of decline and death.

Most of the conceptual smog results from the elementary error of reasoning by inappropriate analogy. The word 'ageing' immediately suggests analogous behaviour in inanimate systems. We hear talk of 'old' red blood cells and 'old' tissue colloids, presumably meaning cells and colloids produced by an 'old' organism and implying that they are as deteriorated as 'old' machines. The error is apparent. As Comfort explains:

The difference between an old cart and an old horse are self-evident: the cart consists of its original material and has never possessed the potentiality of being self-maintaining against wear; the horse contains few or none of its original materials and has for some twenty years been substantially self-repairing, but is losing that power.

'Senescence', in fact, is a generic term for those processes in certain organisms which lead to a decreasing power of homeostasis with increasing chronological age. Decreasing homeostasis with increasing age may have different causes in different phyla. There appears to be no single or 'inherent' process to explain all types of senescence. Though a certain life span is a characteristic of each species, we do not yet know what this means. Conceivably, each species is transmitting from generation to generation an adverse trait which waits to act until the Biblical span is done and the young have been born. This would determine the life span. Obviously, extinction would occur if it acted before a new generation could appear.

The death of organism, of course, ends only one life, not living – life goes on in surviving individuals. Should the environment be altered importantly, *all* individuals could perish at once, or one by one. In a species or society, mass senescence could occur and total death follow. This is extinction. To date, the voids left by the departed millions of extinct forms have been filled by other species and life has gone on. But I see no reason why a major event could not end all life. Unless we have managed to escape into space, the ultimate denouement that is so lugubriously predicted for the earth by sacred and profane alike will be preceded by millions of years of biological senescence. And it is abundantly clear that this process will be greatly accelerated if the background radiation is even slightly increased by the atmospheric pollutions of men who are not primarily interested in the welfare of future generations. Modern war would, at least, bring a livelier finale.

Will the biologist someday synthesize a living organism? I dearly hope so, if only to bring peace of mind and eternal rest to those writers of science fiction, from the author of Frankenstein on down, who seem morbidly preoccupied with this possibility. In view of what we have said about 'life', the synthesis of a living organism may or may not make a fundamental contribution to our understanding. But it surely will not have metaphysical significance except to those who prefer to see it that way. In this sense, it will be rather like aviation's 'breaking the sound barrier'. Once it happened, it became a routine matter. That this, too, will one day happen, I have no doubt. I do doubt, however, that it will become the preferred method of creating life.

In thinking of the future, one comes to realize that biology is destined to have its greatest impact in another realm. This prediction is strengthened by the striking parallels which may be drawn between the history of physics and that of biology. Both sciences had first to find their elementary units – in physics, the atom, in biology, the cell. In Darwin, biology had its Newton, for both gave their science great unifying theories. And, in modern genetics, in whose methodology mutation plays such a large part, we have an analogy to the nuclear physicist's approach to the particles of the atom. For he sees them only as an indirect result of having blasted them with other particles of radiation. What we seek now is that something in biology which will parallel the impact of modern physics upon philosophy. True, Darwinism has already swept into the arena of culture; but for the purposes of our argument, we will set this opposite the philosophy of mechanism that emerged from seventeenth-century physics. No, the new biology has not yet reached out to touch the philosophical balance. I believe, however, that it is now about to – and the questions it will influence will be those concerned with human behaviour and ethical values.

The fragments which together make a possible basis for this belief can be seen in several places. Philosophers have long tussled with the problem of human values, and it is widely believed by analytical thinkers that it is not possible for science to tell us what is right and good, how we *ought* to behave. Science is considered to be ethically neutral: it can tell you how to get what you want but not what you ought to want. This view, I believe, is open to challenge, both on philosophical grounds and on the grounds of what I feel to be a reasonable appraisal of biology's future prospects. I will not presume to discuss the philosophical aspects of ethical theory, except to record my respect for the writings of men like Charles Stevenson and Paul Edwards, who have not been intimidated by the more intractable varieties of logical empiricism. Stevenson, for example, developed the so-called emotive theory of ethics which, in a superficial word, holds that moral behaviour is related to one's own psychological and emotional attitudes and patterns, and that ethical words, therefore, serve both emotional and descriptive purposes. And when experience shows that such and such a property is regularly associated with a 'value attitude', this property comes to serve as a sign of value. While this is not a declaration that ethics is a branch of psychology, it does place ethical decisions within the purview of emotional phenomena.

Next, we note a recent discussion by Priscilla Robertson in which reference is made to three new scientific studies by distinguished biologists who have attempted – apparently successfully – a direct *empirical* attack on the problems of value. Thus, she quotes the work of the psychopathologist Kurt Goldstein, who believes that the soundly functioning human brain involves biological behaviour patterns which have always been termed 'moral values' from other points of view; the British psychologist Money-Kyrle similarly has shown that soundly functioning perceptions lead to reparative consciences, and thus to kindness as well as creativity; and the anthropologist LaBarre, who finds in family love a steady support for human society.

And, finally, we have the unmatched studies of Charles Morris, who, by ingeniously designed questionnaires, empirically examined the life-orientations and preferred value conceptions of many individuals from widely differing cultural backgrounds. Among other things, Morris presents impressive evidence that some of the value dimensions are readily recognizable at the level of organism. Using Sheldon's somatotypes as a biological variable, he shows definite relationships between ectomorphy (fragility and 'linearity' in body build) and detachment, between mesomorphy (predominance of muscle and bone) and dominance through action, and between endomorphy (roundness and softness throughout the body) and receptivity – all of which showed a striking congruence with value ideas.

With this sort of beginning in the biological approach to the problems of ethics, it seems not a very large jump to a future in which neurophysiology will have finally achieved a deeper understanding of the physical basis of mental activity. It is this development to which we may reasonably look for explanations of altruism, goodness, and love in terms of bioelectric circuits! When these things have happened, we will no longer need to concern ourselves with the gap between biology and human culture. For they will then be the same thing.

Who should have imagined that all of this could have come from an ancient sea?

## Second Prologue

And thus we have made the great circle. In human values, we find the product of human needs and desires. In short, we find the essence of humanity, whose embodiment is culture.

We have seen also that neither culture nor science is omnipotent. And if one of these is to be our 'father', it is the task of maturity to reduce him to human dimensions. For human dimensions are not small. Neither are they Promethean except in our wishes.

What we must conclude, then, is that nowhere will we find the Answer. It is not science rampant on a field of analytical philosophers, since science ultimately must rest upon faith – faith in causality or induction or the accessibility of the universe to understanding. But this is not the same as religious faith, for the faith of the scientist consists in what he or anyone else *has to believe* if he wishes to predict or control the course of experience.

Moreover, we must never forget in our enlightenment what lies just beneath the clean surface of enlightenment. There are our feelings, passions, drives, and vulnerabilities, those things which make human existence eternally precarious and potentially tragic – and which continue to keep alive the human search for certainty despite our knowledge that the search must fail.

The human problem, thus, would seem to be the art of avoiding the inevitable consequence of a paternal creed: the surrender of intelligence in the purchase of emotional security – or, in a word, infantilism. For no human institution, not culture, science, history, or the holy hegemony, is going to take care of man. Man, I'm afraid, is going to have to take care of himself.

Realizing this should not strike us rudderless. It should make us band together in strength, in wholeness, in manly purpose. Ambiguity will be our shibboleth and responsibility our creed. Man is capable of these things. As he stands on the seashore, at the edge of a new tomorrow, in control of the energy of the atom, in possession of the exciting knowledge that he is part of wonderful nature, he must realize that it is now time to stick out the chin. Man has already done much, but it is dawn, not midnight, and, in the gathering light, he looks magnificent.

LIST OF BOOKS, ARTICLES, AND
MEMOIRS QUOTED OR CITED
IN THE TEXT

# LIST OF BOOKS, ARTICLES, AND MEMOIRS QUOTED OR CITED IN THE TEXT

ARBER, A.   *The Mind and the Eye*. C.U.P., 1954.

BACON, F.   *Advancement of Learning*. London, 1605.

BAHM, A.   'Teleological Arguments.' *Scientific Monthly*. Vol. 58, 1944.

BELLO, F.   'The Young Scientists.' *Fortune*. Vol. 10, 1954.

BERGSON, H.   *Matter and Memory*. London (Allen & Unwin), 1919.

BERNAL, J. D.   'The Origin of Life.' *New Biology*. Vol. 16, 1954.

BEUTNER, R.   *Life's Beginning on Earth*. Baltimore (Williams & Wilkins), 1938.

BLANSHARD, B.   'The New Philosophy of Analysis.' *Proceedings of the American Philosophical Society*. Vol. 96, 1952.

BLUM, H.   *Time's Arrow and Evolution*. Princeton, 1951.

BORING, E.   'Psychological Factors in the Scientific Process.' *American Scientist*, Vol. 42, 1954.

BOYLE, R.   *The Sceptical Chymist*. O.U.P., 1680.

BRIDGMAN, P. W.   *The Logic of Modern Physics*, New York (Macmillan), 1927.

BRINTON, C.   *Ideas and Men*. New York (Prentice-Hall), 1950.

BROAD, C. D.   *Scientific Thought*. New York (Harcourt, Brace), 1923.

BRONOWSKI, J.   'The Educated Man in 1984.' *Science*. Vol. 123, 1956.

CAJORI, F.   *Sir Isaac Newton's Mathematical Principles of Natural Philosophy and His System of the World* (A. Motte trans.). California, Berkley, 1954.

CALVIN, M.   'Chemical Evolution and the Origin of Life.' *American Scientist*. Vol. 44, 1956.

CAMERON, G. R.   *The Pathology of the Cell*. Springfield (Thomas), 1951.

CANNON, W.   *The Wisdom of the Body*. New York (Norton), 1932.

CASTIGLIONE, A.   *A History of Medicine*. New York (Knopf), 1941.

COHEN, M.   *Studies in Philosophy and Science*. New York (Holt), 1949.

COMFORT, A.   'Biological Aspects of Senescence.' *Biological Reviews*. Vol. 29, 1954.

CONKLIN, E.   'Predecessors of Schleiden and Schwann.' *Biological Symposia*. Vol. 1, 1940.

# List of Books, etc., Quoted or Cited in the Text

DAMPIER, W. C. *A History of Science and Its Relations with Philosophy and Religion.* 4th ed. C.U.P., 1949.

DANTZIG, T. *Number, the Language of Science.* 4th ed. New York (Macmillan), 1954.

DARWIN, C. *The Origin of Species.* New York (Random House ed.), 1936.

DARWIN, C. G. *The Next Million Years.* New York (Doubleday), 1953.

DE KRUIF, P. *Microbe Hunters.* New York (Harcourt, Brace), 1926.

DESCARTES, R. *Philosophical Works.* C.U.P., 1911.

DEWAR, D., and SHELTON, H. *Is Evolution Proved?* London (Hollis & Carter), 1947.

DOBZHANSKY, T. 'A Comment on the Discussion of Genetics by His Holiness, Pius XII.' *Science.* Vol. 118, 1953.

DRIESCH, H. *History and Theory of Vitalism.* New York (Macmillan), 1914.

DUBOS, R. *Louis Pasteur, Free-Lance of Science.* Boston (Little, Brown), 1950.

DU NOÜY, L. *Human Destiny.* Toronto (Longmans), 1947.

EDITORIAL. 'Some Limits to Popular Science.' *Endeavour*, Vol. 59, 1956.

EDWARDS, P. *The Logic of Moral Discourse.* Glencoe, Ill. (Free Press), 1955.

EINSTEIN, A. 'On the Method of Theoretical Physics.' *Philosophy of Science.* Vol. 1, 1934.

EINSTEIN, A. *The Meaning of Relativity.* 5th ed. Princeton, 1955.

EISELEY, L. C. 'Fossil Man,' *Scientific American.* Vol. 189, 1953.

EVANS, E. J. *Biochemical Studies of Bacterial Viruses.* Chicago, 1952.

FEIGL, H. 'Logical Empiricism.' From *Twentieth Century Philosophy*, D. D. Runes, ed. New York (Philosophical Library), 1943.

FEIGL, H. 'The Mind-Body Problem in the Development of Logical Empiricism.' *Revue Internationale de Philosophie.* Vol. 4, 1950.

FRAZER, J. G. *The Golden Bough.* 3rd ed. London (Macmillan), 1911–26.

GAMOW, G. *Biography of the Earth.* New York (Viking), 1941.

GERARD, R. 'The Biological Roots of Psychiatry.' *American Journal of Psychiatry.* Vol. 112, 1955.

GERR, S. 'Language and Science.' *Philosophy of Science.* Vol. 9, 1942.

GHISELIN, B. *The Creative Process.* California, Los Angeles, 1952.

GLASS, B. 'The Long Neglect of a Scientific Discovery: Mendel's

# List of Books, etc., Quoted or Cited in the Text

Laws of Inheritance.' In *Studies in Intellectual History*. Baltimore (Hopkins), 1953.

GOLDSCHMIDT, R. 'Evolution as Viewed by One Geneticist.' *American Scientist*. Vol. 40, 1952.

GOLDSCHMIDT, R. *Understanding Heredity*. New York (Wiley), 1952.

GRANT, M. ' "Proof" Again.' *The Humanist*. Vol. 16, 1956.

GRÜNBAUM, A. 'Modern Science and Refutation of the Paradoxes of Zeno.' *Scientific Monthly*. Vol. 81, 1955.

HALDANE, J. B. S. *A Banned Broadcast and Other Essays*. London (Chatto & Windus), 1946.

HALDANE, J. B. S. *Science and Human Life*. New York (Harper), 1933.

HALDANE, J. S. *The Sciences and Philosophy*. New York (Doubleday), 1929.

HARROD, R. F. *Foundations of Inductive Logic*. New York (Harcourt, Brace), 1957.

HARVEY, W. *On the Motion of the Heart and Blood in Animals*. London ed. 1908.

HEMPEL, C. 'A Logical Appraisal of Operationism.' *Scientific Monthly*. Vol. 79, 1954.

HERTWIG, O. *The Cell and the Tissue*. (Campbell trans.) London, 1895.

HOGBEN, L. *The Nature of Living Matter*. New York (Knopf), 1931.

HOOKE, R. *The Micrographia*. London, 1665.

HOOTON, E. *Up from the Ape*. New York (Macmillan), 1946.

HOROWITZ, N. 'On the Evolution of Biochemical Syntheses.' *Proceedings of the National Academy of Sciences*. Vol. 31, 1945.

HUXLEY, J. *Heredity East and West*. New York (Schuman), 1949.

HUXLEY, J. *Evolution: The Modern Synthesis*. New York (Harper), 1943.

HUXLEY, J. *Man Stands Alone*. New York (Harper), 1940.

HUXLEY, T. 'Biogenesis and Abiogenesis'and 'Yeast.' In *Discourses Biological and Geological*. New York (Appleton), 1898.

HUXLEY, T. *Man's Place in Nature*. New York (Appleton ed.), 1896.

JEANS, J. *The Mysterious Universe*. New York (Cambridge), 1937.

JEFFREYS, H. *Theory of Probability*. O.U.P., 1939.

JOAD, C. E. M. *Guide to Philosophy*. (Gollancz), 1946.

KARLING, J. S. 'Schleiden's Contribution to the Cell Theory.' *Biological Symposia*. Vol. 1, 1940.

# List of Books, etc., Quoted or Cited in the Text

KILLIAN, J. R., JR. 'The Shortage Re-examined.' *American Scientist.* Vol. 44, 1956.

KUBIE, L. 'Some Unsolved Problems of the Scientific Career.' *American Scientist.* Vol. 41, 1953.

LEWIS, C. I. 'Experience and Meaning.' *Philosophical Review.* Vol. 43, 1934.

LOCKE, J. *An Essay Concerning Human Understanding.* London, 1690.

LURIA, S. 'Bacteriophage: An Essay on Virus Reproduction.' *Science.* Vol. 111, 1950.

LURIA, S. *General Virology.* New York (Wiley), 1953.

MC CULLOCH, W. S. 'Mysterium Iniquitatis of Sinful Man Aspiring into the Place of God.' *Scientific Monthly.* Vol. 80, 1955.

MC DOUGALL, W. *The Riddle of Life.* London (Methuen), 1938.

MACH, E. *Science of Mechanics.* (T. McCormack trans.) Open Court, Chicago, 1942.

MACKAY, D. M. 'Mentality in Machines.' *Aristotelian Society, Supplementary Volumes.* Vol. 26, 1952.

MASSERMAN, J. H. 'Faith and Delusion in Psychotherapy.' *American Journal of Psychiatry.* Vol. 110, 1953.

MEDAWAR, P. B. 'Problems of Adaptation.' *New Biology.* Vol 11, 1951.

MONTAGU, M. F. A. 'Vesalius and the Galenists.' *Scientific Monthly.* Vol. 80, 1955.

MORRIS, C. *Varieties of Human Value.* Chicago, 1956.

MULLER, H. J. *The Uses of the Past.* New York (Oxford), 1954.

MULLER, H. J. 'Science in Bondage.' *Science.* Vol. 111, 1951.

MUMFORD, L. *The Condition of Man.* New York (Harcourt, Brace), 1944.

NAGEL, E. 'Mechanistic Explanation and Organismic Biology.' *Philosophy & Phenomenological Research.* Vol. 11, 1951.

NAGEL, E. *Sovereign Reason.* Glencoe, Ill. (Free Press), 1954.

NEEDHAM, J. *Science, Religion, and Reality.* New York (Braziller), 1955.

NEEDHAM, J. *Order and Life.* Yale, New Haven, 1938.

NEWTON, I. *Opticks, or a Treatise on the Reflections, Refractions, Inflections and Colours of Light.* New York (Dover ed.), 1952.

O'MALLEY, C. D., and SAUNDERS, J. B. 'Andreas Vesalius, Imperial Physician.' In *Science, Medicine, and History.* E. Underwood ed. New York (Oxford), 1953.

OPPENHEIMER, J. R.  *The Open Mind*. New York (Simon & Schuster), 1955.

PAGEL, W.  'The Reaction to Aristotle in Seventeenth Century Biological Thought.' In *Science, Medicine, and History*. E. Underwood ed. New York (Oxford), 1953.

PEATTIE, D.  *Green Laurels*. New York (Simon & Schuster), 1936.

PIRIE, N. W.  'The Meaninglessness of the Terms "Life" and "Living." ' In *Perspectives in Biochemistry*. J. Needham and D. Green ed. C.U.P., 1937.

PIRIE, N. W.  'The Origin of Life.' *Discovery*. Vol. 114, 1953.

PIRIE, N. W.  'Vital Blarney.' *New Biology*. Vol. 12, 1953.

RAFFERTY, J. A.  'Mathematical Models in Biological Theory.' *American Scientist*. Vol. 38, 1950.

REICHENBACH, H.  *The Rise of Scientific Philosophy*. California, Los Angeles, 1950.

ROBERTSON, P.  'On Getting Values Out of Science.' *The Humanist*. Vol. 16, 1956.

ROSENBLEUTH, A., WERNER, N., and BIGELOW, J. 'Behaviour, Purpose, and Teleology.' *Philosophy of Science*. Vol. 10, 1943.

ROYAL SOCIETY OF LONDON.  *Newton Tercentenary Celebration*. C.U.P., 1947.

RUSSELL, B.  *Human Knowledge: Its Scope and Limits*. New York (Simon & Schuster), 1948.

RUSSELL, E. S.  *Form and Function*. New York (Dutton), 1917.

SARTON, G.  *Galen of Pergamon*. Kansas, Lawrence, 1954.

SCHLICK, M.  'Meaning and Verification.' *Philosophical Review*. Vol. 45, 1936.

SELYE, H.  'On the Nature of Disease.' *Texas Reports on Biology & Medicine*. Vol. 12, 1954.

SHERRINGTON, C. S.  *Man on His Nature*. C.U.P., 1951.

SHERRINGTON, C. S.  *The Endeavour of Jean Fernel*. C.U.P., 1946.

SHULL, A. F.  *Evolution*. 2nd ed. New York (McGraw-Hill), 1951.

SIMPSON, G. G.  'Evolutionary Determinism and the Fossil Record.' *Scientific Monthly*. Vol. 71, 1950.

SIMPSON, G. G.  *The Major Features of Evolution*. New York (Columbia), 1953.

SIMPSON, G. G.  *The Meaning of Evolution*. New Haven (Yale), 1949.

SINGER, C.  *A History of Biology*. New York (Schuman), 1950.

SINNOTT, E. W.  *The Biology of the Spirit*. New York (Viking), 1955.

# List of Books, etc., Quoted or Cited in the Text

SMITH, H. W.  *From Fish to Philosopher*. Boston (Little, Brown), 1953.

SMITH, H. W.  *Man and His Gods*. Boston (Little, Brown), 1952.

SMITH, J. L. B.  'The Second Coelacanth.' *Nature*. Vol. 171, 1953.

SMITH, W. A.  *Ancient Education*. New York (Philosophical Library), 1955.

SMUTS, J. C.  *Holism and Evolution*. London (Macmillan), 1926.

SOMMERHOFF, G.  *Analytical Biology*. O.U.P., 1950.

STEVENSON, C. L.  *Ethics and Language*. New Haven (Yale), 1943.

STRAUS, W., JR.  'The Great Piltdown Hoax.' *Science*. Vol. 119, 1954.

STUNKARD, H. W.  'Freedom, Bondage, and the Welfare State.' *Science*. Vol. 121, 1955.

SULLIVAN, J. W. N.  *The Limitations of Science*. New York (Viking), 1933.

TARSKI, A. 'The Semantic Conception of Truth and the Foundations of Semantics.' *Philosophy & Phenomenological Research*. Vol. 4, 1944.

TOYNBEE, A.  'Poetic Truth and Scientific Truth in the Light of History.' *International Journal of Psychoanalysis*. Vol. 30, 1949.

UREY, H. C.  'On the Early Chemical History of the Earth and the Origin of Life.' *Proceedings of the National Academy of Sciences*. Vol. 38, 1952.

VAN HOUWENSFELT, S.  *Darwinism Has Deceived Humanity*. London (Routledge), 1931.

VESALIUS, A.  *De humani corporis fabrica*. Basel, 1543.

WADDINGTON, C. H.  'How Do Cells Differentiate?' *Scientific American*. Vol. 189, 1953.

WALD, G.  'The Origin of Life.' *Scientific American*. Vol. 191, 1954.

WALTER, W. G.  'The Imitation of Mentality.' *Nature*. Vol. 177, 1956.

WEINER, J., OAKLEY, K., and CLARK, W.  *Bull. Brit. Mus.* (*Nat. Hist.*), *Geol.* Vol. 2, 1953.

WEISS, P.  'Differential Growth.' In *The Chemistry and Physiology of Growth*. A. Parpart ed. Princeton, 1949.

WELLS, H. G., HUXLEY, J., and WELLS, G. P.  *The Science of Life*. New York (Doubleday), 1935.

WESTERMARCK, E.  *The Origin and Development of Moral Ideas*. London (Macmillan), 1908.

WHITEHEAD, A. N.  *Science and the Modern World*. New York (Macmillan), 1947.

# List of Books, etc., Quoted or Cited in the Text

WIENER, N.    *Cybernetics*. New York (Wiley), 1948.

WIGHTMAN, W. P. D.    *The Growth of Scientific Ideals*. New Haven (Yale), 1953.

WILLIAMS, R. C.    'The Shapes and Sizes of Purified Viruses as Determined by Electron Microscopy.' *Cold Spring Harbour Symposia on Quantitative Biology*. Vol. 18, 1953.

WOODGER, J. H.    *Biological Principles: A Critical Study*. New York (Harcourt, Brace), 1929.

WOODGER, J. H.    *Biology and Language*. C.U.P., 1952.

WOODRUFF, L.    'Microscopy before the 19th Century.' *Biological Symposia*. Vol. 1, 1940.

ZIRKLE, C.    'Citation of Fraudulent Data.' *Science*. Vol. 120, 1954.

ZIRKLE, C.    'The Knowledge of Heredity before 1900.' In *Genetics in the 20th Century*. L. C. Dunn ed. New York (Macmillan), 1951.

301

# INDEX

# INDEX

# Index

309

# Index

# Index

*Some more Pelicans are described
on the following pages*

*John Maynard Smith*

# THE THEORY OF EVOLUTION

A433

All living plants and animals, including man, are the modified descendants of one or a few simple living things. A hundred years ago Darwin and Wallace, in their theory of natural selection, or the survival of the fittest, explained how evolution could have happened, in terms of processes known to take place today. This book describes how their theory has been confirmed, but at the same time transformed, by recent research, and in particular by the discovery of the laws of inheritance.

After stating the problem and Darwin's answer to it, the author describes what can be learnt from laboratory experiments, and then gives the evidence that evolutionary changes are taking place today in wild populations. Later chapters discuss the origins of species, and the special problems which arise in studying the origins of major groups of animals and plants. The book ends by contrasting evolutionary and historical changes, and considers the relative importance of the two processes in the origin and future development of human society.

*J. Bronowski*

# THE COMMON SENSE OF SCIENCE
### A507

We are surrounded by the products of science – washing machines, bottles of aspirin, public opinion surveys; and most people take them very much for granted. Only slowly is the layman becoming aware of the new methods of thought which lie behind the discoveries of science.

A great deal of our ignorance is a result of the jargon that surrounds science. It is Dr Bronowski's achievement in this book to translate science into a language which can be understood by an intelligent person with no scientific knowledge.

He shows that the reader can approach scientific thought through the interests he already possesses – in the everyday affairs of his social life, in history or literature. In this way, Dr Bronowski makes it possible for the layman to comprehend science by tracing its outlook within his own culture.

By Patricia Briggs

*The Mercy Thompson novels*

Moon Called
Blood Bound
Iron Kissed
Bone Crossed
Silver Borne
River Marked
Frost Burned ✓
Night Broken
Fire Touched
Silence Fallen

*The Alpha and Omega novels*

Cry Wolf
Hunting Ground
Fair Game
Dead Heat

Aralorn: Masques and Wolfsb

MOON

...aking with the need to run, I forced mysel...
...n. I waited for him to jump up and grab m...
...ways do in the late-night movies, but he...
...elling of blood and adrenaline.

...A trail of liquid stretched out behind hir...
...ar that had blown a radiator hose and slur...
...r the road – but the liquid that glistened u...
...p was blood.

...Only then did it occur to me that I d...
...m of his heart or the whisper of his br...
...heard a car start up and took my eyes...
...ime to see the black SUV squeal out o...
...turn toward me.

# MOON CALLED

## PATRICIA BRIGGS

www.orbitbooks.net

ORBIT

First published in the United States in 2006 by Ace,
Penguin Group (USA) Inc.
First published in Great Britain in 2008 by Orbit
This paperback edition published in 2011 by Orbit

5 7 9 11 12 10 8 6

A CIP catalogue record for this book
is available from the British Library.

ISBN 978-0-356-50058-4

Typeset in Garamond 3 by Palimpsest Book Production Limited,
Falkirk, Stirlingshire
Printed and bound Great Britain by
Clays Ltd, St Ives plc

Papers used by Orbit are from well-managed forests
and other responsible sources.

This book is for

*Kaye's mom, Almeda Brown Christensen, who likes my books;*
*Alice and Bill Rieckman who like horses as much as I do;*
*and in memory of Floyd 'Buck' Buckner, a good man.*

# ACKNOWLEDGMENTS

As always, this book would not have happened without my personal editorial staff: Michael and Collin Briggs, Michael Enzweiler (who also draws the maps), Jeanne Matteucci, Ginny Mohl, Anne Peters, and Kaye Roberson. I'd also like to thank my terrific editor at Ace, Anne Sowards, and my agent, Linn Prentis. Bob Briggs answered a ton of questions about Montana wildlife and wolves. Finally, Mercedes owes a special debt to Buck, Scott, Dale, Brady, Jason, and all the folks who've worked on our VWs over the years. Thanks, everyone. Any mistakes found in this book are mine.

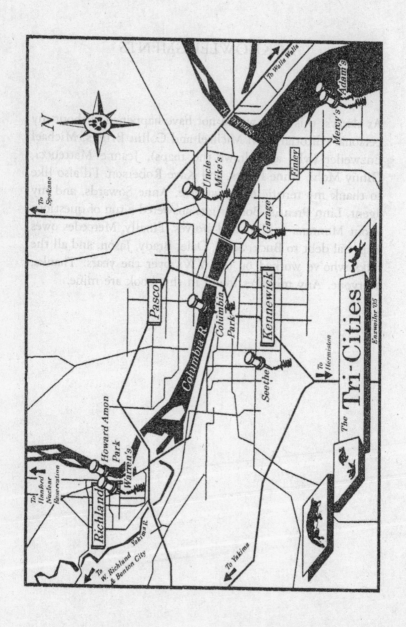

**1**

I didn't realize he was a werewolf at first. My nose isn't at its best when surrounded by axle grease and burnt oil – and it's not like there are a lot of stray werewolves running around. So when someone made a polite noise near my feet to get my attention I thought he was a customer.

I was burrowed under the engine compartment of a Jetta, settling a rebuilt transmission into its new home. One of the drawbacks in running a one-woman garage was that I had to stop and start every time the phone rang or a customer stopped by. It made me grumpy – which isn't a good way to deal with customers. My faithful office boy and tool rustler had gone off to college, and I hadn't replaced him yet – it's hard to find someone who will do all the jobs I don't want to.

'Be with you in a sec,' I said, trying not to sound snappish. I do my best not to scare off my customers if I can help it.

Transmission jacks be damned, the only way to get a transmission into an old Jetta is with muscle. Sometimes being a female is useful in my line of work – my hands are smaller so I can get them places a man can't. However, even weightlifting and karate can't make me as strong as a strong man. Usually leverage can compensate, but sometimes there's no substitute for muscle, and I had just barely enough to get the job done.

Grunting with effort, I held the transmission where it belonged with my knees and one hand. With the other I slipped the first bolt in and tightened it. I wasn't finished,

1

but the transmission would stay where it was while I dealt with my customer.

I took a deep breath and smiled once brightly for practice before I rolled out from under the car. I snagged a rag to wipe the oil off my hands, and said, 'Can I help you?' before I got a good enough look at the boy to see he wasn't a customer – though he certainly looked as though *someone* ought to help him.

The knees of his jeans were ripped out and stained with old blood and dirt. Over a dirty tee, he wore a too-small flannel shirt – inadequate clothing for November in eastern Washington.

He looked gaunt, as though he'd been a while without food. My nose told me, even over the smell of gasoline, oil, and antifreeze permeating the garage, that it had been an equally long time since he'd seen a shower. And, under the dirt, sweat, and old fear, was the distinctive scent of werewolf.

'I was wondering if you had some work I could do?' he asked hesitantly. 'Not a real job, ma'am. Just a few hours' work.'

I could smell his anxiety before it was drowned out by a rush of adrenaline when I didn't immediately refuse. His words sped up until they crashed into one another. 'A job would be okay, too, but I don't have a social security card, so it would have to be cash under the table.'

Most of the people who come around looking for cash work are illegals trying to tide themselves over between harvest and planting season. This boy was white-bread American – except the part about being a werewolf – with chestnut hair and brown eyes. He was tall enough to be eighteen, I supposed, but my instincts, which are pretty good, pinned his age closer to fifteen. His shoulders were wide but bony, and his hands were a little large, as if he still

2

had some growing to do before he grew into the man he would be.

'I'm strong,' he said. 'I don't know a lot about fixing cars, but I used to help my uncle keep his Bug running.'

I believed he was strong: werewolves are. As soon as I had picked up the distinctive musk-and-mint scent, I'd had a nervous urge to drive him out of my territory. However, not being a werewolf, I control my instincts – I'm not controlled by them. Then, too, the boy, shivering slightly in the damp November weather, roused other, stronger instincts.

It is my own private policy not to break the law. I drive the speed limit, keep my cars insured, pay a little more tax to the feds than I have to. I've given away a twenty or two to people who'd asked, but never hired someone who couldn't appear on my payroll. There was also the problem of his being a werewolf, and a new one at that, if I was any judge. The young ones have less control of their wolves than others.

He hadn't commented on how odd it was to see a woman mechanic. Sure, he'd probably been watching me for a while, long enough to get used to the idea – but, still, he hadn't said anything, and that won him points. But not enough points for what I was about to do.

He rubbed his hands together and blew on them to warm up his fingers, which were red with chill.

'All right,' I said, slowly. It was not the wisest answer, but, watching his slow shivers, it was the only one I could give. 'We'll see how it works.

'There's a laundry room and a shower back through that door.' I pointed to the door at the back of the shop. 'My last assistant left some of his old work coveralls. You'll find them hanging on the hooks in the laundry room. If you want to shower and put those on, you can run the clothes you're wearing through the washer. There's a fridge in the laundry room with a ham sandwich and some pop. Eat, then come back out when you're ready.'

I put a little force behind the 'eat': I wasn't going to work with a hungry werewolf, not even almost two weeks from full moon. Some people will tell you werewolves can only shapechange under a full moon, but people also say there's no such things as ghosts. He heard the command and stiffened, raising his eyes to meet mine.

After a moment he mumbled a thank-you and walked through the door, shutting it gently behind him. I let out the breath I'd been holding. I knew better than to give orders to a werewolf – it's that whole dominance reflex thing.

Werewolves' instincts are inconvenient – that's why they don't tend to live long. Those same instincts are the reason their wild brothers lost to civilization while the coyotes were thriving, even in urban areas like Los Angeles.

The coyotes are *my* brothers. Oh, I'm not a werecoyote – if there even is such a thing. I am a walker.

The term is derived from 'skinwalker,' a witch of the Southwest Indian tribes who uses a skin to turn into a coyote or some other animal and goes around causing disease and death. The white settlers incorrectly used the term for all the native shapechangers and the name stuck. We are hardly in a position to object – even if we came out in public like the lesser of the fae did, there aren't enough of us to be worth a fuss.

I didn't think the boy had known what I was, or he'd never have been able to turn his back on me, another predator, and go through the door to shower and change. Wolves may have a very good sense of smell, but the garage was full of odd odors, and I doubted he'd ever smelled someone like me in his life.

'You just hire a replacement for Tad?'

I turned and watched Tony come in from outside through

4

the open bay doors, where he'd evidently been lurking and watching the byplay between the boy and me. Tony was good at that – it was his job.

His black hair was slicked back and tied into a short ponytail and he was clean-shaven. His right ear, I noticed, was pierced four times and held three small hoops and a diamond stud. He'd added two since last time I'd seen him. In a hooded sweatshirt unzipped to display a thin tee that showed the results of all the hours he spent in a gym, he looked like a recruitment poster for one of the local Hispanic gangs.

'We're negotiating,' I said. 'Just temporary so far. Are you working?'

'Nope. They gave me the day off for good behavior.' He was still focused on my new employee, though, because he said, 'I've seen him around the past few days. He seems okay – runaway maybe.' Okay meant no drugs or violence, the last was reassuring.

When I started working at the garage about nine years ago, Tony had been running a little pawnshop around the corner. Since it had the nearest soft drink machine, I saw him fairly often. After a while the pawnshop passed on to different hands. I didn't think much of it until I smelled him standing on a street corner with a sign that said WILL WORK FOR FOOD.

I say smelled him, because the hollow-eyed kid holding the sign didn't look much like the low-key, cheerful, middle-aged man who had run the pawnshop. Startled, I'd greeted him by the name I'd known him by. The kid just looked at me like I was crazy, but the next morning Tony was waiting at my shop. That's when he told me what he did for a living – I hadn't even known a place the size of the Tri-Cities would have undercover cops.

He'd started dropping by the shop every once in a while,

after that. At first he'd come in a new guise each time. The Tri-Cities aren't that big, and my garage is on the edge of an area that's about as close as Kennewick comes to having a high-crime district. So it was possible he just came by when he was assigned to the area, but I soon decided the real reason was he was bothered I'd recognized him. I could hardly tell him I'd just smelled him, could I?

His mother was Italian and his father Venezuelan, and the genetic mix had given him features and skin tone that allowed him to pass as anything from Mexican to African-American. He could still pass for eighteen when he needed to, though he must be several years older than me — thirty-three or so. He spoke Spanish fluently and could use a half dozen different accents to flavor his English.

All of those attributes had led him to undercover work, but what really made him good was his body language. He could stride with the hip-swaggering walk common to handsome young Hispanic males, or shuffle around with the nervous energy of a drug addict.

After a while, he accepted I could see through disguises that fooled his boss and, he claimed, his own mother, but by then we were friends. He continued to drop in for a cup of coffee or hot chocolate and a friendly chat when he was around.

'You look very young and macho,' I said. 'Are the earrings a new look for KPD? Pasco police have two earrings, so Kennewick cops must have four?'

He grinned at me, and it made him look both older and more innocent. 'I've been working in Seattle for the past few months,' he said. 'I've got a new tattoo, too. Fortunately for me it is somewhere my mother will never see it.'

Tony claimed to live in terror of his mother. I'd never met her myself, but he smelled of happiness not fear when he talked of her, so I knew she couldn't be the harridan he described.

6

'What brings you to darken my door?' I asked.

'I came to see if you'd look at a car for a friend of mine,' he said.

'Vee-Dub?'

'Buick.'

My eyebrows climbed in surprise. 'I'll take a look, but I'm not set up for American cars – I don't have the computers. He should take it somewhere they know Buicks.'

'*She's* taken it to three different mechanics – replaced the oxygen sensor, spark plugs, and who knows what else. It's still not right. The last guy told her she needed a new engine, which he could do for twice what the car's worth. She doesn't have much money, but she needs the car.'

'I won't charge her for looking, and if I can't fix it, I'll tell her so.' I had a sudden thought, brought on by the edge of anger I heard in his voice when he talked about her problems. 'Is this *your* lady?'

'She's not my lady,' he protested unconvincingly.

For the past three years he'd had his eye on one of the police dispatchers, a widow with a slew of kids. He'd never done anything about it because he loved his job – and his job, he'd said wistfully, was not conducive to dating, marriage, and kids.

'Tell her to bring it by. If she can leave it for a day or two, I'll see if Zee will come by and take a look at it.' Zee, my former boss, had retired when he sold me the place, but he'd come out once in a while to 'keep his hand in.' He knew more about cars and what made them run than a team of Detroit engineers.

'Thanks, Mercy. You're aces.' He checked his watch. 'I've got to go.'

I waved him off, then went back to the transmission. The car cooperated, as they seldom do, so it didn't take me long. By the time my new help emerged clean and garbed in an

7

old pair of Tad's coveralls, I was starting to put the rest of the car back together. Even the coveralls wouldn't be warm enough outside, but in the shop, with my big space heater going, he should be all right.

He was quick and efficient – he'd obviously spent a few hours under the hood of a car. He didn't stand around watching, but handed me parts before I asked, playing the part of a tool monkey as though it was an accustomed role. Either he was naturally reticent or had learned how to keep his mouth shut because we worked together for a couple of hours mostly in silence. We finished the first car and started on another one before I decided to coax him into talking to me.

'I'm Mercedes,' I said, loosening an alternator bolt. 'What do you want me to call you?'

His eyes lit for a minute. 'Mercedes the Volkswagen mechanic?' His face closed down quickly, and he mumbled, 'Sorry. Bet you've heard that a lot.'

I grinned at him and handed him the bolt I'd taken out and started on the next. 'Yep. But I work on Mercedes, too – anything German-made. Porsche, Audi, BMW, and even the odd Opel or two. Mostly old stuff, out of dealer warranty, though I have the computers for most of the newer ones when they come in.'

I turned my head away from him so I could get a better look at the stubborn second bolt. 'You can call me Mercedes or Mercy, whichever you like. What do you want me to call you?'

I don't like forcing people into a corner where they have to lie to you. If he was a runaway, he probably wouldn't give me a real name, but I needed something better to call him than 'boy' or 'hey, you' if I was going to work with him.

'Call me Mac,' he said after a pause.

The pause was a dead giveaway that it wasn't the name he usually went by. It would do for now.

'Well then, Mac,' I said. 'Would you give the Jetta's owner a call and tell him his car is ready?' I nodded toward the first car we had finished. 'There's an invoice on the printer. His number is on the invoice along with the final cost of the transmission swap. When I get this belt replaced I'll take you to lunch – part of the wages.'

'Okay,' he said, sounding a little lost. He started for the door to the showers but I stopped him. The laundry and shower were in the back of the shop, but the office was on the side of the garage, next to a parking lot customers used.

'The office is straight through the gray door,' I told him. 'There's a cloth next to the phone you can use to hold the receiver so it doesn't get covered with grease.'

I drove home that night and fretted about Mac. I'd paid him for his work in cash and told him he was welcome back. He'd given me a faint smile, tucked the money in a back pocket, and left. I had let him go, knowing that he had nowhere to stay the night because I had no other good options.

I'd have asked him home, but that would have been dangerous for both of us. As little as he seemed to use his nose, eventually he'd figure out what I was – and werewolves, even in human form, do have the strength they're credited with in the old movies. I'm in good shape, and I have a purple belt from the dojo just over the railroad track from my garage, but I'm no match for a werewolf. The boy was too young to have the kind of control he'd need to keep from killing someone his beast would see as a competing predator in his territory.

And then there was my neighbor.

I live in Finley, a rural area about ten minutes from my garage, which is in the older industrial area of Kennewick.

9

My home is a single-wide trailer almost as old as I am that sits in the middle of a couple of fenced acres. There are a lot of small-acreage properties in Finley with trailers or manufactured homes, but along the river there are also mansions like the one my neighbor lives in.

I turned into my drive with a crunch of gravel and stopped the old diesel Rabbit in front of my home. I noticed the cat carrier sitting on my porch as soon as I got out of the car.

Medea gave me a plaintive yowl, but I picked up the note taped to the top of the carrier and read it before I let her out.

*MS THOMPSON*, it said in heavy block letters, *PLEASE KEEP YOUR FELINE OFF MY PROPERTY. IF I SEE IT AGAIN, I WILL EAT IT.*

The note was unsigned.

I undid the latch and lifted the cat up and rubbed my face in her rabbitlike fur.

'Did the mean old werewolf stick the poor kitty in the box and leave her?' I asked.

She smelled like my neighbor, which told me that Adam had spent some time with her on his lap before he'd brought her over here. Most cats don't like werewolves – or walkers like me either. Medea likes everyone, poor old cat, even my grumpy neighbor. Which is why she often ended up in the cat carrier on my porch.

Adam Hauptman, who shared my back fence line, was the Alpha of the local werewolf pack. That there was a were-wolf pack in the Tri-Cities was something of an anomaly because packs usually settle in bigger places where they can hide better, or, rarely, in smaller places they can take over. But werewolves have a tendency to do well in the military and secret government agencies whose names are all acronyms, and the nuclear power plant complex close by the Hanford site had a lot of alphabet agencies involved in it, one way or another.

Why the Alpha werewolf had chosen to buy land right next to me, I suspect, had as much to do with the werewolf's urge to dominate those they see as lesser beings as it did with the superb riverfront view.

He didn't like having my old single-wide bringing down the value of his sprawling adobe edifice – though, as I sometimes pointed out to him, my trailer was already here when he bought his property and built on it. He also took every opportunity to remind me I was only here on his sufferance: a walker being no real match for a werewolf.

In response to these complaints, I bowed my head, spoke respectfully to his face – usually – and pulled the dilapidated old Rabbit I kept for parts out into my back field where it was clearly visible from Adam's bedroom window.

I was almost certain he wouldn't eat my cat, but I'd leave her inside for the next week or so to give the impression I was cowed by his threat. The trick with werewolves is never to confront them straight on.

Medea mewed, purred, and wagged her stub tail when I set her down and filled her food dish. She'd come to me as a stray, and I'd thought for a while that some abusive person had chopped her tail off, but my vet said she was a Manx and born that way. I gave her one last stroke, then went to my fridge to scrounge something for dinner.

'I'd have brought Mac home if I thought Adam would leave him be,' I told her, 'but werewolves don't take to strangers very well. There's all sorts of protocols they insist upon when a new wolf comes into someone else's territory, and something tells me that Mac hasn't petitioned the pack. A werewolf won't freeze to death sleeping outside, however bad the weather. He'll be all right for a little while.'

'Still,' I said, as I got out some leftover spaghetti to nuke, 'if Mac's in trouble, Adam might help him.' It would be better to introduce the subject gently when I knew what the boy's story was.

I ate standing up and rinsed out the dish before curling up on the couch and turning on the TV. Medea yowled and jumped on my lap before the first commercial.

Mac didn't come in the next day. It was a Saturday, and he might not know I worked most every Saturday if there were cars to fix. Maybe he'd moved on.

I hoped Adam or one of his wolves hadn't found him before I'd had a chance to break the news of his presence more gently. The rules that allowed werewolves to live undetected among humankind for centuries tended to have fatal consequences for those who broke them.

I worked until noon, then called to tell the nice young couple that their car was a lost cause. Replacing the engine in it would cost them more than the car was worth. Bad news calls were my least favorite job. When Tad, my old assistant, had been around, I'd made him do them. I hung up almost as depressed as the hapless owners of the shiny, decked-out, well-loved car now destined for a boneyard.

I scrubbed up and got as much of the gunk out from under my nails as was going to come and started in on the never-ending paperwork that had also fallen to Tad. I was glad he'd gotten the scholarship that allowed him to head to the Ivy League college of his choice, but I really missed him. After ten minutes, I decided there was nothing that couldn't be put off until Monday. Hopefully by then I'd have an urgent repair, and I'd be able to put off the paperwork until Tuesday.

I changed into clean jeans and a T-shirt, grabbed my jacket, and headed to O'Leary's for lunch. After lunch I did some desultory grocery shopping and bought a small turkey to share with Medea.

12

My mother called on the cell as I was getting into the car and tried to guilt me into driving up to Portland for Thanksgiving or Christmas. I weaseled my way out of both invitations – I'd had enough of family gatherings in the two years I'd lived with her to last a lifetime.

It's not that they are bad, just the opposite. Curt, my stepfather, is a soft-spoken, no-nonsense sort of person – just the man to balance my mother. I later found out he hadn't known about me until I showed up on his doorstep when I was sixteen. Even so, he opened his house to me without question and treated me as if I were his own.

My mother, Margi, is vivacious and cheerfully flaky. It's not difficult at all envisioning her getting involved with a rodeo rider (like my father) any more than it would be difficult imagining her running off to join the circus. That she is president of her local PTA is far more surprising.

I like my mother and stepfather. I even like all of my half siblings, who had greeted my sudden appearance in their lives with enthusiasm. They all live together in one of those close-knit families that television likes to pretend is normal. I'm very happy to know people like that exist – I just don't belong there.

I visit twice a year so they don't invade my home, and I make certain that it isn't a holiday. Most of my visits are very short. I love them, but I love them better at a distance.

By the time I hung up, I felt guilty and blue. I drove home, put the turkey in the fridge to thaw, and fed the cat. When cleaning the fridge didn't help my mood, though I'm not sure why I expected it to, I got back in the car and drove out to the Hanford Reach.

I don't go out to the Reach often. There are closer places to run, or, if I feel like driving, the Blue Mountains aren't too far away. But sometimes my soul craves the arid, desolate space of the preserve – especially after I get through talking with my mother.

I parked the car and walked for a while until I was reasonably certain there was no one around. Then I took off my clothes and put them in the small daypack and shifted.

Werewolves can take as much as fifteen minutes to shift shape – and shifting is painful for them, which is something to keep in mind. Werewolves aren't the most friendly animals anyway, but if they've just shifted, it's a good policy to leave them alone for a while.

Walkers' shifting – at least my shifting, because I don't know any other walkers – is quick and painless. One moment I'm a person and the next a coyote: pure magic. I just step from one form into the next.

I rubbed my nose against my foreleg to take away the last tingle of the change. It always takes a moment to adjust to moving on four feet instead of two. I know, because I looked it up, that coyotes have different eyesight than humans, but mine is pretty much the same in either form. My hearing picks up a little and so does my sense of smell, though even in human form I've got better senses than most.

I picked up the backpack, now stuffed with my clothes, and left it under a bunch of scrub. Then I shed the ephemera of my human existence and ran into the desert.

By the time I had chased three rabbits and teased a couple in a boat with a close-up glimpse of my lovely, furred self on the shore of the river, I felt much better. I don't have to change with the moon, but if I go too long on two feet I get restless and moody.

Happily tired, in human shape, and newly clothed, I got into my car and said my usual prayer as I turned the key. This time the diesel engine caught and purred. I never know from day to day if the Rabbit will run. I drive it because it is cheap, not because it is a good car. There's a lot of truth in the adage that all cars named after animals are lemons.

On Sunday I went to church. My church is so small that it shares its pastor with three other churches. It is one of those nondenominational churches so busy not condemning anyone that it has little power to attract a steady congregation. There are relatively few regulars, and we leave each other mostly alone. Being in a unique position to understand what the world would be like without God and his churches to keep the worst of the evil at bay, I am a faithful attendee.

It's not because of the werewolves. Werewolves can be dangerous if you get in their way; but they'll leave you alone if you are careful. They are no more evil than a grizzly bear or great white shark.

There are other things, though, things that hide in the dark, that are much, much worse – and vampires are only the tip of the iceberg. They are very good at hiding their natures from the human population, but I'm not human. I know them when I meet them, and they know me, too; so I go to church every week.

That Sunday, our pastor was sick and the man who replaced him chose to give a sermon based upon the scripture in Exodus 22: 'Thou shall not suffer a witch to live.' He extended the meaning to encompass the fae, and from him rose a miasma of fear and rage I could sense from my seat. It was people like him who kept the rest of the preternatural community in hiding almost two decades after the lesser fae were forced into the public view.

About thirty years ago, the Gray Lords, the powerful mages who rule the fae, began to be concerned about advances in science – particularly forensic science. They foresaw that the Time of Hiding was coming to an end. They decided to do damage control, and see to it that the

15

human's realization of the world's magic was as gentle as possible. They awaited the proper opportunity.

When Harlan Kincaid, the elderly billionaire real estate magnate, was found dead near his roses with a pair of garden shears in his neck, suspicion fell upon his gardener Kieran McBride, a quiet-spoken, pleasant-faced man who had worked for Kincaid, a prize-winning gardener himself, for a number of years.

I saw bits of the trial, as most Americans did. The sensational murder of one of the country's wealthiest men, who happened to be married to a beloved, young actress, ensured the highest ratings for the networks.

For several weeks the murder occupied the news channels. The world got to see Carin Kincaid, with tears flowing down her California-tanned cheeks, as she described her reaction to finding her dead husband lying next to his favorite rosebush – which had been hacked to pieces. Her testimony was Oscar-quality, but she was upstaged by what happened next.

Kieran McBride was defended by an expensive team of lawyers who had, amid much publicity, agreed to work pro bono. They called Kieran McBride to the stand and skillfully baited the prosecuting attorney into asking McBride to hold the garden shears in his hand.

He tried. But after only an instant his hands began to smoke before dropping them. At his attorney's request he showed the blistered palms to the jury. He couldn't have been the murderer, the lawyer told the judge, jury, and the rest of the world, because Kieran McBride was fae, a garden sprite, and he couldn't hold cold iron, not even through thick leather gloves.

In a dramatic moment, McBride dropped his glamour, the spell that kept him appearing human. He wasn't beautiful, just the opposite, but anyone who has seen a Shar-pei

16

puppy knows there is great charisma in a certain sort of ugliness. One of the reasons McBride had been chosen by the Gray Lords was because garden sprites are gentle folk and easy to look at. His sorrowful, overly large brown eyes made the covers of magazines for weeks opposite less-than-flattering pictures of Kincaid's wife, who was later convicted of her husband's death.

And so the lesser fae, the weak and attractive, revealed themselves at the command of the Gray Lords. The great and terrible, the powerful or powerfully ugly, stayed hidden, awaiting the reaction of the world to the more palatable among them. Here, said the Gray Lord's spin doctors who had been McBride's lawyers, here are a hidden people: the gentle brownie who taught kindergarten because she loved children; the young man, a selkie, who risked his life to save the victims of a boating accident.

At first it looked as though the Gray Lords' strategy would pay off for all of us preternaturals, fae or not. There were New York and L.A. restaurants where the rich and famous could be waited on by wood sprites or muryans. Hollywood moguls remade *Peter Pan* using a boy who could actually fly and a real pixie for Tinkerbell – the resulting film made box office records.

But even at the beginning there was trouble. A well-known televangelist seized upon fear of the fae to increase his grip over his flock and their bank accounts. Conservative legislators began making noise about a registration policy. The government agencies began quietly making lists of fae they thought they could use – or who might be used against them, because throughout Europe and parts of Asia, the lesser fae were forced out of hiding by the Gray Lords.

When the Gray Lords told Zee, my old boss, that he had to come out five or six years ago, Zee sold the garage to me and retired for a few months first. He'd seen what happened to some of the fae who tried to continue their lives as if nothing had happened.

It was all right for a fae to be an entertainer or a tourist attraction, but the brownie kindergarten teacher was quietly pensioned off. No one wanted a fae for a teacher, a mechanic, or a neighbor.

Fae who lived in upscale suburbs had windows broken and rude graffiti painted on their homes. Those who lived in less law-abiding places were mugged and beaten. They couldn't defend themselves for fear of the Gray Lords. Whatever the humans did to them, the Gray Lords would do worse.

The wave of violence prompted the creation of four large reservations for fae. Zee told me that there were fae in the government who saw the reservations as damage control and used fair means and foul to convince the rest of Congress.

If a fae agreed to live on a reservation, he was given a small house and a monthly stipend. Their children (like Zee's son Tad) were given scholarships to good universities where they might become useful members of society . . . if they could find jobs.

The reservations sparked a lot of controversy on both sides. Personally, I thought the Gray Lords and the government might have paid more attention to the innumerable problems of the Native American reservations – but Zee was convinced the reservations were only a first step in the Gray Lords' plans. I knew just enough about them to admit he might be right – but I worried anyway. Whatever ills it created, the reservation system had lessened the growing problems between the human and fae, at least in the US.

People like the visiting pastor, though, were proof that prejudice and hatred were alive and well. Someone behind me muttered that he hoped Pastor Julio recovered before next week, and a round of mumbled agreement cheered me a little.

I've heard of people who've seen angels or felt their presence. I don't know if it is God or one of his angels I sense, but there is a welcoming presence in most churches. As the pastor continued with his fear-driven speech, I could feel that spirit's growing sadness.

The pastor shook my hand as I left the building.

I am not fae, broad though that term is. My magic comes from North America not Europe, and I have no glamour (or need of it) to allow me to blend with the human population. Even so, this man would have hated me had he known what I was.

I smiled at him, thanked him for the service, and wished him well. Love thy enemies, it says in the scriptures. My foster mother always added, 'At the very least, you will be polite to them.'

# 2

Mac the werewolf was sitting on the step by the office door when I drove up Monday morning.

I kept my face impassive and showed none of the surprisingly fierce satisfaction I felt, just handed him a heavy sack of fast-food breakfast sandwiches so I could get my key out and open the door. I'd been raised around wild animals; I knew how to tame them. A hearty welcome would send him off faster than harsh words if I judged him aright, but food was always a good lure.

'Eat,' I told him as I set out for the bathroom to change into work clothes. 'Save me one – the rest are for you.'

All but one were gone when I came back.

'Thank you,' he told me, watching my feet.

'You'll work it off. Come on, help me get the garage doors up.' I led the way through the office and into the garage. 'There's nothing pending today so we can work on my project Bug.'

The Beetle was unprepossessing at the moment, but when I was finished it would be painted, polished, and purring like a kitten. Then I'd sell it for twice what I had put into it and find another car to resurrect. I made almost half my income refurbishing old VW classics.

We'd worked a few hours in companionable silence when he asked to use the phone to make a long-distance call.

'Long as it's not to China,' I said, coaxing a bolt held in place by thirty-odd years of rust.

I didn't sneak over to the office door to listen in. I don't make a practice of eavesdropping on private conversations. I don't have to. I have very good hearing.

'Hello,' he said. 'It's me.'

My hearing was not so good, however, that I could hear the person he was talking to.

'I'm fine. I'm fine,' he said quickly. 'Look I can't talk long.' Pause. 'It's better you don't know.' Pause. 'I know. I saw a news report. I don't remember anything after we left the dance. I don't know what killed her or why it didn't kill me.'

*Ah, no,* I thought.

'No. Look, it's better just now if you don't know where I am.' Pause. 'I told you, I don't know what happened. Just that I didn't kill her.' Pause. 'I don't know. I just want you to tell Mom and Dad I'm okay. I love them – and I'm looking for the ones who killed her. I have to go now.' Pause. 'I love you, too, Joe.'

There were a dozen stories that could account for the half of his conversation that I heard. Two dozen.

But the most prevalent of the cautionary tales werewolves tell each other is what happens the first time a werewolf changes if he doesn't know what he is.

In my head, I translated Mac's half of the conversation into a picture of a boy leaving a high school dance to make out with his girlfriend under the full moon, not knowing what he was. New werewolves, unless they have the guidance of a strong dominant, have little control of their wolf form the first few times they change.

If Mac were a new werewolf, it would explain why he didn't notice that I was different from the humans around. You have to be taught how to use your senses.

Here in the US, most werewolves are brought over by friends or family. There is a support structure to educate the new wolf, to keep him and everyone around him safe – but there are still the occasional attacks by rogue werewolves. One of the duties of a pack is to kill those rogues and find their victims.

Despite the stories, any person bitten by a werewolf doesn't turn into another werewolf. It takes an attack so vicious that the victim lies near death to allow the magic of the wolf to slip past the body's immune system. Such attacks make the newspapers with headlines like 'Man Attacked by Rabid Dogs.' Usually the victim dies of the wounds or of the Change. If he survives, then he recovers quickly, miraculously – until the next full moon, when he learns that he didn't really survive at all. Not as he had been. Usually a pack will find him before his first change and ease his way into a new way of life. The packs watch the news and read the newspapers to prevent a new wolf from being alone – and to protect their secrets.

Maybe no one had found Mac. Maybe he'd killed his date and when he'd returned to human shape he'd refused to believe what he'd done. What he was. I'd been operating under the impression that he had left his pack, but if he was a new wolf, an untaught wolf, he was even more dangerous.

I broke the rusted-out bolt because I wasn't paying attention. When Mac returned from his phone call, I was working on removing the remnant with an easy out, the world's most misnamed tool – there is nothing easy about it.

I hadn't planned on saying anything to him, but the words came out anyway. 'I might know some people who could help you.'

'No one can help me,' he replied tiredly. Then he smiled, which would have been more convincing if his eyes hadn't been so sad. 'I'm all right.'

I set down the easy out and looked at him.

'Yes, I think you will be,' I said, hoping I wasn't making a mistake by not pushing. I'd have to let Adam know about him before the next full moon. 'Just remember, I've been known to believe as many as six impossible things before breakfast.'

22

His mouth quirked up. 'Lewis Carroll.'

'And they say the youth today aren't being educated,' I said. 'If you trust me, you might find that my friends can help you more than you believed possible.' The phone rang, and I turned back to my work. 'Go answer the phone, please, Mac,' I told him.

That late in the year it was dark out when we finished at six. He stood and watched me as I locked up, obviously thinking about something. I deliberately fumbled with the lock to give him more time, but he didn't take advantage of it.

'See you tomorrow,' he said, instead.

'All right.' Then, impulsively, I asked, 'Do you have a place to sleep tonight?'

'Sure,' he said with a smile, and started off as if he had somewhere to be.

I could have bitten off my tongue because I pushed him into a lie. Once he started lying to me, it would be harder to get him to trust me with the truth. I don't know why it works that way, but it does – at least in my experience.

I kicked myself all the way home, but by the time I had fed Medea and made myself some dinner, I'd figured out a way around it. I'd take him a blanket tomorrow and unlock Stefan's VW bus, which was patiently awaiting brake parts from Oregon. I didn't think Stefan would mind Mac camping out for a night or two.

I called Stefan to make sure, because it's unwise to surprise vampires.

'Sure,' he said, without even asking who I wanted to let sleep in his van. 'That's all right with me, sweetheart. How long until my bus is roadworthy again?'

For a vampire, Stefan was all right.

'Parts are supposed to be in day after tomorrow,' I told him. 'I'll call you when they get here. If you want to help, we can get it done in a couple long evenings. Otherwise, it'll take me a day.'

'Right,' he said, which was apparently good-bye because the next thing I heard was a dial tone.

'Well,' I told the cat, 'I guess I'm headed out to buy a blanket.' It had to be a new blanket: mine would all smell like coyote – and a werewolf who hardly knew me wouldn't be comfortable surrounded by my scent.

I spent several minutes looking for my purse before I realized that I'd left it locked in the safe at work. Happily, my garage was on the way to the store.

Because it was dark, I parked my car on the street behind the garage where there was a streetlight to discourage any enterprising vandals. I walked through the parking lot and passed Stefan's bus, parked next to the office door, and gave it an affectionate pat.

Stefan's bus was painted to match the Mystery Machine, which said a lot about the vampire it belonged to. Stefan told me that he'd briefly considered painting it black a few years ago when he started watching Buffy, but, in the end, he'd decided the vampire slayer was no match for Scooby Doo.

I opened the office door, but didn't bother turning on the lights because I see pretty well in the dark. My purse was where I remembered leaving it. I took it out and relocked the safe. Out of habit, I double-checked the heat to make sure it was set low. Everything had been turned off and put away. All was as it should have been, and I felt the usual sense of satisfaction knowing it was mine – well, mine and the bank's.

I was smiling when I left the office and turned to lock the door behind me. I wasn't moving quietly on purpose, but having been raised by a pack of werewolves makes you learn to be quieter than most.

'Go away.' Mac's voice came from the other side of Stefan's bus. He spoke in a low, growling tone I hadn't heard from him before.

I thought he was talking to me and spun toward the sound, but all I saw was Stefan's bus.

Then someone else answered Mac. 'Not without you.'

The bus had darkened windows. I could see through them well enough to see the side door was open, framing the vague shadowy forms of Mac and one of his visitors. The second one I couldn't see. The wind was right, blowing gently past them to me, and I smelled *two* other people besides Mac: another werewolf and a human. I didn't recognize either one.

Although I know most of Adam's wolves by scent, it wouldn't be odd if he had gotten a new wolf without my hearing about it. But it was the human that told me something was up: I'd never known Adam to send a human out with one of his wolves on business.

Stranger yet was that no one showed any sign they knew I was around. I was quiet, but even so, both werewolves should have heard me. But neither Mac nor the other wolf appeared to notice.

'No,' said Mac, while I hesitated. 'No more cages. No more drugs. They weren't helping.'

*Cages?* I thought. *Someone had been keeping Mac in a cage?* There was no need for that, not with Adam around. Though some Alphas had to depend upon bars to control new wolves, Adam wasn't one of them. Nor did Mac's comments about drugs make sense: there are no drugs that work on werewolves.

'They were, kid. You just need to give them a chance. I promise you we can undo your curse.'

*Undo his curse?* There was no drug in the world that would undo the Change, and darn few werewolves who considered their state a curse after the first few months. Eventually most of them felt that becoming short-tempered and occasionally furry was a small price to pay for extraordinary strength, speed, and senses – not to mention the fringe benefit of a body immune to disease and old age.

Even if the werewolf belonged to Adam, I doubted he knew that one of his pack was telling wild stories. At least I *hoped* he didn't know.

Mac seemed to know these two, though, and I was beginning to feel that his story was more complicated than I had thought.

'You talk like you have a choice,' the third man was saying. 'But the only choice you have is how you get there.'

These weren't Adam's men, I decided. The mention of curses, cages, and drugs made them the enemy. If Mac didn't want to go with them, I wouldn't let them take him.

I took a quick glance around, but the streets were empty. After six the warehouse district is pretty dead. I stripped out of my clothes as quietly as I could and shifted into coyote form.

As a human I didn't stand a chance against a werewolf. The coyote was still not a match – but I was fast, much faster than a real coyote and just a hair quicker than a were-wolf.

I jumped onto the railing and vaulted from there to the top of Stefan's bus for the advantage of the higher position, though I was giving up surprise. No matter how quietly I moved, a werewolf would hear the click of my nails on the metal roof.

I readied myself for launch, but paused. From atop the bus I could see Mac and the two men. None of them seemed to be aware of me. Mac had his back to me, but all the others would have had to do was look up. They didn't. Something wasn't right.

Behind the two strangers was a big black SUV, the kind of car you'd expect bad guys to drive.

'I don't believe there is any way to undo what you did to me,' Mac was saying. 'You can't give me back my life or give Meg back hers. All you can do is leave me alone.'

The human's hair was in a crew cut, but it was the big black gun I could see peeking out of his shoulder holster that first made me think military. Both of the strangers stood like military men – Adam had the posture, too. Their shoulders were just a little stiff, their backs a little too straight. Maybe they did belong to Adam. The thought made me hesitate. If I hurt one of Adam's wolves, there would be hell to pay.

'The moon's coming,' said the longer-haired man, the werewolf. 'Can't you feel it?'

'How're you planning on surviving the winter, kid?' It was Short-hair again. His voice was kindly. Fatherly. Patronizing even. 'It gets cold 'round December, even in this desert.'

I stifled a growl as I tried to determine the best way to help Mac.

'I'm working here,' Mac said, with a gesture at the garage. 'If it gets colder, I think she'll let me sleep in the garage until I find somewhere to live if I ask her.'

'Ask her?' Short-hair looked sympathetic. 'She kept you here for us. She's one of us, kid. How else do you think we found you?'

Mac smelled of shock first, then defeat. Emotions have a smell, but only in my coyote form is my nose good enough to distinguish more than the strongest feelings. My lips curled back over my teeth – I don't like liars, especially when they are lying about me.

The werewolf's voice was dreamy. 'When the moon comes, you can't stop the change.' He swayed back and forth. 'Then

27

you can run and drink the fear of your prey before they die beneath your fangs.'

*Moonstruck*, I thought, shocked out of my anger. If this wolf was so new that he was moonstruck, he certainly wasn't Adam's, and whoever had sent him out was an idiot.

'I'm not coming,' said Mac, taking a step away from them. He took another step back – putting his back against the bus. He stiffened, drew in a deep breath, and looked around. 'Mercy?'

But neither of the men paid attention when Mac caught my scent. The werewolf was still held in his moon dreams, and the human was drawing his gun.

'We tried to do this the easy way,' he said, and I could smell his pleasure. He might have tried the easy way first, but he liked the hard way better. His gun was the kind you find in military catalogues for wanna-be mercenaries, where what it looks like is at least as important as how well it performs. 'Get in the car, kid. I'm packing silver bullets. If I shoot you, you'll be dead.' He sounded like a thug from a fifties gangster movie; I wondered if it was deliberate.

'If I get in the car, I'll be dead anyway, won't I?' Mac said slowly. 'Did you kill the other two who were in the cages by me? Is that why they disappeared?'

None of them had noticed that the werewolf was starting to change, not even the werewolf himself. I could see his eyes gleaming brightly in the darkness and smell the musk of wolf and magic. He growled.

'Quiet,' snapped the human, then he looked. He paused, swallowed, and turned his gun, ever so slightly, toward his erstwhile partner.

As a human, the werewolf probably weighed in at about two hundred pounds. Werewolves, fully changed, weigh upward of two hundred and fifty pounds. No, I don't know where the extra weight comes from. It's magic, not science.

I'm a little large for the average coyote – but that meant that the werewolf was still five times my weight.

I'd been trying to figure out a way to turn my speed to advantage, but when the werewolf, his elongating jaws stretching around sharp, white fangs, focused on Mac and growled again, I knew I'd just run out of time.

I threw myself off the top of the car and onto the werewolf, who was still slowed by his ongoing change. I snapped at him to get his attention and caught his throat, still barren of the thick ruff designed to protect him from such an attack.

I felt my eyeteeth snag flesh, and blood spurted, pushed by his heart and the increased blood pressure that accompanies the change. It wasn't a mortal wound – werewolves heal too fast – but it should slow him down, giving me a head start while he bound the wound.

Only he didn't stop.

He was hot on my heels as I dashed past Stefan's bus, across the alley that allowed access to my garage bays, and leapt over the chain-link fence surrounding the Sav U More Self-Storage facility. If he'd been in full wolf form, he'd have cleared the fence easier than I did, but he was hampered by his awkward shape and had to stop and tear through the fence instead.

Spurred by hunting-rage, he was faster than I was, even on two legs. He shouldn't have been. I've outrun my share of werewolves, and I knew I was faster than they were; but no one had told him that. He was catching up to me. I jumped back over the fence because it had slowed him down the first time.

If there had been homes nearby, the impatient, frustrated whines the werewolf made as it was forced to stop and rip the chain-link fence again would have had the police on their way, but the nearest residences were blocks away. The thought reminded me that I needed to worry about innocent bystanders as well as Mac and myself.

I reversed my direction, running down the road back toward the garage, intent on leading the werewolf away from town rather than into it. But before I reached the garage, my pursuer tripped and fell to the street.

I thought at first that the change had taken him completely, but no werewolf rose on all fours to continue the chase. I slowed, then stopped where I was and listened, but all I could hear was my heart pounding with fear.

He was almost finished with the change, his face entirely wolf though his fur had not yet begun to cover him. His hands, lying limply on the blacktop, were distorted, too thin, with an inhuman distance between his fingers and his thumb. His nails were thickened and had begun to come to a point at the tips. But he wasn't moving.

Shaking with the need to run, I forced myself to approach him. I waited for him to jump up and grab me the way they always do in the late-night movies, but he just lay there, smelling of blood and adrenaline.

A trail of liquid stretched out behind him as if he were a car that had blown a radiator hose and slung antifreeze all over the road – but the liquid that glistened under the street-lamp was blood.

Only then did it occur to me that I did not hear the thrum of his heart or the whisper of his breath.

I heard a car start up and took my eyes off the werewolf in time to see the black SUV squeal out of the parking lot and turn toward me. The big car wobbled as the driver fought his speed and his turn. His headlights blinded me momentarily – but I'd already seen my escape route and took it blind.

He slowed a minute, as if he considered stopping by the body on the street, but then the V-8 roared, and the SUV picked up speed.

He narrowly avoided hitting the lamppost I'd dodged behind. I couldn't tell if Mac was in the car or not. I watched the SUV's taillights until it turned onto the highway and blended in with the traffic there.

I walked to the werewolf just to be certain – but he was well and truly dead.

I'd never killed anyone before. He shouldn't have been dead. Werewolves are hard to kill. If he had bothered to stanch the wound, or if he hadn't chased me, the wound would have healed before he could bleed out.

The taste of his blood in my mouth made me ill, and I vomited beside the body until the taste of bile overwhelmed anything else. Then I left him lying in the middle of the road and ran back to the garage. I needed to check on Mac before I took on the task of dealing with the dead werewolf.

To my relief, Mac was leaning on Stefan's van when I loped into the parking lot. He held a gun loosely in his hand, the barrel bent.

'Mercy?' he asked me, when I approached, as if he expected me to talk.

I ducked my head once, then darted around the front of the garage where I'd left my clothes. He followed me. But when I shifted back, and he saw that I was naked, he turned his back to let me dress.

I pulled on my clothing quickly – it was cold out. 'I'm decent,' I told him, and he faced me again.

'You have blood on your chin,' he said, in a small voice.

I wiped it off with the bottom of my T-shirt. I wasn't going shopping tonight, so it didn't matter if I got blood on my clothes. *Don't throw up again*, I told myself sternly. *Pretend it was a rabbit*. It hadn't tasted like rabbit.

'What are you?' he asked. 'Are you one of theirs? Where is . . . is the wolf?'

'He's dead. We need to talk,' I told him, then paused as

I collected my scattered thoughts. 'But first we need to get the dead werewolf out of the street. And before that, I guess we should call Adam.'

I led him back to the office – this time turning on the light. Not that either of us needed it for anything other than comfort.

He put his hand on top of mine when I reached for the phone. 'Who is Adam, and why are you calling him?' he asked.

I didn't fight his hold. 'The local Alpha. We need to get the body out of the road – unless you want both of us disappeared into some federal laboratory for science to pick over for a few years before they decide they can learn more from us dead than alive.'

'Alpha?' he asked. 'What's that?'

He *was* new.

'Werewolves live in packs,' I told him. 'Each pack has an Alpha – a wolf strong enough to keep the others under control. Adam Hauptman is the local Alpha.'

'What does he look like?' he asked.

'Five-ten, a hundred and eighty pounds. Dark hair, dark eyes. I don't think he has anything to do with your wolves,' I said. 'If Adam wanted you, he'd have you – and he'd have found you a lot sooner. He can be a jerk, but competence is his forte.'

Mac stared at me, his brown eyes looking yellowish in the fluorescent lighting of my office. Truth to tell, I was surprised he was still in human form because watching one wolf change tends to encourage others. I met his gaze calmly, then dropped my eyes until I was looking at his shoulder instead.

'All right,' he said, slowly removing his hand. 'You saved me tonight – and that thing could have torn you apart. I've seen them kill.'

32

I didn't ask when or whom. It was important to take action in the right order to avoid worse trouble. Call Adam. Remove body from the middle of the street where anyone could see it. Then talk. I punched Adam's number from memory.

'Hauptman,' he answered, with just a touch of impatience, on the fourth ring.

'I killed a werewolf at my garage,' I said, then hung up. To Mac's raised eyebrows I said, 'That will get a faster reaction than spending twenty minutes explaining. Come on, you and I need to get the body off the street before someone spots it.' When the phone rang, my answering machine picked it up.

I took Stefan's bus because loading something large into a bus is just easier than loading it into my little Rabbit. The bus smelled of Mac, and I realized he'd not lied to me when he said he had a place to spend the night. He'd been sleeping in it for a couple of nights at least.

The bus was without brakes until we fixed it, but I managed to get it to drift to a stop next to the body. Mac helped me get it in the bus, then dashed back to the garage while I drove. When I arrived, he had the garage open for me.

We set the dead man on the cement floor next to the lift, then I parked the bus back where it had been and pulled down the garage bay door, leaving us inside with the body.

I walked to the corner farthest from the dead werewolf and sat down on the floor next to one of my big tool chests. Mac sat down next to me, and we both stared across the garage at the corpse.

Half-changed, the body looked even more grotesque under the harsh lighting of the second bay than it had under the streetlight, like something out of a black-and-white Lon

33

Chaney movie. From where I sat I could see the slice in his neck that had killed him.

'He was used to healing fast,' I said, to break the silence. 'So he didn't pay attention to his wound. But some wounds take longer to heal than others. He didn't know any more than you do. How long have you been a werewolf?'

'Two months,' Mac said, leaning his head back against the tool chest and looking at the ceiling. 'It killed my girlfriend, but I survived. Sort of.'

He was lucky, I thought, remembering the suppositions I'd had while overhearing his phone call earlier. He hadn't killed his girlfriend after all. He probably wasn't feeling lucky though, and I wasn't going to tell him that it could be worse.

'Tell me about your life afterward. Where did those men come from? Are you from the Tri-Cities?' I hadn't heard of any suspicious deaths or disappearances in the last six months.

He shook his head. 'I'm from Naperville.' At my blank look, he clarified. 'Illinois. Near Chicago.' He glanced at the body, closed his eyes, and swallowed. 'I want to eat him,' he whispered.

'Perfectly natural,' I told him, though I have to admit I wanted to move away from him. Heaven save me, stuck with a new werewolf in a garage with fresh meat was not anyone's idea of safe. But we had to wait here until Adam came. It could have been worse: it could have been nearer the full moon, or he could have been as hungry as he'd been that first day.

'Deer not only tastes better, it's easier to live with afterward,' I said, then reflected that it might be better to talk about something other than food. 'What happened to you after that first attack? Did someone take you to a hospital?'

He looked at me a moment, but I couldn't tell what he was thinking. He said, 'After . . . after the attack, I woke up in a cage in someone's basement. There was someone in the room and when I opened my eyes, he said, "Good, you'll live. Leo will be happy to see it."'

'Wait,' I said. 'Leo. Leo. Chicago.' Then it came to me. 'Leo James? Looks as though he ought to be a Nordic skiing champion? Tall, long, and blond.'

Leo was one of the Chicago Alphas – there were two of them. Leo held territory in the western suburbs. I'd met him once or twice. Neither of us had been impressed, but then, as I said, most werewolves don't take kindly to other predators.

Mac nodded. 'That sounds right. He came down the stairs with the first guy and another man. None of them would talk to me or answer any of my questions.' He swallowed and gave me an anxious glance. 'This shit just sounds so weird, you know? Unbelievable.'

'You're talking to someone who can turn into a coyote,' I told him gently. 'Just tell me what you think happened.'

'All right.' He nodded slowly. 'All right. I was still weak and confused, but it sounded like Leo was arguing money with the third guy. It sounded to me like he sold me for twelve thousand dollars.'

'Leo sold you for twelve thousand dollars,' I said, as much to myself as to Mac. My voice might have been matter-of-fact, but only because Mac was right: it *was* unbelievable. Not that I thought he was lying. 'He had one of his wolves attack you and your girlfriend and when you survived, he sold you to someone else as a newly turned werewolf.'

'I think so,' said Mac.

'You called your family this afternoon?' I asked. I smiled at his wary look. 'I have pretty good hearing.'

'My brother. His cell phone.' He swallowed. 'It's broken. No caller ID. I had to let them know I was alive. I guess the police think I killed Meg.'

'You told him that you were after her killer,' I said.

He gave an unhappy laugh. 'Like I could find him.'

He could. It was all a matter of learning to use his new senses, but I wasn't going to tell him that, not yet. If Mac did find his attacker, chances were Mac would die. A new werewolf just doesn't stand a chance against the older ones.

I patted his knee. 'Don't worry. As soon as we get word to the right people – and Adam is the right people – Leo's a walking dead man. The Marrok won't allow an Alpha who is creating progeny and selling them for money.'

'The Marrok?'

'Sorry,' I said. 'Like I told you, except for the occasional rogue, werewolves are organized into packs under an Alpha wolf.'

It used to be that was as organized as werewolves got. But the only thing it takes to be Alpha is power, not intelligence or even common sense. In the Middle Ages, after the Black Plague, the werewolf population was almost wiped out along with real wolves because some of the Alphas were indiscreet. It was decided then that there would be a leader over all the werewolves.

'In the US, all the packs follow the Marrok, a title taken from the name of one of King Arthur's knights who was a werewolf. The Marrok and his pack have oversight of all the werewolves in North America.'

'There are more of us?' he asked.

I nodded. 'Maybe as many as two thousand in the US, five or six hundred in Canada, and about four hundred in Mexico.'

'How do you know so much about werewolves?'

'I was raised by them.' I waited for him to ask me why, but his attention had drifted toward the body. He inhaled deeply and gave an eager shudder.

36

'Do you know what they wanted with you?' I asked hurriedly.

'They told me they were looking for a cure. Kept putting things in my food – I could smell them, but I was hungry so I ate anyway. Sometimes they'd give me shots – and once when I wouldn't cooperate they used a dart gun.'

'Outside, when you were talking to them, you said they had others like you?'

He nodded. 'They kept me in a cage in a semitrailer. There were four cages in it. At first there were three of us, a girl around my age and a man. The girl was pretty much out of it – she just stared and rocked back and forth. The man couldn't speak any English. It sounded like Polish to me – but it could have been Russian or something. One of the times I was taking a trip on something they pumped in me, I woke up and I was alone.'

'Drugs don't work on werewolves,' I told him. 'Your metabolism is too high.'

'These did,' he said.

I nodded. 'I believe you. But they shouldn't have. You escaped?'

'I managed to change while they were trying to give me something else. I don't remember much about it other than running.'

'Was the trailer here in the Tri-Cities?' I asked.

He nodded. 'I couldn't find it again, though. I don't remember everything that happens when . . .' His voice trailed off.

'When you're the wolf.' Memory came with experience and control, or so I'd been told.

A strange car approached the garage with the quiet purr common to expensive engines.

'What's wrong?' he asked, when I stood up.

'Don't you hear the car?'

He started to shake his head, but then paused. 'I – yes. Yes, I do.'

'There are advantages to being a werewolf,' I said. 'One of them is being able to hear and smell better than the average Joe.' I stood up. 'It's turning into the parking lot. I'm going to look out and see who it is.'

'Maybe it's the guy you called. The Alpha.'

I shook my head. 'It's not his car.'

38

# 3

PATRICIA BRIGGS

I slipped through the office and opened the outside door cautiously, but the smell of perfume and herbs hanging in the night air told me we were still all right.

A dark Cadillac was stretched across the pavement just beyond Stefan's bus. I pushed the door all the way open as the uniformed chauffeur tipped his hat to me, then opened the car's back door, revealing an elderly woman.

I stuck my head back in the office, and called, 'It's all right, Mac. Just the cleanup crew.'

Keeping the humans ignorant of the magic that lives among them is a specialized and lucrative business, and Adam's pack kept the best witch in the Pacific Northwest on retainer. Rumors of Elizaveta Arkadyevna Vyshnevetskaya's origins and how she came to be in the Tri-Cities changed on a weekly basis. I think she and her brood of grandchildren and great-grandchildren encouraged the more outrageous versions. All that I knew for certain was that she had been born in Moscow, Russia, and had lived in the Tri-Cities for at least twenty years.

Elizaveta rose from the depths of the big car with all the drama of a prima ballerina taking her bow. The picture she made was worth all the drama.

She was almost six feet tall and little more than skin and bones, with a long, elegant nose and gray, penetrating eyes. Her style of dress was somewhere between babushka and Baba Yaga. Layers of rich fabrics and textures came down to her calves, all covered with a long wool cape and a worn scarf that wrapped around her head and neck. Her outfit wasn't authentic, at least not to any period or place that I've heard of, but I've never seen anyone brave enough to tell her so.

'Elizaveta Arkadyevna, welcome,' I said, walking past the bus to stand by her car.

She scowled at me. 'My Adamya calls and tells me you have one of his wolves dead.' Her voice had the crispness of a British aristocrat, so I knew she was angry – her usual accent was thick enough I had to make a real effort to understand her. When she was really angry, she didn't speak English at all.

'Werewolf, yes,' I agreed. 'But I don't think it is one of Adam's.' Adamya, I had learned, was an affectionate form of Adam. I don't think she'd ever called him that to his face. Elizaveta was seldom affectionate to anyone likely to overhear her.

'I have the body in my shop,' I told her. 'But there is blood all over here. The werewolf chased me with a torn artery and bled from here over to the storage facility, where he tore up the fence in two places before he bled to death out on the street. The storage facility has cameras, and I used Stefan's bus' – I pointed to it – 'to move the body.'

She said something in Russian to her chauffeur, who I recognized as one of her grandchildren. He bowed and said something back before going around to open the trunk.

'Go,' she told me, and flung her arms in a pushing gesture. 'I will take care of the mess out here without your help. You wait with the body. Adam will be here soon. Once he has seen, he will tell me what he would have me do with it. You killed this wolf? With a silver bullet so I should look for casing?'

'With my fangs,' I told her; she knew what I was. 'It was sort of an accident – at least his death was.'

She caught my arm when I turned to go into the office.

'What were you thinking, Mercedes Thompson? A Little Wolf who attacks the great ones will be dead soon, I think. Luck runs out eventually.'

'He would have killed a boy under my protection,' I told her. 'I had no choice.'

She released me and snorted her disapproval, but when she spoke her Russian accent was firmly in place. 'There is always choice, Mercy. Always choice. If he attacked a boy, then I suppose it must not have been one of Adamya's.'

She looked at her chauffeur and barked out something more. Effectively dismissed, I went back to Mac and our dead werewolf.

I found Mac crouched near the body, licking his fingers as if he might have touched the drying blood and was cleaning them off. Not a good sign. Somehow, I was pretty certain that if Mac were fully in control, he wouldn't be doing that.

'Mac,' I said, strolling past him and over to the far side of the garage, where we'd been sitting.

He growled at me.

'Stop that,' I said sharply, doing my best to keep the fear out of my voice. 'Control yourself and come over here. There are some things you should know before Adam gets here.'

I'd been avoiding a dominance contest, because my instincts told me that Mac was a natural leader, a dominant who might very well eventually become an Alpha in his own right – and I was a woman.

Women's liberation hadn't made much headway in the world of werewolves. A mated female took her pack position from her mate, but unmated females were always lower than males unless the male was unusually submissive. This little fact had caused me no end of grief, growing up, as I did, in the middle of a werewolf pack. But without someone more dominant than he, Mac wouldn't be able to take control of his wolf yet. Adam wasn't there, so it was up to me.

41

I stared at him in my best imitation of my foster father and raised an eyebrow. 'Mac, for Heaven's sake, leave that poor dead man alone and come over here.'

He came slowly to his feet, menace clinging to him. Then he shook his head and rubbed his face, swaying a little.

'That helped,' he said. 'Can you do it again?'

I tried my best. 'Mac. Get over here right now.'

He staggered a little drunkenly over to me and sat at my feet.

'When Adam comes,' I told him firmly, 'whatever you do, don't look him in the eyes for longer than a second or two. Some of this should be instinct, I hope. It isn't necessary to cower – remember that you've done no wrong at all. Let me talk. What we want is for Adam to take you home with him.'

'I'm fine on my own,' Mac objected, sounding almost like himself, but he kept his head turned toward the body.

'No, you're not,' I said firmly. 'If there wasn't a pack, you might survive. But if you run into one of Adam's wolves without being made known to the pack, they'll probably kill you. Also, the full moon is coming soon. Adam can help you get control of your beast before then.'

'I can control the monster?' asked Mac, stilling.

'Absolutely,' I told him. 'And it's not a monster – any more than a killer whale is a monster. Werewolves are hot-tempered and aggressive, but they aren't evil.' I thought about the one who had sold him and corrected myself. 'At least not any more evil than any other person.'

'I don't even remember what the beast does,' Mac said. 'How can I control it?'

'It's harder the first few times,' I told him. 'A good Alpha can get you through that. Once you have control, then you can go back to your old life if you want. You have to be a little careful; even in human form you're going to have to deal with having a shorter temper and a lot more strength than you're used to. Adam can teach you.'

'I can't ever go back,' he whispered.

'Get control first,' I told him. 'There are people who can help you with the rest. Don't give up.'

'You're not like me.'

'Nope,' I agreed. 'I'm a walker: it's different from what you are. I was born this way.'

'I've never heard of a walker. Is that some sort of fae?'

'Close enough,' I said. 'I don't get a lot of the neat things that you werewolves have. No super strength. No super healing. No pack.'

'No chance you might eat your friends,' he suggested. I couldn't tell if he was trying to be funny, or if he was serious.

'There are some benefits,' I agreed.

'How did you find out so much about werewolves?'

I opened my mouth to give him the short version, but decided the whole story might better serve to distract him from the dead body.

'My mother was a rodeo groupie,' I began, sitting down beside him. 'She liked cowboys, any cowboy. She liked a Blackfoot bull-rider named Joe Old Coyote from Browning, Montana, enough to get pregnant with me. She told me that he claimed to come from a long line of medicine men, but at the time she thought he was just trying to impress her. He died in a car accident three days after she met him.

'She was seventeen, and her parents tried to talk her into an abortion, but she would have none of it. Then they tried to get her to put me up for adoption, but she was determined to raise me herself – until I was three months old, and she found a coyote pup in my crib.'

'What did she do?'

'She tried to find my father's family,' I told him. 'She went to Browning and found several families there with that last name, but they claimed they'd never heard of Joe. He was certainly Native American.' I made a gesture to encompass my appearance. I don't look pureblood; my features are too Anglo. But my skin looks tanned even in November, and my straight hair is as dark as my eyes. 'But otherwise I don't know much about him.'

'Old Coyote,' said Mac speculatively.

I smiled at him. 'Makes you think this shifting thing must have run in the family, doesn't it?'

'So how was it that you were raised by werewolves?'

'My great-grandfather's uncle was a werewolf,' I said. 'It was supposed to be a family secret, but it's hard to keep secrets from my mother. She just smiles at people, and they tell her their life stories. Anyway, she found his phone number and called him.'

'Wow,' said Mac. 'I never met any of my great-grandparents.'

'Me either,' I said, then smiled. 'Just an uncle of theirs who was a werewolf. One of the benefits of being a werewolf is a long life.' If you can control the wolf – but Adam could explain that part better than me.

His gaze was drawn back to our dead friend.

'Yes, well.' I sighed. 'Stupidity will still get you killed. My great-grandfather's uncle was smart enough to outlive his generation, but all those years didn't keep him from getting gutted by a moose he was out hunting one night.'

'Anyway,' I continued, 'he came to visit and knew as soon as he saw me what I was. That was before the fae came out and people were still trying to pretend that science had ruled out the possibility of magic. He convinced my mother that I'd be safer out in the hinterlands of Montana being raised by the Marrok's pack – they have their own town in the mountains where strangers seldom bother them. I was fostered with a family there who didn't have any children.'

44

'Your mother just gave you up?'

'My mother came out every summer, and they didn't make it easy on her either. Not overfond of humans, the Marrok, excepting their own spouses and children.'

'I thought the Marrok was the wolf who rules North America,' said Mac.

'Packs sometimes take their public name from their leader,' I told him. 'So the Marrok's pack call themselves the Marrok. More often they find some geographical feature in their territory. Adam's wolves are the Columbia Basin Pack. The only other pack in Washington is the Emerald Pack in Seattle.'

Mac had another question, but I held up my hand for him to be quiet. I'd heard Adam's car pull up.

'Remember what I said about the Alpha,' I told Mac and stood up. 'He's a good man and you need him. Just sit there, keep your eyes down, let me talk, and everything will be all right.'

The heavy garage door of bay one groaned, then rang like a giant cymbal as it was forced all the way open faster than it usually moved.

Adam Hauptman stood in the open doorway, stillness cloaking his body and for an instant, I saw him with just my eyes, as a human might. He was worth looking at.

For all his German last name, his face and coloring were Slavic: dusky skin, dark hair – though not as dark as mine – wide cheekbones, and a narrow but sensual mouth. He wasn't tall or bulky, and a human might wonder why all eyes turned to him when he walked into a room. Then they'd see his face and assume, wrongly, that it was the attraction. Adam was an Alpha, and if he'd been ugly he would have held the attention of anyone who happened to be nearby, wolf or human – but the masculine beauty he carried so unself-consciously didn't hurt.

Under more usual circumstances his eyes were a rich

chocolate brown, but they had lightened with his anger until they were almost yellow. I heard Mac gasp when the full effect of Adam's anger hit him, so I was prepared and let the wave of power wash off me like seawater on glass.

Maybe I should have explained matters better when I had him on the phone, but where's the fun in that?

'What happened?' he asked, his voice softer than the first snowfall in winter.

'It's complicated,' I said, holding his gaze for two full seconds before I turned my head and gestured toward the body. 'The dead one is there. If he belongs to you, he is new – and you haven't been doing your job. He was as deaf and blind as a human. I was able to take him by surprise, then he was too ignorant to realize that the wound wouldn't close as fast as usual if it was given by a preternatural creature. He let himself bleed out because he was too caught up in the chase to—'

'Enough, Mercedes,' he growled as he strode over to the dead wolfman and knelt beside him. He moved the body and one of the corpse's arms flopped down limply on the ground.

Mac whined eagerly, then bowed his head and pressed it against my thigh so that he couldn't see.

The sound drew Adam's attention from the body to the boy at my feet.

He growled. 'This one isn't one of mine – and neither is that.'

'So gracious,' I said. 'Your mother should be complimented on your manners, Hauptman.'

'Careful,' he whispered. It wasn't a threat, it was a warning.

Okay. He was scary. Really scary. He'd probably have been scary even when he was just a human. But it wouldn't do to let him know he intimidated me.

'Adam Hauptman,' I said politely to show him how it

46

was done. 'Allow me to introduce you to Mac – that's all of his name I know. He was attacked by a werewolf in Chicago about two moons ago. The werewolf killed his girlfriend, but he survived. He was taken by his attacker and put in a cage. A man who sounds a lot like the Chicago Alpha Leo sold him to someone who held him inside a cage in a semi-trailer and used him for what sounds like some sort of drug experiments until he broke free. Last Friday he showed up at my door looking for work.'

'You didn't inform me that you had a strange wolf on your doorstep?'

I gave him a put-upon sigh. 'I am not one of your pack members, Adam. I know this is difficult for you to fathom, so I'll speak slowly: I don't belong to you. I am under no obligation to tell you anything.'

Adam swore harshly. 'New werewolves are dangerous, woman. Especially when they are cold and hungry.' He looked at Mac, and his voice changed completely, the heat and anger gone. 'Mercy, come here.'

I didn't look down to see what he'd noticed in Mac's face. I took a step, but Mac was wrapped around my left leg. I stopped before I fell. 'Uhm. I'm a little stuck for the moment.'

'For a smart girl, you're pretty stupid sometimes,' he said, his voice rich and gentle so as not to startle the werewolf by my side. 'Locking yourself in a garage with a new wolf and a dead body isn't the smartest thing you could have done. I don't have a connection with him yet. It would help if you have his real name.'

'Mac,' I murmured. 'What's your name?'

'Alan,' he said dreamily, coming up to his knees so his face was pressed against my belly. 'Alan MacKenzie Frazier after my grandfather who died the year I was born.' The friction of his movement rucked my shirt up and he licked my bare skin. To an outsider it might have looked sensual, but the abdomen is a vulnerable spot on the body, a favorite of predators. 'You smell good,' he whispered.

He smelled like werewolf, and I was starting to panic — which wasn't a very useful thing to do.

'Alan,' said Adam, rolling the name on his tongue. 'Alan MacKenzie Frazier, come here to me.'

Mac jerked his head away from me but tightened his arms painfully on my hips. He looked at Adam and growled, a low rumble that caused his chest to vibrate against my leg. 'Mine,' he said.

Adam's eyes narrowed. 'I don't think so. She is mine.'

It would have been flattering, I thought, except that at least one of them was talking about dinner and I wasn't certain about the other. While Adam had Mac distracted, I reached behind me and grabbed my big crowbar from the shelf directly behind us. I brought it down on Mac's collarbone.

It was an awkward hit because I didn't have much leverage, but the collarbone, even on a werewolf, is not hard to damage. I heard the bone crack and wrenched myself out of Mac's grip and across the garage before he recovered from the unexpected pain.

I didn't like hurting him, but he would heal in a few hours as long as I didn't let him eat me. I didn't think he was the kind of person who would recover from murder as easily as he would a broken bone.

Adam had moved almost as quickly as I had. He grabbed Mac by the scruff of his neck and jerked him to his feet.

'Adam,' I said, from the relative safety of the far end of the garage. 'He's new and untaught. A victim.' I kept my voice quiet so I didn't add to the excitement.

It helped that Mac wasn't looking particularly dangerous at the moment. He hung limply in Adam's grip. 'Sorry,' he said almost inaudibly. 'Sorry.'

Adam let out an exasperated huff of air and lowered Mac to the ground – on his feet at first, but when Mac's knees proved too limp to hold him up, Adam eased him all the way down.

'Hurts,' said Mac.

'I know.' Adam didn't sound angry anymore – of course, he was talking to Mac and not me. 'If you change, it'll heal faster.'

Mac blinked up at him.

'I don't think he knows how to do it on purpose,' I offered.

Adam slanted a thoughtful look at the body, then back at me. 'You said something about a cage and experiments?'

Mac didn't say anything, so I nodded. 'That's what he told me. Apparently someone has a drug that they are trying to get to work on werewolves.' I told him what Mac had told me, then gave him the details of my own encounter with the dead werewolf and his human comrade. I'd already told Adam most of the salient facts, but I wasn't certain how much information made it through his anger, so I just told him all of it again.

'Damn it,' said Adam succinctly when I'd finished. 'Poor kid.' He turned back to Mac. 'All right. You're going to be fine. The first thing we're going to do is call your wolf out so that you can heal.'

'No,' Mac said, looking wildly at me, then at the dead wolfman. 'I can't control myself when I'm like that. I'll hurt someone.'

'Look at me,' said Adam, and even though the dark, raspy voice hadn't been directed at me, I found myself unable to pull my eyes off him. Mac was riveted.

'It's all right, Alan. I won't allow you to hurt Mercy – much as she deserves it. Nor,' Adam continued, proving that he was observant 'will I allow you to eat the dead.'

When Mac hesitated, I walked back over and knelt beside

Adam so I could look Mac in the eye. 'I told you, he can control your wolf until you can. That's why he's Alpha. You can trust him.'

Mac stared at me, then closed his eyes and nodded. 'All right. But I don't know how.'

'You'll get the hang of it,' Adam said. 'But for right now I'll help you.' His knee nudged me away, as he got out his pocket knife. 'This will be easier without your clothing.'

I got up as unobtrusively as I could and tried not to flinch when Mac cried out.

The change is not easy or painless at the best of times, and it was worse without the aid of the moon's call. I don't know why they can't change like I do, but I had to close my eyes against the pained sounds that came from the corner of my garage. Certainly the broken collarbone didn't make the shift any easier for Mac. Some werewolves can change relatively quickly with practice, but a new werewolf can take a lot of time.

I slipped out of the garage through the office and walked out the door, both to give them some privacy and because I couldn't bear Mac's suffering anymore. I sat on the single cement step outside the office and waited.

Elizaveta returned, leaning on her grandson's arm about the same time that Mac's scream turned into a wolf's cry.

'There is another werewolf?' Elizaveta asked me.

I nodded and got to my feet. 'That boy I told you about,' I said. 'Adam's here, though, so it's safe. Did you clean Stefan's van?' I nodded at the bus.

'Yes, yes. Did you think you were dealing with an amateur?' She gave an offended sniff. 'Your vampire friend will never know that his van held a corpse other than his own.'

'Thank you.' I tilted my head, but I couldn't hear anything from inside the garage, so I opened the office door and called, 'Adam?'

'It's all right,' he said, sounding tired. 'It's safe.'

'Elizaveta is here with her chauffeur,' I warned him in case he hadn't noticed them when he'd stormed in.

'Have her come in, too.'

I would have held open the door, but Elizaveta's grandson took it out of my hand and held it for both of us. Elizaveta shifted her bony grasp from his arm to mine, though from the strength of her grip I was pretty certain that she didn't need help walking.

Mac was curled up in the far corner of the garage where I'd left him. His wolf form was dark gray, blending in with the shadows on the cement floor. He had one white foot and a white stripe down his nose. Werewolves usually have markings that are more doglike than wolflike. I don't know why. Bran, the Marrok, has a splash of white on his tail, as though he'd dipped it in a bucket of paint. I think it's cute – but I'd never had the nerve to tell him so.

Adam was kneeling beside the dead man, paying no attention to Mac at all. He looked up when we came in from the office. 'Elizaveta Arkadyevna,' he said in a formal greeting, then added something in Russian. Switching back to English, he continued, 'Robert, thank you for coming tonight, too.'

Elizaveta said something in Russian directed at Adam.

'Not quite yet,' Adam replied. 'Can you reverse his change?' He gestured to the dead man. 'I don't recognize his scent, but I'd like to get a good look at his face.'

Elizaveta frowned and spoke rapidly in Russian to her grandson. His response had her nodding, and they chatted for a few moments more before she turned back to Adam. 'That might be possible. I can certainly try.'

'I don't suppose you have a camera here, Mercy?' Adam asked.

'I do,' I told him. I work on old cars. Sometimes I work on cars that other people have 'restored' in new and interesting fashions. I've found that getting a picture of the cars before I work on them is useful in putting them back together again. 'I'll get it.'

'And bring a piece of paper and an ink stamp pad if you have it. I'll send his fingerprints off to a friend for identification.'

By the time I returned, the corpse was back in human form, and the hole I'd torn in his neck gaped open like a popped balloon. His skin was blue with blood loss. I'd seen dead men before, but none that I was responsible for killing.

The change had torn his clothing – and not in the interesting way that comic books and fantasy artists always depict it. The crotch of his pants was ripped open along with his blood-soaked shirt's neck and shoulder seams. It seemed terribly undignified.

Adam took the digital camera from me and snapped a few pictures from different angles, then tucked it back in its case and slung it over his shoulder.

'I'll get it back to you as soon as I get these pictures off it,' he promised absently as he took the paper and ink stamp and, rather expertly, rolled the limp fingers in the ink, then on the sheet of paper.

Things moved rapidly after that. Adam helped Elizaveta's grandson deposit the body in the luxurious depths of the trunk of her car for disposal. Elizaveta did her mumbles and shakes that washed my garage in magic and, hopefully, left it clean of any evidence that I'd ever had a dead man inside. She took Mac's clothing, too.

'Hush,' said Adam, when Mac growled an objection. 'They were little more than rags anyway. I've clothes that should fit you at my house, and we'll pick up more tomorrow.'

Mac gave him a look.

'You're coming home with me,' said Adam, in a tone that brooked no argument. 'I'll not have a new werewolf running loose around my city. You come and learn a thing or two, then I'll let you stay or go as you choose – but not until I'm satisfied you can control yourself.'

'I am going now; it is not good for an old woman like me to be up this late,' Elizaveta said. She looked at me sourly. 'Don't do anything stupid for a while if you can help it, Mercedes. I do not want to come back out here.'

She sounded as if she came out to clean up my messes on a regular basis, though this was the first time. I was tired, and the sick feeling that killing a man had left in my stomach was still trying to bring up what little was left of my dinner. Her sharpness raised the hackles I was too on edge to pull down, so my response wasn't as diplomatic as it ought to have been.

'I wouldn't want that, either,' I said smoothly.

She caught the implied insult, but I kept my eyes wide and limpid so she wouldn't know whether I meant it or not. Insulting witches is right up there on the stupid list with enraging Alpha werewolves and cuddling with a new wolf next to a dead body: all of which I'd done tonight. I couldn't help it, though. Defiance was a habit I'd developed to preserve myself while growing up with a pack of dominant and largely male werewolves. Werewolves, like other predators, respect bravado. If you are too careful not to anger them, they'll see it as a weakness – and weak things are prey.

Tomorrow I was going to repair old cars and keep my head down for a while. I'd used up all my luck tonight.

Adam seemed to agree because he took Elizaveta's hand and tucked it into the crook of his elbow, drawing her attention back to him as he escorted her back to her car. Her grandson Robert gave me a lazy grin.

'Don't push the babushka too hard, Mercy,' he said softly. 'She likes you, but that won't stop her if she feels you aren't showing her proper respect.'

'I know,' I said. 'I'm going home to see if a few hours of sleep won't curb my tongue before it gets us into trouble.' I meant to sound humorous, but it just came out tired.

Robert gave me a sympathetic smile before he left.

A heavy weight leaned against my hip and I looked down to see Mac. He gave me what I imagined was a sympathetic look. Adam was still with Elizaveta, but Mac didn't seem to be having trouble. I scratched him lightly behind one pricked ear.

'Come on,' I told him. 'Let's lock up.'

This time I remembered to grab my purse.

# 4

Home at last, I decided that there was only one remedy for a night like this. My stash of dark chocolate was gone, and I'd eaten the last gingersnap, so I turned on the oven and pulled out the mixing bowl. By the time someone knocked at my door, I was pouring chocolate chips into the cookie dough.

On my doorstep was a sprite of a girl with Day-Glo orange hair that sprang from her head in riotous curls, wearing enough eye makeup to supply a professional cheerleading squad for a month. In one hand she held my camera.

'Hey, Mercy. Dad sent me over to give you this and to get me out of the way while he dealt with some pack business.' She rolled her eyes as she handed me the camera. 'He acts like I don't know enough to stay out of the way of strange werewolves.'

'Hey, Jesse,' I said and waved her inside.

'Besides,' she continued as she came in and toed off her shoes, 'this wolf was cute. With a little stripe here—' She ran her finger down her nose. 'He wasn't going to hurt me. I was just rubbing his belly and my father came in and had a *cow* – oh yum, cookie dough! Can I have some?'

Jesse was Adam's daughter, fifteen going on forty. She spent most of the year with her mother in Eugene – she must be in town to spend Thanksgiving with Adam. It seemed a little early to me for that, since Thanksgiving wasn't until Thursday, but she went to some private school for brilliant and eccentric kids, so maybe her vacations were longer than the public schools'.

'Did you dye your hair especially for your father?' I asked, finding a spoon and handing it to her with a healthy glob of dough.

'Of course,' she said, taking a bite, then continuing to talk as if her mouth weren't half-full. 'It makes him feel all fatherly if he can complain about something. Besides,' she said with an air of righteousness, 'everyone in Eugene is doing it. It'll wash out in a week or two. When I was tired of the lecture, I just told him he was lucky I didn't use superglue to put spikes in like my friend Jared. Maybe I'll do that next vacation. This is good stuff.' She started to put her spoon in the dough for another round, and I slapped her hand.

'Not after it's been in your mouth,' I told her. I gave her another spoon, finished mixing in the chips, and began dropping cookie dough on the pans.

'Oh, I almost forgot,' she said, after another bite, 'my father sent the camera with a message. It was needlessly cryptic, but I knew you'd tell me what it meant. Are you ready?'

I put the first pan in the oven and started loading the next one. 'Shoot.'

'He said, "Got a hit. Don't fret. He was a hired gun."' She waved her empty spoon at me. 'Now explain it to me.'

I suppose I should have respected Adam's need to protect his daughter, but he was the one who sent her to me. 'I killed a man tonight. Your father found out who he was.'

'Really? And he was a hit man? Cool.' She dropped the spoon in the sink next to the first one, then boosted herself up to sit on my counter and conducted a rapid question and answer session all by herself. 'Was that what you called him about earlier? He was fit to be tied. How come you called Dad? No wait. The man you killed was a werewolf, too, wasn't he? That's why Dad took off so fast. Who is the wolf he came back with?' She paused. '*You* killed a werewolf? Did you have a gun?'

Several. But I hadn't brought one with me to the garage.

She had paused, so I answered her last two questions. 'Yep and nope.'

'Awesome.' She grinned. 'Hey, how'dja do it?'

'It wasn't on purpose,' I told her repressively. I might as well have tried holding back a tidal wave with my bare hands, it would have had as much effect.

'Of course not,' she said. 'Not unless you were really pi—' I raised an eyebrow and she changed the word without slowing down. '—ticked off. Did you have a knife? Or was it a crowbar?'

'My teeth,' I told her.

'Ewwe—' She grimaced briefly. 'Nasty. Oh, I see. You mean that you took him on while you were a coyote?'

Most humans only know about the fae – and there are still a lot of people who think that the fae are just a hoax perpetrated by the government or on the government, take your pick. Jesse, however, as the daughter of a werewolf, human though she was, was quite aware of the 'Wild Things' as she called them. Part of that was my fault. The first time I met her, shortly after the Alpha had moved his family next to my home, she'd asked me if I were a werewolf like her father. I told her what I was, and she nagged me until I showed her what it looked like when I took my other form. I think she was nine and already a practiced steamroller.

'Yep. I was just trying to get his attention so he'd chase me and leave Mac – that's the striped werewolf—' I imitated her finger-down-the-nose gesture. 'He is pretty nice,' I told her. Then, feeling I had to play adult in fairness to her father, I said, 'But he's a newbie, and his control isn't terrific yet. So listen to your father about him, okay? If Mac bit you or hurt you, it would make him feel awful, and he's had a bad enough time of it already.' I hesitated. It really wasn't my business, but I liked Jesse. 'There are a few of your father's wolves that you really do need to stay away from.'

She nodded, but said confidently, 'They won't hurt me, not with *my* father. But you mean Ben, don't you? Dad told me to stay out of his way. I met him yesterday when he stopped by.' She wrinkled her nose. 'He's a snark – even if he has that cool British accent.'

I wasn't certain what a snark was, but I was certain Ben qualified.

We ate the cookies as they came out of the oven, and I gave her a loaded plate covered with tinfoil to take back with her. I went out to the porch with her and saw a sales-lot of cars parked at Adam's house. He must have called in the pack.

'I'll walk you home,' I said, slipping on the shoes I kept on the porch for when it was muddy.

She rolled her eyes, but waited for me. 'Really, Mercy, what'll you do if one of the pack decides to bother us?'

'I can scream really loud,' I said. 'That's if I don't decide to use my newly patented technique and kill him, too.'

'That's right,' she said. 'But I'd stick to screaming. I don't think that Dad would like it if you started killing his wolves.'

Probably none of them would harm a hair of her head, just as she thought. I was almost sure she was right. But one of the cars I could see was Ben's red truck. I wouldn't leave a fifteen-year-old alone if Ben was around no matter whose daughter she was.

No one bothered us as we walked through my back field. 'Nice car,' she murmured, as we passed the donor Rabbit's corpse. 'Dad really appreciates you setting it out here for him. Good for you. I told him the next time he annoyed you, you were likely to paint graffiti on it.'

'Your father is a subtle man,' I told her. 'I'm saving the

58

graffiti for later. I've decided that the next time he gets obnoxious, I'll take three tires off.' I held my hand out and canted it, like a car with one wheel.

She giggled. 'It would drive him nuts. You should see him when the pictures aren't hanging straight on the walls.' We reached the back fence, and she climbed cautiously through the old barbed wire. 'If you do decide to paint it — let me help?'

'Absolutely,' I promised. 'I'll wait here until you're safely inside.'

She rolled her eyes again, but grinned and sprinted for her back porch. I waited until she waved to me once from Adam's back door and disappeared inside.

When I took the garbage out before I went to bed, I noticed that Adam's place was still full of cars. It was a long meeting, then. Made me grateful I wasn't a werewolf.

I turned to go into my house and stopped. I'd been stupid. It doesn't matter how good your senses are if you aren't paying attention.

'Hello, Ben,' I said, to the man standing between me and the house.

'You've been telling tales, Mercedes Thompson,' he said pleasantly. As Jesse had said, he had a nifty English accent. He wasn't bad-looking either, if a trifle effeminate for my taste.

'Mmm?' I said.

He tossed his keys up in the air and caught them one-handed, once, twice, three times without taking his eyes off mine. If I yelled, Adam would hear, but, as I told him earlier, I didn't belong to him. He was possessive enough, thank you. I didn't really believe Ben was stupid enough to do something to me, not with Adam within shouting distance.

'"Stay here a moment, Ben,"' Ben said, with an exaggeration of the drawl that Adam's voice still held from a childhood spent in the deep South. '"Wait until my daughter has had a chance to get to her room. Wouldn't want to expose her to the likes of you."' The last sentence lost Adam's tone and fell back into his own crisp British accent. He didn't sound quite like Prince Charles, but closer to that than to Fagin in *Oliver*.

'I don't know what you think it has to do with me,' I told him with a shrug. 'You're the one who got kicked out of the London pack. If Adam hadn't taken you, you'd have been in real trouble.'

'It wasn't me that done it,' he growled ungrammatically. I refrained from correcting him with an effort. 'And as for what you have to do with it, Adam told me you'd warned him to keep Jesse out of my way.'

I didn't remember doing that although I might have. I shrugged. Ben had come to town a few months ago in a flurry of gossip. There had been three particularly brutal rapes in his London neighborhood, and the police had been looking in his direction. Guilty or not, his Alpha felt it would be good to get him out of the limelight and shipped him to Adam.

The police hadn't anything to hold him on, but after he'd emigrated the rapes stopped. I checked – the Internet is an amazing thing. I remembered speaking to Adam about it, and I warned him to watch Ben around vulnerable women. I'd been thinking about Jesse, but I didn't think I'd said that explicitly.

'You don't like women,' I told him. 'You are rude and abrasive. What do you expect him to do?'

'Go home, Ben,' said a molasses-deep voice from just behind my right shoulder. I needed to get more sleep, darn it, if I was letting everyone sneak up on me.

'Darryl,' I said, glancing back at Adam's second.

Darryl was a big man, well over six feet. His mother had been Chinese, Jesse had told me, and his father an African tribesman who had been getting an engineering degree at an American university when they met. Darryl's features were an arresting blend of the two cultures. He looked like someone who should have been modeling or starring in movies, but he was a Ph.D. engineer working at the Pacific Northwest Laboratories in some sort of government hush-hush project.

I didn't know him well, but he had that eminently respectable air that college professors sometimes have. I much preferred him at my back to Ben, but I wasn't happy being between two werewolves, whoever they were. I stepped sideways until I could see them both.

'Mercy.' He nodded at me but kept his eyes on Ben. 'Adam noticed you were missing and sent me to find you.' When Ben didn't respond, he said, 'Don't screw up. This is not the time.'

Ben pursed his lips thoughtfully, then smiled, an expression that made a remarkable difference to his face. Only for an instant, he looked boyishly charming. 'No fuss. Just telling a pretty lady good night. Good night, sweet Mercedes. Dream of me.'

I opened my mouth to make a smart comment, but Darryl caught my eye and made a cutoff gesture with his hand. If I'd had a really good comeback, I'd have said it anyway, but I didn't, so I kept my mouth shut.

Darryl waited until Ben started off, before saying brusquely, 'Good night, Mercy. Lock your doors.' Then he strode off toward Adam's.

Between the dead wolf and Ben's wish, I suppose I should have had nightmares, but instead I slept deeply and without dreams – none I remembered anyway.

I slept with the radio on, because otherwise, with my

hearing, all I did was catnap all night. I'd tried earplugs, but that blocked sound a little too well for my peace of mind. So I turned music on low to block the normal sounds of night and figured anything louder would wake me up.

Something woke me up that morning about an hour before the alarm, but though I turned down the music and listened, all I heard was a car with a well-muffled Chevy 350 driving away.

I rolled over to go back to sleep, but Medea realized I was awake and began yowling at me to let her out. She wasn't particularly loud, but very persistent. I decided it had been long enough since Adam's note that letting her run wouldn't make him feel like I was deliberately defying him. It would also buy me some quiet so I could catch that last hour of sleep.

Reluctantly, I got out of my warm bed and pulled on jeans and a T-shirt. Happy to have me up and moving, Medea stropped my shins and generally got in the way as I staggered blearily out of my room, across the living room to the front door. I yawned and turned the doorknob, but when I tried to open the door, it resisted. Something was holding it shut.

With an exasperated sigh, I put my shoulder against the door and it moved a reluctant inch or so, far enough for me to catch a whiff of what lay on the other side: death.

Wide-awake, I shut the door and locked it. I'd smelled something else, too, but I didn't want to admit it. I ran back to my room, shoved my feet in my shoes, and opened the gun safe. I grabbed the SIG 9mm and shoved a silver-loaded magazine in it, then tucked the gun into the top of my pants. It was cold, uncomfortable, and reassuring. But not reassuring enough.

I'd never actually shot anything but targets. If I hunted, I did it on four paws. My foster father, a werewolf himself, had insisted I learn how to shoot and how to make the bullets.

If this was werewolf business, and, after the previous night, I had to assume it was – I needed a bigger gun. I took down the .444 Marlin and loaded it for werewolf. It was a short rifle, and small unless you took a good look at the size of the barrel. The lipstick-sized silver bullets were guaranteed, as my foster father used to say, to make even a werewolf sit up and take notice. Then he'd put a finger alongside his nose, smile, and say, 'Or lie down and take notice, if you know what I mean.' The Marlin had been his gun.

The rifle was a comfortable, fortifying presence when I quietly opened my back door and stepped out into the predawn night. The air was still and cold: I took a deep breath and smelled death, undeniable and final.

As soon as I rounded the corner of the trailer I could see the body on my front porch, blocking my front door. He was on his face, but my nose told me who it was – just as it had when I first opened the door. Whoever had dumped him had been very quiet, wakening me only as they drove off. There was no one else there now, just Mac and me.

I climbed the four steps up to my porch and crouched in front of the boy. My breath fogged the air, but there was no mist rising from his face, no heartbeat.

I rolled him onto his back and his body was still warm to my touch. It had melted the frost off the porch where he had lain. He smelled of Adam's home; a fragrant mix of woodsmoke and the pungent air freshener favored by Adam's housekeeper. I couldn't smell anything that would tell me who had killed Mac and left him as a warning.

I sat on the frost-coated wood of the porch, set the rifle beside me, and touched his hair gently. I hadn't known him long enough for him to have a hold on my heart, but I had liked what I'd seen.

The squealing of tires pealing out had me back on my feet with rifle in hand as a dark-colored SUV shot away from Adam's house like the fires of hell were behind it. In the dim predawn light, I couldn't tell what color it was: black or dark blue or even green. It might even have been the same vehicle that the villains had driven last night at the shop – newer cars of a similar make all look alike to me.

I don't know why it had taken me so long to realize that Mac dead on my front porch meant that something bad had happened at Adam's house. I abandoned the dead in hopes of being of use to the living, tearing across my back field at a sprinter's pace, the rifle tucked under my arm.

Adam's house was lit up like a Christmas tree. Unless he had company, it was usually dark. Werewolves, like walkers, do very well in the dark.

When I came to the fence between our properties, I held the rifle away from my body and vaulted the barbed wire with a hand on top of the post. I'd been carrying the Marlin at quarter cock, but as soon as I landed on the other side of the fence, I pulled the hammer back.

I would have gone through the back door if there had not been a tremendous crash from the front. I shifted my goal and made it around the side of the house in time to see the couch land half-in and half-out of the flower bed that lined the porch, evidently thrown through the living room window and the porch rails.

The werewolf I'd killed last night notwithstanding, werewolves are taught to be quiet when they fight – it's a matter of survival. Only with the broken window and the front door hanging wide open, did I hear the snarls.

I whispered the swear words I usually only bring out for rusty bolts and aftermarket parts that don't fit as advertised to give me courage as I ran. *Dear Lord*, I thought, in a sincere prayer, as I ran up the porch stairs, *please don't let anything permanent have happened to Adam or Jesse.*

I hesitated just inside the door, my heart in my mouth and the Marlin at the ready. I was panting, from nerves as much as exertion, and the noise interfered with my hearing.

Most of the destruction seemed to be concentrated in the high-ceilinged living room just off the entryway. The white Berber carpet would never be the same. One of the dining room chairs had been reduced to splinters against the wall, but the wall had suffered, too: broken plaster littered the floor.

Most of the glass from the shattered window was spread outside on the porch; the glass on the carpet was from a mirror that had been jerked off the wall and slammed over someone's head.

The werewolf was still there, a sizable chunk of mirror embedded in her spine. It wasn't a werewolf I knew: not one of Adam's because there were only three females in Adam's pack, and I knew all of them. She was near enough to truly dead that she wasn't going to be a problem for a while, so I ignored her.

I found a second werewolf under the fainting couch. (I liked to tease Adam about his fainting couch – How many women do you expect to faint in your living room, Adam?) He'd have to buy a new one. The seat was broken with splinters of wood sticking through the plush fabric. The second werewolf lay chest down on the floor. His head was twisted backward, and his death-clouded eyes stared accusingly at me.

I stepped over a pair of handcuffs, the bracelets bent and broken. They weren't steel or aluminum, but some silver alloy. Either they were specifically made to restrain a werewolf, or they were a specialty item from a high-ticket BDSM shop. They must have been used on Adam; he'd never have brought a wolf he had to restrain into his house while Jesse was here.

The noises of the fight were coming from around the corner of the living room, toward the back of the house. I ran along the wall, glass crunching under my feet and stopped just this side of the dining room as wood cracked and the floor vibrated.

I put my head around the corner cautiously, but I needn't have worried. The fighting werewolves were too involved with each other to pay attention to me.

Adam's dining room was large and open with patio doors that looked out over a rose garden. The floors were oak parquet – the real stuff. His ex-wife had had a table that could seat fifteen made to match the floor. That table was upside down and embedded in the far wall about four feet from the floor. The front of the matching china closet had been broken, as if someone had thrown something large and heavy into it. The result of the destruction was a fairly large, clear area for the werewolves to fight in.

The first instant I saw them, all I could do was hold my breath at the speed and grace of their motion. For all their size, werewolves still resemble their gracile cousin the timber wolf more than a Mastiff or Saint Bernard, who are closer to their weight. When weres run, they move with a deadly, silent grace. But they aren't really built for running, they are built for fighting, and there is a deadly beauty to them that comes out only in battle.

I'd only seen Adam's wolf form four or five times, but it was something you didn't forget. His body was a deep silver, almost blue, with an undercoat of lighter colors. Like a Siamese cat's, his muzzle, ears, tail, and legs deepened to black.

The wolf he was fighting was bigger, a silvery buff color more common among coyotes than wolves. I didn't know him.

At first, the size difference didn't bother me. You don't get to be the Alpha without being able to fight – and Adam had been a warrior before he'd been Changed. Then I realized that all the blood on the floor was dripping from Adam's belly, and the white flash I saw on his side was a rib bone.

I stepped out where I could get better aim and lifted the rifle, pointing the barrel at the strange werewolf, waiting until I could take a shot without risking hitting Adam.

The buff-colored wolf seized Adam just behind the neck and shook him like a dog killing a snake. It was meant to break Adam's neck, but the other wolf's grip wasn't firm, and instead he threw Adam into the dining table, sending the whole mess crashing onto the floor and giving me the opportunity I'd been waiting for.

I shot the wolf in the back of the head from less than six feet away. Just as my foster father had taught me, I shot him at a slight downward angle, so that the Marlin's bullet didn't go through him and travel on to hit anyone else who happened to be standing in the wrong place for the next quarter mile or so.

Marlin .444's were not built for home defense; they were built to kill grizzlies and have even been used a time or two to take out elephants. Just what the doctor ordered for werewolves. One shot at all but point-blank and he was dead. I walked up to him and shot him one more time, just to make sure.

I'm not usually a violent person, but it felt good to pull the trigger. It soothed the building rage I'd felt ever since I'd knelt on my porch next to Mac's body.

I glanced at Adam, lying in the midst of his dining table, but he didn't move, not even to open his eyes. His elegant muzzle was covered in gore. His silver hair was streaked dark with blood and matted so it was hard to see the full extent of his wounds. What I could see was bad enough.

Someone had done a fair job of gutting him: I could see pale intestines and the white of bone where the flesh had peeled away from his ribs.

He might be alive, I told myself. My ears were still ringing. I was breathing too hard, my heart racing too fast and loud: it might be enough to cover the sound of his heart, of his breath. This was more damage than I'd ever seen a werewolf heal from, far more than the other two dead wolves or the one I'd killed last night.

I put the rifle back on quarter cock, and waded through the remains of the table to touch Adam's nose. I still couldn't tell if he was breathing.

I needed help.

I ran to the kitchen where, in true Adam fashion, he had a tidy list of names and numbers on the counter just below the wall phone. My finger found Darryl's name with his work, home, and pager number printed in black block letters. I set my gun down where I could reach it fast and dialed his home number first.

'You have reached the home of Dr Darryl Zao. You may leave a message after the tone or call his pager at 543—' Darryl's bassy-rumble sounded intimate despite the impersonal message.

I hung up and tried his work number, but he wasn't there either. I'd started dialing his pager, but while I'd been trying to call him, I'd been thinking about our encounter last night.

*'This isn't the time,'* he'd told Ben. I hadn't given it a second thought last night, but had there been a special emphasis in his voice? Had he meant, as I'd assumed: not after all the effort Ben had put into being on his best behavior since his banishment from London? Or had it been more specific as in: not now, when we have greater matters to deal with? Greater matters like killing the Alpha.

In Europe, murder was still mostly the way the rule of

the pack changed hands. The old Alpha ruled until one of the younger, hungrier dominant males decided the old one had grown weak and attacked him. I knew of at least one European Alpha who killed any male who showed signs of being dominant.

In the New World, thanks to the iron hand of the Marrok, things were more civilized. Leadership was mostly imposed from above – and no one challenged the Marrok's decisions, at least not as long as I had known him. But could someone have come into Adam's house and done this much damage without help from Adam's pack?

I hung up the phone and stared at the list of names, none of whom I dared call for help until I knew more about what was going on. My gaze dropped and rested on a photograph in a wooden frame set out beside the list.

A younger Jesse grinned at me with a baseball bat over her shoulder and a cap pulled a little to one side.

*Jesse.*

I snatched up my rifle and sprinted up the stairs to her room. She wasn't there. I couldn't tell if there had been a struggle in it or not – Jesse tended to live in a tumult that reflected itself in the way she kept her room.

In coyote form, my senses are stronger. So I hid both of my guns under her bed, stripped out of my clothes, and changed.

Jesse's scent was all over the room, but I also caught a hint of the human who'd confronted Mac at my garage last night. I followed the trail of his scent down the stairs because Jesse's scent was too prevalent to find a single trail.

I was almost out the door when a sound stopped me in my tracks. I temporarily abandoned the trail to investigate. At first I thought perhaps I had only heard one of the pieces of overturned furniture settling, but then I noticed Adam's left front paw had moved.

Once I saw that, I realized I could hear the almost imperceptible sound of his breathing. Maybe it was only the sharper senses of the coyote, but I would have sworn he hadn't been breathing earlier. If he was alive, there was a very good chance he'd stay that way. Werewolves are tough.

I whined happily, crawled over the wreckage of his table, and licked his bloody face once before resuming my search for his daughter.

Adam's house is at the end of a dead-end road. Directly in front of his house is a turnaround. The SUV I'd seen take off – presumably with Jesse – had left a short trail of burning rubber – but most cars have very little individual scent until they grow old. This one had not left enough behind for me to trail once the tang of burnt rubber faded from its tires.

There was no more trail to follow, nothing I could do for Jesse, nothing I could do for Mac. I turned my attention to Adam.

That he was alive meant I really could not contact his pack, not with him helpless. If any of the dominants had aspirations to become Alpha, they'd kill him. I also couldn't just bring him to my house. First, as soon as someone realized he was missing, they'd check my place out. Second, a badly wounded werewolf was dangerous to himself and everyone around him. Even if I could trust his wolves, there was no dominant in the Columbia Basin Pack strong enough to keep Adam's wolf under control until he was well enough to control himself.

I knew where one was, though.

# 5

PATRICIA BRIGGS

A Vanagon resembles nothing so much as a Twinkie on wheels; a fifteen-foot-long, six-foot-wide Twinkie with as much aerodynamic styling as a barn door. In the twelve years that VW imported them into the US, they never put anything bigger in them than the four-cylinder *wasser-boxer* engine. My 1989 four-wheel-drive, four-thousand-pound Syncro's engine put out a whopping ninety horses.

In layman's terms, that means I was cruising up the inter-state with a dead body and a wounded werewolf at sixty miles an hour. Downhill, with a good tailwind, the van could go seventy-five. Uphill I was lucky to make fifty. I could have pushed it a little faster, but only if I wanted to chance blowing my engine altogether. For some reason, the thought of being stranded by the roadside with my current cargo was enough to keep my foot off the gas pedal.

The highway stretched out before me in gentle curves that were mostly empty of traffic or scenic beauty unless you liked scrub desert better than I did. I didn't want to think of Mac, or of Jesse, scared and alone – or of Adam who might be dying because I chose to move him rather than call his pack. So I took out my cell phone.

I called my neighbors first. Dennis Cather was a retired pipefitter, and his wife Anna a retired nurse. They'd moved in two years ago and adopted me after I fixed their tractor.

'Yes.' Anna's voice was so normal after the morning I'd had, it took me a moment to answer.

'Sorry to call you so early,' I told her. 'But I've been called out of town on a family emergency. I shouldn't be gone

71

long – just a day or two – but I didn't check to make sure Medea had food and water.'

'Don't fret, dear,' she said. 'We'll look after her. I hope that it's nothing serious.'

I couldn't help but glance back at Adam in the rearview mirror. He was still breathing. 'It's serious. One of my foster family is hurt.'

'You go take care of what you need to,' she said briskly. 'We'll see to things here.'

It wasn't until after I cut the connection that I wondered if I had involved them in something dangerous. Mac had been left on my doorstep for a reason – a warning to keep my nose out of someone's business. And I was most certainly sticking my whole head in it now.

I was doing as much as I could for Adam, and I thought of something I could do for Jesse. I called Zee.

Siebold Adelbertsmiter, Zee for short, had taught me everything I knew about cars. Most fae are very sensitive to iron, but Zee was a Metallzauber – which is a rather broad category name given to the few fae who could handle metal of all kinds. Zee preferred the modern American term 'gremlin,' which he felt better fit his talents. I wasn't calling him for his talents, but for his connections.

'Ja,' said a gruff male voice.

'Hey, Zee, it's Mercy. I have a favor to ask.'

'Ja sure, Liebling,' he said. 'What's up?'

I hesitated. Even after all this time, the rule of keeping pack trouble in the pack was hard to break – but Zee knew everyone in the fae community.

I outlined the past day to him, as best I could.

'So you think this baby werewolf of yours brought this trouble here? Why then did they take our kleine Jesse?'

'I don't know,' I said. 'I'm hoping that when Adam recovers he'll know something more.'

'So you are asking me to see if anyone I know has seen these strange wolves in hopes of finding Jesse?'

'There were at least four werewolves moving into the Tri-Cities. You'd think that someone among the fae would have noticed.' Because the Tri-Cities was so close to the Walla Walla Fae Reservation, there were more fae living here than was usual.

'*Ja*,' Zee agreed heavily. 'You'd think. I will ask around. Jesse is a good girl; she should not be in these evil men's hands longer than we can help.'

'If you go by the garage, would you mind putting a note in the window?' I asked. 'There's a "Closed for the Holidays" sign under the counter in the office.'

'You think they might come after me if I opened it for you?' he asked. Zee often ran the garage if I had to be out of town. 'You may be right. *Ja, gut*. I'll open the garage today and tomorrow.'

It had been a long time since Siebold Adelbertsmiter of the Black Forest had been sung about, so long that those songs had faded from memory, but there was something of the spirit of the *Heldenlieder*, the old German hero songs, about him still.

'A werewolf doesn't need a sword or gun to tear you to bits,' I said, unable to leave it alone, though I knew better than to argue with the old gremlin once he'd made up his mind. 'Your metalworking magic won't be much help against one.'

He snorted. 'Don't you worry about me, *Liebling*. I was killing werewolves when this country was still a Viking colony.' Many of the lesser fae talked about how old they were, but Zee had told me that most of them shared a life span similar to humankind. Zee was a lot older than that.

I sighed and gave in. 'All right. But be careful. If you're going to be there, I have a parts order that should be in.

Could you check it for me? I haven't ordered from this place before, but my usual source was out.'

'*Ja wohl*. Leave it to me.'

The next call I made was to Stefan's answering machine. 'Hey, Stefan,' I told it. 'This is Mercy. I'm headed to Montana today. I don't know when I'll be back. Probably late this week. I'll give you a call.' I hesitated, but there really wasn't a good way to say the next part. 'I had to haul a dead body in your van. It's fine; Elizeveta Arkadyevna cleaned it. I'll explain when I get back.'

Mentioning Elizaveta reminded me of something else I needed to do. Adam's house was on the end of the road, but it was clearly visible from the river. Someone would notice that the couch was sitting in the flowerbeds and call the police if the mess wasn't cleaned up soon.

I had her number on my phone, though I'd never had occasion to use it before. I got her answering machine and left a message telling her there was a mess at Adam's house, there had been a dead man on my porch, Jesse was missing, and I was taking Adam, who was wounded, somewhere he'd be safe. Then I closed the phone and put it away. I didn't know what happened at Adam's house, but that didn't stop me from feeling guilty and responsible. If I hadn't interfered last night when the two bullies came to find Mac, would everyone still be alive? If I'd sent Mac to Montana, to the Marrok, rather than letting Adam take him, what would that have changed?

Taking Mac to the Marrok had never even occurred to me. I hadn't contacted Bran since he'd sent me away from the pack, and he'd returned the favor. I took a quick glance behind my seat at the blue tarp concealing Mac's body. Well, I was bringing Mac to him now.

I found myself remembering the shy grin Mac had worn when I told him my name. I wiped my cheeks and fiercely blinked back further tears, but it was no use. I cried for him, for his parents and his brother who didn't even know he was dead. Doubtless they were all sitting beside their phones, waiting for him to call again.

I was coming down the grade into Spokane before more pressing worries distracted me from grief and guilt: Adam began stirring. My fear that Adam would die was instantly overwhelmed by the worry that he'd heal too fast.

I still had well over two hundred miles to go, most of it two-lane mountain highway meandering through dozens of small towns at twenty-five miles an hour. The last sixty miles was on a road marked 'other' on the state highway map – as opposed to highway or road. As I recalled, it was gravel most of the way. I figured it would take me at least four more hours.

Dominant wolves heal faster than the submissive wolves. By my rough estimate, it would be no more than two days before Adam was recovered enough to control his wolf – which would be capable of mayhem long before that. I needed Bran before Adam was mobile, and, if he was stirring already, I was going to be lucky if I made it.

When I hit Coeur d'Alene, where I'd have to leave the interstate for highway, I gassed up then drove to the first fast-food burger place I found and bought thirty cheese-burgers. The bemused teenager who started handing me bags through the service window peered curiously at me. I didn't explain, and she couldn't see my passengers because of the van's curtains.

I parked in the restaurant's parking lot, snatched a couple of the bags, stepped over Mac, and began stripping the buns off the meat. Adam was too weak to do more than growl at me and snatch the cheese-and-catsup-covered meat as fast as I could toss it to him. He ate almost twenty patties before he subsided into his previous comalike state.

The first few flakes of snow began falling on us as I took the highway north.

I drove into Troy, Montana, cursing the heavy wet snow that had distracted me so I missed my turnoff, which should have been several miles earlier. I topped off my gas tank, got directions, chained up, and headed back the way I'd come.

The snow was falling fast enough that the snow crews hadn't been able to keep up with it. The tracks of the cars preceding me were rapidly filling.

The gas station clerk's directions fresh in my mind, I slowed as I crossed back over the Yaak River. It was a baby river compared to the Kootenai, which I'd been driving next to for the past few hours.

I watched the side of the road carefully, and it was a good thing I did. The small green sign that marked the turnoff was half-covered in wet snow.

There was only one set of tracks up the road. They turned off at a narrow drive and, after that, I found my way up the road by driving where there were no trees. Happily, the trees were dense and marked the way pretty clearly.

The road twisted up and down the narrow river valley, and I was grateful for the four-wheel drive. Once, a couple of black-tailed deer darted in front of me. They gave me an irritated glance and trotted off.

It had been a long time since I'd been that way – I hadn't even had my driver's license then. The road was unfamiliar, and I began to worry I'd miss my turn. The road divided, one-half clearly marked, but the other half, the one I had to take, was barely wide enough for my van.

'Well,' I told Adam, who was whining restlessly, 'if we end up in Canada and you haven't eaten me yet, I suppose we can turn around, come back, and try again.'

I'd about decided I was going to have to do just that,

when I topped a long grade and saw a hand-carved wooden sign. I stopped the van.

*Aspen Creek*, the sign read in graceful script, carved and painted white on a dark brown background, *23 miles*. As I turned the van to follow the arrow, I wondered when Bran had decided to allow someone to post a sign. Maybe he'd gotten tired of having to send out guides — but he'd been adamant about keeping a low profile when I left.

I don't know why I expected everything to be the same. After all, I'd changed a good deal in the years since I'd last been there. I should have expected that Aspen Creek would have changed, too. I didn't have to like it.

The uninitiated would be forgiven for thinking there were only four buildings in Aspen Creek: the gas station/post office, the school, the church, and the motel. They wouldn't see the homes tucked unobtrusively up the draws and under the trees. There were a couple of cars in front of the gas station, but otherwise the whole town looked deserted. I knew better. There were always people watching, but they wouldn't bother me unless I did something unusual — like dragging a wounded werewolf out of my van.

I stopped in front of the motel office, just under the *Aspen Creek Motel* sign, which bore more than a passing resemblance to the sign I'd followed to town. The old motel was built the way the motor hotels had been in the middle of the last century — a long, narrow, and no-frills building designed so guests could park their vehicles in front of their rooms.

There was no one in the office, but the door was unlocked. It had been updated since I'd been there last and the end result was rustic charm — which was better than the run-down 1950s tacky it had been.

I hopped over the front desk and took a key marked #1.

Number one was the Marrok's safe room, specially designed to contain uncooperative werewolves.

I found a piece of paper and a pen and wrote: *Wounded in #1. Please Do Not Disturb.* I left the note on the desk where it couldn't be missed, then I returned to the van and backed it up to the room.

Getting Adam out of the van was going to be rough no matter what. At least when I dragged him into it, he'd been unconscious. I opened the reinforced metal door of the motel room and took a look around. The furnishing was new, but sparse, just a bed and a nightstand that was permanently fixed against the wall – nothing to help me get a werewolf who weighed twice what I did out of the van and into the room without hurting one or the other of us. There was no porch as there had been at Adam's house, which left almost a four-foot drop from the back of the van to the ground.

In the end I decided calling for help was better than hurting Adam worse. I went back to the office and picked up the phone. I hadn't called Sam's number since I'd left, but some things are just ingrained. Even though he was the reason I'd left here, he was the first one I thought to call for help.

'Hello,' answered a woman's voice that sounded completely unfamiliar.

I couldn't speak. I hadn't realized how much I'd been counting on hearing Samuel until I heard someone else's voice instead.

'Marlie? Is there something wrong at the motel? Do you need me to send Carl?' She must have caller ID, I thought stupidly.

She sounded frantic, but I recognized her voice at last, and felt a wave of relief. I don't know why Lisa Stoval was answering this number, but the mention of Carl and the sudden tension in her voice cued me in. I guess she had just never sounded cheerful when she talked to me.

Some things might have changed, but some things I had just forgotten. Aspen Creek had a population of about five hundred people, and only about seventy were werewolves, but I seldom thought about the human majority. Lisa and her husband Carl were both human. So was Marlie, at least she had been when I left. She'd also been about six years old.

'I don't know where Marlie is,' I told her. 'This is Mercedes, Mercedes Thompson. There's no one in the motel office. I'd really appreciate it if you'd send Carl down here, or tell me who else to call. I have the Alpha from the Columbia Basin Pack in my van. He's badly wounded, and I need help getting him into the motel room. Even better would be if you could tell me how to get ahold of Bran.'

Bran didn't have a telephone at his home – or hadn't when I left. For all I knew he had a cell phone now.

Lisa, like most of the women of Aspen Creek, had never liked me. But she wasn't one of those people who let a little thing like that get in the way of doing what was right and proper.

'Bran and some of the others have taken the new wolves out for their first hunt. Marlie's probably holed up somewhere crying. Lee, her brother, was one of the ones who tried to Change. He didn't make it.'

I'd forgotten. How could I have forgotten? The last full moon of October, all of those who chose to try to become werewolves were allowed to come forward. In a formal ceremony they were savaged by Bran, or by some other wolf who loved them, in the hopes that they would rise Changed. Most of them didn't make it. I remembered the tension that gripped the town through October and the sadness of November. Thanksgiving had a different meaning to the residents of Aspen Creek than it did for the rest of America.

'I'm sorry,' I said inadequately, feeling rawly incapable of dealing with more dead youngsters – I remembered Lee, too. 'Lee was a good kid.'

'I'll send Carl.' Lisa's voice was crisp, denying me the right to grieve or sympathize. She hung up without saying good-bye.

I avoided thinking – or looking at the tarp that covered Mac – while I sat in the van waiting for help. Instead, I fed Adam the remaining hamburgers while we waited. They were cold and congealed, but it didn't seem to bother the wolf. When they were gone, he closed his eyes and ignored me.

At long last, Carl pulled up next to me in a beat-up Jeep and climbed out. He was a big man, and had always been more of a man of action than words. He hugged me and thumped me on my back.

'Don't be such a stranger, Mercy,' he said, then laughed at my look of shock and ruffled my hair. I'd forgotten he liked to do that, forgotten the easy affection he showed to everyone – even Bran. 'Lisa said you have Adam here and he's in bad shape?'

Of course he'd know who the Alpha of the Columbia Basin Pack was. Adam's pack was closest to Aspen Creek.

I nodded and opened the back of my van so he could see what we were dealing with. Adam looked better than he had when I first put him in the van, but that wasn't saying much. I couldn't see the bones of his ribs anymore, but his coat was matted with blood and covered with wounds.

Carl whistled through his teeth, but all he said was, 'We'll need to tie his jaws shut until we get him in. I've got something we can use in the Jeep.'

He brought an Ace bandage and we wound it round and round Adam's muzzle. The wolf opened his eyes once, but didn't struggle.

It took a lot of grunting, a few swear words, and a little sweat, but the two of us managed to get Adam out of the van and into the room. Once we had him on the bed, I made Carl get back before I unwound the bandage and freed the wolf. I was fast, but even so, Adam caught my forearm with an eyetooth and drew blood. I jumped back as he rolled off his side and struggled to stand – driven to defend himself against the pain we'd caused him.

'Out,' Carl said, holding the door for me.

I complied and we shut the door behind us. Carl held it shut while I turned the key in the dead bolt. Unlike most motel rooms, this dead bolt operated by key from both sides – for just such situations. The windows were barred, the vents sealed. Number one served as prison and hospital on occasion: sometimes both.

Adam was safe – for now. Once he'd regained a little more strength things could still get problematical unless I tracked down Bran.

'Do you know where Bran took the new wolves?' I asked, shutting the back hatch of the van. Carl hadn't asked me about Mac – he didn't have a wolf's nose to tell him what was in the tarp – and I decided that Mac could ride with me for a while longer. Bran could decide what to do with his body.

'You don't want to go after him, Mercy,' Carl was saying. 'Too dangerous. Why don't you come home with me. We'll feed you while you wait.'

'How many wolves are left in town?' I asked. 'Is there anyone who could resist Adam's wolf?'

That was the downside of being dominant. If you did go moonstruck, you took everyone who was less dominant with you.

Carl hesitated. 'Adam's pretty weak yet. Bran will be back by dark.'

Something hit the door, and we both jumped.

'He took them up to the Lover's Canyon,' Carl told me, giving in to the obvious. 'Be careful.'

'Bran will have control of the new ones,' I told him. 'I'll be all right.'

'I'm not worried about them. You left enemies behind you, girl.'

I smiled tightly. 'I can't help what I am. If they are my enemies, it was not by my choice.'

'I know. But they'll still kill you if they can.'

The lovers were a pair of trees that had grown up twined around each other near the entrance to a small canyon about ten miles north of town. I parked next to a pair of old-style Land Rovers, a nearly new Chevy Tahoe, and a HumVee – the expensive version. Charles, Bran's son, was a financial genius, and the Marrok's pack would never be begging on street corners. When I left here, I'd had ten thousand dollars in a bank account, the result of part of my minimum wage earnings invested by Charles.

I stripped off my clothes in the van, jumped out into knee-deep snow, and shut the door. It was colder up in the mountains than it had been in Troy, and the snow had a crust of hard ice crystals that cut into the bare skin of my feet.

I shifted as fast as I could. It might have been safer to go as a human, but I didn't have the right kind of clothing on for a winter hike in Montana. I am not absolutely sure there *is* a right kind of clothing for a winter hike in Montana. Running as a coyote, I don't mind the cold all that much.

I'd grown used to city scents and sounds. The forest scents were no less strong, just different: fir, aspen, and pine instead of exhaust, fried grease, and humans. I heard the distinctive

rat-a-tat of a woodpecker, and, faintly, the howl of a wolf —
too deep to be that of a timber wolf.

The fresh snow, which was still falling, had done a fair
job of hiding their tracks, but I could still smell them. Bran
and his mate, Leah, both had brushed against the bough of
a white pine. Charles had left tracks where the ground was
half-sheltered by a boulder. Once my nose drew me to the
right places, I could see where the old snow had been broken
by paws before the snow had begun, and the tracks weren't
difficult to follow.

I hesitated when the wolves' tracks began to separate.
Bran had taken the new wolves — there seemed to be three
of them — while his sons, Charles and Samuel, and Leah,
Bran's mate, broke off, probably to hunt up game in the
hopes of chasing it back to the rest.

I needed to find Bran to tell him what had happened, to get
his help for Adam — but I followed Sam's trail instead. I couldn't
help it. I'd been in love with him since I was fourteen.

*Not that I am in love with him now*, I assured myself, following
his tracks down an abrupt drop and back up to a ridgetop
where the snow wasn't as deep because the wind periodically
swept it clean.

*I was only a teenager when I last saw him*, I thought. I hadn't
spoken to him since then, and he hadn't tried to contact me
either. Still, it had been his number I had called for help. I
hadn't even thought about calling anyone else.

On the tail of that thought, I realized the forest had fallen
silent behind me.

The winter woods were quiet. The birds, except for a scat-
tering of nut hatches, cedar waxwings, and a few others like
the woodpecker I'd heard, had gone south. But there was an
ominous quality to the silence behind me that was too heavy
to be only winter's stillness. I was being stalked.

I didn't look around, nor did I speed up. Werewolves chase things that run from them.

I wasn't really frightened. Bran was out there somewhere, and Samuel was even nearer. I could smell the earth-and-spice musk that belonged to him alone; the wind carried it to me. The tracks I was following had been laid several hours ago. He must have been returning the way he'd come; otherwise, he'd have been too far away for me to scent.

The new wolves were all with Bran, and the one following me was alone: if there had been more than one, I would have heard something. So I didn't have to be worried about the new wolves killing me by mistake because they thought I was a coyote.

I didn't think it was Charles stalking me either. It would be beneath his dignity to frighten me on purpose. Samuel liked playing practical jokes, but the wind doesn't lie, and it told me he was somewhere just ahead.

I was pretty sure it was Leah. She wouldn't kill me no matter what Carl had implied – not with Bran sure to find out – but she would hurt me if she could because she didn't like me. None of the women in Bran's pack liked me.

The wind carrying Samuel's scent was coming mostly from the west. The trees on that side were young firs, probably regrowing after a fire that must have happened a decade or so in the past. The firs were tucked together in a close-packed blanket that wouldn't slow me at all, but a werewolf was a lot bigger than I.

I scratched my ear with a hind foot and used the movement to get a good look behind me. There was nothing to see, so my stalker was far enough away for me to reach the denser trees. I put my foot down and darted for the trees.

The wolf behind me howled her hunting song. Instinct takes over when a wolf is on the hunt. Had she been thinking,

Leah would never have uttered a sound – because she was immediately answered by a chorus of howls. Most of the wolves sounded like they were a mile or so farther into the mountains, but Samuel answered her call from no more than a hundred yards in front of me. I altered my course accordingly and found my way through the thicket of trees and out the other side where Samuel had been traveling.

He stopped dead at my appearance – I suppose he was expecting a deer or elk, not a coyote. Not me.

Samuel was big, even for a werewolf. His fur was winter white, and his eyes appeared almost the same shade, an icy white-blue, colder than the snow I ran through, all the more startling for the black ring that edged his iris. There was plenty of room for me to dive under his belly and out the other side, leaving him between me and my pursuer.

Before he had a chance to do more than give me that first startled look, Leah appeared, a gold-and-silver huntress, as beautiful as Samuel in her own way: light and fire where he was ice. She saw Samuel and skidded ungracefully to a halt. I suppose she'd been so hot on the chase she hadn't been paying attention to Samuel's call.

I could see the instant he realized who I was. He cocked his head, and his body grew still. He recognized me all right, but I couldn't tell how he felt about it. After the space of a deep breath, he turned back to look at Leah.

Leah cringed and rolled onto her back – though as Bran's wife she should have outranked Samuel. Unimpressed by the show, he curled his lips away from his fangs and growled, a deep rumbling sound that echoed in my chest. It felt just like old times: Samuel protecting me from the rest of the pack.

A wolf howled, nearer than before, and Samuel stopped growling long enough to answer. He looked expectantly toward the north, and in a few minutes two wolves came into sight. The first one was the color of cinnamon with four black feet. He was a shade bigger even than Samuel.

The second werewolf was considerably smaller. From a distance he could have passed as one of the wolves that had only this decade begun to return to Montana. His coat was all the shades between white and black, combining to make him appear medium gray. His eyes were pale gold, and the end of his tail was white.

Charles, the cinnamon wolf, stopped at the edge of the trees and began to change. He was an oddity among werewolves: a natural-born werewolf rather than made. The only one of his kind that I have ever heard of.

Charles's mother had been a Salish woman, the daughter of a medicine man. She had been dying when Bran came across her, shortly after he arrived in Montana. According to my foster mother, who told me the story, Bran had been so struck with her beauty that he couldn't just let her die, so he Changed her and made her his mate. I never could wrap my imagination around the thought of Bran being overcome by love at first sight, but maybe he had been different two hundred years ago.

At any rate, when she became pregnant, she used the knowledge of magic her father had given her to keep from changing at the full moon. Female werewolves cannot have children: the change is too violent to allow the fetus to survive. But Charles's mother, as her father's daughter, had some magic of her own. She managed to carry Charles to term, but was so weakened by her efforts that she died soon after his birth. She left her son with two gifts. The first was that he changed easier and faster. The second was a gift for magic that was unusual in werewolves. Bran's pack did not have to hire a witch to clean up after them; they had Charles.

Bran, the smaller of the two wolves, continued on to

where I stood awaiting him. Samuel stepped aside reluctantly, though he was still careful to keep between Leah and me.

There was no sense of power about Bran, not like the one his sons and Adam carried – I'm not certain how he contained it. I've been told that sometimes even other werewolves, whose senses are sharper than mine, mistake him for a real wolf or some wolf-dog hybrid to account for his size.

I don't know how old he is. All I know is that he was old when he came to this continent to work as a fur trapper in the late eighteenth century. He'd traveled to this area of Montana with the Welsh cartographer David Thompson and settled to live with his Salish mate.

He padded up to me and touched his muzzle behind my ear. I didn't have to sink submissively to be lower than he, but I hunched down anyway. He took my nose between his fangs and released it, a welcome and a gentle chiding all in one – though I wasn't certain what he was chiding me for.

Once he released me, he stalked past Samuel and stared down at his wife, still lying in the snow. She whined anxiously and he bared his teeth, unappeased. It seemed that even though he'd once asked me to leave, I wasn't to be viewed as fair game.

Bran turned his back on her to look at Charles, who had completed his transformation and stood tall and human. Charles's features were pure Salish, as if the only thing that he'd gotten from his father was the ability to change.

I've been told that the Native Americans were shy about their bodies. It was certainly true of Charles. He'd used his magic to clothe himself and stood garbed in fur-lined buckskins that looked as if they had come out of another century.

I, like most shapeshifters, was nearly as comfortable naked as clothed – except in the middle of November, high up in the Rockies of Montana with a chill Canadian wind blowing from the northwest and the temperature beginning to drop as the snow quit falling at last. And as soon as Charles started to speak, I was going to have to become human so I could talk to him.

'My father bids you welcome to the territory of the Marrok,' Charles said, his voice carrying the flat tones of his mother's people with just a hint of the Welsh lilt Bran no longer spoke with unless he was really angry. 'He wonders, however, why you have chosen now to come.'

I took human form, quickly kicked snow away from me, then knelt to keep myself lower than Bran. I sucked in my breath at the chill of the wind and the snow under my shins. Samuel moved between me and the worst of the wind. It helped, but not enough.

'I came on pack business,' I told them.

Charles raised his eyebrows. 'You come smelling of blood and death.' Charles had always had a good nose.

I nodded. 'I brought the Columbia Basin Alpha here. He's been badly wounded. I also brought the body of another wolf, hoping someone here could tell me how he died and who killed him.'

Bran made a soft sound, and Charles nodded. 'Tell us what is necessary now. You can give us the details later.'

So I told them what I knew, as succinctly as possible, beginning with Mac's story, as he had told it to me, and ending with Mac's death, Adam's wounds, and Jesse's kidnapping. By the time I was finished, my teeth were chattering, and I could barely understand myself. Even when I shifted back into coyote form, I couldn't quite warm up.

Bran glanced at Samuel, who gave a woof and took off at a dead run.

'Bran will finish the hunt with the new ones,' Charles told me. 'It is their first hunt, and should not be interrupted. Samuel is going back to take care of Adam. He'll take a shorter route than the automobiles can manage, so he'll be there before us. I'll ride back with you and take care of your dead.'

On the tail end of Charles's words, Bran trotted off into the forest without looking at me again. Leah rose from her submissive pose, growled at me – like it was my fault she'd gotten herself in trouble – and followed Bran.

Charles, still in human form, strode off in the direction of the cars. He wasn't talkative at the best of times and, with me still four-footed and mute, he didn't bother to say anything at all. He waited politely on the passenger side of the van while I transformed again and dove into my clothes.

He didn't object to my driving as Samuel would have. I'd never seen Charles drive a car; he preferred to ride horseback or run as a wolf. He climbed into the passenger seat and glanced once behind him at the tarped body. Without commenting, he belted himself in.

When we got back to the motel, I pulled in at the office door. Carl was in the office with a red-eyed young woman who must be the missing Marlie, though I couldn't see the six-year-old I'd known.

'Mercedes needs a room,' Charles told them.

Carl didn't question him, just handed me a key. 'This is on the side away from the road, as far from #1 as we get.'

I looked down at the #18 stamped on the key. 'Don't you know that you're not supposed to put the room number on the key anymore?' I asked.

'We don't have much trouble with burglary,' Carl said, smiling. 'Besides, I know you spent a couple of years working here. Except for number one, there are only three different locks for all the rooms.'

I smiled at him and tossed the key up once and caught it. 'True enough.'

Charles opened the door for me as we left. 'If you'll get

your luggage and give me your car keys, I'll take care of the body.'

I must have looked surprised.

'Don't worry,' he told me dryly. 'I'll have Carl drive.'

'No luggage,' I told him. I pulled out my keys and gave them to him, but caught his hand before he pulled away. 'Mac was a good man,' I told him. I don't know why I said it.

Charles didn't touch anyone casually. I had always thought he rather despised me, though he treated me with the same remote courtesy he used with everyone else. But he put his free hand on the back of my head and pulled my forehead briefly against his shoulder.

'I'll take care of him,' he promised as he stepped back.

'His full name was Alan MacKenzie Frazier.'

He nodded. 'I'll see that he is treated well.'

'Thank you,' I told him, then turned and walked toward my room before I could start to cry again.

There was a pile of *National Geographics* and a paperback mystery stacked neatly on the nightstand. As I recall, the reading material was put there originally to make up for the absence of a TV. When I'd cleaned rooms here, you couldn't get reception so far in the mountains. Now there was a dish on top of the motel and a small TV positioned so you could watch it either from the bed or the small table in the kitchenette.

I wasn't interested in watching old reruns or soap operas so I flipped desultorily through the magazines. They looked familiar. Maybe they were the same stack that had been here when I'd last cleaned this room: the newest one was dated May of 1976, so it was possible. Or maybe random stacks of *National Geographics* have a certain sameness gained from years of appearing in waiting rooms.

I wondered if Jesse were lying in a hospital somewhere. My mind flashed to a morgue, but I brought it back under control. Panic wouldn't help anyone. I was doing the best that I could.

I picked up the lone book and sat on the bed. The cover was not prepossessing, being a line drawing of a Wisconsin-style barn, but I opened it anyway and started reading. I closed it before I'd read more than the first sentence. I couldn't bear sitting here alone, doing nothing.

I left the room. It was colder than it had been, and all I had was my T-shirt, so I ran to number one. I had the key in the pocket of my jeans, but when I tried the door, it opened.

Adam lay on top of the bed on his side, his muzzle wrapped with a businesslike strap. Samuel was bent over him wearing a pair of jeans, plastic gloves, and nothing else. It was a measure of my concern for Adam that my eyes didn't linger. Charles, leaning against the wall, glanced at me but said nothing.

'Shut the door,' Samuel snapped, without looking up. 'Damn it, Mercy, you should have set the break before you threw him in the car and drove all day – you of all people know how fast we heal. I'll have to rebreak his leg.'

Samuel had never yelled at me before. He was the least volatile male werewolf I'd ever met.

'I don't know how to set bones,' I said, wrapping my arms around myself. But he was right. I knew werewolves heal incredibly fast – I just hadn't thought about what that meant as far as broken bones were concerned. I hadn't even known his leg was broken. I'd been stupid. I should have just called Darryl.

'How much training does it take to set a leg?' Samuel continued with barely a pause. 'All you have to do is pull it straight.' His hands were gentle as they stretched out Adam's leg. 'He'd have had someone with medic training in his pack. You could have called for help if you didn't have the guts for it yourself.' Then to Adam he said, 'Brace yourself.' From my position by the door, I couldn't see what he did, but I heard a bone snap, and Adam jerked and made a noise I never want to hear again.

'I was worried that someone from his pack was involved in the attack,' I whispered. 'Adam was unconscious. I couldn't ask him. And they don't have anyone strong enough to control Adam's wolf.'

Samuel glanced back at me, then swore. 'If all you can do is snivel, then get the hell out of here.'

Despite his condition, Adam growled, swiveling his head to look at Samuel.

92

'I'm sorry.' I said, and left, closing the door tightly behind me.

I'd spent twenty minutes staring at the first page of the mystery when someone knocked on the door. My nose told me it was Samuel, so I didn't answer right away.

'Mercy?' His voice was soft, just as I remembered it, with just a touch of Celt.

If I left early in the morning, I could get a head start on looking for Jesse, I thought, staring at the door. Someone else could take Adam back when he was ready to travel. If I left early enough, I could avoid talking to Samuel altogether.

'Mercy. I know you're listening to me.'

I stared at the door, but didn't say anything. I didn't want to talk to him. He'd been right. I had been useless – subjecting Adam to a six-hour drive because of a chance remark of Darryl's, a remark that I was beginning to think meant nothing. Of course, as I'd told Samuel earlier, the pack would have had to bring Adam to Montana or at least send for a dominant until Adam could control himself – but they would have set his broken leg immediately. Darryl and the pack could be out looking for Jesse with Adam safely on the road to recovery if I hadn't been so stupid.

In my own world of engines and CV joints, I'd grown used to being competent. If Adam had been a car, I'd have known what to do. But in Aspen Creek, I'd always been not quite good enough – some things, it seemed, hadn't changed.

'Mercy, look, I'm sorry. If you didn't know first aid, and you couldn't trust his pack, there's nothing else you could have done.'

His voice was soft and sweet as molasses; but my mother once told me that you had to trust that the first thing out of a person's mouth was truth. After they have a chance to think about it, they'll change what they say to be more socially acceptable, something they think you'll be happier with, something that will get the results they want. I knew what he wanted, what he had always wanted from me, even if – while he had been working on Adam's injuries – Samuel, himself, had forgotten.

'Adam tore a strip off me for being so hard on you,' he said, his voice coaxing. 'He was right. I was mad because I don't like hurting someone unnecessarily, and I took it out on you. Can I come in and talk to you instead of the door?'

I rubbed my face tiredly. I wasn't sixteen anymore, to run away from difficult things, no matter how attractive that option was. There were, I thought reluctantly, things I needed to say to him as well.

'All right,' he said. 'All right, Mercy. I'll see you in the morning.'

He had turned around and was already walking away when I opened the door.

'Come in,' I said and shivered when the wind blew through my shirt. 'But you'd better hurry. It's colder than a witch's britches out there.'

He came back and stomped his feet hard on the mat, leaving behind clumps of snow before stepping inside my room. He took off his coat and set it on the table near the door, and I saw he'd found a shirt somewhere. They kept stashes of clothes around town, in case someone needed to dress quickly; unisex things mostly, like jeans, T-shirts, and sweats. The T-shirt he wore was a little small and clung to him like a second skin. If he'd had an extra ounce of fat or a little less muscle, it would have looked stupid, but he was built like a Chippendales' dancer.

His body was lovely, but I don't know if anyone else would have called him handsome. He certainly didn't have Adam's strikingly beautiful features. Sam's eyes were deeply set, his nose was too long, his mouth too wide. His coloring in human form was much less striking than his wolf: light blue-gray eyes and brown hair, streaked just a bit from the sun.

Looking at his face, I wasn't objective enough to decide how attractive he was: he was just Sam who had been my friend, my defender, and my sweetheart.

I glanced away from his face, dropping my own so that he couldn't read my anger — and whatever other emotion was hammering at me — until I'd gotten it under control. If he read the wrong thing into it, that wasn't my fault. I hadn't let him in to argue with him.

'I didn't think you were going to talk to me,' he said, with a shadow of his usual warm smile in his voice.

'Me either,' I agreed grimly to my shoes — I wasn't going to get through this if I had to look at him. 'But I owe you an apology, too.'

'No.' His tone was wary. Apparently he was too smart to believe my submissive gaze. 'You have nothing to be sorry for. I shouldn't have snapped your nose off earlier.'

'It's all right,' I told him. 'You were probably right. I found Mac dead and Adam almost in the same shape — and I panicked.' I walked to the bed and sat on it, because it was as far away from him as I could get in the motel room. Only then did I dare to look at him again. '*My* apology is years overdue. I should have talked to you before I left. I should have told you I'd decided to go to Portland.' *But I was afraid I might do something stupid like shoot you or, worse, cry* — but he didn't need to know that part.

The humor that usually touched his face leaked away, leaving behind neutral wariness, as if he were watching for a trap. 'My father told me he'd spoken to you and persuaded you to go to your mother's house instead of running off with me,' he said.

'How long did you wait for me?' After Bran had caught us necking in the woods and told me he was sending me to Portland, Samuel had decided that he'd take me away with him instead. I was supposed to sneak out and meet him in the woods a mile or so from my house. But the Marrok knew, he was like that. He told me why Samuel wanted to take me as his mate – and it hadn't been for any reason I could accept.

So while Samuel waited for me, Charles was driving me down to Libby to catch the train to Portland that morning instead.

Samuel looked away from me without answering.

In his own way, Samuel was the most honorable person I'd ever known – something that made his betrayal hurt worse because I knew that he'd never meant me to believe he loved me. He'd told me he would wait for me, and I knew he'd waited long after he'd realized I wasn't going to come.

'That's what I thought,' I said in a small voice. *Damn it, he shouldn't still affect me this way.* I found that I was taking deeper breaths than I normally did, just to breathe in his scent.

'I should have told you I'd changed my mind,' I told him, clinging by my fingernails to the threads of what I needed to tell him. 'I'm sorry for abandoning you without a word. It was neither right nor kind.'

'Father told you to go without talking to me again,' Samuel said. He sounded detached, but he'd turned his back on me and was staring at a damp spot on the rug near his boots.

'I am not of his pack,' I snapped. 'That has always been made perfectly clear to me. It means I didn't have to obey Bran then. I shouldn't have, and I knew it at the time. I'm sorry. Not for leaving, that was the right decision, but I should have told you what I was doing. I was a coward.'

'My father told me what he told you.' His voice started calmly enough, but there was a tinge of anger weaving itself through his words as he continued. 'But you should have known all of that already. I didn't hide anything.'

There was no defensiveness in his voice or in his posture; he really didn't understand what he'd done to me – as stupid as that made him in my eyes. It was still good, somehow, to know that the hurt he'd caused me had been unintentional.

He turned, his eyes met mine, and I felt the zing that had once been as familiar as his face. Part of it was attraction; but part of it was the power of a dominant wolf. The attraction brought me to my feet and halfway across the room before I realized what I was doing.

'Look, Samuel,' I said, coming to an abrupt halt before I touched him. 'I'm tired. It's been a rough day. I don't want to fight with you over things that are long past.'

'All right.' His voice was soft, and he gave a little nod to himself. 'We can talk more tomorrow.'

He put his coat back on, started for the door, then turned back. 'I almost forgot, Charles and Carl took the body—'

'Mac,' I told him sharply.

'Mac,' he said, gentling his tone. I wished he hadn't done that, because his sympathy brought tears to my eyes. 'They took Mac to our clinic and brought back your van. Charles gave me the keys. He would have returned them himself, but you left the room too quickly. I told him I was coming to deliver an apology, so he gave them to me.'

'Did he lock the van?' I asked. 'I've a pair of guns in there, loaded for werewolves—' Mention of the guns reminded me of something else, something odd. 'Oh, and there's a tranquilizer dart of some sort that I found near Adam when I moved him.'

'The van's locked,' he said. 'Charles found the dart and

left it at the lab because he said it smelled of silver and Adam. Now that I know where you found it, I'll make sure to look it over carefully.'

'Mac said someone was using him to experiment on,' I told him. 'They'd found some drugs that worked on were-wolves, he said.'

Samuel nodded. 'I remember you telling us that.'

He held out my keys and, careful not to touch his hand, I took them from him. He smiled as if I'd done something interesting and I realized I shouldn't have been so careful. If I had felt nothing for him, touching his hand wouldn't have bothered me. Living among normal humans, I'd forgotten how difficult it was to hide anything from werewolves.

'Good night, Mercy,' he said.

Then he was gone, and the room felt emptier for his leaving it. *I'd* better *go in the morning*, I thought, as I listened to the snow squeak under his feet as he walked away.

I was busy reading page fourteen for the third time when someone else knocked on the door.

'I brought dinner,' said a man's pleasant tenor.

I set the book down and opened the door.

A sandy-haired young man with a nondescript face held a plastic tray loaded with two plastic-wrapped sub sand-wiches, a pair of styrofoam cups of hot chocolate, and a dark blue winter jacket. Maybe it was the food, but it occurred to me that if Bran looked that much like the cliché of a delivery boy, it was probably on purpose. He liked to be unobtrusive.

He gave me a small smile when I didn't step away from the door right away. 'Charles told me that Adam is going to be fine, and Samuel made a fool of himself.'

'Samuel apologized,' I told him, stepping back and letting him into the room.

The kitchenette had a two-burner stove, six-pack-sized

fridge, and a small, Formica-covered table with two chairs. After tossing the coat on the bed, Bran set the tray on the table and rearranged the contents until there was a sandwich and cup on each side.

'Charles told me that you didn't have a coat, so I brought one. I also thought you might like something to eat,' he said. 'Then we can discuss what we're to do with your Alpha and his missing daughter.'

He sat down on one side and gestured for me to take the other seat. I sat and realized I hadn't eaten anything all day – I hadn't been hungry. I still wasn't.

True to his word, he didn't talk while he ate and I picked. The sandwich tasted of refrigerator, but the cocoa was rich with marshmallows and real vanilla.

He ate faster than I did, but waited patiently for me to finish. The sandwich was one of those huge subs, built to feed you for a week. I ate part of it and wrapped the rest in the plastic it had come in. Bran had eaten all of his, but werewolves need a lot of food.

My foster mother had liked to say, 'Never starve a were-wolf, or he might ask you to join him for lunch.' She'd always pat her husband on the head afterward, even if he was in human form.

I don't know why I thought of that right then, or why the thought tried to bring tears to my eyes. My foster parents were both of them almost seventeen years dead. She died trying to become a werewolf because, she'd told me, every year she got older and he didn't. There are a lot fewer women who are moon called, because they just don't survive the Change as well. My foster father died from grief a month later. I'd been fourteen.

I took a sip of cocoa and waited for Bran to talk.

He sighed heavily and leaned back in the chair, balancing it on two legs, his own legs dangling in the air.

'People don't do that,' I told him.

He raised an eyebrow. 'Do what?'

'Balance like that – not unless they're teenage boys showing off for their girlfriends.'

He brought all four legs back on the floor abruptly. 'Thank you.' Bran liked to appear as human as possible, but his gratitude was a little sharp. I took a hasty sip of cocoa so he wouldn't see my amusement.

He put his elbows on the table and folded his hands. 'What are your intentions now, Mercy?'

'What do you mean?'

'Adam's safe and healing. We'll find out how your young friend was killed. What are *you* planning to do?'

Bran is scary. He's a little psychic – at least that's what he says if you ask. What that means is that he can talk to any werewolf he knows, mind to mind. That's why Charles was able to be his spokesperson out in the woods. Bran uses that ability, among others, to control the North American packs. He claims it is all one way, that he can make people hear him but not the other way around.

The pack whisperers say he has other abilities, too, but no one knows exactly what they are. The most common rumor is that he really can read minds. Certainly he always knew who was responsible for what mischief around the town.

My foster mother always laughed and said it was his reputation for knowing everything that allowed him to appear infallible: all he had to do was walk through the room and see who looked guiltiest when they saw him. Maybe she was right, but I tried looking innocent the next time, and it didn't work.

'I'm leaving in the morning.' *Early*, I thought. *To get away without talking to Samuel again – but also to get started looking for Jesse.*

Bran shook his head and frowned. 'Afternoon.'

I felt my eyebrows rise. 'Well,' I said gently, 'if you knew what I was going to be doing, why didn't you just tell me instead of asking?'

He gave me a small smile. 'If you wait until afternoon, Adam will be ready to travel, and Samuel should know something about how your young man . . . Alan MacKenzie Frazier died. He's staying up tonight to perform the autopsy and run tests in the lab.'

He leaned forward. 'It's not your fault, Mercy.'

I spilled the cocoa all down the front of my T-shirt. 'Sh—' I bit off the word. Bran didn't approve of swearing. 'You *can* read minds.'

'I know the way your mind works,' Bran said, with a little smile that managed to be not quite smug. But he was quick enough retrieving a roll of paper towels stored under the sink and handed them to me as I held my shirt away from my body. The cocoa was still hot, though not scalding.

As I mopped myself up at the sink, he continued, 'Unless you've changed more than I can believe, if something happens, if someone gets hurt, it must be your fault. I had the story from Adam, as far as he knows it, and it had nothing to do with you.'

'Hah – you can read minds. He's in wolf form, and can't talk,' I said. I'd done the best I could with the shirt, but I wished I had an extra change of clothing.

Bran smiled. 'He's not now. Sometimes the change helps us heal faster. Usually we change from human to wolf, but the other way works as well. He was not happy with Samuel.' Bran's smile deepened. 'He spent his first words chewing him out. Told him that second-guessing the man in the field was an amateur's mistake. He said he'd rather not have someone who didn't know what they were doing "mucking about" with his wounds. He also said that you had more guts than sense sometimes.' Bran tipped his styrofoam cup in my direction. 'As it happens I agree — which is why I asked Adam to keep an eye on you for me when you moved into his territory.'

Ah, I thought and tried not to look as devastated as I felt. So Adam had been ordered to look after me? I had rather thought that the odd relationship we had was based on something else. Knowing that Bran had told him to watch me changed the shading of every conversation we'd ever had, lessened it.

'I don't like lies,' said Bran, and I knew I'd failed to keep the pain of his revelation from my face. 'Not even lies of omission. Hard truths can be dealt with, triumphed over, but lies will destroy your soul.' He looked as though he had personal knowledge of it. 'That distaste leads me to meddle where perhaps I should step back.'

He paused, as if to let me speak, but I had no idea where he was going with this.

He sat down and took another sip of cocoa. 'There were those who thought the truth of Bryan's death should be kept from you.' Bryan had been my foster father.

I remembered waking up shortly after Christmas to Bran's low-key voice in the kitchen. When I came out of my room. Bran told me that the police had found Bryan's body in the Kootenai River.

Suicide is difficult for werewolves. Even silver bullets don't always defeat the wolf's ability to heal itself. Decapitation is effective, but rather difficult to achieve in a suicidal situation. Drowning works very well. Werewolves are very densely muscled; they tend to have a difficult time swimming even if they want to, because, like chimpanzees, they have too much muscle and not enough fat to float.

'Some of the pack would have told you that Bryan had an accident.' Bran's voice was contemplative. 'They told me that fourteen was too young to deal with a suicide, especially on top of the death of Bryan's mate.'

'Her name was Evelyn,' I told him. Bran had a tendency to dismiss the humans around him as if they didn't exist. Samuel once told me that it was because humans were so fragile, and Bran had seen too many of them die. I thought that if I could handle Evelyn's death when I was fourteen, then, by hang, Bran could, too.

He gave me a quelling look. When I didn't look down as protocol demanded, his lips turned up before he hid them with the cup.

'Evelyn, indeed,' he said, then sighed. 'When you chose to live alone, rather than go to your mother, I agreed to that, too. You had proven your mettle to me; I thought you had earned the right to make your own choices.' His eyes roved around the room. 'Do you remember the last time you and I talked?'

I nodded and sat down finally. Even if he wasn't insisting on protocol tonight, it felt awkward to be standing while he was sitting in the chair.

'You were sixteen,' he said. 'Too young for him – and too young to know what it was that he wanted from you.'

When Bran had caught Samuel kissing me in the woods, he'd sent me home, then shown up the next morning to tell me that he'd already spoken with my real mother, and she would be expecting me at the end of the week. He was sending me away, and I should pack what I wanted to take.

I'd packed all right, but not to go to Portland; I was packed to leave with Samuel. We'd get married, he'd said. It never occurred to me that at sixteen, I'd have trouble getting married without parental permission. Doubtless Samuel would have had an answer for that as well. We'd planned to move to a city and live outside of any pack.

I loved Samuel, had loved him since my foster father had died and Samuel had taken over his role as my protector. Bryan had been a dear, but Samuel was a much more effective defense. Even the women didn't bother me as much once I had Samuel at my back. He'd been funny and charming. Lightheartedness is not a gift often given to werewolves, but Samuel had it in abundance. Under his wing, I learned joy – a very seductive emotion.

'You told me that Samuel didn't love me,' I told Bran, my mouth tasting like sawdust. I don't know how he'd found out what Samuel had planned. 'You told me he needed a mate who could bear his children.'

Human women miscarry a little over half of the children they conceive by a werewolf father. They carry to term only those babies who are wholly human. Werewolf women miscarry at the first full moon. But coyotes and wolves can interbreed with viable offspring, so why not Samuel and me? Samuel believed that some of our children would be human, maybe some would be walkers like me, and some would be born werewolves – but they all would live.

It wasn't until Bran explained it all to me that I understood the antagonism Leah had toward me, an antagonism that all the other females had adopted.

'I should not have told you that way,' Bran said.

'Are you trying to apologize?' I asked. I couldn't understand what Bran was trying to say. 'I was sixteen. Samuel may seem young, but he's been a full-grown adult as long as I can remember – so he's what, fifty? Sixty?'

I hadn't worried about it when I had loved him. He'd never acted any older than I. Werewolves didn't usually talk about the past, not the way humans do. Most of what I knew about Bran's history, I picked up from my human foster mother, Evelyn.

'I was stupid and young,' I said. 'I needed to hear what

you told me. So if you're looking for forgiveness, you don't need it. Thank you.'

He cocked his head. In human form his eyes were warm hazel, like a sunlit oak leaf.

'I'm not apologizing,' he said. 'Not to you. I'm explaining.' Then he smiled, and the resemblance to Samuel, usually faint, was suddenly very apparent. 'And Samuel is a wee bit older than sixty.' Amusement, like anger, sometimes brought a touch of the old country – Wales – to Bran's voice. 'Samuel is my firstborn.'

I stared at him, caught by surprise. Samuel had none of the traits of the older wolves. He drove a car, had a stereo system and a computer. He actually liked people – even humans – and Bran used him to interface with police and government officials when it was necessary.

'Charles was born a few years after you came here with David Thompson,' I told Bran, as if he didn't know. 'That was what . . . 1812?' Driven by his association to Bran, I'd done a lot of reading about David Thompson in college. The Welsh-born mapmaker and fur trader had kept journals, but he hadn't ever mentioned Bran by name. I wondered when I read them if Bran had gone by another name, or if Thompson had known what Bran was and left him out of the journals, which were kept, for the most part, more as a record for his employers than as a personal reminiscence.

'I came with Thompson in 1809,' Bran said. 'Charles was born in the spring of, I think, 1813. I'd left Thompson and the Northwest Company by then, and the Salish didn't reckon time by the Christian calendar. Samuel was born to my first wife, when I was still human.'

It was the most I'd ever heard him say about the past. 'When was that?' I asked, emboldened by his uncustomary openness.

'A long time ago.' He dismissed it with a shrug. 'When

I talked to you that night, I did my son a disservice. I have decided that perhaps I was overzealous with the truth and still only gave you part of it.'

'Oh?'

'I told you what I knew, as much as I thought necessary at the time,' he said. 'But in light of subsequent events, I underestimated my son and led you to do the same.'

I've always hated it when he chose to become obscure. I started to object sharply – then realized he was looking away from my face, his eyes lowered. I'd gotten used to living among humans, whose body language is less important to communication, so I'd almost missed it. Alphas – especially this Alpha – never looked away when others were watching them. It was a mark of how bad he felt that he would do it now.

So I kept my voice quiet, and said simply, 'Tell me now.'

'Samuel is old,' he said. 'Nearly as old as I am. His first wife died of cholera, his second of old age. His third wife died in childbirth. His wives miscarried eighteen children between them; a handful died in infancy, and only eight lived to their third birthday. One died of old age, four of the plague, three of failing the Change. He has no living children and only one, born before Samuel Changed, made it into adulthood.'

He paused and lifted his eyes to mine. 'This perhaps gives you an idea of how much it meant to him that in you he'd found a mate who could give him children less vulnerable to the whims of fate, children who could be born werewolves like Charles was. I have had a long time to think about our talk, and I came to understand that I should have told you this as well. You aren't the only one who has mistaken Samuel for a young wolf.' He gave me a little smile. 'In the days Samuel walked as human, it was not uncommon for a sixteen-year-old to marry a man much older than she. Sometimes the world shifts its ideas of right and wrong too fast for us to keep up with it.'

Would it have changed how I felt to know the extent of Samuel's need? A passionate, love-starved teenager confronted with cold facts? Would I have seen beyond the numbers to the pain that each of those deaths had cost?

I don't think it would have changed my decision. I knew that because I still wouldn't have married someone who didn't love me; but I think I would have thought more kindly of him. I would have left him a letter or called him after I reached my mother's house. Perhaps I'd even have gathered the courage to talk to him if I hadn't been so hurt and angry.

I refused to examine how Bran's words changed my feelings about Samuel now. It wouldn't matter anyway. I was going home tomorrow.

'There were also some things I didn't know to tell you.' Bran smiled, but it wasn't a happy smile. 'I sometimes believe my own press, you know. I forget that I don't know everything. Two months after you left, Samuel disappeared.'

'He was angry at your interference?'

Bran shook his head. 'At first, maybe. But we talked that out the day you left. He would have been more angry if he hadn't felt guilty about taking advantage of a child's need.' He reached out and patted my hand. 'He knew what he was doing, and he knew what you would have felt about it, whatever he tells himself or you. Don't make him out to be the victim.'

*Not a problem.* 'I won't. So if he wasn't angry with you, why did he leave?'

'I know you understand most of what we are because you were raised among us,' Bran told me slowly. 'But sometimes even I miss the larger implications. Samuel saw in you the answer to his pain, and not the answer to his heart. But that wasn't all Samuel felt for you – I doubt he knew it himself.'

'What do you mean?' I asked.

'He pined when you left,' Bran said, the old-fashioned wording sounding odd coming from the young man he looked to be. 'He lost weight, he couldn't sleep. After the first month he spent most of his time as a wolf.'

'What *do* you think was wrong with him?' I asked carefully.

'He was grieving over his lost mate,' said Bran. 'Werewolves aren't that different from our wild cousins in some respects. It took me too long to figure it out, though. Before I did, he left us without a word. For two years, I waited for the newspapers to report his body discovered in the river like Bryan's had been. Charles tracked Samuel down when he finally started to use the money in his bank account. He'd bought some papers and gone back to college.' Samuel had been through college at least once before that I knew of, for medicine. 'He became a medical doctor again, set up a clinic in Texas for a while, then came back to us about two years ago.'

'He didn't love me,' I said. 'Not as a man loves a woman.'

'No,' agreed Bran. 'But he had chosen you as his mate.' He stood up abruptly and put on his coat. 'Don't worry about it now. I just thought you ought to know. Sleep in tomorrow.'

# 7

I ventured out to the gas station the next morning in my borrowed coat and bought a breakfast burrito. It was hot, if not tasty, and I was hungry enough to eat almost anything.

The young man working the till looked as though he'd have liked to ask questions, but I cowed him with my stare. People around here know better than to get into staring contests. I wasn't a were-anything, but he didn't know that because he wasn't either. It wasn't nice to intimidate him, but I wasn't feeling very nice.

I needed to do something, *anything*, and I was stuck waiting here all morning. Waiting meant worrying about what Jesse was suffering at the hands of her captors and thinking of Mac and wondering what I could have done to prevent his death. It meant reliving the old humiliation of having Bran tell me the man I loved was using me. I wanted to be out of Aspen Creek, where the memories of being sixteen and alone tried to cling no matter how hard I flinched away; but obedience to Bran was too ingrained – especially when his orders made sense. I didn't have to be nice about it, though.

I'd started back to the motel, my breath raising a fog and the snow crunching beneath my shoes, when someone called out my name.

'Mercy!'

I looked across the highway where a green truck had pulled over – evidently at the sight of me, but the driver didn't look familiar. The bright morning sun glittering on the snow made it hard to pick out details, so I shaded my eyes with my hand and veered toward him for a better look.

As soon as I changed directions, the driver turned off the truck, hopped out, and jogged across the highway.

'I just heard that you were here,' he said, 'but I thought you'd be long gone this morning or else I'd have stopped in earlier.'

The voice was definitely familiar, but it didn't go with the curling red hair and unlined face. He looked puzzled for a moment, even hurt, when I didn't recognize him immediately. Then he laughed and shook his head. 'I forgot, even though every time I look in a mirror it still feels like I'm looking at a stranger.'

The eyes, pale blue and soft, went with the voice, but it was his laugh that finally clued me in. 'Dr Wallace?' I asked. 'Is that really you?'

He tucked his hands in his pockets, tilted his head, and gave me a wicked grin. 'Sure as moonlight, Mercedes Thompson, sure as moonlight.'

Carter Wallace was the Aspen Creek veterinarian. No, he didn't usually treat the werewolves, but there were dogs, cats, and livestock enough to keep him busy. His house had been the nearest to the one I grew up in, and he'd helped me make it through those first few months after my foster parents died.

The Dr Wallace I'd known growing up had been middle-aged and balding, with a belly that covered his belt buckle. His face and hands had had been weathered from years spent outside in the sun. This man was lean and hungry; his skin pale and perfect like that of a twenty-year-old – but the greatest difference was not in his appearance.

The Carter Wallace I'd known was slow-moving and gentle. I'd seen him coax a skunk out of a pile of tires without it spraying everything, and keep a frightened horse still with his voice while he clipped away the barbed wire it had become tangled in. There had been something peaceful about him, solid and true like an oak.

Not anymore. His eyes were still bright and kind, but there was also something predatory that peered out at me. The promise of violence clung to him until I could almost smell the blood.

'How long have you been wolf?' I asked.

'A year last month,' he said. 'I know, I know, I swore I'd never do it. I knew too much about the wolves and not enough. But I had to retire year before last because my hands quit working right.' He looked down, a little anxiously, at his hands and relaxed a bit as he showed me he could move all his fingers easily. 'I was all right with that. If there is anything a vet gets used to – especially around here – it is aging and death. Gerry started in on me again, but I'm stubborn. It took more than a little arthritis and Gerry to make me change my mind.' Gerry was his son and a werewolf.

'What happened?' I asked.

'Bone cancer.' Dr Wallace shook his head. 'It was too far gone, they said. Nothing but months in a bed hoping you die before the morphine quits working on the pain. Everyone has their price, and that was more than I could bear. So I asked Bran.'

'Most people don't survive the Change if they're already too sick,' I said.

'Bran says I'm too stubborn to die.' He grinned at me again, and the expression was beginning to bother me because it had an edge that Dr Wallace's, *my* Dr Wallace's, had never had. I'd forgotten how odd it was to know someone from both sides of the Change, forgotten just how much the wolf alters the human personality. Especially when the human wasn't in control.

'I thought I'd be practicing again by now,' Dr Wallace

said. 'But Bran says not yet.' He rocked a little on his heels and closed his eyes as if he could see something I didn't. 'It's the smell of blood and meat. I'm all right as long as nothing is bleeding.' He whispered the last sentence and I heard the desire in his voice.

He gathered himself together with a deep breath, then looked at me with eyes only a shade darker than the snow. 'You know, for years I've said that werewolves aren't much different from other wild predators.' Like the great white, he'd told me, or the grizzly bear.

'I remember,' I said.

'Grizzly bears don't attack their families, Mercy. They don't crave violence and blood.' He closed his eyes. 'I almost killed my daughter a few days ago because she said something I disagreed with. If Bran hadn't stopped by . . .' He shook his head. 'I've become a monster, not an animal. I'll never be able to be a vet again. My family never will be safe, not while I'm alive.'

The last two words echoed between us.

*Damn, damn, and damn some more*, I thought. He should have had more control by now. If he'd been a wolf for a full year and still couldn't control himself when he was angry, he'd never have the control he needed to survive. Wolves who can't control themselves are eliminated for the safety of the pack. The only question, really, was why Bran hadn't already taken care of it – but I knew the answer to that. Dr Wallace had been one of the few humans Bran considered a friend.

'I wish Gerry could make it back for Thanksgiving,' Dr Wallace told me. 'But I'm glad I got a chance to see you before you left again.'

'Why isn't Gerry here?' I asked. Gerry had always traveled on business for Bran, but surely he could come back to see his father before . . .

Dr Wallace brushed his hand over my cheek, and I realized I was crying.

'He's on business. He's in charge of keeping an eye on the lone wolves who live where there is no pack to watch them. It's important.'

It was. But since Dr Wallace was going to die soon, Gerry should be here.

'Livin's easier than dyin' most times, Mercy girl,' he said kindly, repeating my foster father's favorite saying. 'Dance when the moon sings, and don't cry about troubles that haven't yet come.'

His smile softened, and for a minute I could see the man he used to be quite clearly. 'It's cold out here, Mercy, and that coat isn't helping you much. Go get warm, girl.'

I didn't know how to say good-bye, so I didn't. I just turned and walked away.

When the clock in the motel room ticked over to noon, I walked out to the van, which Charles – or Carl – had parked just outside the door to number one. *If Adam isn't ready to go, he'll just have to find another ride. I can't stand another minute here.*

I opened the back to check my antifreeze because the van had a small leak I hadn't fixed yet. When I shut the back hatch, Samuel was just there, holding a bulging canvas bag.

'What are you doing?' I asked warily.

'Didn't my father tell you?' He gave me the lazy grin that had always had the power to make my heart beat faster. I was dismayed to see that it still worked. 'He's sending me with you. Someone's got to take care of the rogues who attacked Adam, and he's barely mobile.'

I turned on my heel, but stopped because I had no idea where to find Bran. And because Samuel was right, damn him. We needed help.

113

Happily, before I had to come up with something suitable to say in apology for my too-obvious dismay, the door to room one opened.

Adam looked as though he'd lost twenty pounds in the last twenty-four hours. He was wearing borrowed sweat-pants and an unzipped jacket over the bare skin of his chest. Most of the visible skin was bruised, mottled technicolor with purple, blue, and black touched with lighter spots of red, but there were no open wounds. Adam was always meticulous in his dress and grooming, but his cheeks were dark with stubble, and his hair was uncombed. He limped slowly onto the sidewalk and kept a tight grip on a cane.

I hadn't expected him to be walking this soon, and my surprise must have shown on my face because he smiled faintly.

'Motivation aids healing,' he said. 'I need to find Jesse.'

'Motivation aids stupidity,' muttered Samuel beside me, and Adam's smile widened, though it wasn't a happy smile anymore.

'I have to find Jesse,' was all that Adam said in reply to Samuel's obvious disapproval. 'Mercy, if you hadn't arrived when you did, I'd have been a dead man. Thank you.'

I hadn't figured out yet exactly what our relationship was, and knowing that Bran had told him to look after me hadn't helped. Even so, I couldn't resist the urge to tease him – he took life so seriously.

'Always happy to come to your rescue,' I told him lightly, and was pleased at the temper that flashed in his eyes before he laughed.

He had to stop moving and catch his breath. 'Damn it,' he told me, with his eyes shut. 'Don't make me do that.'

Samuel had stepped unobtrusively closer, but relaxed when Adam resumed his forward progress without toppling over. I opened the sliding door behind the passenger seat.

'Do you want to lie down?' I asked him. 'Or would you rather sit up on the bench seat? Sitting shotgun is out – you need something easier to get in and out of.'

'I'll sit up,' Adam grunted. 'Ribs still aren't happy about lying down.'

When he got close to the van, I backed out of the way and let Samuel help him up.

'Mercy,' said Bran behind my shoulder, surprising me because I'd been paying attention to the expression on Adam's face.

He was carrying a couple of blankets.

'I meant to get here sooner to tell you that Samuel was coming with you,' Bran said, handing the blankets to me. 'But I had business that took a little longer than I expected.'

'Did you know that you were sending him with me when you talked to me last night?' I asked.

He smiled. 'I thought it was probable, yes. Though I had another talk with Adam after I left you, and it clarified some things. I'm sending Charles to Chicago with a couple of wolves for backup.' He smiled wider, a nasty predatory smile. 'He will find out who is out trying to create new wolves without permission and see that it is stopped in such a way that we'll not see a problem like this again.'

'Why not send Samuel and give me Charles?'

'Samuel has too weak a stomach to handle Chicago,' said Adam, sounding breathless. I glanced at him and saw that he was sitting upright on the short middle bench seat, a sheen of sweat on his forehead.

'*Samuel* is a doctor and dominant enough to keep Adam from eating anyone until he gets better,' responded Samuel, climbing back out of the van and snatching the blankets out of my hands.

Bran's smile softened with amusement. 'Samuel was gone for a long time,' he explained. 'Other than Adam, I think that only Darryl, Adam's second, has ever met him. Until we know what is going on, I'd rather not have everyone know I'm investigating matters.'

'We think the time is coming when we will no longer be able to hide from the humans,' said Samuel, who had finished wrapping Adam in the blankets. 'But we'd rather control how that happens than have a group of murdering wolves reveal our existence before we're ready.'

I must have looked shocked because Bran laughed.

'It's only a matter of time,' he said. 'The fae are right. Forensics, satellite surveillance, and digital cameras are making the keeping of our secrets difficult. No matter how many Irish Wolfhounds and English Mastiffs George Brown breeds and crossbreeds, they don't look like werewolves.'

Aspen Creek had three or four people breeding very large dogs to explain away odd tracks and sightings – George Brown, a werewolf himself, had won several national titles with his Mastiffs. Dogs, unlike most cats, tended to like werewolves just fine.

'Are you looking for a poster boy like Kieran McBride?' I asked.

'Nope,' Adam grunted. 'There aren't any Kieran McBrides who make it as werewolves. Harmless and cute we are not. But he might be able to find a hero: a police officer or someone in the military.'

'You knew about this?' I asked.

'I'd heard rumors.'

'What we don't need right now is a murdering bastard running free around the Tri-Cities, using werewolves to kill people,' Bran said. He looked over my shoulder at his son. 'Find the blackguard and eliminate him before he involves the humans, Samuel.' Bran was the only person I knew who could use words like 'blackguard' and make them sound like swear words – but then he could have said 'bunny rabbit' in that tone of voice and weakened my spine with the same shiver of fear.

But I shivered more from the cold than fear. In the Tri-Cities it was still above freezing most days. It wasn't particularly cold for November in Montana – for instance, my nostrils weren't sticking together when I breathed, so it wasn't ten below zero yet – but it was considerably colder than I was used to.

'Where's your coat?' asked Bran, his attention drawn to my chattering teeth.

'I left it in the room,' I said. 'It's not mine.'

'You are welcome to it.'

'I'm out here now,' I said.

He shook his head. 'You'd better get going then, before you freeze to death.' He looked at Samuel. 'Keep me apprised.'

'Bran,' said Adam. 'Thank you.'

Bran smiled and brushed past me so he could reach in the van and take one of Adam's battered hands in a gentle grip. 'Anytime.'

When he stepped back he shut the sliding door with just the right amount of push so it didn't bounce back open. It had taken me three months to learn how to do it right.

He reached into the pocket of his coat and gave me a card. It was plain white with his name and two phone numbers in simple black lettering. 'So you can call me if you want to,' he said. 'The top number is my cell phone – so you won't have to risk talking to my wife.'

'Bran?' I asked him impulsively. 'What is it that Gerry is doing that is so important he can't come home to be with Dr Wallace?'

'Feeling sorry for himself,' snapped Samuel.

Bran put a hand on Samuel's arm, but spoke to me. 'Carter's case is tragic and unusual. Usually when a wolf lives through the Change but doesn't survive his first year, it is because the human cannot control the instincts of the wolf.'

'I thought it was always a matter of control,' I told Bran.

He nodded his head, 'It is. But in Carter's case it is not a lack of self-control, it is too much.'

'He doesn't want to be a werewolf,' said Samuel. 'He doesn't want to feel the fire of the killing instinct or the power of the chase.' For a moment the sun caught Samuel's eyes, and they glittered. 'He's a healer, not a taker of life.'

*Ah*, I thought, *that rankled, didn't it, Dr Samuel Cornick?* Samuel hadn't been given to in-depth talks – although that might have been as much a function of my age as his inclination – but, I remembered that he had trouble, sometimes, because his instinct to heal was not as strong as his instinct to kill. He told me that he always made certain to eat well before performing any kind of surgery. Did he think that Dr Wallace was the better man for choosing not to live with that conflict?

'Unless Carter allows the wolf to become part of him, he can't control it.' Bran's mouth turned down. 'He's dangerous, and he gets more dangerous every moon, Mercy. But all it would take was for him to compromise his damn hardheaded morals just once, so he can accept what he is and he'd be fine. But if it doesn't happen soon, it won't happen at all. I can't let him see another full moon.'

'Gerry's the one who talked him into Changing,' said Samuel, sounding tired. 'He knows that the time is coming when someone is going to have to deal with Carter. If he's here, it will be his duty – and he can't handle that.'

'I'll take care of it,' said Bran, taking a deep breath. 'I've done it before.' He moved the hand on Samuel's arm to his shoulder. 'Not everyone is as strong as you, my son.' There was a world of shared sorrow in his words and in his posture – and I remembered the three of Samuel's children who hadn't survived the Change.

118

'Get in the van, Mercy,' said Samuel. 'You're shivering.'

Bran put his hands on my shoulders and kissed me on the forehead, then ruined it by saying, 'Let the boys take care of this, eh, Mercedes?'

'Sure thing,' I said, stepping away from him. 'Take care, Bran.'

I stalked around the front of the bus. The only reason I wasn't muttering under my breath was because the werewolves would all hear what I was saying.

I started the van – it protested because of the cold, but not too much. I let it warm up while Bran said a few last words to Samuel.

'How well does Bran know you?' asked Adam quietly. The noise of the engine and the radio would most likely keep the others from hearing us.

'Not very well if he thinks that I'll leave things to you and Samuel,' I muttered.

'That's what I was hoping,' he said, with enough satisfaction that I jerked around to look at him. He smiled tiredly. 'Samuel's good, Mercy. But he doesn't know Jesse, doesn't care about her. I'm not going to be good for much for a while: I need you for Jesse's sake.'

The passenger door opened and Samuel pulled himself up into the seat and shut the door.

'Da means well,' Sam told me, as I started backing out, proving that he knew me better than his father did. 'He's used to dealing with people who listen when he tells them something. Mercy, he's right, though. You aren't up to dealing with werewolf business.'

'Seems to me that she's been dealing just fine,' Adam said mildly. 'She killed two of them in as many days and came out of it without a scratch.'

'Luck,' said Samuel.

'Is it?' In my rearview mirror, I saw Adam close his eyes

119

as he finished in almost a whisper. 'Maybe so. When I was in the army, we kept lucky soldiers where they would do us the most good.'

'Adam wants me to help find Jesse,' I told Samuel, putting my foot on the gas as we left Aspen Creek behind us.

The conversation went downhill from there. Adam dropped out after a few pointed comments, and sat back to enjoy the fireworks. I didn't remember arguing with Samuel much before, but I wasn't a love-struck sixteen-year-old anymore either.

After I pointedly quit talking to him, Samuel unbuckled his seat belt and slipped between the front seats to go back and sit next to Adam.

'Never argue with Mercy about something she cares about,' Adam advised, obviously having enjoyed himself hugely. 'Even if she stops arguing with you, she'll just do whatever she wants anyway.'

'Shut up and eat something,' growled Samuel, sounding not at all like his usual self. I heard him lift the lid on a small cooler and the sweet-iron smell of blood filled the van.

'Mmm,' said Adam without enthusiasm. 'Raw steak.'

But he ate it, then slept. After a while Samuel came back to the front and belted himself in.

'I don't remember you being so stubborn,' he said.

'Maybe I wasn't,' I agreed. 'Or maybe you didn't used to try to order me around. I'm not a member of your pack or Bran's pack. I'm not a werewolf. You have no right to dictate to me as if I were.'

He grunted, and we drove a while more in silence.

Finally, he said, 'Have you had lunch?'

I shook my head. 'I thought I'd stop in Sandpoint. It's grown since last time I drove through there.'

'Tourists,' said Samuel in disgust. 'Every year there are

more and more people.' I wondered if he was remembering what it had been like when he'd first been there.

We stopped and got enough fried chicken to feed a Little League team – or two werewolves, with a little left over for me. Adam ate again with restrained ferocity. Healing was energy-draining work, and he needed all the protein he could get.

When he was finished, and we were back on the road, with Samuel once again in the front, I finally asked, 'What happened the night you were attacked? I know you've told Bran and probably Samuel, too, already – but I'd like to know.'

Adam wiped his fingers carefully on the damp towelette that had come with our chicken – apparently he didn't think it was finger-lick'n good. 'I'd pulled the pack in to introduce Mac, and to tell them about your adventures with his captors.'

I nodded.

'About fifteen minutes after the last of them left, about three-thirty in the morning, someone knocked on the door. Mac had just managed to regain his human form, and he jumped up to answer the door.' There was a pause, and I adjusted the rearview mirror so I could see Adam's face, but I couldn't read his expression.

'I was in the kitchen, so I don't know exactly what happened, but from the sounds, I'd say they shot him as soon as he opened the door.'

'Which was stupid,' commented Samuel. 'They'd know you had to hear the shots – even a tranq gun makes a pretty good pop.'

Adam started to shrug – then stopped with a pained expression. 'Damned if – excuse me, Mercedes – I'll be darned if I know what they were thinking.'

'They didn't kill him on purpose, did they?' I said. I'd

121

been thinking, too. A gun with silver bullets is a much more certain thing than a dart full of experimental drugs.

'I don't think so,' Samuel agreed. 'It looked like a massive allergic reaction to the silver.'

'There was silver in the dart Mercedes found? Just like Charles thought?' asked Adam.

'Yes,' said Samuel. 'I've sent the dart off to the lab along with a sample of Mac's blood for proper analysis, but it looks to me as though they combined silver nitrate with DMSO and Special K.'

'What?' I asked.

'Special K is Ketamine,' Adam said. 'It's been used as a recreational drug for a while, but it started out as an animal tranquilizer. It doesn't work on werewolves. Silver nitrate is used to develop film. What's DMSO?'

'Silver nitrate is a convenient way to get silver in a solution,' Samuel said. 'It's used to treat eye infections, too – though I wouldn't recommend it for a werewolf.'

'I've never heard of a werewolf with an eye infection,' I said, though I understood his point.

He smiled at me, but continued to talk to Adam. 'DMSO – Dimeythyl Sulfoxide. It has a lot of odd properties, but the one of most interest here is that it can carry other drugs with it across membranes.'

I stared at the road ahead of me and put my right hand in front of the heater to warm it. The seals on my windows needed replacing, and the heater wasn't keeping up with the Montana air. Funny, I didn't remember being cold on the way over. No room for simple discomfort when you are trying to save someone, I guess.

'There was something in chem lab my freshman year,' I said. 'We mixed it with peppermint oil and put a finger in it – I could taste peppermint.'

'Right,' said Samuel. 'That's the stuff. So take DMSO and

mix it with a silver solution, and presto, the silver is carried throughout the werewolf's body, poisoning as it goes so that the tranquilizer, in this case, Ketamine, goes to work without interference from the werewolf metabolism that would normally prevent the drug from having any effect at all.'

'You think Mac died from the silver rather than an over-dose of Ketamine?' asked Adam. 'They only shot him twice. I took at least four hits, maybe more.'

'The more recent exposure you have to silver, the worse the reaction,' said Samuel. 'I'd guess that if the boy hadn't spent the last few months in their tender care being dosed up with silver, he'd have made it just fine.'

'Obviously the silver nitrate and the Ketamine are rela-tively easily obtainable,' Adam said after a while. 'What about this DMSO?'

'I could get it. Good stuff is available by prescription – I'd bet you could buy it at any veterinary supply, too.'

'So they'd need a doctor?' I asked.

But Samuel shook his head. 'Not for the veterinary supply. And I'd expect you could get it fairly easily from a phar-macy, too. It's not one of the drugs they'd track carefully. I'd expect they could make as much of their cocktail as they wanted to without much trouble.'

'Great.' Adam closed his eyes, possibly envisioning an invading army armed with tranquilizer dart guns.

'So they killed Mac,' I said when it became apparent that Adam wasn't going to continue. 'Then what happened?'

'I came charging out of the kitchen like an idiot, and they darted me, too.' Adam shook his head. 'I've grown used to being damn near bulletproof – served me right. Whatever they gave me knocked me for a loop, and when I woke up, I was locked up, wrist and ankle in cuffs. Not that I was in any shape to do anything. I was so groggy I could barely move my head.'

'Did you see who they were?' I asked. 'I know one of them was the human who accompanied the werewolf I killed at the garage. I smelled him in Jesse's room.'

Adam shifted on the bench seat, pulling a little against the seat belt.

'Adam.' Samuel's voice was quiet but forceful.

Adam nodded and relaxed a little, stretching out his neck to release the build-up of tension. 'Thank you. It's harder when I'm angry. Yes, I knew one of them, Mercedes. Do you know how I became a werewolf?'

The question seemed to come from left field – but Adam always had a reason for everything he said. 'Only that it was during Vietnam,' I answered. 'You were Special Forces.'

'Right,' he agreed. 'Long-range recon. They sent me and five other men to take out a particularly nasty warlord – an assassination trip. We'd done it before.'

'The warlord was a werewolf?' I asked.

He laughed without humor. 'Slaughtered us. It was one of his own people who killed him, while he was eating poor old McCue.' He shut his eyes, and whispered, 'I can still hear him scream.'

We waited, Samuel and I, and after a moment Adam continued. 'All the warlord's people ran and left us alone. At a guess they weren't certain he was really dead, even after he'd been beheaded. After a while – a long while, though I didn't realize that until later – I found I could move. Everyone was dead except Spec 4 Christiansen and me. We leaned on each other and got out of there somehow, hurt badly enough that they sent us home: Christiansen was a short-timer, anyway, and I guess they thought I was mostly crazy – raving about wolves. They shipped us out of there fast enough that none of the docs commented about how quickly we were recovering.'

'Are you all right?' asked Samuel.

Adam shivered and pulled the blankets closer around himself. 'Sorry. I don't talk about this often. It's harder than I expected. Anyway, one of my army buddies who'd come back to the States a few months earlier heard I was home and came to see me. We got drunk – or at least I tried. I'd just started noticing that it took an awful lot of whiskey to do anything, but it loosened me up enough that I told him about the werewolf.

'Thank goodness I did because he believed me. He called in a relative and between them they persuaded me that I was going to grow furry and kill something the next full moon. They pulled me into their pack and kept everyone safe until I had enough control to do it myself.'

'And the other man who was wounded?' I asked.

'Christiansen?' He nodded. 'My friends found him. It should have been in time, but he'd come home to find that his wife had taken up with another man. He walked into his house and found his bags packed and his wife and her lover waiting with the divorce papers.'

'What happened?' asked Samuel.

'He tore them to pieces.' His eyes met mine in the rearview mirror. 'Even in that first month, if you get angry enough, it is possible to Change.'

'I know,' I told him.

He gave me a jerky nod. 'Anyway, they managed to persuade him to stay with a pack, who taught him what he needed to know to survive. But as far as I know he never did join a pack officially – he's lived all these years as a lone wolf.'

A lone wolf is a male who either declines to join a pack or cannot find a pack who will take him in. The females, I might add, are not allowed that option. Werewolves have not yet joined the twentieth century, let alone the twenty-first, as far as women are concerned. It's a good thing I'm not a werewolf – or maybe it is a pity. Someone needs to wake them up.

'Christiansen was one of the wolves who came to your house?' I asked.

He nodded. 'I didn't hear him or see him – he stayed away from me – but I could smell him. There were several humans and three or four wolves.'

'You killed two,' I told him. 'I killed a third.' I tried to remember what I'd smelled in his house, but I had only been tracking Jesse. There had been so many of Adam's pack in the house, and I only knew some of them by name. 'I'd know the man, the human, who confronted Mac and me earlier that night, but no one else for certain.'

'I'm pretty sure they intended I stay out until they'd done whatever they came for, but their whole plan was a botch job,' Adam said. 'First, they killed Mac. Obviously, from their attempt to take him at your shop, they wanted him, but I don't think they meant to kill him in my house.'

'They left him on my doorstep,' I said.

'Did they?' Adam frowned. 'A warning?' I could see him roll the thought around and he came up with the same message I had. 'Stay out of our business, and you won't end up dead.'

'Quick thinking for the disposal of a body they didn't know they were going to have,' I commented. 'Someone drove to my house to dump his body and was gone when I came outside. They left some people at your house who took off hell-bent-for-leather, probably with Jesse. I made it to your house in time to kill the last werewolf you were fighting.' I tried to think about what time that was. 'Four-thirty in the morning or thereabouts, is my best guess.'

Adam rubbed his forehead.

Samuel said, 'So they shot Mac, shot Adam, then waited around until Mac died. They dropped the body at your house

— then Adam woke up, and they grabbed Jesse and ran, leaving three werewolves behind to do something — kill Adam? But then why take Jesse? Presumably they weren't supposed to just die.'

'The first wolf I fought was really new,' I said slowly. 'If they were all that way, they might have just gotten carried away, and the others fled because they couldn't calm them down.'

'Christiansen isn't new,' said Adam.

'One of the wolves was a woman,' I told him. 'The one I killed was a buff color — almost like Leah but darker. The other was a more standard color, grays and white. I don't remember any markings.'

'Christiansen is red-gold,' Adam said.

'So did they come to kidnap Jesse in the first place or was her kidnapping the result of someone trying to make the best of a screwup?'

'Jesse.' Adam sounded hoarse, and when I glanced back at him I could see that he hadn't heard Samuel's question. 'I woke up because Jesse screamed. I remember now.'

'I found a pair of broken handcuffs on the floor of your living room.' I slowed the van so I didn't tailgate an RV that was creeping up the side of the mountain we were climbing. I didn't have to slow down much. 'Silver wrist cuffs — and the floor was littered with glass, dead werewolves, and furniture. I expect the ankle cuffs were around there somewhere.' I thought of something. 'Maybe they just came to get Mac and maybe punish Adam for taking him in?'

Samuel shook his head. 'Mercy, *you* they might leave warnings for — or try to teach a lesson. A pack of newbie werewolves — especially if they're headed by an experienced wolf — is not going to tick off an Alpha just to "punish" him for interfering in their business. In the first place, there's no better way I can think of to get the Marrok ticked off. In the second place there's Adam himself. He's not just the Columbia Basin Alpha, he's damn near the strongest Alpha in the US, present company excluded, of course.'

Adam grunted, unimpressed with Samuel's assessment. 'We don't have enough information to make an educated guess at what they wanted. Mac's dead, either accidentally or on purpose. They half killed me, and they took Jesse. The human you knew implies that it has something to do with Mac's story – and Christiansen's presence implies it has something to do with me. I'll be darned if I know what Mac and I have in common.'

'Mercy,' said Samuel.

'I forgot to tell you that I joined the secret society of villains while I was away,' I told Samuel, exasperated. 'I am now trying to put together a harem of studly, musclebound werewolves. *Please*. Remember, I didn't know Mac until he dropped in my lap sometime *after* the villains screwed up his life.'

Samuel, having successfully baited me, reached over and patted my leg.

I just happened to glance at Adam's face, and I saw his eyes lighten from chocolate to amber as his gaze narrowed on Samuel's hand before I had to return my eyes to the road to make sure the RV ahead of me hadn't slowed down again. There were four cars trailing slowly behind us up the mountain.

'Don't touch her,' whispered Adam. There was a shadow of threat in his voice, and he must have heard it, too, because he added, 'Please.'

The last word stopped the nasty comment I'd readied because I remembered that Adam was still hurt, still struggling to control his wolf, and the conversation we'd been having hadn't been designed to calm him.

But it wasn't my temper I should have been worried about.

Samuel's hand turned until his fingers spanned the top of my thigh, and he squeezed. It wasn't hard enough to hurt. I'm not certain Adam would have even noticed except that Samuel accompanied it by a throaty half growl of challenge.

I didn't wait to see what Adam would do. I yanked the wheel to the right and slammed on the brakes as soon as the van was on the shoulder of the road. I unsnapped my seat belt and twisted around to meet Adam's yellow gaze. He was breathing heavily, his reaction to Samuel's taunt tempered by the pain my jerky driving had caused.

'You,' I said firmly, pointing at him. 'Stay right there.' Sometimes, if you tell them firmly enough, even Alphas will listen to commands, Especially if you tell them to sit still while they're too hurt to move.

'You' – I turned my attention to Samuel – 'outside, right now.'

Then I jerked my leg out from under Samuel's hand and jumped out of the van, narrowly avoiding getting the door taken off as a truck passed by.

I wasn't certain either of them would listen to me, but at least I wouldn't have to try to drive with a pair of wolves trying to tear each other apart. However, Samuel opened his door as I stalked around the front of the van. By the time I walked a half dozen steps away from the van, he was beside me, and the van's doors were closed.

'Just what did you think you were doing?' I yelled at him, raising my voice over the passing cars. Okay, I was mad, too. 'I thought you were here to make sure no one challenged Adam until he was well – not challenge him yourself.'

'You don't belong to him,' he snapped back, his white teeth clicking together sharply.

'Of course not!' I huffed in exasperation – and a little in

desperation. 'But I don't belong to *you* either! For Pete's sake, Sam, he wasn't telling you that I belonged to him – just that he felt like you were invading his territory. He was asking you for help.' Someone should have awarded me a Ph.D. in werewolf psychology and counseling – surely I deserved something for putting up with this garbage. 'It wasn't a challenge, stupid. He's trying to control his wolf after nearly being killed. Two unmated male werewolves always get territorial in the presence of a female – you know that better than I do. You're supposed to be the one with all this control, and you're behaving worse than he is.' I sucked in air tainted by the traffic.

Samuel paused, then settled his weight on his heels – a sign that he was considering backing off from this fight. 'You called me Sam,' he said in an odd voice that frightened me as much as the violence I could still smell on him, because I didn't know what was causing him to act like this. The Samuel I knew had been easygoing – especially for a were-wolf. I was beginning to think that I wasn't the only one who'd changed over the years.

I didn't know how to respond to his comment. I couldn't see what my calling him Sam had to do with anything, so I ignored it. 'How can you help him control himself if your control isn't better than this? What is wrong with you?' I was honestly bewildered.

Samuel was good at calming the dangerous waters. One of his jobs had been teaching the new wolves control so they could be allowed to live. It is not an accident that most were-wolves are control freaks like Adam. I didn't know what to do with Samuel – except that he wasn't getting back into that van until he had a handle on whatever was bothering him.

'It isn't just that you are female,' he muttered at last, though I almost didn't hear him because two motorcycles blew past us.

'What is it then?' I asked.

He gave me an unhappy look, and I realized that he hadn't intended for me to hear what he'd said.

'Mercedes . . . Mercy.' He looked away from me, staring down the slope of the mountain as if the meadows below held some secret he was looking for. 'I'm as unsettled as a new pup. *You* eat my control.'

'This is all *my* fault?' I asked incredulously. It was outside of enough that he was scaring the bejeebers out of me – I certainly wasn't about to accept the blame for it.

Unexpectedly, he laughed. And as easily as that the smoldering anger, the bright violence, and the dominant power that had been making the air around us feel heavier than it could possibly be floated away. It was just the two of us and the warm scent of Samuel, who smelled of home and the woods.

'Stay out here and enjoy the diesel fumes, Mercy,' he said as a delivery van in need of a new engine chugged past us in a cloud of black smoke. 'Give me a few minutes to clear the air with Adam before you come back in.' He turned and took two steps back to the van. 'I'll wave to you.'

'No violence?' I said.

He put his hand over his heart and bowed. 'I swear.'

It took long enough that I got worried, but finally he opened the door and called me over. He hadn't rolled down the window because I had the keys and the windows were electric. For some reason I still hadn't tracked down, the windows only worked one at a time even with the car running.

I scooted in the driver's seat and gave Adam a cautious look – but his eyes were closed.

# 8

As soon as 'roaming' quit appearing on my phone, I called Zee.

'Who's this?' he answered.

'Mercy,' I told him.

'Didn't tell me the part was for the *vampire's* bus,' he said shortly.

I rubbed my face. 'I couldn't afford to pay them the percentage you were,' I explained, not for the first time.

In the Columbia Basin, which included Richland, Kennewick, and Pasco as well as the smaller surrounding towns like Burbank and West Richland, every business the vampires considered under their jurisdiction (meaning anyone touched by the supernatural who was too powerless to stand against them) paid them protection money. And yes, just like the mob, the vampires only protect you from themselves.

'They agreed I could repair their cars instead – and they pay me for parts. That way they save face, and I only have to repair Stefan's bus and an occasional Mercedes or BMW. Stefan's not bad for a vampire.'

There was a growl from the seat beside me.

'It's okay,' Adam told Samuel. 'We keep an eye on her. And she's right, Stefan's not bad for a vampire. Word is that he runs a little interference so she's not bothered.'

I hadn't known any of the vampires had *intended* to bother me – or that Stefan would care enough to stop them.

'I didn't know that,' said Zee, who'd obviously overheard Adam's comment. He hesitated. 'Vampires are bad news,

Mercy. The less you have to do with them the better – and writing a check and mailing it every month is safer than dealing with them face-to-face.'

'I can't afford it,' I told him again. 'I'm still paying the bank and will be until I'm as old as you are.'

'Well, it doesn't matter,' he said at last. 'I didn't have to deal with him, anyway. Your new supply house sent the wrong part. I sent it back to them and called with a word to their sales manager. The right part should be here on Friday – best he could do with Thanksgiving tomorrow. I called the number on the vampire's file and left a message. What kind of vampire plays the Scooby Doo song on his answering machine?' It was a rhetorical question, because he continued. 'And a woman came by and said your *Politzei* friend had sent her.'

I rubbed my forehead. I'd forgotten about Tony's girl. 'Did you figure out what's wrong with her car?'

'Mercy!' he snapped, insulted.

'No insult meant. Was it something worth fixing?'

'Wiring harness is bad,' he said. 'Mercy . . .'

I grinned because I'd seen the effect this woman had on 'I'm married to my job' Tony. 'You like her,' I told him.

Zee grunted.

'Did you give her a quote?'

'Haven't talked to her yet,' he said. 'She's got poor and proud written all over her. She wouldn't let me give her a lift, so she and her kids walked home. She doesn't have a phone number except a work phone.'

I laughed to myself. There was more than one reason that Zee didn't have the kind of money the older fae generally amass. Well, I'm probably never going to be rich either.

'Okay,' I said. 'What kind of deal are we talking about?'

'I called the *Politzei*,' Zee said. He knew what Tony's name was; he even liked him, though he did his best to hide it.

He just disapproved of letting the human authorities get too close. He was right, too – but I don't always follow the rules of wisdom. If I did, I wouldn't be hauling two werewolves in my van.

'What did he say?' I asked.

'He said that she has an older boy who's been looking for work after school.'

I let him say it; it was just too fun to listen to him squirm. He liked to play the gruff, nasty old man – but he had a marshmallow heart.

'With my Tad gone, you're short a pair of hands.'

*And with Mac dead.* I lost interest in teasing the old gremlin.

'It's fine, Zee. If you talk to her, you can tell her that her son can work off the bill. If he works out, I'll offer him Tad's job. I assume you've already fixed the car?'

'*Ja,*' he said. 'You'll have to talk to the lady yourself, though, unless you need me tomorrow, too. She works day shift.'

'No, I won't need you. Tomorrow is Thanksgiving. I'll leave the shop closed – if you would remember to put up a sign in the window.'

'No problem.' He hesitated. 'I might have a lead for you on Jesse. I was just getting ready to call you. One of the fae who is still in hiding told me she might be able to help, but she wouldn't tell me without talking to you.'

'Still in hiding' meant either that the Gray Lords hadn't noticed her yet, or that she was of the terrible or powerful sort.

This time it was Adam who growled. Such are the joys of trying to have a private phone call in the presence of werewolves. Somehow it didn't bother me so much when I was the eavesdropper.

'We're about an hour out of town,' I said. 'Could you set up a meeting tonight at a place of her choice?'

134

'All right,' he said, and hung up.

'You caught all of that?' I asked them.

'Adam can't go,' Samuel said firmly. 'No, Adam, you know it yourself.'

Adam sighed. 'All right. I even agree I'm not fit to be on my own – but I want Mercy there. We can call Darryl and—'

Samuel held up a hand. 'Mercy,' he said, 'what caused you to bring Adam all the way to Montana rather than calling on his pack for help?'

'It was stupid,' I said.

'Maybe, but tell us anyway.'

'I was trying to get in touch with Darryl, and I suddenly felt uneasy. I remembered a snippet of conversation between Ben and Darryl earlier that night, but in retrospect it wasn't much.'

'What were Ben and Darryl doing talking to you?' asked Adam in that mild voice he used to cozen people into thinking he wasn't angry.

'I can take care of myself, Adam,' I told him. 'I was taking the trash out and ran into them. All Darryl did was tell Ben to leave me alone. He said, "Not now." I don't know why I decided it meant he knew that something was going to happen.'

'First you felt uneasy,' said Samuel. 'Then you came up with this stupid reason.'

'Yes.' I felt my face flush.

'How do you feel about his pack now?'

I opened my mouth, then shut it again. 'Damn it. Something's wrong. I don't think Adam should go to the pack until he can defend himself.'

Samuel settled back with a small, smug smile.

'What?' I asked.

'You noticed something,' Adam said. 'A scent or something

at my house that makes you think someone from my pack is involved. Instincts.' He sounded grim. 'I thought it was odd that they came so soon after my wolves left.'

I shook my head. 'Look, I don't know anything.'

'We're not going to kill anyone,' said Samuel. 'Not on the basis of your instincts, anyway – but what's the harm in being careful? Call your friend back. We'll see to his information tomorrow, when Adam has enough control to be on his own.'

'No,' said Adam.

'Damned if I will.' It felt odd not to be arguing with Adam. 'The faster we find Jesse, the better.'

'I can't be in two places at once,' Samuel said. 'And I won't allow you to go out on your own and talk to who knows what kind of fae.'

'We need to find Jesse,' I said.

'My daughter comes first.'

Samuel twisted around to look at Adam. 'You have a dominant wolf in your pack that you trust? Someone not in line to be pack leader?'

'Warren.' Adam and I said his name in the same instant.

Warren was my favorite of Adam's pack, and the only wolf whose company I sought out. I met him shortly after I moved to the Tri-Cities, before I even knew there was a pack in town.

I hadn't met a werewolf since I'd left Montana, and I certainly hadn't expected to meet one working the night shift at the local Stop and Rob. He'd given me a wary look, but there were other people in the store, so he accepted my payment without a word. I accepted my change with a nod and a smile.

After that we'd mostly ignored each other, until the night a woman with a fresh shiner came into the store to pay for the gas her husband was pumping. She gave Warren the money, then took a firmer grip on the hand of the boy at her side, and asked Warren if he had a back door she could use.

He smiled gently at her and shepherded the two frightened people into a small office I'd never noticed before at the back of the store. He left me to watch the till and went out and had a short talk with the man at the pump. When he came back, he had two hundred dollars cash for her, and her husband drove away with a speed indicating either terror or rage.

Warren and I waited with the battered pair until the lady who ran the local women's shelter drove over to collect her newest clients. When they left, I turned to him and finally introduced myself.

Warren was one of the good guys, a hero. He was also a lone wolf. It had taken him a while to trust me enough to tell me why.

Perhaps in other ages, in other places, it wouldn't have mattered that he was gay. But most of the werewolves in power in the US had been born in a time when homosexuality was anathema, even punishable by death in some places.

One of my professors once told me that the last official act of the British monarchy was when Queen Victoria refused to sign a law that made same-sex acts illegal. It would have made me think more highly of her, except the reason she objected was because she didn't believe women would do anything like that. Parliament rewrote the law so it was specific to men, and she signed it. A tribute to enlightenment, Queen Victoria was not. Neither, as I have observed before, are werewolf packs.

There was no question of Warren's staying in the closet, either, at least not among other werewolves. As demonstrated by Adam and Samuel just a few hours ago, werewolves are very good at sensing arousal. Not just smells, but elevated temperature and increased heart rate. Arousal in werewolves tends to bring out the fighting instinct in all the nearby males.

Needless to say, a male wolf who is attracted to other male wolves gets in a lot of fights. It spoke volumes about Warren's fighting ability that he survived as long as he had. But a pack won't accept a wolf who causes too much trouble, so he'd spent his century of life cut off from his kind.

It was I who introduced Adam and Warren, about the time Adam moved in behind me. I'd had Warren to dinner and we'd been laughing about something, I forget what, and one of Adam's wolves howled. I'll never forget the desolation on Warren's face.

I'd heard it all the time when I was growing up – wolves are meant to run in a pack. I still don't understand it completely myself, but Warren's face taught me that being alone was no trivial thing for a wolf.

The next morning, I'd knocked on Adam's front door. He listened to me politely and took the piece of paper with Warren's phone number on it. I'd left his house knowing I'd failed.

It was Warren who told me what happened next. Adam summoned Warren to his house and interrogated him for two hours. At the end of it, Adam told Warren he didn't care if a wolf wanted to screw ducks as long as he'd listen to orders. Not actually in those words, if Warren's grin as he told me about it was an accurate measure. Adam uses crudeness as he uses all of his weapons: seldom, but with great effect.

I suppose some people might think it odd that Warren is Adam's best friend, though Darryl is higher-ranking. But they are heroes, both of them, two peas in a pod – well, except Adam isn't gay.

The rest of the pack weren't all happy when Warren came in. It helped a little that most of Adam's wolves are even younger than he, and the last few decades have seen a vast improvement over the rigid Victorian era. Then, too, none of the pack wanted to take on Adam. Or Warren.

Warren didn't care what the rest of the wolves thought, just that he had a pack, a place to belong. If Warren needed friends, he had me and he had Adam. It was enough for him.

Warren would never betray Adam. Without Adam, he would no longer have a pack.

'I'll give him a call,' I said with relief.

He picked up on the second ring, 'Warren, here. Is this you, Mercy? Where have you been? Do you know where Adam and Jesse are?'

'Adam was hurt,' I said. 'The people who did it took Jesse.'

'Tell him not to let anyone else know,' said Samuel.

'Who was that?' Warren's tone was suddenly cool.

'Samuel,' I told him. 'Bran's son.'

'Is this a coup?' Warren asked.

'No,' answered Adam from the backseat. 'At least not on Bran's part.'

'Excuse me,' I said. 'But this is *my* phone call. Would you all *please* pretend that it is a private conversation? That includes you, Warren. Quit listening to the other people in my van.'

'All right,' agreed Warren. Having heard Adam, his voice relaxed into its usual lovely south Texas drawl. 'How are you today, Mercy?' he asked sweetly, but as he continued his voice became gradually sharper. 'And have you heard the startling news that our Alpha's house was broken into and he and his daughter disappeared? That the only clue is the phone message left on the *damned* Russian witch's phone? A message that she has refused to let anyone else listen to? Rumor has it that the message is from you, and no one can find you either.'

Samuel leaned his head back, closed his eyes, and said, 'Tell him you'll explain when we get there.'

I smiled sweetly. 'I'm doing better all the time, Warren. Thank you for asking. Montana is nice, but I don't recommend a November vacation unless you ski.'

'Haven't put on skis for twenty years,' murmured Warren, sounding a little happier. 'Has Adam taken up skiing during this jaunt of yours to Montana?'

'He has skis,' I said, 'but his health wasn't up to it this time. I brought back a doctor, but the two of us found out that we need to go out tonight and were wondering if you were up for a little nursing.'

'Glad to,' said Warren. 'I don't work tonight, anyway. Did you say Jesse's been kidnapped?'

'Yes. And for right now, we need you to keep it under your hat.'

'I drove by your houses on the way back from work this morning,' Warren said slowly. 'There's been a lot of activity there. I think it's just the pack watching, but if you want to avoid them, maybe you all ought to spend the night at my place.'

'You *think* it's the pack?' asked Adam.

Warren snorted. 'Who'd call and talk to me about it? Darryl? Auriele called to tell me you were missing, but without you, the women are mostly left out of the business, too. The rest of the pack is supposed to be keeping their eyes out for you – all three of you – but that's all I know. How long do you need to keep them in the dark?'

'For a day or two.' Adam's voice was neutral, but the words would tell Warren all he needed to know.

'Come to my house. I don't think that anyone except you and Mercy even know where I live. I've got enough room

140

for all of you — unless there are a couple of people who haven't spoken up.'

Each of the Tri-Cities has its own flavor, and it is in Richland that the frenzy of the dawn of the nuclear age has pressed most firmly. When the government decided to build weapons-grade plutonium here, they had to build a town, too. So scattered over the city are twenty-six types of buildings designed to house the workers for the nuclear industry. Each kind of house was given a letter designation beginning with A and ending Z.

I don't recognize them all, but the big duplexes, the A and B houses, are pretty distinctive. The A houses look sort of like Eastern farmhouses — two-story, rectangular, and unadorned. B houses are single-story rectangles. Most of them have been changed a little from what they once were, porches added, converted from duplexes to single-family dwellings — and back again. But no matter how much they are renovated, they all have a sort of sturdy plainness that overcomes brick facades, decks, and cedar siding.

Warren lived in half an A duplex with a big maple tree taking up most of his part of the front lawn. He was waiting on his porch when I drove up. When I'd met him, he'd had a sort of seedy I've-been-there-and-done-everything kind of look. His current lover had coaxed him into cutting his hair and improving his dress a little. His jeans didn't have holes in them, and his shirt had been ironed sometime in the not-too-distant past.

I was able to park directly in front of his home. As soon as I stopped, he hopped down the stairs and opened the van's sliding door.

He took in Adam's condition in one swift glance.

'You say this happened night before last?' he asked me.

'Yep.' His accent is thick enough that I sometimes found

myself falling into it — even though I'd never been to Texas.

Warren stuck his thumbs in his pockets and rocked back on the heels of his battered cowboy boots. 'Well, boss,' he drawled, 'I expect I ought to feel lucky you're alive.'

'I'd feel lucky if you could see your way to helping me up,' Adam growled. 'I wasn't feeling too bad this morning, but this thing's springs leave a lot to be desired.'

'We can't all drive a Mercedes,' I said lightly, having gotten out myself. 'Warren, this is Bran's son, Dr Samuel Cornick, who has come down to help.'

Warren and Samuel assessed each other like a pair of cowboys in a fifties movie. Then, in response to some signal invisible to me, Samuel held out a hand and smiled.

'Good to meet you,' he said.

Warren didn't say anything, but he shook Samuel's hand once and looked as if he took pleasure in the other man's greeting.

To Adam, Warren said, 'I'm afraid it'll be easier to carry you, boss. There's the front stairs, then the flight up to the bedrooms.'

Adam frowned unhappily, but nodded. 'All right.'

Warren looked a little odd carrying Adam because, while not tall, Adam is wide, and Warren is built more along the lines of a marathon runner. It's the kind of thing werewolves have to be careful not to do too often in public.

I opened the door for them but stayed in the living room while Warren continued up the stairs. Samuel waited with me.

Warren's half of the duplex had more square footage than my trailer, but between the small rooms and the stairways, my house always felt bigger to me.

He'd furnished the house comfortably with garage-sale finds and bookcases filled eclectically with everything from scientific texts to worn paperbacks bearing thrift-store price tags on the spines.

Samuel settled on the good side of the plush sofa and stretched out his legs. I turned away from him and thumbed through the nearest bookcase. I could feel his gaze on my back, but I didn't know what he was thinking.

'Oh, Mercy,' sighed a soft voice. 'This one is pretty. Why aren't you flirting with him?'

I looked at the kitchen doorway to see Kyle, Warren's current lover, leaning against the doorway of the kitchen in a typical Kyle pose designed to show off the toned body and tailored clothes.

The pose was deceptive; like Kyle's lowered eyelids and pouty, Marilyn Monroe expression, it was designed to hide the intelligence that made him the highest-paid divorce attorney in town. He told me once that being openly gay was as good for his business as his reputation as a shark. Women in the middle of a divorce tended to prefer dealing with him even over female lawyers.

Samuel stiffened and gave me a hard look. I knew what it meant: he didn't want a human involved in werewolf business. I ignored him; unfortunately Kyle didn't – he read the disapproval and mistook its cause.

'Good to see you,' I said. 'This is an old friend visiting from Montana.' I didn't want to get too detailed, because I thought it was up to Warren how much he told Kyle. 'Samuel, this is Kyle Brooks. Kyle, meet Dr Samuel Cornick.'

Kyle pushed himself off the doorframe with his shoulders and strolled into the living room. He stopped to kiss me on the cheek, then sat down on the sofa as close to Samuel as he could get.

It wasn't that he was interested in Samuel. He'd seen Samuel's disapproval and had decided to exact a little revenge. Warren usually retreated from the frowns of others or ignored

143

them. Kyle was a different kettle of fish entirely. He believed in making the bastards squirm.

I'd like to say that he had a chip on his shoulder, but he had no way of knowing that it wasn't his sexual orientation causing Samuel's reaction. Warren hadn't told him he was a werewolf. It was strongly discouraged to discuss the matter with anyone other than permanent mates – and to werewolves that meant male and female pairings – and the punishment for disobedience was harsh. Werewolves don't have jails. The people who break their laws are either punished physically or killed.

To my relief, Samuel seemed more amused than offended by Kyle's blatant come-on. When Warren came down the stairs, he paused a little at the sight of Kyle's hand on Samuel's thigh. When he started down again, his movements were easy and relaxed, but I could smell the tension rising in the air. He was not pleased. I couldn't tell if he was jealous or worried for his lover. He didn't know Samuel, but he knew, better than most, what the reaction of most werewolves would be.

'Kyle, it might be a good idea to take a few days and check out the state of your house.' Warren's tone was even, but his drawl was gone.

Kyle had his own house, an expensive place up on one of the hills in West Richland, but he'd moved in with Warren when Warren had refused to move in with him. At Warren's words, he stilled.

'I'm hiding someone for a few days,' Warren explained. 'It's not illegal, but it won't be safe here until he's gone.'

Samuel might have turned invisible for all the attention Kyle paid him. 'Darling, if you don't want me around, I'm gone. I suppose I'll accept Geordi's invitation for Thanksgiving, shall I?'

'It's just for a couple of days,' said Warren, his heart in his eyes.

'This have something to do with what you've been so upset about the past couple of days?'

Warren glanced at Samuel, then nodded once, quickly.

Kyle stared at him for a moment, then nodded back. 'All right. A couple of days. I'll leave my stuff here.'

'I'll call you.'

'You do that.'

Kyle left, closing the door behind him gently.

'You need to tell him,' I urged. 'Tell him the whole thing or you're going to lose him.' I liked Kyle, but more than that, a blind person could have seen that Warren really loved him.

Warren gave a pained half laugh. 'You think he'd be over-joyed to hear that he was sleeping with a monster? Do you think that would make everything okay?' He shrugged and tried to pretend it didn't matter. 'He'll leave me one way or another anyway, Mercy. He graduated from Cornell and I work nights at a gas station. Hardly a match made in Heaven.'

'I've never seen that it bothered him,' I said. 'He bends over backwards to keep you happy. Seems to me that you might give him a little something back.'

'It's forbidden,' Samuel said, but he sounded sad. 'He can't tell him.'

'What do you think Kyle'd do,' I said indignantly. 'Tell everyone that Warren's a werewolf? Not Kyle. He didn't get where he is by shooting off his mouth – and he's not the kind of person to betray anyone. He's a lawyer; he's good at keeping secrets. Besides, he's got too much pride to allow himself to be just another tabloid headline.'

'It's all right, Mercy.' Warren patted me on my head. 'He hasn't left me yet.'

'He will if you have to keep lying to him,' I said.

The two werewolves just looked at me. Warren loved Kyle, and he was going to lose him because someone had decided you had to be married before you told your spouse what you were — as if that wasn't a recipe for disaster.

I was pretty certain Kyle loved Warren, too. Why else would he live at Warren's when he had a huge, modern, air-conditioned monstrosity with a swimming pool? And Warren was going to throw it all away.

'I'm going for a walk,' I announced, having had enough of werewolves for one day. 'I'll come back when Zee calls.'

I wasn't as civilized as Kyle. I slammed the door behind me and started off down the sidewalk. I was so mad, I almost walked right past Kyle who was just sitting in his Jag, staring straight ahead.

Before I could think better of it, I opened the passenger door and slid in.

'Take us to Howard Amon Park,' I said.

Kyle gave me a look, but his lawyer face was on, so I couldn't tell what he thought, though my nose gave me all sorts of information on what he was feeling: angry, hurt, and discouraged.

What I was about to do was dangerous, no question. It wasn't just a werewolf's obligation to obey his Alpha that kept Warren's mouth shut. If Kyle did start telling everyone about werewolves, he would be silenced. And like me or not, if Adam or Bran found out I was the one who told him, they'd silence me, too.

Did I know Kyle well enough to trust him with our lives?

The Jag slid through the sparse Wednesday-after-work traffic like a tiger through the jungle. Neither Kyle's driving, nor his face, gave any sign of the anger that had raised his pulse rate, or the pain that fueled his anger — but I could smell them.

He pulled into Howard Amon near the south end and parked the car in one of the empty spaces. There were a lot of empty parking slots: November is not a time when most people decide to head to a river park.

'It's cold,' he said. 'We could talk in the car.'

'No,' I said, and got out. He was right, it was chilly. The wind was mild that day, but the Columbia added moisture to the air. I shivered in my cocoa-stained T-shirt – or maybe with nerves. I was going to do this and hope I wasn't wrong about Kyle.

He opened the trunk of his car and pulled a light jacket out and put it on. He took out a trench coat, too, and handed it to me.

'Put this on before you turn blue,' he said.

I wrapped myself in his coat and in the smell of expensive cologne. We were much of a size, so his coat fit me.

'I like it,' I told him. 'I need to get one of these.'

He smiled, but his eyes were tired.

'Let's walk,' I said, and tucked my arm in his, leading him past empty playground equipment and onto the path that ran along the river.

Warren was right, I thought. Having Kyle know he was a monster might not help matters between them at all – but I had the feeling that today would be the final straw if someone didn't clue Kyle in.

'Do you love Warren?' I asked. 'Not the good sex and great company kind of love. I mean the I'll-follow-you-to-death-and-beyond kind.'

It made me feel better that he paused before he answered. 'My sister Ally is the only one of my family I still talk to. I told her about Warren a few months ago. I hadn't realized, until she mentioned it, that I'd never told her about any of my other lovers.'

He put his hand over mine where it rested on his arm, warming it. 'My parents denied what I was for years. When I finally confronted them about it after my mother set me up with yet another young woman with a good pedigree, my father disinherited me. My sister Ally called as soon as she heard — but, after that first conversation, we avoid talking about my being gay. When I talk to her, I feel as if I have a scarlet letter sewn on my chest, and we are both trying to pretend it's not there.' He gave a bitter, angry laugh that changed subtly at the end. When he spoke again his voice was subdued. 'Ally told me to bring him to visit.' He looked at me and shared what that invitation meant to him.

We'd set out at a fast pace, and the park had narrowed to a strip of lawn on either side of the path. The riverbank exchanged its well-groomed look for a more natural growth of bushes and winter-yellowed, knee-high grass. There was a metal porch-type swing set on the top of a rise, set to look out over the river. I tugged him to it and sat down.

It was so important to get this right. Now that the time had come, I was afraid I'd ruin everything.

Swinging lazily, we watched the water flow past us, almost black in the growing shadows of the overcast sky. After a moment he rubbed his face briskly to warm it — and to wipe away incipient tears.

'God,' he said, and I flinched. I'm not a vampire, who can't bear to hear His name, but I don't like it used in vain. When he continued, though, I thought perhaps it hadn't been in vain at all.

'I love him.' It sounded as though the words were ripped from his throat. 'But he won't let me *in*. People call in the middle of the night, and he leaves without telling me where he's going.'

A lone bicyclist, wearing the skintight uniform of the die-hard enthusiast, appeared from the way we'd come. He passed us in a blur of spokes and Superman blue lycra.

'Nice legs,' said Kyle.

It was an old game. Kyle and I comparing notes on men while Warren pretended exasperation.

I leaned my head against Kyle's shoulder. 'Too small. I don't like it when I outweigh my men.'

Kyle leaned back until he was looking at the sky rather than the river. 'When we were in Seattle last month, he drove away a group of drunken, redneck gay-bashers, just scared them off with a few words. But that Darryl treats him like . . . like dirt, and Warren just puts up with it. I don't understand. And this stuff tonight . . .' He sucked air in to steel himself. 'Is he involved with drug dealers?'

I shook my head quickly. 'No. Nothing illegal.' Not yet anyway.

'Is he a fae, then?' he asked, as if it wouldn't bother him much.

'The fae all came out years ago.'

He snorted. 'You're not that dumb. I know a few doctors and teachers who are still in the closet about being gay – and all they have to worry about is losing their jobs, not having a group of idiots burn their houses down.' I could feel him deciding Warren was fae, and his agitation dropped appreciably. 'That would explain some things, like how strong he is and how he knows who's coming before he answers the door.'

Well, I thought feeling hopeful, being fae wasn't quite the same as being a werewolf. But if he could accept the one, maybe the other wouldn't be too big a stretch.

'He's not fae,' I said. I started to tell him just what Warren was, but the words caught in my throat.

'Warren should be the one telling me this,' said Kyle.

'Right,' I agreed. 'But he can't.'

'You mean he won't.'

'No. Can't.' I shook my head. 'I don't have many friends,' I said. 'Not "come over and eat popcorn and watch a stupid

PATRICIA BRIGGS

movie" friends. You and Warren are sort of it.' I don't have many girlfriends. My work isn't conducive to meeting other women.

'Pretty sad,' Kyle commented. Then he said, 'You and Warren are the only people I eat popcorn with, too.'

'Pathetic.' The banter helped. I drew in a breath and just said it. 'Warren's a werewolf.'

'A what?' Kyle stopped the swing.

'A werewolf. You know. The moon-called, run-on-four-feet-with-big-fangs kind of werewolf.'

He looked at me. 'You're serious.'

I nodded. 'And you're not going to breathe a word of it.'

'Oh?'

'That's why Warren couldn't tell you. That and because Adam – the pack Alpha – forbade it. If you go out now and talk to the authorities or the papers, even if they don't believe you, the pack will kill you.' I knew I was speaking too fast, but I couldn't seem to slow down. In Warren's house, with only Samuel and Warren, it hadn't seemed so dangerous. Samuel and Warren might care for me, but there were plenty of werewolves right here in town who would be happy to see me – and Kyle – dead for what I had just told him. 'Warren will fight them, but there are too many of them. He'll die, and you'll die with him.'

Kyle held up a hand. 'Hold on. It's a little soon for you to have Warren and me dead, don't you think?'

I took a deep breath. 'I hope so. You have to believe me on this – they take their secrecy very seriously. How do you think they've remained undetected for so long?'

'Mercy.' He caught my hand – his own felt cold, but that might have been from the wind. 'A werewolf?'

He didn't really believe me – that might be more dangerous. 'Twenty years ago no one believed in the fae, either. Look, I can prove it to you.'

150

I looked at a thicket of leafless bushes. They weren't really thick enough for me to strip and shift in, but there weren't any boats out on the water, and as long as we didn't get another biker at the wrong moment . . . I could just shift in my clothes – I get smaller, not bigger – but I'd rather be given a ticket for indecent exposure. A coyote in human clothes looks ridiculous.

'Wait here.' I gave him the trench coat so it wouldn't get dirty, then hopped off the swing and waded through the old grass into the bushes. I took off my clothes as fast as I could and shifted as soon as I dropped the last piece of clothing.

I stopped on the path and sat down, trying to look harmless.

'Mercy?' Kyle had his lawyer face on, which told me how shocked he was. He really hadn't believed me.

I wagged my tail and made a crooning noise. He got out of the swing like an old, old man and approached me.

'A coyote?' he asked.

When I went down to get my clothes, he followed me. I shifted right in front of him – then scrambled back into my clothes as I heard another bicycle coming along.

'I'm not a werewolf,' I told him, running my fingers through my hair. 'But I'm as close as you're going to get until you talk Warren into changing for you.'

Kyle made an impatient sound and pulled my hands away, rearranging my hair himself.

'Werewolves are bigger,' I said, feeling as though I ought to warn him. 'A lot bigger. They don't look like wolves. They look like really, really big wolves who might eat you.'

'Okay,' he said, stepping back. I thought he was talking about my hair, until he continued. 'Warren's a werewolf.'

I looked at his lawyer face and sighed. 'He couldn't tell you. If I tell you, and you don't do anything stupid – you and he are both safe. But if he told you, no matter how you reacted, he would have disobeyed a direct order. The penalty for that is brutal.'

He still wasn't giving anything away. He was so closed off, I couldn't sense what he was feeling. Most humans don't have that kind of control over themselves.

'Won't his pack—' He stumbled over that word a little. 'Won't they think he told me?'

'A lot of werewolves can smell a lie,' I said. 'They'll know how you found out.'

He went back to the swing, picked up the trench coat, and held it out to me. 'Tell me about werewolves.'

I was in the middle of trying to explain just how dangerous a werewolf could be and why it wasn't a good idea for him to flirt with Samuel – or Darryl – when my cell phone rang.

It was Zee.

'Business?' Kyle asked when I hung up.

'Yes.' I bit my lip.

He smiled. 'It's all right. I think I've heard enough secrets for one day. I take it you need to go back to Warren's?'

'Don't talk to him yet,' I said. 'Wait for it to sink in. If you have other questions, you can call me.'

'Thanks, Mercy.' He wrapped an arm around my shoulder. 'But I think I need to talk the rest out with Warren – after his business is finished.'

# 9

Samuel and Warren were seated on opposite sides of the living room when I walked in, and the air smelled thick with anger. I couldn't tell, just by looking at them, whether they were angry with each other or something else. But then, werewolves are always ready to be angry about something. I'd forgotten what it was like.

Of course, I wasn't the only one with a nose. Warren, sitting closest to the door, took a deep breath.

'She's been with Kyle,' he said, his voice flat. 'She smells like the cologne I gave him. You told him.' He swore at me, but there was more pain than anger in it. I felt a sharp twinge of guilt.

'*You* weren't going to tell him,' I said. I was *not* apologizing. 'And he deserved to know that all the crap he has to put up with is not all your doing.'

Warren shook his head and gave me a despairing glance. 'Do you have a death wish? Adam could have you and Kyle executed for it. I've seen it done.'

'Just me, not Kyle,' I said.

'Yes, damn it, Kyle, too.'

'Only if your lover decides to take it to the news or police.' Samuel's voice was mild, but Warren glared at him anyway.

'You risked too much, Mercy,' said Warren, turning back to me. 'How do you think I'd feel if I lost both of you?' All the anger left him suddenly, leaving only misery behind. 'Maybe you were right. It was still my job. My risk. If he was going to know, it should have been me telling him.'

'No. You are pack and sworn to obedience.' Adam swayed

at the top of the stairs, leaning a little on his cane. He was wearing a white shirt and jeans that fit. 'If you'd told him, I'd have had to enforce the law or risk a rebellion in the pack.'

He sat down on the top stair more abruptly than he meant to, I think, and grinned at me. 'Samuel and I both can witness that Warren didn't tell Kyle anything, you did. Despite Warren's objections, I might add. And, as you keep insisting, you are not pack.' He looked over at Warren. 'I'd have given you permission a long time ago, but I have to obey orders, too.'

I stared at him a moment. 'You knew I was going to tell Kyle.'

He smiled. 'Let's just say that I thought I was going to have to come down and order you not to tell him so you would storm out the door before Kyle drove off.'

'You manipulative bastard,' I said, with a tinge of awe. That was it, three tires were going to come off that old Rabbit.

'Thank you.' He gave me a modest smile.

*And* when we got Jesse back, she could help me with the graffiti.

'How did he take it?' asked Warren. He'd gotten off the couch and stood staring out his window. His hands hung loose and relaxed by his side, giving nothing of his feelings away.

'He's not gone running to the police,' I told Adam and Samuel. I searched for something more hopeful to tell Warren, but I didn't want to raise his expectations in case I was wrong about Kyle.

'He said he'd talk it over with you,' I told him at last. 'After this business is finished.'

He raised his hands to his face abruptly, in a gesture very like the one Kyle had used. 'At least it's not over, yet.'

He wasn't talking to any of us, but I couldn't stand the bleakness of his voice. I touched his shoulder, and said, 'Don't screw it up anymore and I think he'll be okay with it.'

Samuel and I headed out to meet with Zee and his informant, and I was still trying to figure out if I should have been mad at Adam for manipulating me like that. Except that he actually hadn't done any manipulation, had he? All he'd done was claim credit for my actions afterward.

The light turned red, and I had to stop behind a minivan a little closer than I usually did. Samuel's hand braced itself on my dash and he sucked in his breath. I made a face at the kid in the backseat of the van who had twisted around in his seat belt to look at us. He pulled his lower eyelids down and stuck out his tongue.

'It's not that I object to being in a car wreck,' Samuel said. 'I just prefer to have them on purpose.'

'What?' I glanced over at him, then looked in front of us. The back of the other van made an all-encompassing wall about two feet from our windshield. Sudden comprehension made me grin. 'Vanagons have no nose,' I said gently. 'Our bumper is about a foot from your toes. You could walk between our cars.'

'I could reach out and touch that boy,' he said. The boy had made another face, and Samuel made one back, sticking his thumbs in his ears and spreading his fingers out like moose antlers. 'You know, one of Adam's jobs was to make sure you didn't run around telling the world about werewolves.'

The light turned green, and the kid waved sadly as his van accelerated onto the interstate ramp. We were accelerating, too, but the ramp curled around in an uphill slant so it would take us a while to get to interstate speed.

I snorted. 'Kyle's not the world.' I glanced at him. 'Besides, you knew what I was going to do as well as Adam did. If you'd really objected, you could have stopped me before I left.'

'Maybe I think Kyle is trustworthy.'

I snorted. 'Maybe the moon is made of green cheese. You don't care. You think the werewolves need to come out in public like the fae.' Samuel had never been afraid of change.

'We aren't going to be able to hide much longer,' Samuel said, confirming my guess. 'When I went back to school, I realized just how far forensic medicine has come. Ten years ago, when it was just the military and the FBI labs we had to worry about, having a few wolves in the right places was sufficient. But there aren't enough wolves to infiltrate every small-town police laboratory. Since the fae came out, the scientists are paying closer attention to abnormalities they used to attribute to lab equipment failure or specimen contamination. If Da doesn't pick his time soon, it'll pick him.'

'You're the reason he's considering it at all.' That made sense. Bran had always given close consideration to Samuel's advice.

'Da's not stupid. Once he understood what we faced, he came to the same conclusion. He has a meeting scheduled for all the Alphas this coming spring.' He paused. 'He considered using Adam – the handsome Vietnam war hero.'

'Why not you?' I asked. 'The handsome, selfless doctor who has been keeping people alive for centuries.'

'That's why Da's in charge and you're just a minion,' he said. 'Remember, popular culture holds that all you need to become a werewolf is to have one bite you – not unlike AIDS. It will be a while before they're comfortable rubbing elbows up close and personal. Better to leave them thinking that all the wolves are in the military and the police. You know – "To Serve and Protect".'

'I'm not a minion,' I objected hotly. 'Minions have to be followers.' He laughed, pleased at having gotten my goat again.

'You don't mind that I told Kyle early?' I asked after a while.

'No, you were right. He has too much to lose by going to the tabloids, and he's the kind of people we need behind us – to keep the mobs under control.'

'Educated, well-spoken, well-bred lawyer?' I tried. Yes, that all fit Kyle. 'But he's not exactly mainstream.'

Samuel shrugged. 'Being gay has a certain cachet today.'

I thought of the story Kyle had told me about his family and thought Samuel was mistaken, at least in some quarters. But all I said was, 'I'll tell Kyle he has a certain cachet with you.'

Unexpectedly, Samuel grinned. 'I'd rather you didn't. He'll just flirt with me some more.'

'Speaking of uncomfortable,' I said, 'what had you and Warren so uptight?'

'It was mostly Warren,' he said. 'I'm a stranger, a dominant wolf in his territory – and he was already upset because he thought he was losing the love of his life. If I'd realized how dominant he was, I'd have taken myself elsewhere for the night. We'll manage, but it won't be comfortable.'

'He's Adam's third.'

'Would have been nice if someone had seen fit to tell me that,' Samuel groused good-naturedly. 'With Adam wounded and the second not there, that sticks Warren in the Alpha role – no wonder he was so wound up. I was ready to go out and take a walk myself when you showed up.' He gave me a sharp look. 'Odd how you showing up let him back down. Just as if Adam's second were there – or his mate.'

'I'm not pack,' I said shortly. 'I'm not dating Adam. I have no status in the pack. What I did have was a long overdue conversation with Kyle – which is what distracted Warren.'

Samuel continued to watch me. His mouth was quirked up, but his eyes were full of things I couldn't read, as he said, 'Adam's staked his claim on you before his pack. Did you know that?'

I hadn't. It made me suck in an angry breath before I realized why he might have done that. 'He had to keep his pack from killing me somehow. Wolves kill coyotes who are in their territory. A formal claim of me as his mate would keep me safe. I understand that was something Bran asked him to do. It doesn't make me pack, it doesn't make me his mate. The first is out because I'm a coyote, the second because somebody has to ask me before he can claim me for a mate.'

Samuel laughed, but there was no amusement in it. 'You can think as you please. How much time do we have before we find this bar?'

'It's in the far side of Pasco,' I said. 'We'll be there in ten minutes.'

'Well,' he said, 'why don't you tell me about Zee and this fae we are supposed to meet?'

'I don't know a lot,' I told him. 'Not about the fae. Just that she's got some information we might be interested in. As for Zee, he's a gremlin. He gave me my first job out of college, and I bought the garage from him when he retired. He still helps out when I need him – or when he gets bored. He likes to take things apart and see what's wrong with them, but he usually lets me put them back together again.'

'There's a fae reservation near here.'

I nodded. 'About forty miles away. Just outside of Walla Walla.'

'Adam says that having so many lesser fae around has attracted more of the greater fae.'

'I don't know about that,' I said. 'I can smell their magic, but I can't tell how strong they are.'

'He thinks that's also why there are more vampires, ghosts, and whatnot around the Tri-Cities than, say Spokane, which is a larger city.'

'I try to stay out of the other species' business,' I told him. 'I can't avoid the werewolves, not with Adam living right next door, but I try. The only fae I associate with are Zee and his son Tad.'

'The fae are willing to talk to you.' Samuel stretched his legs out and clasped his hands behind his neck, sticking his elbows out like wings. 'Adam says your old boss is one of the oldest of the fae — and, just so you know, the metal-smiths — gremlins — are not included with the lesser fae. Also, Warren told me that Stefan the vampire visits you quite often. Then there's this human police officer. Drawing the attention of the police is dangerous.'

It did sound as if I had my finger in all sorts of pies.

'Zee was forced public by the Gray Lords,' I said. 'So someone considers him to be one of the lesser fae. Stefan loves his bus, and I let him help me fix it.'

'You *what*?'

I forgot he'd never met Stefan. 'He's not like most vampires,' I tried to explain. Even though Stefan was the only vampire I'd ever met, I knew how they were supposed to act: I went to movies just like everyone else.

'They are *all* like most vampires,' Samuel said darkly. 'Some of them are just better at hiding it than others.'

It wouldn't do any good to argue with him — especially since I agreed with him in principle.

'And the police officer wasn't my fault,' I muttered, taking my exit into Pasco. It seemed like a good time to change the subject, so I said, 'The Fairy Mound in Walla Walla is the bar where tourists go to see the fae. The fae who don't want to be gawked at mostly hang out at Uncle Mike's here in Pasco. Zee says there's a spell on it that makes humans avoid it. It doesn't affect me, but I don't know about werewolves.'

'You aren't going in without me,' he said.

'Fine.' *Never argue with werewolves before you need to*, I reminded myself.

Uncle Mike's was across the Columbia River from my garage, which put it near Pasco's Industrial Park. The old building had once been a small warehouse, and there were warehouses on either side, both heavily tagged by the local kids. I wasn't sure if magic kept the kids away, or someone with a lot of paint and a brush, but Uncle Mike's exterior was always pristine.

I pulled into the parking lot and turned off my lights. It was about seven, still a little early for the regular crowd, and there were only four other cars in the lot, one of which was Zee's truck.

Inside, the bar was dark enough that a human might stumble over the stairs that led from the entry to the bar proper. Samuel hesitated in the doorway, but I thought that it was a tactical thing and not a reaction to a spell. The bar took up all of the wall to our right. There was a small dance floor cleared in the center of the room, with clusters of small tables scattered around the outside.

'There they are,' I told Samuel, and headed for the far corner, where Zee sat looking relaxed next to a moderately attractive woman in conservative business dress.

I've never seen Zee without his glamour; he told me he'd worn it so long that he was more comfortable in human guise. His chosen form was moderately tall, balding, with a little potbelly. His face was craggy, but not unattractively so – just enough to give it character.

He saw us coming and smiled. Since he and the woman already had the defensive seats, setting their backs against the wall, Samuel and I sat across from them. If having the rest of the room behind him, mostly empty as it was, bothered Samuel, I couldn't tell. I hitched my chair around until I could at least get a glimpse of the rest of the room.

'Hey, Zee,' I said. 'This is Dr Samuel Cornick. Samuel, meet Zee.'

Zee nodded, but didn't try to introduce his companion. Instead, he turned to her, and said, 'These are the ones I told you about.'

She frowned and tapped the table with long, manicured nails. Something about the way she used them made me think that beneath the glamour she might have claws. I'd been trying to pin down her scent, but finally was forced to conclude that either she didn't have one or that she smelled of iron and earth just like Zee.

When she looked up from contemplating her nails, she spoke to me and not to Samuel. 'Zee tells me there is a child missing.'

'She's fifteen,' I said, wanting to be clear. The fae don't like it if they think you've lied to them. 'The local Alpha's human daughter.'

'This could be trouble for me,' she said. 'But I have talked to Zee, and what I have to tell you has nothing to do with the fae, and so I am at liberty to share it. I would not usually help the wolves, but I do not like those who take their battles to the innocents.'

I waited.

'I work at a bank,' she said at last. 'I won't tell you the name of it, but it is the bank that the local seethe of vampires uses. Their deposits follow a regular pattern.' Meaning that most of their victims' payments were monthly. She sipped her drink. 'Six days ago, there was an unexpected deposit.'

'Visitors paying tribute,' I said, sitting up straighter in my chair. This sounded promising. A single fae or wolf or whatever wouldn't have paid a tribute high enough to catch anyone's eye.

'I took the liberty of speaking to Uncle Mike himself before you came,' said Zee quietly. 'He's heard of no new visitors, which means these people are keeping very quiet.'

'We need to talk to the vampires,' said Samuel. 'Adam will know how to do it.'

'That will take too long.' I took out my cell phone and dialed Stefan's number. It was early for him to be up, but he'd called me not much later than this.

'Mercy,' he said warmly. 'Are you back from your trip?'

'Yes. Stefan, I need your help.'

'What can I do for you?' Something changed in his voice, but I couldn't worry about that.

'Tuesday night or early Wednesday morning, a group of people including out-of-territory werewolves kidnapped the Alpha's daughter. She's a personal friend of mine, Stefan. Someone told me that your seethe might know of a visiting pack.'

'Ah,' he said. 'That's not in my area of responsibility. Do you want me to inquire for you?'

I hesitated. I didn't know much about the vampires except that smart people avoid them. Something about the formality of his question made me think it was a bigger question than it sounded.

'What does that mean, exactly?' I asked suspiciously.

He laughed, a cheerful unvampire-like sound. 'Good for you. It means that you are appointing me your representative and that gives me certain rights to pursue this that I might not otherwise have.'

'Rights over me?'

'None that I will take advantage of,' he said. 'I give you

162

my word of honor, Mercedes Thompson. I will force you to do nothing against your will.'

'All right,' I said. 'Then yes, I would like you to inquire for me.'

'What do you know?'

I glanced at the woman's expressionless face. 'I can't tell you everything – just that I've been told that your seethe knows of visitors to the Tri-Cities who might be the group I'm looking for. If that group doesn't have any werewolves, then they're the wrong ones. They might be doing something experimental with medicines or drugs.'

'I'll inquire,' he said. 'Keep your cell phone at hand.'

'I'm not certain that was wise,' said Zee, after I hung up.

'You said she deals with the werewolves.' The woman curled her upper lip at me. 'You didn't tell me she also deals with the undead.'

'I'm a mechanic,' I told her. 'I don't make enough money to pay off the vampires in cash, so I fix their cars. Stefan has an old bus he's restoring. He's the only one I've ever dealt with personally.'

She didn't look happy, but her lip uncurled.

'I appreciate your time,' I said, narrowly skirting an outright thank you – which can get you in trouble. The wrong kind of fae will take your thanks as an admission that you feel obligated to them. Which means that you must then do whatever they ask. Zee had been very careful to break me of that habit. 'The Alpha will also be happy to recover his daughter.'

'It is always good for the Alpha to be happy,' she said; I couldn't tell if she was being honest or sarcastic. She stood up abruptly and smoothed down her skirts to give me time to move my chair so she could exit. She stopped by the bar and spoke to the bartender before she left.

'She smells like you,' Samuel said to Zee. 'Is she a metal-smith, too?'

'Gremlin, please,' said Zee. 'It may be a new name for an old thing, but at least it is not a bad translation. She is a troll – a relative, but not a close one. Trolls like money and extortion, a lot of them go into banking.' He frowned at me. 'You don't go into that nest of vampires alone, Mercy, not even if Stefan is escorting you. He appears better than most, but I have been around a long time. You cannot trust a vampire. The more pleasant they appear, the more dangerous they are.'

'I don't plan on going anywhere,' I told him. 'Samuel is right, the wolves don't pay tribute here. Likely they are people who have nothing to do with taking Jesse.'

My phone rang.

'Mercy?'

It was Stefan, but there was something about his voice that troubled me. I heard something else, too, but there were more people in the bar and someone had turned up the music.

'Wait a moment,' I said loudly – then lied. 'I'm sorry I can't hear you. I'm going outside.' I waved at Samuel and Zee, then walked outside to the quieter parking lot.

Samuel came with me. He started to speak but I held up a finger to my lips. I didn't know how good a vampire's hearing was, but I didn't want to risk it.

'Mercy, can you hear me now?' Stefan's voice was overly crisp and even.

'Yes,' I said. I could also hear the woman's voice that said sweetly, 'Ask her, Stefan.'

He sucked in his breath as if the unknown woman had done something that hurt.

'Is there a strange werewolf with you at Uncle Mike's?' he asked.

'Yes,' I said, looking around. I couldn't smell anything

like Stefan nearby, and I was pretty certain I'd have noticed. The vampires must have a contact at Uncle Mike's, someone who could tell Samuel was a werewolf and who knew Adam's werewolves.

'My mistress wonders that she was not informed of a visitor.'

'The wolves don't ask permission to travel here, not from your seethe,' I told him. 'Adam knows.'

'Adam has disappeared, leaving his pack leaderless.' They spoke together, his words so tight on the end of hers that he sounded like an echo.

I was relatively certain she didn't know I could hear her – though Stefan did. He knew what I was because I'd shown him. Apparently he hadn't seen fit to inform the rest of his seethe. Of course, someone as relatively powerless as I was of little interest to the vampires.

'The pack is hardly leaderless,' I said.

'The pack is weak,' they said. 'And the wolves have set precedent. They paid for permission to come into our territory because we are dominant to Adam's little pack.'

Samuel's eyes narrowed, and his mouth tightened. The vampire's contributors were the people who'd killed Mac, the people who had Jesse.

'So the new visitors have werewolves among them,' I said sharply. 'They are not Bran's wolves. They cannot be a pack. They are less than nothing. Outlaws with no status. I killed two of them myself, and Adam killed another two. And you know I am no great power. Real wolves, wolves who were pack, would never have fallen to something as weak as I.' That was the truth, and I hoped they both could hear it.

There was a long pause, I could hear murmuring in the background, but I could not tell what they said.

'Perhaps that is so,' said Stefan at last, sounding tired. 'Bring your wolf and come to us. We'll determine if he needs a visitor's pass. If not, we see no reason not to tell you what we know of these outlaws who are so much less than pack.'

'I don't know where your seethe is,' I said.

'I'll come and get you,' said Stefan, apparently speaking on his own. He hung up.

'I guess we're going to visit the vampires tonight,' I said. Sometime during the conversation, Zee had come out as well. I hadn't noticed when, but he was standing beside Samuel. 'Do you know vampires?'

Samuel shrugged. 'A little. I've run into one a time or two.'

'I'll go with you,' the old mechanic said softly, and tossed back the last of the scotch in the shot glass he'd brought out with him. 'Nothing I am will help you – metal is not their bane. But I know something of vampires.'

'No,' I said. 'I need you for something else. If I don't call you tomorrow morning, I want you to call this number.' I pulled an old grocery receipt out of my purse and wrote Warren's home number on the back of it. 'This is Warren's, the wolf who's Adam's third. Tell him as much as you know.'

He took the number. 'I don't like this.' But he shoved the note into his pocket in tacit agreement. 'I wish you had more time to prepare. Do you have a symbol of your faith, Mercy, a cross, perhaps? It is not quite as effective as Mr Stoker made it out to be, but it will help.'

'I'm wearing a cross,' Samuel said. 'Bran makes us all wear them. We don't have vampires in our part of Montana, but there are other things crosses are good for.' Like some of the nastier fae – but Samuel wouldn't mention that in front of Zee – it would be rude. Just as Zee would never mention that the third and fourth bullets in the gun he carried were silver – I made them for him myself. Not that he couldn't do it better himself, but if he got tangled up with were-wolves, I figured it would be because of me.

'Mercy?' asked Samuel.

I don't like crosses. My distaste has nothing to do with the metaphysical like it does for vampires; when I lived in Bran's pack, I wore crosses, too. I have a whole spiel about how sick it is to carry around the instrument of Christ's torture as a symbol for the Prince of Peace who taught us to love one another. It's a good spiel, and I even believe it.

Really though, they just give me the willies. I have a very vivid memory of going to church with my mother on one of her rare visits when I was four or five. She was poor and living in Portland; she just couldn't afford to come very often. So when she could come, she liked to do something special. We went to Missoula for a mother-daughter weekend and, on Sunday, picked a church to attend at random – more, I think, because my mother felt she ought to take me to church than because she was particularly religious.

She stopped to talk to the pastor or priest, and I wandered farther into the building so I was alone when I turned the corner and saw, hanging on the wall, a bigger-than-life-size statue of Christ dying on the cross. My eyes were just level with his feet, which were tacked to the cross with a huge nail. It wouldn't have been so bad, but someone with talent had painted it true to life, complete with blood. We didn't go to church that day – and ever since then, I couldn't look at a cross without seeing the son of God dying upon it.

So, no crosses for me. But, having been raised in Bran's pack, I carried around something else. Reluctantly, I pulled out my necklace and showed it to them.

Samuel frowned. The little figure was stylized; I suppose he couldn't tell what it was at first.

'A dog?' asked Zee, staring at my necklace.

'A lamb,' I said defensively, tucking it safely back under my shirt. 'Because one of Christ's names is "The Lamb of God."'

Samuel's shoulders shook slightly. 'I can see it now, Mercy holding a roomful of vampires at bay with her glowing silver sheep.'

I gave his shoulder a hard push, aware of the heat climbing up my cheeks, but it didn't help. He sang in a soft taunting voice, 'Mercy had a little lamb . . .'

'I've been told it's the faith of the wearer that matters,' Zee said, though he sounded doubtful, too. 'I don't suppose you've ever used your lamb against a vampire?'

'No,' I said shortly, still huffy over the song. 'But if the Star of David works, and Bran says it does, then this should, too.'

We all turned to watch a car drive into the parking lot, but its occupants got out and, after the driver tipped an imaginary hat at Zee, walked into Uncle Mike's. No vampires in that lot.

'Is there anything else we should know?' I asked Zee, who seemed to be the most informed of us. All I knew for certain about vampires came under the heading of 'Stay Away From.'

'Prayer doesn't work' he said. 'Though it seems to have some effect on demons and some of the oldest of the dark fae. Garlic doesn't work—'

'Except like insect repellent,' said Stefan, just appearing between two parked cars behind Zee. 'It doesn't hurt, but it smells bad and tastes worse. If you don't irritate one of us, and make sure you bring a friend who hasn't eaten garlic, it'll at least put you last on the menu.'

I hadn't heard him come, hadn't seen him or sensed him at all until he spoke. From somewhere, Zee drew a dark-bladed dagger as long as my arm and stepped between me and the vampire. Samuel growled.

'I'm sorry,' Stefan apologized humbly, as he noticed how badly he'd startled us. 'Moving unseen is a talent of mine, but I usually don't use it on my friends. I've just had an unpleasant episode, and it left me with my guard up.'

Stefan was tallish, but he always seemed to take up less space than he should, so I seldom thought of him as being a big man unless he was standing next to someone else. He was, I noticed, just exactly the same height as Samuel and nearly as broad in the shoulders, though he lacked some of the werewolf's bulk.

His face had regular features and in repose he might be handsome, I suppose. But his expressions were so big that I lost the shape of his features for the bright engagement of his grin.

Just then, though, he frowned at me. 'If I am to take you before the Mistress, I'd rather you had dressed up a bit more.'

I looked down and realized I was wearing the clothing I'd had on when I'd gone over to check out Adam's house. It seemed like a week ago, rather than the night before last. The T-shirt was one Stefan himself had given me for teaching him how to correct the timing on his bus. It read 'Happiness is German engineering, Italian cooking, and Belgian chocolate' and bore a large stain from the cocoa I spilled on it. Thinking about how long I'd been wearing it made me realize that it smelled a little bit stronger than it usually did – and not of detergent and fabric softener either.

'We just came back into town late this afternoon,' I apologized. 'I haven't had a chance to go home and change yet. But you're not much better.'

He looked down at himself, rocking back on his heels and spreading his hands like a vaudeville comic exaggerating his motions for an audience. He was wearing a casual black long-sleeved shirt unbuttoned over a plain white T-shirt, and jeans with a hole over one knee. I've never seen him wearing anything more formal, but for some reason his casual clothes always looked . . . wrong somehow, as if he were wearing a costume.

'What, this?' he asked. 'This is my best down-at-the-heels vampire look,' he said. 'Maybe I should have worn black jeans and a black shirt, but I hate overdoing it.'

'I thought you were picking us up.' I looked around pointedly. 'Where's your car?'

'I came the fast way.' He didn't explain what that was, but continued, 'I see you have your van. There should be plenty of room for the four of us.'

'Zee's staying here,' I said.

Stefan smiled. 'To bring in the troops.'

'Do you know where the people who attacked Adam are?' I asked, rather than commenting on Stefan's observation.

He shook his head regretfully. 'The Mistress didn't see fit to tell me any more than I conveyed to you.' His face grew still for a moment. 'I'm not even certain what she told me was truth. She may know nothing. You might want to find an excuse for not going, Mercy.'

'These visitors have already killed one man and made a mess of Adam's house,' I told him. 'If your Mistress knows where they are, we need to go ask.'

He gave me an oddly formal bow and turned to look at Samuel, giving him a wide smile that managed to keep from displaying his fangs. 'I don't know you. You must be the new wolf in town.'

I made introductions, but it was obvious that Samuel and Stefan were not going to be instant friends – and it wasn't Stefan's fault.

I was a little surprised. Both men shared the easygoing charm that usually had other people smiling. But Samuel's manner was unusually grim. Obviously, he didn't like vampires.

I hopped in my van and waited while Stefan and Samuel

had a very polite argument about where they would sit. Both of them wanted the backseat. I was willing to believe that Stefan was trying to be considerate, but Samuel didn't want the vampire sitting behind him.

Before he dropped his politeness and told Stefan so, I broke in. 'I need Stefan in front so he can tell me where we're going.'

Zee knocked on my window and, when I turned on the power to roll it down, he gave me the dagger he'd pulled when Stefan first emerged from the shadows, along with a handful of leather that looked to be a sheath and belt.

'Take this,' he said. 'The belt ties so you can adjust it to fit you.'

'May I?' Stefan asked diffidently, as he settled himself in the front seat. When Zee gave a curt nod, I handed it over.

The vampire held the blade up and turned it back and forth under the van's dome light. He started to hand it back to me, but Samuel reached between the seats and took it from him. He tested the sharpness of the edge, pricking himself lightly on the thumb. Sucking in his breath, he jerked his hand away and put his thumb in his mouth.

For a moment nothing happened. Then power washed through the van, not like the power the Alphas could call, nor did it feel like the magic Elizaveta Arkadyevna used. It was akin somehow to the fae power of glamour and tasted like metal and blood in my mouth. After a bare moment, the night was quiet again.

'I would suggest that feeding old blades your blood is not a good idea,' said Stefan mildly.

Zee laughed, a full-throated openmouthed sound that made him throw his head back. 'Listen to the vampire, Samuel Bran's Son. My daughter likes the taste of you a little too well.'

Samuel handed the dagger and its accouterments back to

me. 'Zee,' he said, then, as if he'd just realized something he continued in German, '*Siebold Adelbertkrieger aus dem Schwarzenwald.*'

'Siebold Adelbertsmiter from the Walla Walla Fae Preserve,' Zee said mildly.

'Siebold Adelbert's Smiter from the Black Forest,' I translated, using my required two years of a foreign language course for the first time ever. It didn't matter; in German or in English, the words, which Sam made sound like a title of honor, still meant nothing to me.

Go to any Irish village and they'll tell you the names of the fae who interacted with their ancestors. There are rocks and ponds that bear the names of the brownies or kelpies that live there. The German stories tended to concentrate on the heros. Only a few of the German fae, like Lorelei and Rumpelstiltskin, have stories that tell you their names and give you fair warning about the fae you might be dealing with.

Samuel, though, knew something about Zee.

Zee saw the look in my eye and laughed again. 'Don't you start, girl. We live in the present and let the past take care of itself.'

I have a degree in history, which is one of the reasons I'm an auto mechanic. Most of the time, I satisfy my craving for the past by reading historical novels and romances. I'd tried to get Zee to tell me stories before, but like the werewolves, he would not say much. The past holds too many shadows. But armed with a name, I was going to hit the Internet as soon as I finally got to go home.

Zee looked at Stefan, and the laughter faded from his eyes. 'The dagger probably won't help a great deal against vampires, but I'll feel better if she has something to defend herself.'

Stefan nodded. 'It will be allowed.'

The dagger lay on my lap just like any other blade, but I remembered the caress of power and slid it carefully into its sheath.

'Don't look them in the eyes,' Zee told me abruptly. 'That means you, too, Dr Cornick.'

'Don't play dominance games with vampires,' said Samuel. 'I remember.'

The second half of that old wolf aphorism is 'just kill them.' I was happy that he'd left it out.

'Do you have any other warnings, vampire who is Mercy's friend?' Zee asked Stefan.

He shrugged. 'I wouldn't have agreed to this if I truly thought the Mistress had harm in mind. Mostly she just grows bored. Mercy is very good at soft answers that don't promise anything. If the wolf can manage the same, we should all be safe in our beds before dawn.'

# 10

I don't know where I expected the vampires to live. I suppose I'd been influenced by all those late night flicks and imagined a large Victorian mansion in a disreputable part of town. There are a few along the downtown area in Kennewick, most of them polished and painted like old opera stars. And, while there are a few run-down neighborhoods around, they tend to be populated with houses too small to house even a small seethe.

It shouldn't have surprised me to be driving along a street with Mercedes, Porsches, and BMWs in every elegant cobbled driveway. The road had been cut into the side of a hill that overlooked the town, and for thirty years, doctors, lawyers, and CEOs had been building their four-thousand-square-foot homes on the steeply sloped lots. But, as Stefan told us, the vampires had been there first.

At the end of the main street, a smaller gravel road broke off and cut between a pair of two-story brick edifices. It looked almost like it might be a driveway, but continued past the houses and into the undeveloped area behind them.

We drove through about a quarter mile of the usual eastern Washington scrub — cheat grass, sagebrush, and tackweed mostly — and then up over a small ridge that was just large enough to hide a two-story, sprawling hacienda surrounded by an eight-foot wall. As the road came down the hill our view of the house was limited to what we could see through the double, wrought-iron gates. I thought the sweeping Spanish arches that graced the sides of the building did a wonderful job of disguising the scarcity of windows.

At Stefan's direction, I parked just outside the walls, where the ground had been leveled. The vampire jumped out and was around to open my door before Samuel got out of the van.

'Should I leave this?' I asked Stefan, holding up Zee's dagger. On the way, I'd decided that since it was too big to be hidden without fae glamour – which I don't have – it might be a good thing not to take it in at all.

Stefan shrugged, his hands patting lightly on his thighs as if he heard music I didn't. It was a habitual thing with him; he was seldom absolutely still.

'Carrying an artifact this old could make them respect you more,' said Samuel, who'd come around the van. 'Wear it.'

'I was worried about setting the wrong tone,' I explained.

'I don't expect things to get violent tonight,' said Stefan. 'The dagger is not going to start anything.' He grinned at me. 'It is illegal in this state, though. You'll have to remember to take it off when you leave.'

So I wrapped the leather belt around my hips a few times. There was a handmade buckle without a pin on one end, and I wove the other end of the belt through and tied it off.

'It's too loose,' said Stefan, reaching for it – but Samuel got there first.

'Tighten it around your waist,' he said, adjusting it for me. 'Then pull it over your hips so the weight of the blade doesn't slide the whole thing down around your ankles.'

When he was satisfied, he stepped away.

'I'm not the enemy,' Stefan told him mildly.

'We know that,' I said.

Stefan patted my shoulder, but continued, 'I am not your enemy, Wolf. I've risked more than you know by taking both of you under my protection. The Mistress wanted to send others for you – and I don't think you'd have enjoyed that.'

'Why take the risk?' Samuel asked. 'Why take us under

PATRICIA BRIGGS

your protection? I know something of what that means. You don't know me – and Mercy is just your mechanic.'

Stefan laughed, his hand still on my shoulder. 'Mercy is my friend, Dr Cornick. My mother taught me to take care of my friends, didn't yours?'

He was lying. I don't know how I was so certain of it, but I was.

Some werewolves can tell if a person is lying. I can only do it if it is someone I know really well, *and* I'm paying attention. It has to do with the change in the normal sounds a person makes – breathing and pulse, things like that. Usually I'm not paying that much attention. I've never been able to tell a thing about Stefan, not even the usual emotions that carry such distinctive smells. And Stefan's pulse and breathing tended to be erratic. I sometimes thought he only breathed because he knew how uncomfortable he made people when he didn't.

Nonetheless, I knew he had lied.

'You just lied to us,' I told him. 'Why *are* you helping us?' I pulled out from under his hand so I could turn and face him, putting Samuel at my back.

'We don't have time for this,' Stefan said, and some of the usual liveliness faded from his face.

'I need to know if we can trust you,' I told him. 'Or at least how far we can trust you.'

He made one of those grand stage magician gestures, throwing his hands up and tossing his head – but I felt a fine cloak of real magic settling around us. Like Zee, it tasted of earth, but there were darker things in Stefan's spell than anything the gremlin had done around me.

'Fine,' he said. 'Just don't blame me when she's in a rotten mood because we kept her waiting. You called me tonight with a question.'

'What did you just do?' asked Samuel quietly.

176

Stefan let fall an exasperated sigh. 'I made certain that the three of us are the only ones participating in this conversation, because there are things that hear very well in the night.'

He turned his attention back to me. 'When I called our accountant she put me right through to our Mistress — which is not standard procedure. Our Mistress was obviously more interested in your Dr Cornick than she was with your question. She came to me and had me call you back — she didn't intend me to escort you. She didn't want you to have even that much protection, but once I offered, she could not contradict me. I am here, Mercy, because I want to know what is going on that stirs my Mistress from the lethargy that has been her usual state since she was exiled here. I need to know if it is a good thing, or something very bad for me and my kind.'

I nodded. 'All right.'

'But I would have done it for friendship's sake,' he added.

Unexpectedly, Samuel laughed a little bitterly. 'Of course. We all do things for our Mercy for friendship's sake,' he said.

Stefan didn't take us through the front gates, which were large enough to drive a semi through, but led the way around the side to a small, open door in the wall.

In contrast to the undeveloped scrub outside the gates, the interior grounds were elaborate. Even in November, the grass, under the moon's waxing light, was dark and luxurious. A few roses peeked out from protected areas near the house, and the last of the mums still had a few blooms. It was a formal French-style garden, with organized beds and meticulous grooming. Had the house been a Victorian- or Tudor-style home, it would have looked lovely. Next to a Spanish-style adobe house it just looked odd.

Grapevines, bare in their winter guise, lined the wall. In

the moonlight they looked like a row of dead men, hanging arms spread wide and crucified on the frames that supported them.

I shivered and moved closer to Samuel's warmth. He gave me an odd look, doubtless scenting my unease, but set his hand on my shoulder and pulled me closer.

We followed a cobbled path past a swimming pool, covered for the winter, around the corner of the house to a broad swath of lawn. Across the lawn there was a two-story guest-house almost a third the size of the main house. It was to this smaller building that Stefan led us.

He knocked twice at the door, then opened and waved us into an entry hall decorated aggressively in the colors and textures of the American Southwest, complete with clay pots and kachina dolls. But even the decor was overwhelmed by the smell of mostly unfamiliar flowers and herbs rather than the scents of the desert.

I sneezed, and Samuel wrinkled his nose. Perhaps all the potpourri was designed to confuse our noses – but it was only strong, not caustic. I didn't enjoy it, but it didn't stop me from smelling old leather and rotting fabrics. I took a quick, unobtrusive look around, but I couldn't see anything to account for the smell of rot; everything looked new.

'We'll wait for her in the sitting room,' Stefan said, leading the way through the soaring ceilings of a living room and into a hall.

The room he took us to was half again the size of the biggest room in my trailer. From what I'd seen of the house, though, it was cozy. We'd left behind the Southwest theme for the most part, though the colors were still warm earth tones.

The seats were comfortable, if you like soft fluffy furniture. Stefan settled into a chair with every sign of relaxation as the furniture swallowed him. I scooted toward the front edge of the love seat, which was marginally firmer, but the cushions would still slow me down a little if I had to move quickly.

Samuel sat in a chair that matched Stefan's, but rose to his feet as soon as he started to sink. He stalked behind my love seat and looked out of the large window that dominated the room. It was the first window I'd seen in the house.

Moonlight streamed in, sending loving beams over his face. He closed his eyes and basked in it, and I could tell it was calling to him, even though the moon was not full. She didn't speak to me, but Samuel had once described her song to me in the words of a poet. The expression of bliss on his face while he listened to her music made him beautiful.

I wasn't the only one who thought so.

'Oh, aren't you lovely?' said a voice; a throaty, lightly European voice that preceded a woman dressed in a high-cut, semiformal dress of gold silk that looked rather odd combined with jogging shoes and calf-high athletic socks.

Her reddish blond curls were pulled up with elegant whimsy and lots of bobby pins, revealing dangling diamond earrings that matched the elaborate necklace at her throat. There were faint lines around her eyes and mouth.

She smelled a little like Stefan, so I had to assume she was a vampire, but the lines on her face surprised me. Stefan looked scarcely twenty, and I'd somehow assumed that the undead were like the werewolves, whose cells repaired themselves and removed damage of age, disease, and experience.

The woman padded into the room and made a beeline for Samuel, who turned to regard her gravely. When she leaned against him and stood on tiptoe to lightly lick his neck, he slid a hand up around to the base of her skull and looked at Stefan.

I shifted a little farther toward the edge of my seat and twisted so I could watch them over the back of the love seat.

I wasn't too worried about Samuel – he was poised to break her neck. Maybe a human couldn't have managed it, but he wasn't human.

'Lilly, my Lilly fair.' Stefan sighed, his voice puncturing the tension in the room. 'Don't lick the guests, darling. Bad manners.'

She paused, her nose resting against Samuel. I gripped the hilt of Zee's dagger and hoped I didn't have to use it. Samuel could protect himself, I hoped, but he didn't like hurting women – and Stefan's Lilly looked very feminine.

'She said we had guests for entertainment.' Lilly sounded like a petulant child who knows the promised trip to the toy store is about to be delayed.

'I'm sure she meant we had guests for *you* to entertain, my sweet.' Stefan hadn't moved from his chair, but his shoulders were tight, and his weight was forward.

'But he smells so good,' she murmured. I thought she darted her head forward, but I must have been mistaken because Samuel didn't move. 'He's so warm.'

'He's a werewolf, darling Lilly. You'd find him a difficult meal.' Stefan got up and walked slowly around my couch. Taking one of Lilly's hands in his, he kissed it. 'Come entertain us, my lady.'

He pulled her gently off Samuel and escorted her formally to an upright piano tucked into one corner of the room. He pulled out the bench and helped her settle.

'What should I play?' she asked. 'I don't want to play Mozart. He was so rude.'

Stefan touched her cheek with the tips of his fingers. 'By all means, play whatever you wish, and we will listen.'

She sighed, an exaggerated sound with an accompanying shoulder droop, then, like a marionette she straightened from head to toe and placed her hands just so on the keys.

I don't like piano music. There was only one music teacher

in Aspen Creek when I grew up, and she played piano. For four years I banged out tunes for a half hour a day and hated the piano more each year. It hated me back.

It took only a few measures for me to realize I'd been wrong about the piano – at least when Lilly played it. It didn't seem possible that all that sound came from the little upright piano and the fragile woman sitting before us.

'Liszt,' whispered Samuel, stepping away from the window and sitting on the back of my seat. Then he closed his eyes and *listened*, just as he'd listened to the moon.

Stefan stepped away from the piano once Lilly was focused on her music. He drifted back to stand beside me, then he held out a hand.

I glanced at Samuel, but he was still lost in the music. I took Stefan's hand and let him pull me to my feet. He took me to the far side of the room before releasing me.

'It isn't being a vampire that made her this way,' he said, not whispering, exactly, but in low tones that didn't carry over the music. 'Her maker found her playing piano at an expensive brothel. He decided he wanted her in his seethe, so he took her before he understood that she was touched. In the normal course she would have been mercifully killed: it is dangerous to have a vampire who cannot control herself. I know the werewolves do the same. But no one could bear to lose her music. So she is kept in the seethe and guarded like the treasure she is.'

He paused. 'But usually she is not allowed to wander about at will. There are always attendants who are assigned to keep her – and our guests – safe. Perhaps our Mistress amuses herself.'

I watched Lilly's delicate hands flash across the keys and produce music of power and intellect that she didn't possess herself. I thought about what had happened when Lilly had come into the room.

'If Samuel had reacted badly?' I asked.

'She'd have no chance against him.' Stefan rocked back on his heels unhappily. 'She has no experience at taking unwilling prey, and Samuel is old. Lilly is precious to us. If he had hurt her, the whole seethe would have demanded retribution.'

'Shh,' said Samuel.

She played Liszt for a long time. Not the early lyrical pieces, but the ones he composed after hearing the radical violinist Paganini. But, right in the middle of one of his distinctively mad runs of notes, she switched into a blues piece I didn't recognize, something soft and relaxed that lazed in the room like a big cat. She played a little Beatles, some Chopin, and something vaguely oriental in style before falling into the familiar strains of *Eine Kleine Nachtmusik*.

'I thought you weren't going to play Mozart,' said Stefan when she'd finished the song and begun picking out a melody with her right hand.

'I like his music,' she explained to the keyboard. 'But he was a pig.' She crashed her hands on the keys twice. 'But he is dead, and I am not. Not dead.'

I wasn't going to argue with her. Not when one of those delicate fingers broke the key beneath it. No one else said anything either.

She got up from the piano abruptly and strode through the room. She hesitated in front of Samuel, but when Stefan cleared his throat, she trotted up to him and kissed him on the chin. 'I'm going to eat now,' she said. 'I'm hungry.'

'Fine.' Stefan hugged her, then directed her out of the room with a gentle push.

She hadn't once so much as looked at me.

'So you think we're being set up?' asked Samuel, with lazy geniality that seemed somehow out of place.

Stefan shrugged. 'You, I, or Lilly. Take your pick.'

'It seems like a lot of trouble to go to,' I ventured. 'If Samuel died, Bran would tear this place apart. There wouldn't be a vampire left in the state.' I looked at Stefan. 'Your lady may be powerful, but numbers matter. The Tri-Cities isn't that big. If there were hundreds of you here, I'd have noticed it. Bran can call upon every Alpha in North America.'

'It is nice to know how we are esteemed by the wolves. I'll make certain our Mistress knows to leave the wolf alone because she should fear them,' said a woman from just behind me.

I jumped forward and turned, and Stefan was suddenly between me and the new vampire. This one was neither ethereal nor seductive. If she hadn't been a vampire, I'd have put her age somewhere around sixty, every year etched in the lines of grim disapproval that traversed her face.

'Estelle,' said Stefan. I couldn't tell if it was a greeting, introduction, or admonition.

'She has changed her mind. She doesn't want to come up to visit with the wolf. They can come to her instead.' Estelle didn't seem to react to Stefan at all.

'They are under my protection.' Stefan's voice darkened in a way I'd never heard it before.

'She said you may come, too, if you wish.' She looked at Samuel. 'I'll need to take any crosses or holy objects you are wearing, please. We do not allow people to go armed in the presence of our Mistress.'

She held out a gold-embossed leather bag, and Samuel unhooked his necklace. When he pulled it out of his shirt, the necklace didn't blaze or glow. It was just a bit of ordinary metal, but I saw her involuntary shudder when it brushed close to her skin.

She looked at me and I pulled out my necklace and showed her my sheep. 'No crosses,' I said in a bland voice. 'I didn't expect to be out speaking to your Mistress tonight.'

183

She didn't even glance at Zee's dagger, dismissing it as a weapon. After pulling the drawstring tight, she let the bag dangle from it. 'Come with me.'

'I'll bring them down in a minute,' Stefan said. 'Go tell her we are coming.'

The other vampire raised her eyebrows but left without a word, carrying the bag with Samuel's cross in it.

'There's something more happening than I thought,' Stefan said rapidly. 'Against most of those here, I can protect you, but not the Mistress herself. If you'd like, I'll get you out of here and see if I can find the information without you.'

'No,' said Samuel. 'We're here now. Let us finish this.'

Samuel's words slurred a little, and I saw Stefan give him a sharp glance.

'Once more I offer you escort away from here.' This time Stefan looked at me. 'I would have no harm come to you and yours here.'

'Can you find out where the other wolves are, if she doesn't want you to?' I asked him.

He hesitated, which was answer enough.

'We'll go talk to her, then,' I said.

Stefan nodded, but not like he was happy about it. 'Then I find myself echoing your gremlin. Keep your eyes away from hers. She'll probably have others with her, whether she allows you to see them or not. Don't look at anyone's eyes. There are four or five here who could entangle even your wolf.'

He turned and led the way through the house to an alcove sheltering a wrought-iron spiral staircase. As we started down, I thought we were going to the basement, but the stairway went deeper. Small lights on the cement wall surrounding the stairs turned on as Stefan passed them. They allowed us to see the stairs – and that we were traveling down a cement tube, but they weren't bright enough to do much more. Fresh air wafted out of small vents that kept the air moving, but it also kept me from smelling anything from deeper down.

'How far down are we going?' I asked, trying to fight off the claustrophobic desire to run back the way we'd come.

'About twenty feet from the surface.' Stefan's voice echoed a little – or else something below us made a noise.

Maybe I was just jumpy.

Eventually the stairway ended in a pad of cement. But even with my night vision, the darkness was so absolute I could see only a few yards in any direction. The smell of bleach danced around several scents I'd never encountered before.

Stefan moved and a series of fluorescent lights flickered to life. We stood in an empty room with cement floors, walls, and ceilings. The overall effect was sterile and empty.

Stefan didn't pause, just continued through the room and into a narrow tunnel that sloped gently upward as we walked. Steel doors without knobs or handles lined the tunnel at even intervals. I could hear things moving behind the doors and scooted up until I could touch Samuel's shoulder for reassurance. As I passed the last door, something slammed against it, ringing with a hollow boom that echoed away from us. Behind another door someone – or something – began a high-pitched hopeless cascade of laughter that ended in a series of screams.

By the end of it, I was all but crawling up on top of Samuel, but he was still relaxed, and his breathing and pulse hadn't even begun to speed up. Damn him. I didn't take a deep breath until we'd left the doors behind.

The tunnel took a narrow turn, and the floor became a steep upward set of twelve stairs that ended in a room with curved plastered walls, wooden floors, and soft lighting. Directly opposite the stairway was a sumptuous mocha leather couch whose curves echoed the walls.

A woman reclined on two overstuffed tapestry-covered pillows braced against one of the couch's arms. She wore silk. I could smell the residue of the silkworms, just as I could smell the faint scent I was learning to identify with vampire.

The dress itself was simple and expensive, revealing her figure in swirling colors ranging from purple to red. Her narrow feet were bare except for red and purple toenail polish. She had them braced so her knees came up and provided backing to support the paperback she was reading.

She finished the page, dog-eared one corner, and set it carelessly on the floor. She swung her legs off the couch and shifted so that her face was toward us before she raised her gaze to look at us. It was so gracefully done that I barely had time to drop my own eyes.

'Introduce us, Stefano,' she said, her voice a deep contralto made the richer by a touch of an Italian accent.

Stefan bowed, a formal gesture that should have looked odd with his torn jeans, but somehow came out gracefully old-fashioned instead.

'*Signora* Marsilia,' he said, 'may I introduce you to Mercedes Thompson, auto mechanic extraordinaire and her friend Dr Samuel Cornick, who is the Marrok's son. Mercy, Dr Cornick, this is Signora Marsilia, Mistress of the Mid-Columbia Seethe.'

'Welcome,' she said.

It had been bothering me how human the two women upstairs had seemed with their wrinkles and imperfections. Stefan, himself, had a touch of otherness that I could see. I had known him for inhuman the first time I'd seen him, but, except for the distinctive scent of vampire, the other two women would have passed for human.

This one would not have.

I stared at her, trying to nail down what was making the hair on the back of my neck rise. She looked like a woman in her early twenties, evidently having died and become vampire before life had marked her. Her hair was blond, which was not a color I associated with Italy. Her eyes were dark, though, as dark as my own.

Hastily, I jerked my gaze from her face, my breath coming more rapidly as I realized how easy it was to forget. She hadn't been looking at me though. Like the other vampires, her attention was on Samuel, and understandably so. He was the son of the Marrok, Bran's son, a person of influence rather than a VW mechanic. Then, too, most women would look at him rather than me.

'I have said something to amuse you, Mercedes?' Marsilia asked. Her voice was pleasant, but there was power behind it, something akin to the power the Alphas could call upon.

I decided to tell her the truth and see what she made of it. 'You are the third woman tonight who has virtually ignored me, Signora Marsilia. However, I find it perfectly understandable, since I have trouble taking my attention off Dr Cornick, too.'

'Do you often have such an effect on women, Dr Cornick?' she asked him archly. See, her attention was still really on him.

Samuel, unflappable Samuel, stuttered. 'I-I haven't . . .' He stopped and sucked in air, then, sounding a little more like himself, he said, 'I expect that you have more luck with the opposite sex than I do.'

She laughed, and I realized finally what it was that bothered me. There was something off about her expressions and her gestures, as if she were only aping humans. As if, without us here to perform for, she would not appear human at all.

Zee told me that modern advances in CGI allowed film-makers to create computer-animated people who seemed very nearly human. But they found that after a certain point, the closer the characters looked to real, the more they repelled their audience.

I knew now exactly what he meant.

She had everything *almost* right. Her heart beat, she breathed regularly. Her skin was flushed slightly, like a person who has just finished walking in the cold. But her smiles were just slightly wrong: coming too late or too early. Her imitation of a human was very close, but not quite close enough to be real – and that small difference was giving me the creeps.

Generally, I don't have the control problems that the werewolves do – coyotes are adaptable, amiable beasts. But at that moment, if I had been in coyote form, I'd have been running away as fast as I could.

'My Stefano tells me that you want to know about the visitors who paid me so nicely to leave them alone.' She had gone back to ignoring me again – something I wasn't really unhappy with.

'Yes.' Samuel kept his voice soft, almost dreamy. 'We will eventually find them ourselves, but your information would help.'

'After I give you this information,' her voice rumbled in her throat like a cat's, 'we shall talk a little about the Marrok and what he will give me for cooperation.'

Samuel shook his head. 'I am sorry, Signora, I do not have authority to discuss this matter. I will be happy to forward any messages you might have to my father.'

She pouted at him, and I felt the impact of her intent upon him, could smell the beginnings of his arousal. The scary things making noise behind steel doors hadn't caused his pulse to increase, but the Mistress of the seethe could. She leaned forward, and he closed the distance between them until her face was only inches from his groin.

'Samuel,' said Stefan quietly. 'There is blood on your neck. Did Lilly cut you?'

'Let me see it,' suggested the Signora. She breathed in deeply, then made a hungry noise that sounded like the rattle of old dry bones. 'I will take care of it for you.'

That sounded like a really bad idea somehow. I wasn't the only one who thought so.

'They are under my protection, Mistress,' Stefan said, his voice stiffly formal. 'I brought them here so you could speak to the Marrok's son. Their safety is my honor – and it was almost lost earlier when Lilly came to us unescorted. I should hate to think your wishes were opposed to my honor.'

She shut her eyes and dropped her head, resting her forehead on Samuel's belly. I heard her take in another deep breath, and Samuel's arousal grew as if she called it from him as she inhaled.

'It has been so long,' she whispered. 'His power calls to me like brandy on a winter night. It is difficult to think. Who was in charge of Lilly when she wandered into my guests?'

'I will find out,' Stefan said. 'It would be my pleasure to bring the miscreants before you and see you once more attend your people, Mistress.'

She nodded, and Samuel groaned. The sound made her open her eyes, and they were no longer dark. In the dimly lit room, her eyes gleamed red-and-gold fire.

'My control is not as good as it once was,' she murmured. Somehow I'd expected her voice to harshen with the heat of the flames in her eyes, but instead her voice softened and deepened seductively, until my own body was reacting – and I don't care for other women that way as a rule.

'This would be a good time for your sheep, Mercy.' Stefan's attention was so focused upon the other vampire it took me a moment to realize he was speaking to me.

I'd been edging closer to Samuel. Five years of study in the martial arts had given me a purple belt, the muscles to

189

heft car parts around almost as well as a man, and the understanding that my paltry skills weren't worth a damn thing
against a vampire.

I'd debated the wisdom of knocking Samuel away from
her, but something my senses had been trying to tell me for
a while had finally kicked in: there were others here, other
vampires I couldn't see or hear – only scent.

Stefan's advice gave me something better to do. I pulled
out my necklace. The chain was long enough that I could
tug it over my head, and I let it dangle from my hand just
as Marsilia moved.

I grew up with werewolves who ran faster than grey-
hounds, and I am a little faster yet – but I never saw Marsilia
move. One moment she was pressed against the front of
Samuel's jeans, and the next her legs were wrapped around
his waist and her mouth was on his neck. Everything that
followed seemed to happen slowly, although I suppose it was
only a few seconds.

The illusion hiding the other vampires dissipated in the
frenzy of Marsilia's feeding, and I saw them, six vampires
lined up against the wall of the room. They were making
no attempt to appear human, and I gathered a hurried impression of gray skin, hollow cheeks, and eyes glittering like
backlit gemstones. None of them moved, though Stefan had
wrapped himself around Marsilia and was trying to pull her
off. Nor did they interfere when I closed the distance between
Samuel and me, the silly necklace wrapped around my wrist.
I suppose they didn't consider either of us a threat.

Samuel's eyes were closed, his head thrown back to give
Marsilia better access. So scared I could barely breathe, I
pressed the silver lamb against Marsilia's forehead and said
a hurried, but fervent prayer, that the lamb would work the
same way a cross did.

The little figure pressed into her forehead, but Marsilia,

as absorbed in the feeding as Samuel, paid me no mind. Then several things happened almost at the same time – only afterward did I put them in their probable order.

The sheep under my hand blazed up with the eerie blue flame of a well-adjusted Bunsen burner. Marsilia was suddenly crouched on the back of the couch, as far from my necklace – and Samuel – as she could get. She shrieked, a high-pitched noise just barely within the range of my hearing, and made a gesture with her hands.

Everyone dropped to the floor, Samuel, Stefan, and Marsilia's guards, leaving me standing, my little sheep aglow like an absurdly small blue neon sign, facing the Mistress of the nest. I thought at first that the others had fallen voluntarily, reacting to some secret sign I hadn't seen. But Marsilia jerked her chin, a quick, inhuman motion, and screamed again. The bodies on the floor twisted a little, as if something hurt, but they could not move to alleviate it – and I finally realized that it was magic as well as fear that was stealing my breath. Marsilia was doing something to hurt them all.

'Stop it,' I said, with all the authority I could muster. My voice came out thin and shaky. Not impressive.

I cleared my throat and tried again. Surely if I could face down Bran after the time I ran his Porsche into a tree without either a driver's license or permission to drive it, I could steady my voice so it didn't squeak. 'Enough. No one has harmed you.'

'No harm?' she hissed, tossing her head so her mane of hair fell away from her forehead to reveal a nasty-looking burn vaguely in the shape of my necklace.

'You were feeding upon Samuel without his permission,' I said firmly, as if I knew that her action had given me the right to defend him – I wasn't certain it was true, but bluffing worked with the wolves. And vampires seemed to be big on manners.

She raised her chin but didn't reply. She took a deep breath, and I realized she hadn't been breathing since I'd driven her off Samuel. Her eyelids fluttered as she took in the smell of the room — I could smell it, too: fear, pain, blood, and something sweet and compelling brushed with the scents of those present.

'It has been a long time since I had such presented for me,' she said. 'He was bleeding and half-caught already.' Her tone wasn't apologetic, but I'd settle for mere explanations if it only got us all out of here alive.

Stefan managed to get out a single word. 'Trap.'

She drew a quick circle in the air and dropped her hand out and away. In response, all the men on the floor went limp. Samuel, I noticed with relief, was still breathing.

'Explain, Stefan,' she said, and I took a deep, relieved breath at having her attention somewhere else.

'A trap for you, Mistress,' Stefan said, his voice hoarse like a man who has been screaming. 'Bleed the wolf and present him to you as if he were gift-wrapped. They were good. I didn't notice that he was under thrall until I saw the blood.'

'You may be right,' she said. She gave me an irritated look. 'Put that thing away, please. You don't need it now.'

'It's all right, Mercy,' said Stefan, his voice still whisper-thin. He hadn't raised himself off the floor, but lay with his eyes closed, as if he'd come to the end of his strength.

I hid the necklace again, and the room looked even dimmer in the remaining, more mundane, lighting.

'Tell me about this trap, Stefano,' she said briskly as she climbed from the back of the couch and into her seat. If her eyes dwelled a moment too long upon Samuel, who was still limp, at least their inhuman flames had died to flickers.

The vampires were all showing signs of life, but only

Stefan was moving. He groaned as he sat up and rubbed his forehead as if it hurt. His movements were jerky, inhuman.

'Lilly was sent to us without her attendant. I thought she was sent to create an incident. If Samuel had killed her, it would be war between our seethe and the Marrok. But perhaps it was more than that. I thought we got him away before she marked him, but looking back, I believe he was in thrall from that moment on. They sent him down here bleeding like a rare steak and presented him to you. If you had killed Samuel – and I think it likely, half-starved as you've been keeping yourself—' I could hear the disapproval in his voice. 'If you had killed Samuel . . .' He let his words trail off.

She licked her lips as if there was still a trace of blood left. I saw a flash of regret on her face as she stared at Samuel, as if she wished no one had stopped her.

'If I had killed him, there would have been war.' She looked away from Samuel and met my eyes – but nothing happened. She frowned at me, but seemed less surprised than I was. But maybe the little sheep who must have protected me from her magic was still at work. She tapped her long, manicured nails together, looking as if she were considering something.

'We would be badly outnumbered,' Stefan said, when she said no more. He gathered himself visibly before getting to his feet. 'If war broke out, we would be forced to leave this country.'

She stilled, as if his words were of great significance. 'To leave this cursed desert and return *home*' – she closed her eyes – 'now that is a prize that many here might risk my wrath to gain.'

The other vampires were stirring by then. I moved between them and Samuel, trusting Stefan to keep his mistress off us. As they rose, they seemed to be more focused on Samuel than on Marsilia. Like most everyone else tonight, they ignored me as they slowly began closing in.

'Wake up, Sam.' I nudged him with the heel of my foot.

Stefan said something in liquid tones with the unmistakable cadence of Italian. Like they were in a peculiar game of 'Swing the Statue,' the other vampires simply stopped moving, though it left some of them in awkward poses.

'What's wrong with Samuel?'

I asked the question of Stefan, but it was Marsilia who answered. 'He is bespelled by my bite,' she said. 'Some do die of the Kiss, but it will probably do no permanent harm to a werewolf. If I were less, then he would not have succumbed.' She sounded pleased.

'Then how did Lilly manage?' asked Stefan. 'It wasn't a full Kiss, but he was in thrall.'

She crouched by my feet and touched Samuel's neck. I didn't like the way she just kept appearing places, especially when she did it near Samuel who couldn't defend himself.

'That is a good question,' she murmured. 'He is a dominant, this son of Bran?'

'Yes,' I answered. I knew that humans had trouble telling a dominant from a submissive wolf. I hadn't thought the same would be true of a vampire.

'Then Lilly could not enthrall him. But . . . perhaps she could have been loaned the power.' She brought her fingers to her lips and licked Samuel's blood off them. Her eyes were glowing again.

I reached into my shirt and started to draw out the sheep, but a pale hand wrapped around my wrist and jerked me against a body, all cold bone and sinew.

By the time I realized I'd been grabbed, I'd already thrown him. If I'd had time to think, I'd never have tried to throw a vampire the way I would a human, but it was a reflexive thing born of hundreds of hours in the dojo.

He landed right on top of Samuel because Marsilia had gotten out of the way. The creature twisted, and I thought he was coming at me again, but he was after Samuel instead. He struck at Samuel's bleeding neck.

Marsilia jerked her vampire off, leaving torn skin where his fangs had already locked onto flesh. Without visible effort or emotion, she tossed him into the nearest wall. Plaster flew, but he bounced to his feet with a snarl that died as soon as he saw who had thrown him the second time.

'Out, my dears.' I noticed that the burn mark on her forehead was healing. 'Out before we lose all honor, overcome by such sweetness as is laid out here before us like a tempting feast.'

I'd gotten my sheep out finally, but before it started glowing we were alone, Stefan, Samuel, and I.

# 11

There was an elevator hidden behind one of the doors in the corridor. Stefan leaned wearily against the wall; he carried Samuel, who was bloodstained, limp, but still breathing.

'You're sure he's all right?' I asked, not for the first time.

'He'll not die of it,' he said, which was not quite the same thing.

The elevator came to a smooth stop, and the doors slid open to reveal a kitchen. Bright lights gleamed on bird's-eye maple cabinetry and creamy stone countertops. There were no windows, but a clever use of mirrors and backlit stained-glass panels made up for the lack. Next to the refrigerator was something I was a lot more interested in, an outside door. I didn't wait for Stefan, but opened the door and ran out to the manicured lawn. As I sucked in a shaky breath of air that smelled of dust and exhaust rather than vampires, I realized that I'd come out of the main house.

'The houses are connected by the tunnels,' I said, as Stefan came down the back steps.

'There's no time to talk,' grunted Stefan.

I looked at him and saw that he was struggling with Samuel's weight.

'I thought vampires were strong enough to upend trees,' I said.

'Not after Marsilia gets finished with them,' said Stefan. He shifted Samuel, trying to get a better grip.

'Why not a fireman's carry?' I asked.

'Because I don't want to be carrying him that way when he starts waking up – he's not going to be a happy wolf.

This way I can put him down and get out of the way if I need to.'

'I'll carry him,' said a stranger's voice.

Stefan turned with a snarl and, for the first time ever, I saw his fangs, white and sharp in the night.

Another vampire stood near us, wearing jeans and one of those white, piratey shirts, open to the waist, that you see at Renaissance Fairs and Errol Flynn movies. It didn't look good on him. His shoulders were too narrow, and his flat stomach just looked cadaverous rather than sexy – or maybe I'd just had enough of vampires that night.

'Peace, Stefan.' The vampire held up a hand. 'Marsilia thought you could use some help.'

'You mean she didn't want Dr Cornick to be here when he came out of the Kiss's hold.' Stefan relaxed a little. 'All right.'

They transferred Samuel from one vampire to the other – the newcomer apparently wasn't suffering from Stefan's worries because he lifted the werewolf over his shoulder.

The night was quiet, but there was a waiting quality to it that I recognized from the hunt. Someone was watching us – big surprise. None of us talked as we made our way through the garden and out the main gates, which someone had propped open while we had been inside.

I slid the door of the van open and pointed to the long bench seat. The pirate-clad vampire pulled Samuel off his shoulder and put him on the far backseat. I decided that much strength was creepier in vampires than it was in were-wolves – at least the wolves looked like people who should be strong.

With Samuel safely stowed, the vampire turned directly to me.

'Mercedes Thompson,' he said. 'My mistress thanks you for your visit, which has allowed us to discover problems that otherwise might have gone unnoticed. She also thanks you for allowing her to keep her honor and that of her vassal, Stefano Uccello.' He saw the skepticism on my face and smiled. 'She said that she'd never been repulsed by a sheep before. Crosses, scriptures, and holy water, but not a sheep.'

'The Lamb of God,' explained Stefan. He was looking almost like his usual self, with one elbow propped against the door of the van. 'I didn't think it would work either. Otherwise, of course, I would have told her to give it to Estelle.'

'Of course.' The other vampire gave me another quick, charming smile. 'In any case, I am to extend Signora Marsilia's apologies for any discomfort you or yours experienced this night and we hope that you will extend our apologies also to Dr Cornick. Please explain that the Mistress intended him no hurt, but that her recent indisposition has allowed some of her people to become . . . obstreperous. They will be punished.'

'Tell the Signora that I find her apologies gracious and that I, too, regret any trouble she suffered this night,' I lied. But I must have done it well, because Stefan gave me a half nod of approval.

The vampire bowed, then, holding it gingerly by its chain, handed me Samuel's cross and a small sheet of paper, the thick handmade kind. It smelled of the same herbs that scented the house and upon it, written in a flourishing hand that had learned to write with a quill, was a Kennewick address.

'She had intended to give this to you herself, but has asked me to tell you more. The wolves paid us just under ten thousand dollars for the rights to live at this address for two months.'

Stefan straightened. 'That's too much. Why did she charge them so much?'

'She didn't. They paid us without any negotiation. I

expressed my concerns about the oddity of the transaction to the Signora, but . . .' He glanced at Stefan and shrugged.

'Marsilia has not been herself since she was exiled here from Milan,' Stefan told me. He looked at the other vampire, and said, 'It is a good thing that happened tonight. To see our Mistress potent with her hunger again is wondrous, Andre.'

'Wondrous' was not the word I'd have chosen.

'I hope so,' said the other harshly. 'But she has been asleep for two centuries. Who knows what will happen when the Mistress awakens? You may have outsmarted yourself this time.'

'It was not I,' murmured Stefan. 'Someone was trying to stir up trouble again. Our Mistress has said I might investigate.'

The two vampires stared at each other, neither of them breathing.

At last Stefan said, 'Whatever their purpose, they have succeeded in awakening Her at last. If they had not put my guests in danger, I would not willingly hunt them.'

*Vampire politics*, I thought. *Humans, werewolves, or, apparently, vampires, it doesn't matter; get more than three of them together and the jockeying for power begins.*

I understood some of it. The older wolves pull away from the world as it changes until some of them live like hermits in their caves, only coming out to feed and eventually even losing interest in that. It sounded as if Marsilia suffered from the same malady. Evidently some of the vampires were happy with their Mistress's neglect while Stefan was not. Andre sounded as if he didn't know which side he was on. I was on whichever side meant that they left me alone.

'The Mistress told me to give you something, too,' Andre told Stefan.

There was a sound, like the crack of a bullet, and Stefan

staggered back against the van, one hand over his face. It wasn't until the faint blush of a handprint appeared on Stefan's cheek that I realized what had happened.

'A foretaste,' Andre told him. 'Today she is busy, but tomorrow you will report to her at dusk. You should have told her what Mercedes Thompson was when you first knew. You should have warned the Mistress, not let her find out when the walker stood against her magic. You should not have brought *her* here.'

'She brought no stake or holy water.' Stefan's voice gave no indication that the blow bothered him. 'She is no danger to us – she barely understands what she is, and there is no one to teach her. She does not hunt vampires, nor attack those who leave her in peace.'

Andre jerked his head around faster than anyone should and looked at me. 'Is that true, Mercedes Thompson? You do not hunt those who merely frighten you?'

I was tired, worried about Samuel, and somewhat surprised to have survived my encounter with Signora Marsilia and her people.

'I don't hunt anything except the occasional rabbit, mouse, or pheasant,' I said. 'Until this week, that was it for me.' If I hadn't been so tired, I'd never have uttered that last sentence.

'What about this week?' It was Stefan who asked.

'I killed two werewolves.'

'You killed two werewolves?' Andre gave me a look that was hardly flattering. 'I suppose you were defending yourself and just happened to have a gun at hand?'

I shook my head. 'One of them was moonstruck – he'd have killed anyone near him. I tore his throat out and he bled to death. The other one I shot before he could kill the Alpha.'

'Tore his throat out?' murmured Stefan, while Andre clearly didn't know whether to believe me or not.

'I was coyote, and trying to get his attention so that he'd chase me.'

Stefan frowned at me. 'Werewolves are fast.'

'I know that,' I said irritably. 'I'm faster.' I thought about the wild chase with Bran's mate, and added, 'Most of the time anyway. I didn't intend to kill—'

Someone screamed, and I quit talking. We waited, but there were no more sounds.

'I had better attend the Signora,' said Andre, and was gone, just gone.

'I'll drive,' Stefan told me. 'You'll need to ride in the back with Dr Cornick so he has someone he trusts with him when he wakes up.'

I gave him the keys and hopped in the back.

'What's going to happen when he wakes up?' I asked as I settled onto the backseat, lifting Samuel's head so I could scoot underneath it and sit down. My hands smoothed over his hair and slid over his neck. The marks of the vampires were already scabbed over, rough under my light touch.

'Maybe nothing will happen,' Stefan said, getting in the driver's seat and starting the van. 'But sometimes they don't react well to being Kissed. Signora Marsilia used to prefer wolves to more mundane prey – that's why she lost her place in Italy and was sent here.'

'Feeding off of werewolves is taboo?' I asked.

'No.' He turned the van around and started back up the drive. 'Feeding off the werewolf mistress of the Lord of Night is taboo.'

He said Lord of Night as if I should know who that was, so I asked, 'Who is the Lord of Night?'

'The Master of Milan – or he was last we heard.'

'When was that?'

'Two hundred years, more or less. He exiled Signora Marsilia here with those who owed her life or vassalage.'

'There wasn't anything here two hundred years ago,' I said.

'I was told he stuck a pin in a map. You are right; there was nothing here. Nothing but desert, dust, and Indians.' He'd adjusted the rearview mirror so he could see me, and his eyes met mine as he continued. 'Indians and something we'd never encountered before. Mercy. Shapeshifters who were not moon called. Men and women who could take on the coyote's form as they chose. They were immune to most of the magics that allow us to live among humans undetected.'

I stared at him. 'I'm not immune to magic.'

'I didn't say you were,' he answered. 'But some of our magics pass you by. Why do you think you stood against Marsilia's rage when the rest of us fell?'

'It was the sheep.'

'It wasn't the sheep. Once upon a time, Mercedes, what you are would have been your death sentence. We killed your kind wherever we found them, and they returned the favor.' He smiled at me, and my blood ran chill at the expression in those cool, cool eyes. 'There are vampires everywhere, Mercedes, and you are the only walker here.'

I'd always thought of Stefan as my friend. Even in the heart of the vampires' seethe I hadn't questioned his friendship, not really. Stupid me.

'I can drive myself home,' I told him.

He returned his gaze to the street in front of him and laughed softly as he pulled the van over. He got out and left it running. I loosened my grip on Samuel's shoulder and forced myself away from the safety of the back bench seat.

I didn't see Stefan or smell him when I got out of the van and moved to the driver's seat, but I could feel his eyes on my back. I started to drive off, then pulled my foot off the gas and stomped on the brakes.

I rolled down the window and spoke to the darkness. 'I know you don't live there – you smell of woodsmoke and popcorn. Do you need a ride home?'

He laughed. I jumped, then jumped again when he leaned in the window and patted my shoulder.

'Go home, Mercy,' he said, and was gone – for real this time.

I chugged along behind semis and Suburbans and thought about what I'd just learned.

I knew that vampires, like the fae, and werewolves and their kindred were all Old World preternatural creatures. They'd come over for the same reasons most humans did: to gain wealth, power, or land, *and* to escape persecution.

During the Renaissance, vampires had been an open secret; being thought one added power and prestige. The cities of Italy and France became havens for them. Even so, their numbers were not great. Like werewolves, humans who would become vampires died more often than they accomplished their goal. Most of the princes and nobles believed to be vampires were just clever men who saw the claim as a way to discourage rivals.

The Church saw it differently. When the Spanish invasion of the New World filled the coffers of the Church so they no longer had to depend upon the favor of the nobles, they went after the vampires as well as any other preternatural creature they could find.

Hundreds of people died, if not thousands, accused of vampirism, witchcraft, or lycanthropy. Only a small percentage of those who died actually were vampires, but those losses were still severe – humans (lucky for them) breed much faster than the undead.

So vampires came to the New World, victims of religious persecution like the Quakers and the Puritans – only different.

Werewolves and their moon-called kindred came to find new territory to hunt. The fae came to escape the cold iron of the Industrial Revolution, which followed them anyway. Together these immigrants destroyed most of the preternatural creatures who had lived in the Americas, until at last, even the bare stories of their existence were mostly gone.

My people, apparently, among them.

As I took the on-ramp onto the highway to Richland, I remembered something my mother once told me. She hadn't known my father very well. In my mostly empty jewelry box was a silver belt buckle he'd won in a rodeo and given her. She told me his eyes were the color of sunlit root beer, and that he snored if he slept on his back. The only other thing I knew about him was that if someone had found his wrecked truck sooner, he might have lived. The wreck hadn't killed him outright. Something sharp had sliced open a big vein, and he bled to death.

There was a noise from the back of the van. I jerked the rearview mirror around until I could see the backseat. Samuel's eyes were open, and he was shaking violently.

Stefan hadn't told me what the bad reaction to the Kiss might be, but I was pretty sure I was about to find out. I was already passing the exit for Columbia Park, but I managed to take it without getting rear-ended.

I drove until I came to a small parking lot next to a maintenance shed. I parked, killed the lights, then slipped between the seats of the van and approached Samuel cautiously.

'Sam?' I said, and for a heartbeat his struggles slowed down.

His eyes gleamed in the shadows of the van's depths. I smelled adrenaline, terror, sweat, and blood.

I had to fight not to flee. Part of me knew that so much fear must have a cause. The rest of me figured out why some werewolves had a bad reaction to the vampire's Kiss – waking up unable to move, his last memory being something sucking his blood was bound to hit every panic button in a were-wolf's arsenal.

'Shhh,' I said, crouching in the space between the second seat and the sliding door. 'The vampires are gone. What you are feeling is something they can do with their bite. It makes their victims passive so they can feed without drawing attention. It's wearing off now – Stefan said it will leave no ill effects.'

He was beginning to listen to me. I could see it in the softening of his shoulders – then my cell phone rang.

I answered it, but the sudden noise had been too much. The van bumped and bobbed as Samuel scrambled over the backseat and into the luggage space behind the seat.

'Hey,' I said, keeping my voice soft.

'Mercy.' It was Warren, his voice urgent. 'You need to come here as soon as you can – and bring Samuel.'

Samuel was making harsh noises behind the seat. Changing was painful for the wolves at the best of times – when they are comfortable and eager to hunt. Changing when the air is thick with fear and blood would not be good. Not good at all.

'Samuel is indisposed,' I said, as he screamed, a roar of agony and despair. He was fighting the change.

Warren swore. 'Tell me this then. Is Adam afraid someone in the pack betrayed him?'

'That's my fault,' I said. 'Warren, is the pack coming to your house?'

He grunted. I assumed it was a yes.

'Tell Adam.'

'I made steaks and fed him about an hour ago, and he's sleeping it off. I tried to wake him up before I called, but he's shut down hard in a healing sleep. I don't know what it would take to wake him up.'

'Dr Cornick would,' I muttered, wincing at the noises Sam was making in the back of the van. 'But he's not available to come to the phone right now.'

'It's all right, Mercy.' He sounded suddenly calm. 'I'll take care of it. If that's Samuel in the middle of an involuntary change, you need to get away from there and give him time to calm down.'

'What? And leave Samuel to go hunting in the middle of Kennewick? I don't think so.'

'He won't know you, not if he's changing like that. It won't be Samuel Bran's son, it will be only the wolf.'

The sounds behind the seat were becoming more canid and less human.

'Mercy, get out of there.'

'It's all right, Warren,' I said, hoping I was right.

Wolves, the real wolves, are not usually vicious animals unless they are frightened, hurt, or cornered. Werewolves are always vicious, always ready for the kill.

'If this doesn't work – tell him the vampires got me,' I said. 'I don't think he'll remember. It'll be true enough. The vampires are what forced this change. You tell him that.' I hung up the phone.

It was already too late to run, but I wouldn't have anyway. Leave Samuel to deal with the aftermath of his wolf's rampage? Samuel was a healer, a defender of the weak. I wasn't certain that he would live with innocent blood on his hands.

I'd deserted him once, a long time ago. I wouldn't do it again.

The sounds died down until all I could hear was the harsh panting of his breath, but I could smell his rage. I didn't bother undressing before I shifted – it would have taken too long. When Samuel's white head appeared over the top of the seat, I was backing out of my T-shirt and bra.

I stopped what I was doing and crouched on the floor of the van, tail tucked between my legs. I didn't look up, but I felt the springs give way as he climbed slowly over the back and stood on the seat.

I was so scared it was hard to breathe. I knew what I had to do next, but I wasn't certain I could manage it. If some part of me weren't absolutely convinced that Sam, my Sam, could never hurt me, I wouldn't have been able to do the next part.

He was utterly silent. In Montana, on a hunt, the wolves howl and cry, but in the city all hunting is done soundlessly. Growls, whines, and barks are all bluffing tools — it is the quiet wolf that will kill you.

With Samuel perched silently on the backseat, I rolled over onto my back and exposed my belly to his jaws. I stretched my chin so that my neck was vulnerable to him as well. It was one of the hardest things I'd ever done. It wasn't as if he couldn't kill me as easily if I were lying on my belly, but there was something worse about exposing my unprotected underside. Being submissive is a bitch.

The van dipped again as he jumped down, landing almost on top of me. I could smell his anger — the sour smell of his fear had faded all away with his humanity, leaving only the wolf. Hot breath moved my fur as he sniffed his way upward, his nose parting my hair as he went. Slowly the anger faded along with the intensity that had allowed me to know what he was feeling.

I tilted my head and risked a glance. Samuel filled the space between the short bench seat and the sliding door. Caught beneath him, one front paw on either side of my shoulders, I felt a sudden claustrophobia and instinctively tried to roll over.

I stopped the movement as soon as it began, but Samuel lunged forward with a warning growl and a snap of teeth in my face. I tried to take comfort from the growl, since theoretically, if he was growling he wasn't likely to kill me – but I was too aware of the volatile nature of the werewolves.

He moved suddenly, closing his mouth over my throat – but too wide for a jugular strike. I could feel his teeth through the fur on my neck, but they stopped as soon as they touched my skin.

I prayed then that Bran was right, and Samuel's wolf looked upon me as his mate. If he was wrong, then both Samuel and I would pay the price.

I held very still as my heart tried desperately to pound its way out of my rib cage. He released me, nipped gently at my nose, then slipped soundlessly away.

I rolled to my feet and shook my fur to resettle it, shedding my bra at last. Samuel was stretched along the backseat, watching me with his beautiful white eyes. He blinked at me once, then resettled his muzzle on his front paws and closed his eyes, saying, as clearly as he could without words, that the two halves of his soul were together again.

I heard the quiet purr of a big engine coming down the park road. I shifted to human as quickly as I could and began scrambling for clothes. My underwear was pale green and I found them first. The sports bra went on easier than it had come off, and I found my T-shirt when my foot touched it.

The car slowed as it approached, its headlights glinting through the window of my van.

'Pants, pants, pants,' I chanted as I brushed my hands over the floor. My fingers found them as tires crunched gravel and the car parked behind us. They also found Zee's dagger. I shoved it under the rubber mat near the side of the van farthest from the sliding door.

Feverishly, I jerked my pants up, zipped, and buttoned them as the driver's side door of the other car opened. Shoes.

Luckily they were white and I snatched them up and pulled them on over my bare feet without untying them.

I gave the hulking brute stretched across the full length of the van's backseat a frantic look. Samuel wouldn't be able to change back for a while yet, probably a few hours. A forced change takes time to recover from, even for a wolf of Samuel's power, and it was too late to try to hide him.

'You're a good dog, Samuel,' I told him sternly. 'Don't scare the nice police officer. We don't have time to be escorted down to the station house.'

A flashlight found me, and I waved, then slowly opened the sliding door.

'Jogging, Officer,' I said. The flashlight kept me from picking out a face.

There was a long pause. 'It's one in the morning, ma'am.'

'I couldn't sleep.' I gave him an apologetic smile.

'Jogging alone at night isn't safe, ma'am.' He lowered the flashlight, and I blinked rapidly, hoping the residual after-images would fade soon.

'That's why I always take him,' I said, and jerked a thumb toward the back of the van.

The policeman swore. 'Sorry, ma'am. That's just the biggest damn dog I've ever seen – and I grew up with Saint Bernards.'

'Don't ask me what he is,' I said, sliding through the door so I stood beside the policeman rather than below him. 'I got him from the pound when he was a puppy. My vet says he might be an Irish Wolfhound cross of some sort, maybe with something with a little wolf like a Husky or Samoyed.'

'Or Siberian Tiger,' he muttered, not intending me to hear. In a louder voice, he said, 'Why don't you let me see your license, registration, and insurance, ma'am.' He was relaxed, now, not expecting trouble.

I opened the front passenger door and retrieved my purse

from the jockey box, where I'd tucked it when we'd stopped at Uncle Mike's. Right next to the registration, insurance cards and my SIG.

Life would be much easier if the nice police officer didn't see that – or the .444 Marlin in the far back. I had a concealed carry permit, but I'd rather keep this low-key. Especially since, according to Stefan, Zee's dagger was not legal.

I gathered the insurance card and registration, then shut the jockey box – gingerly, so the SIG didn't rattle. I needn't have worried. When I looked for him, the police officer was sitting on the floor of the van petting Samuel.

Any other werewolf of my acquaintance I'd have been worried about – they aren't pets, and some of them resent being treated like one. Samuel canted his face so that the policeman's fingers found just the right spot behind his ear and groaned with pleasure.

Samuel liked humans. I remember him coming down to play with the elementary-school kids – all human – at recess. Most werewolves avoid children, but not Samuel. They all knew who he was, of course, and when they saw him as a man they called him Dr Cornick and treated him as they would have treated any other adult. But when he came to school as a wolf, they put him to work playing pony, runaway dog, and ferocious, but loyal, wolf-friend. He did it with the same fierce enjoyment as the children.

'He's beautiful,' the policeman said, getting out of the van at last and taking my paperwork. 'How big is he when he's standing up?'

I clicked my fingers. 'Samuel, come.'

He stood up on the bench seat, and the top of his back brushed the roof of the van. Then he stretched and hopped off the seat and onto the gravel road without touching the floor of the van. He deliberately moved like a big dog, a little clumsy and slow. His thick winter coat and the night provided some camouflage of the differences that no amount of mixed breeding could account for.

Werewolves' front legs are built more like a bear's or a lion's than a timber wolf's. Like the former two, werewolves used their claws to rip and tear flesh, and that means their musculature is different, too.

The policeman whistled and walked around him. He was careful to keep the flashlight out of Samuel's eyes. 'Look at you,' he murmured. 'Not an ounce of fat and every bit of two hundred pounds.'

'You think so? I've never weighed him,' I said. 'I know he's heavier than I am, and that's good enough for me.'

The policeman gave me back my license and assorted papers without actually looking at any of them. 'I'd still be happier if you ran in the daylight, ma'am. In any case, this park is closed at night – safer for everyone.'

'I appreciate your concern for my safety,' I said earnestly, patting the werewolf lightly on the head.

The police officer moved his car, but he waited while I closed Samuel back into the van and followed me out of the park as far as the on-ramp to the highway – so I couldn't stop to put my socks on. I hate going barefoot in leather tennis shoes.

Samuel levered his bulk up on the front passenger seat and stuck his head out the window, flattening his ears against the tear of the wind.

'Stop that,' I chided him. 'Keep all your body parts in the van.'

He ignored me and opened his mouth, letting his tongue get swept back like his ears. After a while, he pulled his head in and grinned at me.

'I've always wanted to do that,' I confessed. 'Maybe when this is all over, you can drive, and I'll stick my head out the window.'

He turned toward me and let his front paws rest on the floor between our seats. Then he stuck his nose in my midriff and whined.

'Stop that!' I shrieked, and slapped his muzzle. 'That's just rude.'

He pulled his head back and gave me a quizzical look. I took the opportunity to glance at my speedometer and make sure I wasn't speeding.

'You're going to cause a wreck, Samuel Llewellyn Cornick. Just you keep your nose out of my business.'

He snorted and put one paw on my knee, patted it twice – then stuck his nose in my belly button again. He was quicker than my slap this time, withdrawing all the way back onto his seat.

'My tattoo?' I asked, and he yipped – a very bassy yip. Just below my navel I had a pawprint. He must have seen it while I was scrambling into my clothes. I have a couple on my arms, too.

'Karen, my college roommate, was an art major. She earned her spending money giving people tattoos. I helped her pass her chemistry class, and she offered to give me one for free.'

I'd spent the previous two years living with my mother and pretending to be perfect, afraid that if I weren't, I'd lose my place in my second home as abruptly as I had the first. It would never have occurred to me to do something as outrageous as getting a tattoo.

My mother still blames Karen for my switching my major from engineering to history – which makes her directly responsible for my current occupation, fixing old cars. My mother is probably right, but I am much happier as I am than I would have been as a mechanical engineer.

'She handed me a book of tattoos that she had done and about halfway through was a guy who'd had wolf tracks tattooed across his back from one hip to the opposite shoulder.

212

I wanted something smaller, so we settled on a single pawprint.'

My mother and her family had known what I was, but they'd asked no questions, and I'd hidden my coyote self from them, becoming someone who fit their lives better. It had been my own choice. Coyotes are very adaptable.

I remember staring at the man's back and understanding that, although I must hide from everyone else, I could not hide from myself anymore. So I had Karen put the tattoo on the center of my body, where I could protect my secret and it could keep me whole. I'd finally started to enjoy being who I was instead of wishing that I were a werewolf or human so I'd fit in better.

'It's a coyote pawprint,' I said firmly. 'Not a wolf's.'

He grinned at me and stuck his head out the window again; this time his shoulders followed.

'You're going to fall out,' I told him.

# 12

'The pack is coming,' I told Samuel, as we cruised slowly by Warren's house for a look-see. 'I don't know how much you remember from while you were changing, but Warren called for help. Adam was sleeping and couldn't be woken up—' With Samuel safe, I could worry about Adam. 'Is that normal?'

Samuel nodded, and I felt a wave of relief. Clearing my throat, I continued, 'Since we can't trust the pack, I think Warren is going to try to keep them away from Adam – which would be fine except that Darryl is Adam's second.' Which meant a fight.

Samuel told me once that, despite all the physical benefits they gain, the average life span of a werewolf from his first Change until his death is ten years. People, like my old friend Dr Wallace, who had to be eliminated within their first year, accounted for some of that. But most werewolves died in dominance fights with other wolves.

I didn't want Warren or even Darryl to die tonight – and if one of them did, it would be my fault. Without my flash of intuition or paranoia that there was something wrong with the pack, Warren wouldn't have been trying to keep Darryl away from Adam.

Richland was quiet, but both sides of the street on Warren's block were solid with parked cars. I recognized Darryl's '67 Mustang as I passed it: the pack was already here. I parked a block away and jogged back with Samuel at my side.

A woman stood under the porch overhang in front of Warren's door. Her black, black hair was pulled back into a waist-length ponytail. She folded her sleekly muscled arms and widened her stance when she saw me. She was a chemistry teacher at Richland High and Darryl's mate.

'Auriele,' I said, climbing up the stairs until I shared the porch with her.

She frowned at me. 'I told him that you wouldn't do anything to hurt Adam, and he believed me. I told him you would not act against the pack. You have some explanations to give.'

As Darryl's mate, Auriele ranked high in the pack. Normally I'd have discussed the matter with her politely – but I needed to get past her and into Warren's home before someone got hurt.

'Fine,' I said. 'But I need to explain myself to Darryl, *not* you, and *not* right now.'

'Darryl is busy,' she said, not buying my argument. I'd noticed before that teaching classrooms of teenagers made Auriele hard to bluff.

I opened my mouth to try again, when she said, 'We keep the Silence.'

Wolves have little magic, as most people think of it. Sometimes there will be one, like Charles, who has a gift, but for the most part they are limited to the change itself, and a few magics that allow them to stay hidden. One of those is Silence.

I glanced around and saw four people (doubtless there were others if I cared to look) standing unobtrusively around Warren's duplex, their eyes closed and their mouths moving in the chant that brought Silence upon all that stood within their circle.

It was to keep the battle inside from disturbing anyone. It meant that the fight had already begun; the pack would not willingly break the Silence and let me through.

'This fight is without merit,' I told her urgently. 'There is no need for it.'

Her eyes widened. 'There is every need, Mercy. Darryl is second, and Warren defies him. It cannot go without answer. You can talk after he is through disciplining that one.' Her mobile brows drew together as she stared at Samuel. In a completely different voice, she asked, 'Who is that? There were strange wolves dead at Adam's house.'

'This is Samuel,' I said impatiently starting up the stairs. 'I'm going in.'

She'd started forward to intercept me, then hesitated as she took in Samuel's unusual coloration. 'Samuel who?' she asked.

Twice a year the Alphas met with Bran in Bran's corporate headquarters in Colorado. They sometimes brought their seconds or thirds – but never the women. Part of that was practicality. Alphas are uncomfortable outside their own territory, and they interact badly with other Alphas. With their mates beside them, all of that discomfort and territorialism had a greater tendency to turn toward violence.

That meant Auriele had never met Samuel, but she'd heard of him. White wolves named Samuel are not very common.

'This is Dr Samuel Cornick,' I told her firmly. 'Let us through. I've got information about the people who attacked Adam.'

I was tired and worried about Warren – and Darryl; otherwise, I wouldn't have made such an obvious misstep: I doubt she heard anything except my command.

She wasn't stupid; she knew I was not Adam's mate, no matter that he'd claimed me before the pack. I was not werewolf, not pack, not her dominant, and she could not listen to me and keep her place.

All hesitation left her manner, and she closed with me. I was a fair bit taller than she, but it didn't slow her down. She was a werewolf, and when she put her hands on my shoulders and pushed, I stumbled back three or four steps.

'You are not in charge here,' she said in a voice I'm certain worked very well in her classrooms.

She tried to push me again. Her mistake. She was a lot stronger than I, but she didn't have any experience in fighting in human shape. I moved aside, letting her momentum do most of my work. I helped her fall down the stairs with only a gentle push to keep her off-balance and make her lose control of her landing. She landed hard on the sidewalk, hitting her head on a stair.

I didn't wait around to make sure she was all right. It would take a lot more than a header down the stairs to slow a werewolf down much. The wolf closest to me started to move, but had to stop because it would have ruined the spell of Silence.

The door wasn't locked, so I opened it. Samuel brushed past me. The sound of Auriele's enraged snarl sent me scrambling in after him.

Warren's living room was a mess of scattered books and bits of broken furniture, but both Warren and Darryl were in human form. It told me that Darryl was still trying to keep the fight from being a fight to the death – and so was Warren. Werewolves in human form might be very strong, but they weren't half as deadly as the wolf.

Warren took one of his dining-room chairs and broke it over Darryl's face. The sound of the blow was absorbed by the pack's spell casting, so I could only judge the force by the size of the pieces the chair broke into and by the spraying blood.

In a move so quick my eyes couldn't quite catch it, Darryl had Warren on the ground with a lock on his throat.

Samuel darted in and closed his mouth over Darryl's wrist – then danced back out of reach. The unexpectedness of it – Darryl hadn't heard us come in – loosened Darryl's hold, and Warren broke out of it, scrambling away to get some room.

That meant Samuel could take up a position between both of them. Warren, breathing hard, sagged against a wall and wiped blood out of his eyes. Darryl had taken two swift steps forward before he recognized Samuel and almost fell over backward to keep from touching him, an expression of absolute astonishment on his face.

As soon as I was certain neither Darryl nor Warren was going to continue the fight, I tapped Samuel on the shoulder to get his attention. When he looked at me, I pointed to my mouth and ears. There wasn't a chance in hell that the werewolves outside would listen to me and stop their chanting – and we all needed to talk.

I expected Samuel to go outside, but he did something else. His power rushed through the house with the force of a firestorm after some idiot opens a door to let oxygen into a room that has been smoldering for hours. The air filled with him, with his scent and power; it popped and crackled until I felt as though I was breathing the sparklers that children play with on the Fourth of July. Discharges of power sparked on my skin until it felt raw, loosening my control of my extremities. I fell helplessly to my knees. My vision began to sparkle, too. Black swirls and bright snapping lights made me drop my head on my knees as I fought to keep conscious.

'Enough, Samuel,' said a voice I dimly recognized as Adam's. 'I think you made your point, whatever it was.'

I left my head on my knees. If Adam was here, everything else could wait until I caught my breath.

Footsteps came down the stairs with the light, quick movements I associated with Adam – he had been doing some rapid healing. I raised my head too soon and had to put it back down. Adam rested his hand on the top of my head, then moved away.

'What was this about?' he asked.

'We've been looking for you for two days, Adam.' Darryl's voice sounded a little distorted. 'All we had was a message on Elizaveta Arkadyevna's answering machine that she told us was from Mercy — and your wrecked house with three dead werewolves that no one could put names to. You, Jesse, and Mercy were all missing. We've been watching your house, but it was sheer dumb luck that one of the pack saw Mercy riding around with Kyle earlier. When I called Warren, he wouldn't admit you were here, but he didn't say you weren't either, so I called the pack and came over.'

I looked up again, and this time the world didn't spin. Darryl and Warren were both kneeling on the floor, near where they'd been fighting when I'd last seen them. I saw the reason for the odd enunciation problem Darryl was having — a nasty cut on his lip was visibly healing.

'I couldn't lie to Darryl,' explained Warren. 'You were in a healing sleep, and I couldn't wake you up. I couldn't let any of the pack up there while you were vulnerable.'

Samuel sat beside me and licked my face, whining softly.

'Ish,' I said, thrusting him away. 'That's just gross. Stop it, Samuel. Didn't Bran teach you any manners at all?'

It was a deliberate distraction, designed to give us all a chance to decide how to handle the situation without more bloodshed.

'Warren was acting under my orders,' said Adam slowly.

'I see,' said Darryl, his face becoming carefully expressionless.

'Not against you.' Adam waved his hand at chest height — *don't feel hurt*, the gesture said, *it wasn't personal*.

'Then who?'

'We don't know,' I told him. 'There was just something that bothered me.'

'Tell them what happened that night,' Adam said.

So I did.

To my surprise, when I told them that I'd had a bad feeling about calling in the pack, Darryl just nodded, saying, 'How did they know where Adam lived? Or when the meeting was over? How did they know he didn't have an army at his house like some of the Alphas do? Jesse's not stupid. When she heard the sound of the tranq guns firing, she wouldn't have screamed – but they knew where she was anyway.'

I thought about that. 'There was just the one human they sent up after her – and he went right to her room.'

Darryl made a sweeping gesture. 'I'm not saying that there are not explanations other than a betrayal by one of the pack – but you made the right choice.'

It shouldn't have made me feel good – but I'm as much a sucker for a pat on the back as the next woman.

'Go on, Mercy,' said Adam.

So I continued the explanation as succinctly as possible – which meant I left out any details that weren't their business, such as my past relationship with Samuel.

The rest of the pack filtered in while I talked, taking up seating on the floor – moving broken furniture out of the way as necessary. It wasn't the whole pack, but there were ten or fifteen of them.

Auriele sat next to Darryl, her knee just brushing his. She had a nasty bruise on her forehead, and I wondered if she would continue to treat me with the cool courtesy she'd always extended to me – or if she, like the females in Bran's pack, would consider me an enemy from now on.

Warren, I thought, with Adam's support, had just cemented his place in the pack – at least with Darryl, whose body language told the rest of the pack that Warren was not in disgrace. Darryl valued loyalty, I thought, suddenly certain it wasn't Darryl who had betrayed Adam.

*Who then?* I looked out over the faces, some familiar, some less so; but Adam was a good Alpha, and other than Darryl, there were no wolves dominant enough to be Alphas themselves.

I got to our decision to bring Adam to Warren's, saying only that we thought it would be a better hiding place than his house or mine, and stopped because Darryl was all but vibrating with his need to ask questions.

'Why did they take Jesse?' he asked, as soon as I quit speaking.

'Warren tells me there haven't been any ransom calls,' Adam said. He'd begun pacing sometime during my story. I couldn't see any sign he'd ever been hurt, but I suspect some of that was acting; an Alpha never admits weakness in front of the pack. 'I've been thinking about it, but I honestly don't know. One of the wolves who came to my house was someone I once knew – thirty years ago. We were both turned at the same time. His experience was . . . harrowing, because he Changed without help.' I saw several of the wolves wince. 'He might bear a grudge because of it, but thirty years is a long time to wait if revenge is the only reason for taking Jesse.'

'Does he belong to a pack?' Mary Jo asked from the back of the room. Mary Jo was a firefighter with the Kennewick FD. She was small, tough-looking, and complained a lot because she had to pretend to be weaker than all the men on her team. I liked her.

Adam shook his head. 'David is a lone wolf by choice. He doesn't like werewolves.'

'You said they had humans with them, and new wolves,' Warren said.

Adam nodded, but I was still thinking about the lone

wolf. What was a man who had been a lone wolf for thirty years doing running in a pack of new wolves? Had he Changed them himself? Or were they victims like Mac had, been?

Samuel laid his muzzle on my knee, and I petted him absently.

'You said they used silver nitrate, DMSO, and Ketamine,' said Auriele, the chemistry teacher. 'Does that mean they have a doctor working for them? Or maybe a drug pusher? Ketamine isn't as common as meth or crack, but we see it in the high school now and then.'

I straightened up. 'A doctor or a vet,' I said. Beside me Samuel stiffened. I looked at him. 'A vet would have access to all of those, wouldn't he, Samuel?'

Samuel growled at me. He didn't like what I was thinking.

'Where are you going with this?' asked Adam, looking at Samuel, though he was talking to me.

'Dr Wallace,' I said.

'Carter is in trouble because he can't accept being a were-wolf, Mercy. It is too violent for him, and he'd rather die than be what we are. Are you trying to say that he is involved in a plot where young wolves are held in cages while experiments are performed upon them? Have you ever heard what he has to say about the animal experimentation and the cosmetics industry?'

For a moment I was surprised Adam knew so much about Dr Wallace. But I knew from the reactions of the people in Aspen Creek that Adam had spent time there. I suppose it only made sense that he would know about Dr Warren's troubles. From the murmurs around us, the rest of the pack didn't, though.

Adam stopped arguing with me to explain to everyone who Dr Wallace was. It gave me time to think.

'Look,' I said when he'd finished. 'All these chemicals for the drug they shot you with are readily available – but who

222

would think to combine them and why? Who would want to be able to tranquilize a werewolf? Dr Wallace is in danger of losing control – I saw it myself this week. He is worried about his family. He wouldn't have developed a way to administer drugs to werewolves in order to kidnap Jesse, but he might have developed a tranquilizer for people to use on him – in case he lost all control, and his wolf attacked someone.'

'Maybe,' Adam said slowly. 'I'll call Bran tomorrow and have him ask Dr Wallace about it. No one can lie to Bran.'

'So what do they stand to gain with Jesse?' Darryl asked. 'Money seems ridiculous at this point. It seems that this attack was directed at the Columbia Basin Pack's Alpha rather than at Adam Hauptman, businessman.'

'Agreed.' Adam frowned at him. 'Possibly someone wants control of the pack? There isn't much I would not do for my daughter.'

*Control of the pack or control of Adam*, I wondered, *and is there a difference between the two?*

'Whoever it is and whatever they want, we should know before dawn. We know where they are staying,' I said, reaching into the pocket of my jeans and pulling out the paper the vampires had given me and handing it to Adam. 'Zee's informant said that our enemies paid the vampires almost ten thousand dollars to leave them alone while they were here,' I told Adam.

Adam's eyebrows shot up even though he clutched the paper with white fingers. 'Ten thousand is way too much,' he said. 'I wonder why they did that?'

He glanced at the paper and looked around the room. 'Darryl? Warren? Are you up to another adventure tonight?'

'Nothing's broken,' Darryl said.

'Not anymore,' agreed Warren. 'I'm up for it.'

'Samuel?'

The white wolf grinned at him.

'We can take my van,' I offered.

'Thank you,' said Adam, 'but you are staying here.'

I raised my chin, and he patted my cheek – the patronizing bastard. He laughed at my expression, not like he was making fun of me, but like he was really enjoying something . . . me.

'You are not expendable, Mercedes – and you are not up to facing a pack war.' By the time he'd finished speaking the smile had left his face, and he was watching the people in the room.

'Listen, buddy,' I said. 'I killed two werewolves – that makes my kill sheet as high as yours this week – and I didn't do so badly getting that address from the vampires either.'

'*You* got the address from the *vampires*?' said Adam, in a dangerously soft voice.

'Patronizing bastard,' I muttered, driving my van through the empty streets of East Kennewick. 'I am *not* pack. He does *not* have the right to tell me what to do or how to do it. He has no right to yell at me for talking to the vampires. He is *not* my keeper.'

He was, I'd finally had to concede, right about how little help I'd be in a fight with another pack of werewolves. Warren had promised to call me when they were through.

I yawned and realized I'd been up for nearly twenty hours – and I'd spent that last night tossing on a strange motel bed, alternately dreaming of Mac dying because of something I hadn't done and of Jesse alone and crying for help.

I pulled into my driveway and didn't bother parking the van in its usual place, safe in the pole-built garage. I'd clean out the wrappers and the socks in the morning and put it away. Zee's dagger, which I'd put back on before I left Warren's to make certain I didn't just leave it in the van, got tangled in my seat belt. I was so tired I was in tears by the time I finally was free.

Or maybe I was crying like the kid who gets picked last for the softball team at school — and is told to go somewhere and not get in the way while the rest of them played ball.

I remembered to get the guns out of the van and to grab my purse. As I started up my steps, I realized that Elizaveta Arkadyevna hadn't gotten around to cleaning the porch yet because I could still smell Mac and the distinctive scents that accompany death.

No, I decided, my lips peeling back from my teeth in a snarl, I was crying because I wanted to be in on the kill. These people had come into my territory and hurt people I cared about. It was my duty, my right, to punish them.

As if I could do anything against a pack of werewolves. I brought my hand down on the safety rail and snapped the dry wood as easily as if it had been resting on cinder blocks at the dojo. A small, soft presence rubbed against my ankles and welcomed me with a demanding mew.

'Hey, Medea,' I said, wiping my eyes before I picked her up and tucked her under the arm that wasn't holding my guns. I unlocked my door, not bothering with the light. I put the guns away. I set my cell phone in its charger beside the regular phone, then curled up on the couch with a purring Medea and fell asleep waiting for Warren's call.

The sun in my eyes woke me up. For the first few moments I couldn't remember what I was doing sleeping on the couch. The clock on my DVD player read 9:00 A.M., which meant it was ten in the morning. I never reset it to account for daylight savings.

I checked my messages and my cell phone. There was a call from Zee asking me to check in, but that was it. I called Zee back and left a message on *his* machine.

I called Adam's home phone, his cell phone, and his pager. Then I called Warren's home number, too. I looked Darryl's phone number up in the phone book and called him, writing down the other numbers his machine purred at me. But he wasn't answering his cell phone either.

After a moment of thought I turned the TV onto the local station, but there were no emergency broadcasts. No one had reported a bloodbath in West Richland last night. Maybe no one had found the bodies yet.

I took my cell, got in the Rabbit, and drove to the address the vampires had given me – I might have given Adam the paper, but I remembered the address. The house was completely empty with a FOR SALE sign on the front lawn. I could smell the pack faintly around the perimeter of the building, but there was no sign of blood or violence.

If the address had been false, where was everyone?

I drove to my shop before I remembered it was Thanksgiving and no one would be bringing in cars for me to fix. Still, it was better than sitting home and wondering what had happened. I opened one of the big garage doors and started to work on my current project.

It was difficult getting anything done. I'd had to take off my phone so I didn't break it while I was working, and I kept thinking I heard it ring. But no one called, not even my mother.

An unfamiliar car drove up and stopped out front, and a tiny woman dressed in red sweats and white tennis shoes got out. She met my gaze, nodded once, and, having acquired a target lock, walked briskly over to me.

'I am Sylvia Sandoval,' she said, extending her hand.

'You don't want to shake my hands just now,' I said with a professional smile. 'I'm Mercedes Thompson. What can I do for you?'

'You already have.' She put her hand down and nodded

back at her car, a been-there-done-that Buick that was, despite rust spots and a ding on the right front fender, spotlessly clean. 'Since your Mr Adelbertsmiter fixed it, it has been running like new. I would like to know how much I owe you, please. Mr Adelbertsmiter indicated that you might be interested in exchanging my son's labor for your time and trouble.'

I found a clean rag and began rubbing the worst of the grease off my hands to give myself time to think. I liked it that she had taken time to learn Zee's name. It wasn't the easiest name to wrap your lips around, especially if your first language was Spanish.

'You must be Tony's friend,' I said. 'I haven't had time to look at the bill Zee prepared – but I am shorthanded. Does your son know anything about fixing cars?'

'He can change the oil and rotate the tires,' she said. 'He will learn the rest. He is a hard worker and learns fast.'

Like Zee, I found myself admiring her forthright, determined manner. I nodded. 'All right. Why don't we do this. Have your son come' – When? I had no idea what I was going to be doing for the next couple of days – 'Monday after school. He can work off the repairs, and, if we suit, he can keep the job. After school and Saturday all day.'

'His school comes first,' she said.

I nodded. 'I can live with that. We'll see how it works.'

'Thank you,' she said. 'He'll be here.'

I watched her get into her car and reflected that Bran was lucky she wasn't a werewolf or he might find himself having trouble keeping his place as Alpha.

I paused and stared at my dirty hands. Last night someone had asked what the kidnappers wanted. They didn't need Adam's place in the pack, not if they had their own pack. If they wanted money, surely there were easier targets than the Alpha's daughter. So there was something special about

Adam. Among the werewolves, it is a matter of safety always to know where you rank in the pack. In the hierarchy of the Marrok it was not so important – as long as everyone remembered that Bran was on top. But people kept track anyway.

I had a very clear memory of my foster father crouching in front of my chair and naming off names on my fingers when I was four or five. 'One is Bran,' he said. 'Two is Charles, and three is Samuel. Four is Adam of the Los Alamos Pack. Five is Everett of the Houston Pack.'

'One is Bran,' I said now. 'Two is Charles, and three Samuel, both Bran's sons. Four is Adam, now of the Columbia Basin Pack.'

If there was something special about Adam, it was that – other than Bran's sons, he was the nearest challenger for the title of Marrok.

I tried to dismiss it at first. If I wanted to get Adam to fight Bran, I certainly wouldn't start by kidnapping his daughter. But maybe they hadn't.

I sat down in the Bug's driver's seat, and the old vinyl cracked under me. What if they had come to talk to Adam rather than attack him? I closed my eyes. Suppose it was someone who knew Adam well like his old army buddy. Adam had a hot temper, explosive even – although he could be persuaded to listen, once he'd calmed down again.

Given that the enemy was a werewolf, he would be afraid of Adam, or at least cautious. That's the way the dominance game works. Meeting an Alpha on his home territory puts him in a superior position. Can't take a gun loaded with silver ammunition because that would be a declaration of war – he'd have to kill Adam or die himself. Suppose this enemy had on hand a drug, something to calm a werewolf down. Something to keep Adam from killing him if negotiations went poorly.

But things don't work out right. Someone panics and shoots the person who opens the door – less dominant werewolves would have a tendency to panic when invading an Alpha's home. Suppose they shoot him several times. A mistake, but not irreparable.

Except that then Adam attacks. So they shoot Adam, too, and chain him so they can hold him until he listens. But Mac dies and Adam is not in any mood to listen. He begins to break free, and when you have enough drug in him to stop that, he is too far under to discuss anything.

They are panicking. They have to come up with a new plan. How can they get Adam to cooperate?

'Jesse's upstairs,' I said, snapping my fingers in a quick rhythm that answered the speed of my thoughts.

Take Jesse, then force Adam to listen. Or, if he won't listen, then threaten to kill Jesse.

It made as much sense as anything else. So where did Mac and the drug experiments come in?

I scrabbled out of the Bug and jogged into my office to locate a notebook. I had no proof of any of it, just instincts – but my instincts were sometimes very good.

On one page, I wrote down: *Drug experiments/buying new werewolves?* and on the next *Why replace Bran with Adam?*

I set a hip over a three-legged stool and tapped my pen on the paper. Other than the tranquilizers that had killed Mac, there was no physical evidence of any other drugs, but Mac's experiences seemed to indicate that there were more. After a moment I wrote down: *Were Ketamine/silver nitrate/DMSO the only drugs?* Then I wrote down the names of people likely to have knowledge of all the drugs. *Samuel, Dr Wallace*, and after a thoughtful pause I wrote *Auriele*, the chemistry teacher. With a sigh I admitted: *it could be anybody*. Then, stubbornly, I circled Dr Wallace's name.

He had the ability and a motive for making a tranquilizer

that would render him harmless to the people he loved. I quit playing with my pen. *Or would it?*

Wasn't the vampire's Kiss a tranquilizer? It was possible a submissive werewolf might have come out of it like any other tranquilized animal, groggy and quiet. Stefan had said that only some wolves became problematic. Samuel had come out fighting, with his wolf ready to attack, just as if he'd been trapped.

I thought of the broken manacles Adam had left behind in his house. He'd put his reaction down to Jesse's kidnapping — but maybe that was only part of it. But, that was a side issue for now.

I looked at the second page. *Why replace Bran with Adam?*

I brushed my finger over the words. I wasn't certain that was the motive, but it was the kind of motive that would leave bodies on the ground without discouraging the perpetrators. They left Adam alive when they could easily have killed him, so they wanted something from him.

Bran had been Marrok for almost two centuries. Why would someone get desperate to change the way things ran just now?

I wrote down: *want change.*

Bran could be a bastard. He was a ruler in the old-fashioned despot sense — but that was something the werewolves seemed to want. Under his rule the werewolves in North America had prospered, both in power and numbers — while in Europe the wolves waned.

But would Adam be any different? Well, yes, but not in any way that I could see would benefit anyone. If anything, Adam would be more despotic. Samuel said that Bran had considered using Adam as the poster child for the werewolves — but it would never have worked. Adam was too hot-tempered. Some reporter would shove a camera in his face and find himself flattened on the pavement.

*That was it.*

I sucked in my breath. It wasn't change that someone wanted – it was *to keep everything the same*. Bran was planning on bringing the wolves out.

Suddenly it didn't seem so odd that one of Adam's wolves might have betrayed him. (I wasn't as confident that my instincts were right as everyone else seemed to be.) But I could see how one of Adam's wolves could feel that aiding the enemy had not been a betrayal. They were preparing the way for him to take power. No harm was supposed to have come from their raid on Adam's house – but they wouldn't be discouraged by the deaths there. Werewolves die – and their wolves had died for a cause. A wolf like Mac, who wasn't even pack, wouldn't be a great loss when measured by what was at risk.

The betrayer could be anyone. None of Adam's pack had any personal loyalty to Bran.

I took out the card Bran had given me and called the top number. He picked up on the second ring.

'Bran, this is Mercy.' Now that I had him on the phone I wasn't certain how much to tell him – far too much of what I'd put together was pure speculation. Finally, I asked, 'Have you heard from Adam?'

'No.'

I tapped my toe. 'Is . . . is Dr Wallace still there?'

Bran sighed. 'Yes.'

'Could you ask him if he developed a tranquilizer that works on werewolves?'

His voice sharpened. 'What do you know?'

'Nothing. Not a damn thing, including where Adam and your son are right now. Just when are you considering bringing the werewolves out in public?'

'Samuel's missing?'

'I wouldn't go that far. The whole pack is with them – they just haven't bothered to check in with me.'

231

'Good,' he said, obviously not surprised that they hadn't seen fit to keep me updated. 'In answer to your previous question – I believe it is something that must be done soon. Not this week nor next, but not a year from now either. My contacts in the FBI laboratories tell me that our existence is an all-but-open secret right now. Like the Gray Lords, I've come to the conclusion that since coming out is inevitable – it is imperative to control how it is done.'

See? Werewolves *are* control freaks.

'How many people . . . how many *wolves* know about this?' I asked.

There was a pause. 'This is pertinent to the attack on Adam?'

'I believe so, yes.'

'Most of the wolves here would know,' he said. 'I haven't been keeping it a secret. Next month at the Conclave I am going to make a general announcement.'

He didn't say anything more, just waited for me to tell him what I'd been thinking. It was pure speculation, and I was opening myself up to ridicule by saying anything at all. I sat on that stool and realized that I had my loyalties, too. I was not a werewolf, but Bran was still my Marrok. I had to warn him.

'I have no proof,' I told him. 'Just a theory.' And I told him what I thought had happened and why.

'I don't have any idea who it is,' I told the silence at the other end of the line. 'Or if I'm right.'

'If it is a werewolf who is unhappy about revealing himself to humans, it seems odd that there would be humans working with him,' Bran said, but he didn't say it like he thought my theory was stupid.

I'd almost forgotten about the humans. 'Right. And I don't have much of an explanation about the drug tests that Mac told us about either – other than maybe they were worried about dosage or side effects. Paying for new-made werewolves seems like a lot of risk with very little benefit.'

'When two wolves are fighting, having one of them drugged could greatly influence the outcome,' said Bran. 'I like your theory, Mercedes. It isn't perfect, but it feels like you're on the right trail.'

'He wouldn't have to worry about the loyalties of humans,' I said, thinking out loud.

'Who?'

'Adam says that one of the wolves who attacked his house was someone he knew, a wolf who shared his rebirth.'

'David Christiansen.'

'Yes.' It didn't surprise me that the Marrok would know who I was talking about. Bran managed to give the impression that he knew every werewolf anywhere personally. Maybe he did.

'David works with humans,' Bran said slowly. 'But not with other werewolves. I wouldn't have thought he would ever be a part of a plot that included rape – Changes like that experienced by your Alan MacKenzie Frazier. Still it is something to consider. I'll call Charles and see what he makes of it.'

'He's still in Chicago?'

'Yes. You were right; it was Leo. Apparently his salary wasn't enough to support the kind of living he wanted to enjoy.' Bran's voice sounded neutral. 'He didn't know the wolf he sold the young victims like your Alan MacKenzie Frazier to – there were six of them altogether. He didn't know what they wanted the young ones for, either. Stupid of him. The Alpha's second is the one who set up the deal, but Charles is having difficulty getting any more information out of the second because he has left town. It may take us a while to find him. The rest of the pack seems to have been unaware of what was going on, but we are breaking them up anyway.'

'Bran? If you hear from Samuel or Adam, will you tell them to call me?'

'I'll do that,' he said gently and hung up.

# 13

I was in no mood for working on the Beetle after talking to Bran, so I closed up shop and went home. Bran had thought my ideas had merit, which was all well and good, except it did not answer the tightness in my belly that told me I should have gotten a call by now. My nose had told me that Adam hadn't found Jesse at the empty house in West Richland, but it didn't tell me where they'd gone afterward.

I paused again on my porch at the smell of death that still lingered there. I decided Elizaveta Arkadyevna was punishing me for not telling her what was going on. I'd have to clean the porch myself or be reminded of Mac's death every time I walked in my house for the next few months.

I opened the door, still thinking of Mac, and realized what else my senses had been trying to tell me a moment too late. All I had time to do was drop my chin so that the man who'd been standing behind the door didn't get the choke-hold he'd gone after, but his arm was still tight around my head and neck.

I twisted around sharply in his grip until I faced him, then threw everything I had into a short, sharp punch into the nerve center on the outside of the big muscle of his thigh. He swore, his grip loosened, and I pulled free and started fighting in earnest.

My style of karate, Shi Sei Kai Kan, was designed for soldiers who would be encountering multiple opponents — which was good because there were three men in my living room. One of them was a werewolf – in human form. I didn't have time to think, only react. I got in some good hits, but it rapidly became apparent that these men had studied violence a lot longer than I.

About the time I realized the only reason I was still up and fighting was because they were being very careful not to hurt me, the werewolf hit me once, hard, square in my diaphragm, then, while I was gasping for air, tossed me on the floor and pinned me there.

'Broke my f—'

'Ladies present,' chided the man who held me in an implacable grip that was as gentle as a mother holding her babe. His voice had the same soft drawl that sometimes touched Adam's voice. 'No swearing.'

'Broke my *freaking* nose then,' said the first voice dryly, if somewhat muffled – presumably by the broken nose.

'It'll heal.' He ignored my attempts to wriggle out of his hold. 'Anyone else hurt?'

'She bit John-Julian,' said the first man again.

'Love nip, sir. I'm fine.' He cleared his throat. 'Sorry, sir. It never occurred to me that she'd have training. I wasn't ready.'

'It's water under the bridge now. Learn from it, boy,' my captor said. Then he leaned down and, in a voice of power that vibrated down my spine, said, 'Let us chat a little, hmm? The idea is not to hurt you. If you hadn't struggled, you wouldn't even have the bruises you do now. We could have hurt you much worse if we had wanted to.' I knew he was right – but it didn't make him my best friend.

'What do you want?' I asked in as reasonable a tone as I could manage, flattened, as I was, on the floor beneath a strange werewolf.

'That's my girl,' he approved, while I stared at the floor between my couch and end table, about two feet from my left hand, where Zee's dagger must have fallen when I went to sleep last night.

'We're not here to hurt you,' he told me. 'That's the first thing you need to know. The second is that the werewolves who have been watching your house and the Sarge's have been called off – so there's no one to help you. The third is—' He stopped speaking and bent his head to take a deeper breath. 'Are you a were? Not a werewolf. You don't smell right for that. I thought it might just be the cat – never had a cat – but it's you that smells like fur and the hunt.'

'Grandpa?'

'It's all right,' the werewolf answered, 'she's not going to hurt me. What are you, girl?'

'Does it matter?' I asked. He'd called Adam 'Sarge' – as in 'Sergeant'?

'No,' he said. He lifted his weight off me and released me. 'Not in the slightest.'

I rolled toward the couch, and grabbed the dagger, shaking it free of sheath and belt. One of the intruders started forward, but the werewolf held up a hand and the other man stopped.

I kept moving until I was crouched on the back of the couch, the dagger in my hand and my back to the wall.

The werewolf's skin was so dark the highlights were blue and purple rather than brown. He knelt on the floor where he'd moved as soon as he let me up. He wore loose khaki pants and a light blue shirt. At another gesture, the two men backed up farther, giving me as much room as they could. They were lean and tough-looking and like enough to be twins. Like the werewolf, they were very dark-skinned. Between skin tone, general build, and that 'Grandpa,' I was betting that they were all related.

'You're Adam's army buddy,' I told the werewolf, trying to sound relaxed, like it made me think he might be on my side, like I didn't know that he'd been involved in the debacle at Adam's house. 'The one who was Changed with him.'

'Yes'm,' he said. 'David Christiansen. These are my men. My grandsons, Connor and John-Julian.' They nodded as he said their names. John-Julian was rubbing his shoulder where I'd gotten a good grip with my teeth, and Connor was holding a wad of tissue to his nose with one hand while the other held my Kleenex box.

'Mercedes Thompson,' I told him. 'What do you want?'

David Christiansen sat down on the floor, making himself as vulnerable as a werewolf could get.

'Well, now, ma'am,' he said. 'We've gotten ourselves into something of a fix, and we're hoping you can help us out of it. If you know who I am, you probably know I've been a lone wolf by choice since the Change.'

'Yes,' I said.

'I never finished high school, and the military was all I knew. When an old buddy recruited me for a mercenary troop, I was happy to go. Eventually I got tired of taking orders and formed up my own troop.' He smiled at me. 'When my grandsons resigned their commissions and joined us, I decided to quit fighting other people's wars for them. We specialize in extracting kidnapped victims, ma'am. Businessmen, Red Cross, missionaries, whatever, we get them out of the hands of the terrorists.'

My legs were getting tired, so I sat down on the back of the couch. 'What does this have to do with me?'

'We find ourselves somewhat embarrassed,' the werewolf said.

'We're on the wrong side,' said the man who'd answered to John-Julian.

'Gerry Wallace came to you,' I whispered, as if a loud noise would destroy my sudden comprehension. It was David's talking about being a lone wolf that had done it. Lone wolves and Dr Wallace meant Gerry, the Marrok's liaison with packless wolves. 'He told you that Bran intended to tell the world about the werewolves.' No wonder Gerry was too busy to spend time with his father.

'That's right, ma'am,' agreed David. He frowned at me. 'You aren't a werewolf, I'd swear to it, so how do you know so much about us——' He broke off his speech as a look of sudden comprehension came into his face. 'Coyote. You're the girl who turns into a coyote, the one raised by the Marrok.'

'That's me,' I said. 'So Gerry talked to you about Bran's decision to bring the werewolves out into the public?'

'Bran is abandoning the wolves to the humans, just like the Gray Lords did their people,' said Connor of the bloody nose. My strangeness evidently took second place to his indignation toward Bran. 'He's supposed to protect his people. *Someone* needed to challenge him before he could do it.'

'So you suggested Adam?'

'No, ma'am.' David's voice was mellow, but I bet if he'd been in wolf form, his ears would have been pinned against his skull. 'That was Gerry. He wanted me to come talk to him, one old friend to another.'

'Bran is not one of the Gray Lords. He would never abandon his wolves. I suppose it never occurred to you to call Adam on the phone and talk to him – or even Bran, for that matter,' I said.

'We were just back from a mission,' David said. 'We had the time. Some things just work better in person.'

'Like kidnapping?' I asked dryly.

'That was unplanned,' Connor said, a touch of heat in his voice.

'Was it?' murmured David. 'I've been wondering. The whole thing came off so badly – with four of Gerry's wolves dead – that I can't help but wonder if it was planned that way.'

'Three of his wolves dead,' I said. 'Mac was ours.'

David smiled, more with his eyes than his lips. 'Yes, ma'am. Three of his wolves died, then, and one of Adam's.'

'Why would he want to kill his own wolves?' asked Connor.

'We'd have to look at the wolves who died.' David looked thoughtful. 'I wonder if they were dominant wolves. I didn't know any of them well – except for Kara. *She* wouldn't have liked taking orders from Gerry for long. The boy, Mac, betrayed him by going to Adam for help.'

'You make Gerry sound like a psychopath,' said John-Julian. 'He didn't strike me as crazy.'

'He's a werewolf,' David told him. 'We're a little more conscious of the chain of command than humans. If he wants to stay in control, he'd have to get rid of the wolves who were more dominant – and, eventually, the wolves who betrayed the pack.'

I looked at David. 'I don't know Gerry well, but if I were to guess, I'd say you were dominant to him, too.'

David grimaced. 'I have my people. I don't want Gerry's, he knows that better than anyone. He's watched me for years.'

'So he felt safe calling you in,' I said tentatively. 'Knowing you wouldn't challenge his leadership.'

'Gerry told Grandpa that Adam didn't want to challenge Bran, but he might listen to an old friend,' said John-Julian mildly. 'He offered to fly us out here to talk, so we agreed. It didn't take long before we realized matters were a little different than presented.'

'I'd made inquiries.' David took over the narrative. 'I called friends and found out that Bran really does intend to tell the Alphas at the December meeting that he is going to take us public. So we came here to talk to Adam. I didn't think it would do much good. Adam likes the Marrok too much to challenge him.'

'But matters weren't quite as they were presented,' said Connor. 'Gerry never told us he was assembling an army of mercenaries and werewolves.'

'An army?' I said.

'A small army. Two or three of the lone wolves like Kara, who couldn't find a pack of their own,' John-Julian explained. 'And a small group of mercenaries, loners he apparently offered to turn into werewolves.'

'I should have put a stop to it when the damn fool armed a bunch of frightened idiots with tranquilizer guns.' David shook his head. 'Maybe if I'd realized Gerry'd come up with something that could hurt a werewolf . . . Anyway, from that moment on it was a classic SNAFU.'

'Adam said they shot Mac when he opened the door,' I said.

'Gerry'd gotten them so worked up about how dangerous Adam was that before they even checked to see who it was, they shot him.' John-Julian's voice held only mild regret – and I had a feeling that was mostly for the stupidity of the shooting rather than Mac's death.

'Did you know Mac?' I asked, looking down at Zee's dagger because I didn't want them all to know how angry I was. But, of course, the werewolf knew.

'No, they didn't,' David said. 'We flew in last Monday afternoon.' He gave me an assessing look. 'We were there when one of Gerry's mercenaries, a human, came in thoroughly spooked.'

'The man said someone killed his partner,' said John-Julian looking at me, too. 'A demon.'

'No demons.' I shrugged. 'It doesn't take a demon to kill an untrained, newbie werewolf who was too stupid to live.'

I swallowed my anger – it wasn't their fault they didn't know Mac. I looked at them and hesitated. Maybe they should.

My inclination was to trust them. Part of it was that their story rang true – though I didn't know them well enough to tell for sure. Part of it was remembering Adam's voice as he talked about David Christiansen.

'Let me tell you about Mac, the boy who died on my porch,' I said, then told them about his Change, the Chicago Alpha who sold him to Gerry, and the drug experiments.

'All we saw were the tranq guns,' said John-Julian, slowly. 'But two shots killed the young wolf – and they shot Adam with five before he was doped enough they could bind him.'

'Our metabolisms are put out of commission by the silver while this DMSO carries the drug more quickly into our blood system?' asked David. 'Does that mean someone could just substitute something else for the Ketamine?'

'I'm not a doctor,' I told him. 'It sounded like something like that would work, though.'

'Maybe that's what it sounded like to Gerry, too, and he was testing it out,' said David. 'With a real pack, it wouldn't have worked, but with this mix of lone wolf deviants and new wolves born of mercenaries who also have to work alone – there's no one who would feel it necessary to protect the prisoners.'

That was nature's balance to the role of the dominant wolf. As strong as the instinct of wolves to follow those who were dominant, was the instinct of dominants to protect those weaker than themselves.

'All lone wolves aren't deviants,' protested Connor.

David smiled. 'Thank you. But werewolves need packs. It takes something stronger to keep them away. A few are like me, we hate what we are too much to live within a pack. Most of them, though, are outcasts, men the pack wouldn't accept.'

His smile changed, grew bleak. 'I have my pack, Connor. It's just not a pack of werewolves—' He looked at me. 'I left the other members of our team with Gerry to keep an eye on the situation there. There are six of us. A small pack, but it works for me. Most wolves who live very long outside of a pack go a little crazy. Mercenaries are a little the same way. A mercenary who only works alone usually does so because no one else will work with him because he's stupid or crazy – and the stupid ones are mostly dead.'

'Not someone I'd want to meet as a werewolf,' I said, as my phone rang. 'Excuse me a minute,' I said, and fished around in my pockets for my cell, which had miraculously escaped damage.

'Happy Thanksgiving, Mercy!'

'Happy Thanksgiving, Mom,' I said. 'Can I call you back? I'm a little busy right now.'

'Your sister has just told us she's engaged . . .' said my mother, blithely ignoring me. So I sat and listened to her chatter about my siblings and my stepfather while three mercenaries sat in my living room and watched me.

'Mom,' I said, when she showed signs of slowing down. 'Mom, I have company over.'

'Oh, good!' she said. 'I was worried about you all alone on Thanksgiving. Is it Warren and that nice young man of his? I hope he keeps this one. Do you remember the last one? Easy on the eyes, I must say, but he wasn't someone you could have a conversation with, was he?'

'No, Mom,' I said. 'These are new friends. But I have to go, or they're going to feel like I'm ignoring them.'

I hung up the phone gently a few minutes later.

'I forgot today was Thanksgiving,' David said, but I couldn't tell if it bothered him or not.

'I've been thinking about these drug experiments, sir,' said Connor. 'Most men who are trying to assassinate a ruler intend to set themselves up instead.'

'These are werewolves,' his grandfather said. 'Not humans. Gerry could never be Marrok. Oh, he's a dominant – but I doubt he'd ever be strong enough to be Alpha of any pack, let alone all the packs. He knows that.'

'But does he like it?' asked Connor. 'Have you watched him among his wolves? Did you notice that the mercenaries he has who are still human show signs of being dominant? He tells them that he can't risk losing them right now — but I think he's being cautious. He doesn't like it when you give his wolves orders and they obey.'

'He can't change what he is,' said David, but not like he was disagreeing.

'No, sir. But he has Adam under his control now, doesn't he? Between finding the right combination of drugs and Adam's daughter, he could have Adam under his control all the time.'

David tilted his head, then shook it. 'It wouldn't work. Not for long. An Alpha would kill himself fighting before he'd submit for very long. He'd defeat the drugs or die.'

I wasn't so certain. I don't think anyone knew exactly how the drug cocktails would work — not even Gerry, who had been experimenting with new wolves and not powerful ones like Adam.

'It doesn't matter what we think. Could Gerry believe they would work on Adam?' asked John-Julian.

For some reason, they looked at me, but all I could do was shrug. 'I don't know Gerry. He didn't spend much time with the pack, and he traveled a lot with his job.' I hesitated. 'Bran wouldn't put a stupid person in a position like that.'

David nodded. 'I never thought Gerry was stupid before this. But that bloodbath has had me rethinking my opinions.'

'Look,' I said. 'I'd love to discuss Gerry, but why don't you tell me what you are doing here and what you want from me first.'

'I still don't like what Bran's doing,' David rumbled. 'Not at all. But I like what Gerry is doing even less.'

'Gerry asked us to deliver the boy's body to your doorstep,' explained John-Julian. 'He said that you needed a warning to stay out of wolf business. We met him back at the house he was using for headquarters and that was when we found out that he'd kidnapped Adam's daughter and left three of his wolves to die.'

'You don't leave your men behind,' said Connor.

'You don't attack the innocents,' John-Julian told me. It sounded like a creed.

David gave me a half smile. 'And, though I think Bran needs to be brought up short, only a fool would think he could get Adam to move a step he doesn't choose to. I'd leave Gerry to learn his lesson, but our honor is at stake. We don't hurt the innocents – so we're getting Adam and his daughter away tonight.'

'They have Adam?' It wasn't really a surprise. What else could have kept the pack away from phones all day? It was even a relief to know because there had been a dozen other, worse things that had occurred to me.

What did come as a surprise was the door opening, though I hadn't sensed anyone on my front porch. Samuel, back in his human shape, let himself into my house. He was wearing only jeans. Even his feet were bare, and he limped a little as he came to me. 'They have Adam,' he confirmed.

I might not have heard him or smelled him, but David didn't look surprised. He'd made a subtle gesture that kept his men where they were – though I could see they were tense and ready to act.

'David Christiansen, meet Dr Samuel Cornick,' I said. 'Samuel, this is David, Adam's old army buddy. He's here to get Adam and Jesse out.'

'So I heard,' Samuel said, sitting down on the couch next to my feet.

'What happened to you?' I asked.

'We got to the address we had for the other wolves and found a few signs, but nothing definite. We wandered around quite a while before Darryl realized the reason Adam wasn't recalling us from the hunt was because he was gone, along with his car. Someone saw him with a cell phone – which he didn't have when we left Warren's house. Several wolves noticed the car drive away, but no one thought to question Adam.'

'Wait a minute,' I said, because I was getting a very bad feeling. 'Wait a minute. The vampires would have checked out the address – Bran says there's nothing more paranoid than a vampire. They'd have made certain there were wolves where they were supposed to be, don't you think? Even just to make certain that it was wolves who'd come. But when half our pack shows up, they can't find enough scent to track the others?' I looked at David. 'And when Mac's body was left on my porch, I couldn't scent anyone else who shouldn't have been there – I didn't smell you.' I hunched my shoulders. 'I should have realized it then, shouldn't I? It's not just Gerry, is it?' I saw Samuel stiffen and remembered he hadn't known. 'Gerry Wallace is working with our witch.'

There were a lot of witches who could sterilize a body so that not even the keenest nose, or the best-equipped, best-trained forensics team could find a clue. But Elizaveta Arkadyevna was one of the few witches who could have removed the scent of David and his men without removing the scent of Adam's house.

'There's a Russian witch,' David said.

'If the wolf packs come out into the open, witches will lose a lot of business,' I said. 'Staying hidden bears a high price – and the witches are some of the people who benefit.

I'm not even certain it would be a breach of contract, not as long as Gerry wants to make Adam the Marrok.'

'What?' Samuel's voice was so quiet it made me nervous.

'Gerry doesn't want the wolves to be made public,' I explained. 'He decided Adam is the only one who can prevent it – by killing Bran.'

He held up a hand, his eyes cool as they watched the other men. 'I think that Mr Christiansen should tell me what he believes is happening.' So Samuel could see if he was lying or not. Samuel was one of the wolves who could do that.

David knew it, too, I could see it in his smile. 'Gerry Wallace told me that Bran was abandoning his people. He asked me if I would speak to Adam and see if I could get him to object.'

'Meaning fight the Marrok for leadership,' clarified Samuel.

'Yes. To that end he flew me and my boys out here. I was *surprised* at the method he chose. I would not have brought armed men to confront an Alpha in his own home – but I could not object more strongly without a fight that would have left me in charge of Gerry's wolves – and a sadder bunch of wolves you've never seen. I knew that Adam was capable of defending himself, so I went along with it.'

David shrugged. 'Talking to Ms Thompson, we've pretty much decided that Gerry intended that blood be spilled because the wolves who died would have been trouble for him. I think he intended blackmail rather than talk from the beginning.'

Samuel inclined his head. 'He knows Adam. Adam wouldn't challenge my father – even if he disagreed with what Bran was doing. He doesn't want to be Marrok.'

'He doesn't know Adam very well if he thinks he can control him by threatening his daughter,' said David.

'I think you're wrong,' I said. 'I think Adam would do anything to save Jesse.'

'You all sound as if it is a given that Adam would kill my father.'

I considered that. 'Gerry's the one who believes it. Maybe he intends to do something to ensure Bran's death. He still thinks that he's the only one who knows about the tranquilizers.'

Samuel growled, and I patted him on the top of the head. The back of the couch wasn't as comfortable as the seat – but I liked being taller than the two werewolves. Samuel pulled my hand down to his shoulder and held it there.

'So why did you come here?' he asked David. 'Couldn't you find Adam's pack?'

'I wasn't looking for the pack,' David said. 'Gerry's got Adam drugged to the gills. I went in to talk to him and he almost tore through his chains. From what he said, he thinks he's got a traitor in his pack – I think he's right. I suspect that's how they took him. Even so, I think the drug is making him more paranoid. Getting him out safely with his human child is going to require his cooperation.

'He doesn't trust me – and I'm sorry to say he has reason.' He looked at Samuel. 'I don't think he'll trust you either – not another male when his daughter is there.' He turned back to me. 'But you have his scent all over your van, and he has a picture of you in his bedroom.'

Samuel gave me a sharp look. 'In his bedroom?'

It was news to me, too. But I was more worried about Adam and Jesse than a picture.

'All right,' I said. 'Where are they holding him?'

With two exceptions, Samuel didn't seem to have a problem letting David make all the plans. First, Samuel insisted on calling in the wolf pack – though he agreed they were only to be backup, waiting a few minutes away. Only Darryl would know what was up, until the very last minute.

He also insisted on calling his father and telling him what we knew.

'Adam won't fight him,' Samuel told David's frozen face. 'I know he doesn't like coming out, but he understands my father's reasons.' He sighed. 'Look, none of us are happy about it, not even the Marrok. But my father has had several wolves report that one of the government agencies is threatening them with exposure if they won't cooperate.'

Some expression crossed David's face too quickly for me to read, but Samuel nodded. 'I wondered if someone had talked to you, too. The others were all military. We've become an open secret – and that's not safe. Frankly, I'm surprised that Bran's managed to keep us hidden this long. I thought that once the public accepted the fae they'd discover all of us.'

'They didn't want to know,' I said. 'Most of them like their safe little world.'

'What will your father do to Grandpa?' asked Connor.

Samuel raised his eyebrows. 'I can't think of anything he's done wrong. He's sworn no oaths to Bran or anyone else – nor done anything to betray our secrets. Just the opposite.'

My cell phone rang again – it was Bran. That werewolf was uncanny. 'Mercedes, let me speak to my son.'

I looked at Samuel, and said, 'He's not here. I told you earlier that I haven't heard from him since last night.'

'Enough games,' Bran told me. 'Give the phone to Samuel.'

Raising my eyebrows at David Christiansen and his men, I handed the phone over and listened to Samuel explain matters. Bran had probably heard the lie in my voice when I told him Samuel wasn't here. Probably. But David, who had heard both sides of the conversation, was going to be forever convinced that the Marrok *knew* that Samuel was sitting beside me.

I hid my satisfaction. The more powerful the wolves believed Bran, the safer he was.

# 14

We rode with Christiansen and his grandsons for most of the way, me as human and Samuel in wolf form. He'd shifted again at my house because other wolves can sense the change.

David dropped us off about a mile from the site with directions on how to get there. The idea was for me and Samuel to sneak up on our own. Then I'd see if I could wriggle my way through a hole in the side of the warehouse where Adam and Jesse were being kept, and Samuel would rendezvous with Adam's pack and wait until they were called in.

Adam and Jesse were being held at a tree farm, nestled in the rolling lands just south of Benton City, a small town about twenty minutes outside of Richland.

Though the tree farm was closed, there were still acres of trees unharvested. I recognized various maples and oaks as we passed, as well as a few pines.

A huge pole building, obviously the warehouse David had told me about, was nestled well behind the manufactured home. The house was boarded up, and there was a Realtor's sign beside it proudly proclaiming it SOLD.

Samuel at my side, I crouched in a ditch surrounded by a thicket of Russian olive and gave the place a good looking over. From where I sat, I couldn't see any vehicles, so they were probably all parked on the other side of the warehouse.

Christiansen had told us that the tree farm had been purchased by a local winery that intended to use the land to grow grapes. Since they wouldn't plant until the coming spring, the whole thing – house and warehouse – was supposed to be empty until then.

The Realtor's sign told me that one of Adam's wolves had indeed betrayed him and gave me a name.

I pulled out my cell phone and called Darryl's number. By this time, I had it memorized.

'Have you gotten in touch with John Cavanaugh, yet?' I asked. John Cavanaugh was one of the wolves I didn't know very well – he'd been at Warren's for our council of war.

'We haven't been able to locate him.'

I heaved a sigh of relief that Darryl ignored, still lost in his irritation at not being told exactly what we were doing. He wasn't happy at having to follow Samuel's orders, either.

'As *instructed*, I'm not leaving messages on answering machines. That means we are going to be short a lot of people.'

'I'm looking at John Cavanaugh's name on a Realtor's sign outside of the tree farm where they're holding Adam,' I told him.

There was a long pause.

'I see,' he said thoughtfully, and hung up. Not one for long good-byes, our Darryl, but a smart man. John Cavanaugh wouldn't be called for this rescue – or any other. Maybe it should have bothered me more that I had just signed a man's death warrant, but I'd wait and see how Adam and Jesse came out of it before I felt sorry for Cavanaugh.

Beside me, Samuel whined softly.

'All right,' I told him, and began disrobing. It was cold out. Not as cold as Montana, but too chilly to do anything but fling clothes off as fast as I could – while being careful not to stick myself on the Russian-olive thorns. I folded my clothes, somewhat haphazardly, and turned off my cell phone.

'You don't have to wait for me to get in,' I told him again.

He just stared at me.

I heaved a put-upon sigh, then I shifted. Delightfully

warm again, I stretched, wagged my tail at Samuel, and headed out for the warehouse. It was still daylight, so I took a circuitous route to avoid being seen. I was aware of Samuel trailing me, though I never saw him. Quite impressive considering his coloring – white is good for a Montana winter, but winter in eastern Washington is usually gray and brown.

One corner of the aluminum side of the warehouse was bent up, just a little, right where Christiansen had told me it would be. I had to work at it, but I got inside at the cost of a little fur. My nose told me that another coyote and several smaller critters had used the same route within the past few months. If Gerry or one of his wolves caught my scent, hopefully they'd just think another coyote had gotten in.

The interior of the warehouse was cavernous and no warmer than it had been outside. Somehow, though Christiansen had said I wouldn't have any problem finding a place to hide, I'd expected it to be empty. Instead it was filled with hundreds, maybe thousands of crates, pallet-sized with three-foot-tall plywood sides, warped by moisture and wear. The crates were stacked three high on racks that reached to the ceiling, maybe thirty feet over my head.

The air smelled musty. As I looked around, I saw there was a sprinkler system set up and drains in the floor. It made sense, I suppose. When the warehouse was full of trees, they would have had to keep the plants moist somehow until they shipped them.

I found a stack whose bottom crate bore a sheet of paper that said '*Hamamelis Virginiana – Witch Hazel 3'–4'*.' It was empty, but the astringent smell of the shrub still clung to the gray wood. I could have hidden inside the top crate, but I'd be easy to see while I was jumping in or out. Instead, I curled up on the cement between the bottom crate and the metal exterior wall, as safe as I could be under the circumstances.

The plan was for me to wait for one of David's sons to come and get me. They were going to 'do the extraction' (David's words) at night, which was still a few hours away.

Gerry had been having problems with Adam. Even with the tranquilizer, they'd found that having guards in the room they were keeping him in made him too agitated. They remembered the way he'd broken through their restraints at his house, so they did their best to keep him calm: that meant most of the time he and Jesse were alone with a guard outside the room. Gerry's scent bothered Adam enough that he'd had to stay out of the warehouse entirely.

Although we weren't getting Jesse and Adam out for a few hours, I could go in with them and do my best to get Adam ready to be rescued.

We'd argued about that. David had wanted me to wait until his man was on guard duty near dusk, but I didn't want to leave Adam and Jesse alone any longer than they had to be. David thought the risk of discovery was too high.

Samuel settled the argument. 'Let her go. She's going to do it anyway, and this way we can reduce the risks.'

David hadn't been happy, but he'd bowed to higher authority – and better judgment. Samuel was right. I wasn't about to let Adam and Jesse wait around without protection when I could be there with them. Gerry was the only wolf who would know my scent, and he was staying away from the warehouse. All the other wolves would just assume I was a coyote, and there were lots of coyotes around.

I still had to wait for escort, though, which might be a long time coming, but it was safer than having me wander around looking for where they were hiding Adam and Jesse.

It is impossible to stay in the state of readiness while

waiting motionless. Eventually I fell into a light doze that lasted for maybe an hour before the newly familiar smell of John-Julian woke me.

I crept out cautiously, but he was alone, with my pack over one shoulder. He didn't talk to me, just turned and threaded his way through the crates to a section of the warehouse that looked as though it had been offices. Like the crates, they were stacked one atop the other, three high.

He climbed the stairs to the middle tier, where the far door had a bright and shiny dead-bolt lock that made it stand out from the others. When he turned the bolt and opened the door, I darted inside and stopped.

No wonder Gerry left them with only one guard at a time. There was no chance either Jesse or Adam would escape on their own.

Jesse was lying on a bare mattress. Someone had wrapped duct tape around the lower half of her face, covering her mouth, hair, and neck. Getting it off was going to be nasty business. Handcuffs held her wrists together, and a climber's rope secured the handcuffs to the two-by-four bed frame. Her ankles were bound together and tied to the foot of the bed, making it impossible for her to do much more than wiggle.

She stared at John-Julian with dull eyes — and didn't seem to notice me at all. She was wearing pajamas, probably what she'd been wearing when they'd taken her, those soft cottony plaid things with a T-shirt top. On the white underside of her left arm was a bruise so dark it appeared black rather than purple.

Adam was seated in a chair obviously made by the same style-impaired carpenter who'd thrown together the bed frame. It was crude, made of two-by-fours and lag bolts, though I don't suppose they were worried about style. Heavy manacles, just like something you'd expect in a wax museum or medieval torture chamber – held his wrists onto the chair arms and a second set held his ankles to the chair legs. But even destroying the chair wouldn't free him because there were enough silver chains wrapped around him to have funded the local school system for a year.

'Gerry won't come here,' said John-Julian to me. Adam opened his eyes, just a bare fraction, and I saw that his irises were yellow gold and blazing with rage. 'His presence has the same effect on Adam that my grandfather's does. Not even the drugs are enough to keep Adam calm – so Gerry will stay away. Our man is only on guard for another five minutes. The next one is the enemy; but after that, Shawn, one of our men, takes over for a two-hour shift.'

John-Julian continued giving me information I already knew, repeated to make sure I understood. 'Shawn'll come in to help you as he can. The guards are supposed to stay downstairs, except when they first come on shift. But you need to leave both of them bound until Shawn takes over guard duty in case they don't. There's one guard watching the prisoners, and there are four men on patrol over the property. One of those is supposed to just walk around the outside of the warehouse. There's electricity and satellite TV in the house, so most of them are in there when they're not on duty. No one really expects Adam's pack to find them this soon, so they're not on high alert.'

David's men were doing the lion's share of guarding the prisoners because Gerry didn't have many people he could trust with a helpless fifteen-year-old girl – that not being a talent much in demand in the world of crazy mercenaries and lone wolves. David said that Gerry had paid them to stay and work guard duty. Gerry seemed to believe that David wouldn't work against him as long as he was paying them.

While John-Julian was talking, I glanced around the

room, which wasn't exactly bursting with places to hide. As long as they didn't come all the way in, I could conceal myself behind the door or in the big, sliding-door closet – some clichés are clichés because they work. There was no reason for the guards to search the room as long as Adam and Jesse were still there.

Jesse finally stirred as she realized he wasn't talking to her. She twisted awkwardly until she got a good look at me, then made a harsh noise behind her gag.

'Shh,' he told her, then said to me. 'You've got about four hours. We'll create a diversion – not my job, but you'll know it when you hear it. Your job is to get these two down the stairs and into the room nearest the big garage door. Grandpa will find you there, and we'll escort you out.'

I nodded, and he set the pack he carried on the floor.

'Good luck,' he said quietly, and left, locking the door behind him.

I shifted as soon as the door closed and opened the pack, pulling out underwear, a dark T-shirt, and a pair of old sweats. I dressed, put on my shoulder harness and slid my SIG into it. It was chambered and ready to go. I'd brought my foster-father's Smith & Wesson, too. It was too big for a shoulder harness, and I couldn't fire it as often, but the .44 magnum bullets packed more punch than the 9mm. If everything went right, I wouldn't have need for either.

I heard someone coming up the stairs and realized that I hadn't heard John-Julian go down – which was pretty good for a human. Assuming that this was the new guard, I grabbed my pack and hid in the closet, the SIG back in my hand. The closet had a sliding door, but I left the side farthest from the door open, just as it had been.

I could see Jesse jerk against her ropes as someone turned the bolt and threw open the outer door.

'Hey, pretty thing,' said the guard. I could smell the garlic he'd eaten recently, and something unhealthy and sour. He wasn't a werewolf, but he wasn't anyone I particularly wanted around Jesse either. 'I'm here to take you to the bathroom. If you're nice to me, I'll even let you eat something. I bet you're hungry by now.'

He walked over to Jesse and I had a perfect shot at his back. The temptation to take it was made stronger by the panic in Jesse's eyes and the smell of fear that washed off her.

Adam snarled, and the guard drew his gun and turned toward him. He pulled the trigger and Jesse made a horrible, disbelieving sound. I had my gun out and was tightening my own finger when I realized that the gun had made a soft pop rather than a bang – it was an air-powered tranq gun. If he'd had a werewolf's hearing, I'd have had to shoot him anyway because I couldn't help the gulp of air I'd taken when he shot Adam.

'That'll keep you for a while,' he said, presumably to Adam. He holstered the gun and bent over to work on the knots at Jesse's feet. If he'd turned around, he could have seen me – just as Jesse did.

I shook my head at her and touched my eyes, then pointed at the guard. She got the point because she quit looking at me – staring fixedly at the ceiling instead.

He didn't seem to hear it, but someone was jogging up the stairs – possibly drawn by the sound of the gun's discharge, soft as it had been. The door was hanging open so the second man came right in. This one was a werewolf. I couldn't see him, but I could smell him just fine.

'Smells like animals in here,' he said, in a voice that echoed in a bass so low that it sounded muffled.

At first, I was sure he was talking about me.

The guard I could see jerked around, obviously caught by surprise. If he'd shifted his eyes ten degrees, he'd have been staring right at me, but the second guard held his attention instead.

'You an animal, Jones?' the second man asked with a soft eagerness in his voice. 'I am.'

Jones backed up until the bed caught him behind the knees and he sat down, half on top of Jesse. I could have told him that was stupid. You don't back away from preda-tors – it gives them the wrong idea.

When Jones didn't say anything, the werewolf laughed. 'I thought the boss told you he didn't want you anywhere near this child. Am I right?'

I don't know what the werewolf was doing, but it must have been frightening because Jones was making small noises. The werewolf moved at last, a big redheaded man with a dark beard cut close to his face. He grabbed Jones, a hand on each shoulder of his shirt, and picked him up off the bed with a grunt of effort. He turned toward the door and tossed the lighter man across the room. I didn't see Jones hit the floor, but I heard him gasp.

'Go,' the werewolf said.

I heard Jones scramble down the stairs, but I wasn't certain that it was an improvement. The man who was left was far more dangerous. He'd made that remark about animals. Had he scented me? Or was he just taunting Jones?

I stood motionless, except for a slight tremor I couldn't control, and tried to think good thoughts. Fear is a strong scent, and while Jesse was scared enough for the both of us, I was hoping to stay unnoticed.

'All right, Angel, let's get you untied,' the werewolf said to Jesse in a gentle voice that might have been more reas-suring if I hadn't been able to smell his lust. Jesse was unable to do so, and I saw her relax fractionally.

His big hands made short work of the knots, and he helped her sit up like a gentleman, giving her time to work out the stiffness in her shoulders and back. She, smart girl that she was, positioned herself so that his gaze was away from the closet.

He gave her a gentle boost so she could stand, then steadied her with light hands as she walked out of my view and out the door. I leaned against the wall, closed my eyes, and prayed I'd made the right decision, that he wasn't going to do anything more than take her to use a rest room.

In the meantime, I needed to check on Adam.

The dart was still stuck in his neck, and I pulled it out and dropped it on the floor. He opened his eyes when I touched him, but I don't think he saw anything.

'It's all right, now,' I told him, rubbing gently at the bloodstain on his neck. 'I'm here, and we're going to get you and Jesse out. We know who at least one of the traitors is, and the rest won't be able to cause any harm.'

I didn't tell him who 'we' encompassed. I wasn't sure he was hearing me anyway, but I wanted to soothe him rather than rile him. There was another dart tangled in the sleeve of his right arm, and I pulled it out, leaning across his body to do so. His head dropped forward until his face was buried between my shoulder and my neck. I couldn't tell if it had been a purposeful move on his part or if I'd bumped him, but I could hear his breathing deepening.

'That's right,' I told him. 'You sleep and get rid of this poison.'

I stayed there, holding him against me until I heard someone start up the stairs again. I rearranged Adam until he looked like he had when they'd left, minus the darts, then scrambled quietly back into my hiding place.

I waited, worried, as a single set of footsteps came back up the stairs. It wasn't until he came into my view again that I realized the guard was carrying Jesse. She was stiff in his arms and staring at the wall.

'Sorry, Angel,' he crooned, as he tied her up efficiently. 'I'd have given you privacy if it were up to me, but we couldn't chance it, could we?'

He was a dead man, I thought, memorizing his features and the way he moved so I'd know him again – even if Gerry happened to have two six-foot-plus redheaded giants in his pack. I'd heard the satisfaction in his voice, and I'm certain Jesse did as well. He wanted to scare her.

Adam stirred. I could hear it, though he was out of my range of vision. 'Mercy,' he said, his voice a hoarse rasp.

The guard laughed. 'Mercy, is it. You'll find none of that around here.' He reached down and patted Jesse's face. 'Until next time, Angel.'

Adam called her Angel, I remembered, feeling a little sick. The door shut, and the bolt slid home. I waited until he'd gone back down before I moved out of the closet. Jesse was still staring at the wall.

Adam's head had fallen forward again, and I couldn't help but touch him again to make sure he was still breathing. Then I went to his daughter.

She hadn't altered her position since the guard had retied her. Two hours before it was safe to release them, I thought, even while I was digging in the pack for something to cut Jesse's ropes. There was no way I could leave her like this for two more hours.

I don't know why I brought Zee's dagger with me, or why I reached for it instead of the pocketknife I'd also packed, but it came into my hand like it belonged there.

Jesse jerked when I put a knee on the bed, so I touched her shoulder. 'It's me, Mercy. No one's going to hurt you anymore. We've got to wait, yet, but we're going to get you out of here. You need to be quiet. If you can do that for me, I'll get this rope off you and see what I can do about the duct tape.'

She'd gone from being utterly passive to shivering as if

she were frozen as soon as I began talking to her. It was chilly in the room, and they hadn't covered her, so I supposed that might have been part of the problem. But she was sucking in air as hard as she could – a difficult task, since she could only breathe in and out of her nose.

I touched the edge of the dagger to my thumb. It was sharp, but not sharp enough to make cutting through climbing rope very easy. I slid the blade between a strand of the rope and the bed frame and almost stabbed myself when I pulled back and there was no resistance. I thought at first that the dagger had slipped out from under the rope – but the rope was clean-cut.

I gave the dagger a look of respect. I should have realized that any dagger Zee carried about as personal protection would have some surprises in store. I cut the rope at her feet, and she pulled her knees up to her chest and tucked her arms around her middle. Tears slid down her face, and I rubbed her back for a minute. When she seemed to be calming a little, I went back to the pack and pulled out a small, travel-sized can of WD-40.

'Next to vinegar and baking soda, WD-40 is the miracle discovery of the age,' I told her. 'Right now we're going to use it to loosen up this duct tape.'

I wasn't certain it would work, although I had used it to clean up duct tape residue on cars. But as the oil worked into the edge of the tape I was able to peel it slowly off her skin. When enough of the tape was loose, I slid Zee's dagger against the tape and cut through it close to her ear. I wasn't worried about freeing her hair just now – I only needed to get it off her face.

It came up as nicely as any of the stuff I'd peeled off cars. It didn't take very long before her mouth was free, and I sliced the remaining tape so that all she had was a strip stuck in her hair.

'That tastes terrible,' she said hoarsely, wiping her mouth with the bottom of her shirt.

'I don't like it either,' I agreed, having gotten the oil in my mouth a time or two when I forgot I had it on my hands. 'How long since you had something to drink?'

'When they brought Dad in,' she whispered to her knees. 'When I talked, he kept rousing from whatever they keep injecting him with, so they gagged me. I thought were-wolves were impervious to drugs.'

'Not this drug,' I told her as I went back to my pack and pulled out the thermos of coffee. 'Though I don't think it's working as well as they want.

'I should have thought to bring water,' I told her, holding a thermos cup filled with the noxious-smelling black stuff near her face. I know that most people like the smell, but for some reason I can't stand it.

When she didn't move I snapped, 'Come on now, you don't have time to wallow. Tonight, when you're home, you can go catatonic if you want to. You need to help me get your father up and running.'

I felt like I was beating a whimpering dog, but she sat up and took the small metal cup in a trembling hand. I'd been expecting that, and only filled the cup halfway. She grimaced at the taste.

'Drink it,' I told her. 'It's good for what ails you. Caffeine and sugar. *I* don't drink it, so I ran over to your house and stole the expensive stuff in your freezer. It shouldn't be that bad. Samuel told me to make it strong and pour sugar into it. Should taste sort of like bitter syrup.'

She gave me a small smile, then a bigger one, and plugged her nose before she drank it all down in one gulp. 'Next time,' she said in a hoarse voice, 'I make the coffee.'

I grinned at her. 'That's it.'

'Is there any way to get the handcuffs off?' she asked.

'We've got a conspirator coming in a couple of hours,' I told her. 'He'll have keys.'

'Okay,' she said, but her mouth trembled. 'But maybe you could try to pick them. These aren't the good ones, like cops have, but more like the ones you find at BDSM stores.'

'Jessica Tamarind Hauptman,' I said in a shocked voice. 'How would you know about that?'

She gave me a watery giggle. 'One of my friends has a pair he got at a garage sale. He locked himself in and couldn't find a key. He was pretty panicked until his mom picked the lock.'

I took a good look at the keyhole. It looked suspiciously clumsy to me. I didn't have any handy bobby pins or wire hangers, but Zee's dagger had a narrow point.

I took one of the cuffs and tried to insert the narrow end of the dagger. First I thought it wasn't going to fit, but with a little pressure it slid in just fine.

'Ow.' Jesse jerked her arms.

I pulled the dagger back and looked at the scratch on her wrist. Then I looked at the cuff where the dagger had slid through the metal almost as easily as it had the rope.

'Metal mage indeed,' I murmured.

'What kind of a knife *is* that?' Jesse asked.

'A dagger. A borrowed one.' I set it against the chain between the cuffs and watched the chain melt away from the edge of the dark gray blade. 'Hmm. I suppose I'm going to ask more questions next time I borrow something from a fae.'

'Can it cut all the way through the cuffs?' Jess held up the damaged one, which was already half sliced through.

I held it away from her bruised skin and cautiously slid the dagger between her wrist and the cuff. It looked like some bad special effect as the metal parted from the blade.

A filmmaker would have added sparks or a bright red glow – all I could detect was a faint whiff of ozone.

'Who did you borrow it from?' she asked, as I cut through the second cuff. 'Zee?' I saw his status rise from crusty old friend to intriguing mystery. 'How cool.' She sounded almost like herself, and it was a painful contrast to the purpling bruise down one side of her face and the marks around her wrists.

I didn't remember seeing the bruise on her face before the werewolf took her downstairs.

'Did he hit you just now?' I asked, touching her cheek and remembering the sight of the guard carrying her while she tried to be as small as possible.

She withdrew, the smile dying and her eyes growing dull. 'I don't want to think about him.'

'All right,' I agreed easily. 'You don't need to worry about him anymore.'

I'd see to it myself if I had to. The veil of civilization fell away from me rather easily, I thought, taking the empty cup and twisting it back on the thermos. All it had taken was the sight of that bruise, and I was ready to do murder.

'You really ought to have more of this,' I told her. 'But I need the caffeine for your father. Maybe Shawn will bring something with him when he comes.'

'Shawn?'

I explained about David Christiansen and the help they had promised in getting us all out in one piece.

'You trust them?' she asked, and when I nodded, she said, 'Okay.'

'Let's go take a look at your father.'

Once I'd freed Jesse, there was little benefit to leaving Adam in chains, and all that silver couldn't be helping him any. I brought Zee's dagger up to bear, but Jesse caught my hand.

'Mercy?' she said in a small voice. 'When he starts coming out of it, he's . . .'

'Pretty scary?' I patted her hand. I'd thought a time or two that her experience with werewolves had led her to think of them like pets, rather than dangerous predators. It looked as though that wasn't going to be a problem. I remember David saying that Adam had gone crazy when he'd come into the room, and I remembered the ruins of Adam's living room. Maybe the veil had been ripped from her eyes a little too thoroughly.

'What did you expect when he's helpless in the hands of his enemies?' I said reasonably. 'He's trying to defend you as best he can. It takes a tremendous amount of will to overcome the stuff they've been pumping into him. You can't expect the results to be pretty.'

I had been going to start with one of the chains, but Jesse's concerns made me realize that I was a little worried about completely freeing Adam, too. That would never do. Not if I was going to get him up and mobile. If I was afraid of him, it would rouse the predator.

Resolutely, I pressed the knife against the heavy manacle that held his left wrist. I had to be careful because the manacles fit his wrists tighter than the cuffs had fit Jesse. There was not enough space between his skin and the metal to slide the dagger in without cutting him. Remembering how the blade had reacted to cutting Samuel, I thought that might be a bad thing. So I let the knife rest on the metal without adding any force so I could pull it away as soon as it was through.

At first I thought it was the heat of my hands warming the haft, but as the blade broke through the manacle, I had to drop it because it had grown too hot to hold. Adam's hand slid off the chair arm to rest in his lap.

It took almost an hour to cut away the rest of the manacles

and chains. Each time the knife heated up, it did so more quickly and took longer to cool off. There were scorch marks on the linoleum floor and a few blisters on my hand by the time Adam was finally free of the silver chains.

Jesse helped me to gather all the chains together and heap them on the bed. We had to be careful not to drag them on the floor because the sound of metal on hard surfaces tends to carry.

We were just dropping the last of it when I heard the sound of the guard's footstep on the stair. I dropped Zee's dagger on the bed with the silver, pushed Jesse toward the closet, and drew my gun. I aimed it about six feet up the door, and froze, waiting for the bolt to turn on the lock.

He whistled as he inserted the key and I steadied my grip. I planned on hitting him in the middle of his chest first, then two shots into his head. If he wasn't dead after that, he'd be incapacitated so I could finish him off. It would rouse everyone, but I had no options: I had neither time nor inclination to rebind the prisoners.

As I drew in a breath I heard a man's voice, distorted by the door and by distance so I couldn't quite make out what he said. But I heard the man outside our door. If I had to kill someone, I was happy it would be the one who'd hit Jesse.

'Checking on the prisoners,' he said. 'It's about time to shoot Hauptman again.'

The second man said something else.

'I don't need orders to watch the clock,' he said. 'Hauptman needs more of the drug. He's not going to kick the bucket over a little silver. Hang what Wallace says.'

I sucked in my breath as power crept up the stairway. Not Adam's or Samuel's caliber, but power nonetheless, and I guessed that the man talking to our guard was David Christiansen.

The guard growled, but he pulled the key out of the door and tromped down the stairs. I heard the sound of a short, nasty little argument, and when no one came back up the stairs I decided Christiansen had won his point and put my gun away again.

'Well,' I told Jesse as I tried to steady my breathing, 'wasn't that fun.'

She'd curled up in the bottom of the closet. For a moment I thought she was going to stay there – but she was tougher than that. She gathered her courage and got to her feet.

'Now what?'

I looked at Adam. He hadn't moved.

I crossed the room and put my hand against his face. His skin was cool to my touch, which was bad. Because of their high metabolisms, werewolves usually feel warmer to the touch. I wondered how much of that silver they'd pumped into his system.

'I need to get some of that coffee into him,' I told Jesse. 'And I have some food, too – which should help.'

She stood by me and looked at him, then looked at me. 'Okay,' she said finally, 'I give. How are we going to get him to drink coffee?'

In the end, we dragged him out of the chair and propped his head up against Jesse's thigh. We dribbled the coffee, which was still hot, into his mouth. Neither of us could figure out how to make him swallow, but after a few dribbles, he did it on his own.

After the third swallow, he opened his eyes, and they were night-dark velvet. He reached up and grasped Jesse's hand where it lay on his shoulder, but his eyes were on me.

'Mercy,' he mumbled. 'What the *hell* did you do to my French Roast?'

I had a moment to believe all my worries had been for nothing when he dropped Jesse's hand and his spine curled backward, throwing his head farther into her lap. His skin went gray, then mottled, as his hands clenched. His eyes rolled back until all I could see were the whites.

I dropped the coffee and grabbed Jesse under the shoulders and dragged her away from Adam as far and as fast as I could.

'He'll hit his head,' she said, beginning to struggle as she realized, as I had, that he was having a seizure.

'He'll heal a cracked skull, but you can't,' I told her. 'Jesse, he's a werewolf – you can't go anywhere near him when he's like this. If he hits you, he'll break bones.' I thanked the dear Lord sincerely that he'd let go of Jesse's hand before he crushed it.

As if it had been awakened by the same demons that were causing his convulsions, I felt the sweep of power arise from him – as would any other werewolves in the area. Which, if Christiansen's figures were accurate, numbered twelve.

'Can you shoot?' I asked her.

'Yes.' Jesse didn't look away from her father.

I pulled the SIG out and handed it to her.

'Point this at the door,' I said, digging to the bottom of the pack for the .44. 'If I tell you to shoot, pull the trigger. The first pull will be a little stiff. It's loaded for werewolf. We have allies here, so wait until I tell you to shoot.'

I found the revolver. There was no time to check it, but I'd loaded it before I put it in the pack. That would have to do. The Smith & Wesson was a lot heavier than the SIG, and it could do a lot more damage.

'What's wrong?' Jesse whispered, and I remembered she was human and couldn't feel the song of the Alpha's strength.

The music grew, abruptly doubling, and the focus faded until I couldn't tell that it was coming from Adam anymore. Light feet ran up the stairs and the bolt turned on the door.

Jesse was still looking at me, but I had my revolver up and aimed as the door opened.

'Don't fire,' I said, raising my gun and putting my hand on top of hers so that the automatic's nose stayed on the ground. 'He's one of ours.'

The man who stood in front of the door had skin the color of hot chocolate, a green T-shirt that said DRAGONS KILLED THE DINOSAURS, and hazel eyes. It was the shirt that told me he was David's man. He was standing very still, giving us time to decide he was on our side.

'I'm Shawn,' he said, then he saw Adam.

'Damn,' he said, stepping into the room and shutting the door quietly. 'What's going on?' he asked, his eyes on Adam, who was flat on his back, his arms and legs doing a strange, jerky sort of dance.

'I think he's changing,' Jesse answered.

'Convulsions,' I said. 'I'm no doctor, but I think that too much of the silver has worked its way into his nervous system and damaged something important.'

'Will he be okay?' Jesse's voice shook.

'He's tough,' I told her, hoping she wouldn't notice I hadn't answered the question. How much silver did it take to kill a werewolf? Usually it was a function of power – but there were some werewolves who were more sensitive to it than others.

'I was switching guard duty with Hamilton when the captain picked a fight with Connor and gave me the high sign to get my ass up here,' Shawn said. 'I hadn't taken three steps when every werewolf on the place was converging on the captain. I take it that something about this fit called them all?'

I nodded and explained to both of them as best I could. 'I don't know how Christiansen is doing it,' I told him, 'but he's pulling Adam's power and muddying it. I bet everyone will think it's him.'

'Because of the fight,' Shawn said in an 'ah-hah' voice.

But I'd lost interest in how quick off the mark Christiansen had been, because Adam quieted and lay limp. Jesse would have gone to him then, but I held her back.

'Wait,' I said, using the opportunity to take the automatic back from her so that she didn't fire it by accident. 'Make sure he's finished.'

'He's not dead?' she asked.

'No. I can hear him breathing.' It was faint and shallow, but steady.

I stowed the Smith & Wesson on the top layer in my pack and put the SIG back in its holster. Thanks to Christiansen we weren't going to have a pack of wolves converging on us – but that might change at any time.

Adam hadn't moved, but his breathing grew deeper. I started to tell Jesse that it was all right, when Adam abruptly rolled on his side and jerked into a fetal position with a low groan.

# 15

'*Now* is he shifting?' asked Jesse.

'That would be bad,' said Shawn. 'We don't want him changing until he's kicked off the effects of the drugs. I talked to some of the men who were in your house when he broke free. He was tranqued up then, too.'

'Stop scaring her,' I snapped. 'He'll be all right. Besides, I don't think he's changing.' Actually, that werewolfy feeling of power had died to nothing. I had no idea what he was doing.

The dress shirt Adam wore, dirty, torn, and stained with drops of blood, looked more gray than white. A lot more gray. He'd broken out into a sweat, and the fabric began to cling to him, outlining the taut muscles of his shoulders and back. I could even see the bumps of his spine. The shirt shimmered a little under the cold fluorescent lights as he shivered miserably. I couldn't tell if he was conscious or not.

I holstered the revolver and walked slowly toward him.

'Adam,' I said, because he had his back to me. It is never a good thing to startle a werewolf. 'Are you all right?'

Unsurprisingly, he didn't answer.

I crouched and touched the wet fabric, and he grabbed my wrist – his movement so fast that he was just suddenly there, on his back. I don't remember seeing him roll over. His eyes were yellow and cold, but his grip was light.

'You're safe,' I told him, trying to stay calm. 'Jesse's here, and she's safe, too. We're going to get you on your feet in fighting shape, then we're getting out of here.'

'It's the silver,' said Shawn, awed. 'That's why the shirt

is turning gray. Fu— I mean, damn. *Damn*. He's sweating silver. Damn.'

Adam didn't look away from me, though he flinched subtly at the sound of Shawn's voice. His blazing gold eyes held mine, somehow hot and icy at the same time. I should have looked away – but it didn't seem like a dominance contest. It felt like he was using my eyes to pull himself up from wherever the drugs had forced him. I tried not to blink and break the spell.

'Mercy?' His voice was a hoarse whisper.

'*C'est moi, c'est moi*, 'tis I,' I told him. It seemed appropriately melodramatic, though I didn't know if he'd catch the reference. I shouldn't have worried.

Unexpectedly, he laughed. 'Trust you to quote Lancelot rather than Guinevere.'

'Both of them were stupid,' I told him. 'Arthur should have let them marry each other as punishment and gone off to live happily on his own. I only like *Camelot* for the music.' I hummed a bit.

The mundane talk was working. His pulse was less frantic, and he was taking deep, even breaths. When his eyes went back to normal we'd be out of trouble. Except, of course, for the small matter of a warehouse full of enemies. One trouble at a time, I always say.

He closed his yellow eyes, and momentarily I felt cut adrift and abandoned until I realized he was still holding my wrist as if he were afraid I'd leave if he let go.

'I have the mother of all headaches,' he said, 'and I feel like I've been flattened by a steamroller. Jesse's safe?'

'I'm fine, Dad,' she said, though she obeyed the urgent signal I made with my free hand and stayed where she was. He might have sounded calm, but his scent and the compulsive way he was holding on to my wrist contradicted his apparent control.

'Bruised and scared,' I said. 'But otherwise unhurt.' I realized that I actually didn't know that and gave Jesse a worried glance.

She smiled, a wan imitation of her usual expression. 'Fine,' she said again, this time to me.

His sigh held relief. 'Tell me what's been going on.'

I gave him a short version – it still took a while to tell. Except for when I told him about David Christiansen's invasion of my home, he kept his eyes shut as if it hurt him to open them. Before I finished he was twisting uncomfortably.

'My skin is crawling,' he said.

'It's the silver that's bothering you.' I should have thought of that earlier. Touching his shirt with my free hand, I showed him the gray metal on my index finger. 'I've heard of sweating bullets before, but never silver.' I started to help him remove his shirt when I realized he couldn't run around naked with Jesse here. 'I don't suppose you have any extra clothes, Shawn? If that silver stays against his skin it'll burn him.'

'He can have my shirt,' he said. 'But I can't leave to get clothes; I'm on guard duty.'

I sighed. 'He can have my sweatpants.' The T-shirt I was wearing hit me halfway down my thighs.

Shawn and I stripped Adam as quickly as we could, using the shirt to wipe most of the silver off his skin before covering him in my sweats and Shawn's green T-shirt. Adam was shivering when we finished.

The thermos cup had dumped its sticky contents all over the floor when I dropped it, but both it and the thermos had survived. I had Jesse pour hot coffee down her father as fast as he'd drink it, and, with something to focus on, she steadied. When the coffee was done, she fed him the raw roast from the Ziploc bags without turning a hair.

I was worried because Adam was so passive, not a state I'd ever seen him in before. Samuel had said prolonged exposure to silver increased sensitivity. I thought about Adam's headache and the seizures and hoped lycanthropy was enough to allow him to heal.

'You know,' said Shawn thoughtfully, 'for someone who wants this one to fight the head wolf in a month, Gerry's not taking very good care of him.'

I was frowning at him when I heard the door open.

'Hey, Morris,' said the stranger as he opened the door, 'the boss wants to see you and—' His eyes traveled to Adam and Jesse and he stopped speaking and went for his gun.

If I had been alone, we'd have all been dead. I didn't even think to pull my weapon, just stared in shock, belatedly realizing that Shawn hadn't bolted the door when he'd come in. Shawn's gun popped quietly three times in rapid succession, putting a neat triangle of red over the intruder's heart, making little more noise than someone opening a can of pop. He was shooting a small-caliber automatic with a silencer.

The wounded man fell slowly to his knees, then forward onto his face. I pulled my SIG at last and took aim.

'No,' Adam said. 'Wait.' He looked at his daughter. 'You told me you weren't hurt – is that true?'

Jesse nodded resolutely. 'Just bruises.'

'All right, then,' he said. 'Mercy, we're going to try to leave as many alive as possible – dead men tell no tales, and I want to know exactly what's been going on. We'll be gone before this man heals enough to be a danger. Leave him be.'

'He's not dead?' asked Shawn. 'The captain says you can kill werewolves with lead.'

Not being in the habit of taking on werewolves, Christiansen's men hadn't had silver ammunition, and my supply was limited. Silver bullets are expensive, and I don't go out hunting werewolves on a regular basis. Only Connor had had a gun that could use any caliber I had anyway. I'd given him a half dozen of my 9mm bullets.

'You have to take out the spinal column if you want to kill a werewolf without silver,' I told him. 'And even then . . .' I shrugged. 'Silver ammo makes wounds that don't heal as fast, gives them a chance to bleed out.'

'Damn,' Shawn said, with a last look at the bleeding werewolf he'd shot. He took out a cell phone and dialed in several numbers.

'That'll let everyone know we're on the move,' he told me when he'd finished, tucking the small device back into his pants pocket. 'We've got to get out of here now. With any luck they'll assume someone's out on the range and won't pay attention to my shots. But someone's going to miss Smitty, and we need to be out of here when they do.' Then he got down to business and organized our retreat.

I put the SIG back in its holster and took out the .44 magnum. I didn't have a holster for it so I'd just have to carry it. I shoved the extra magazine for the SIG into my bra because I didn't have any better place to store it.

We dragged the wounded werewolf out of the doorway, then Shawn and Jesse got Adam to his feet. Shawn because he was the strongest of us, Jesse because I knew how to shoot a gun. I went out the door first.

This part of the warehouse was set apart from the main room. The offices had been set into a section half the width of the building, and below me was a bare strip of cement wide enough for two trucks to drive side by side. Leaning over the railing to check beneath the stairway, I could tell that there was no one nearby, but I couldn't see very well into the rest of the building because of the racks of giant crates.

As soon as the others were out of the room and onto the landing, I ran down ahead of them to the second-floor landing, where I could guard their descent. Shawn's plan was that we were going to try to get Adam to the cars. One of Gerry's men drove a classic Chevy truck that Shawn said he could hot-wire faster than he could put a key in the ignition.

I tried to control my breathing so I could listen, but the warehouse was silent except for my comrades coming down the stairs and the ringing in my ears that could have obscured the movements of an army.

There was a garage door right next to the offices, the kind that is double-wide and double-high so a semi can drive through it. Shawn told me it was kept padlocked from the outside, and Gerry had shot the motor that opened it when he'd decided to keep Jesse in one of the offices here where he could control who had access to her. We'd have to make our way back toward the other side of the warehouse and go out a person-sized door, which was the only one unlocked.

As I waited at the bottom of the stairs, trying to see into the warehouse past the impossible maze of crates that could conceal a dozen werewolves with a host of hiding places to spare, I thought about what Shawn had said at last. He was right. If Gerry wanted Adam to kill Bran, he'd need him in a lot better shape. It wouldn't take Bran more than a few seconds to kill Adam in his present condition.

Gerry wasn't stupid, Samuel had told me. So maybe that was the result he intended.

It occurred to me that there were an awful lot of things that didn't make sense if Gerry wasn't stupid – and Samuel was a pretty good judge of character. David seemed to think that the bloodbath at Adam's house had served to rid Gerry of some unwanted competition – but it had also drawn the Marrok's attention. And it would have drawn Bran's eye, even if I hadn't taken Adam to him. An attack at an Alpha's home was important. Then there was that payment to the vampires. I might have found out about it sooner than expected, but if Bran had come sniffing around, I was pretty sure he'd've discovered it, too.

If I were trying to get someone to challenge for Marrok, I wouldn't make my candidate hate me by kidnapping his daughter. If I were going to use underhanded methods to force a challenge I wasn't certain my candidate would win, I would make sure to cover my tracks so Bran would never find out – and Bran had a deserved reputation for finding out everything.

Gerry had all but painted a billboard that said, 'Look at what I'm doing!' and, if he wasn't stupid, he'd done it on purpose. Why?

'Mercy.' Shawn's whisper jerked me back to the present. They were down the stairs, and I was blocking their way.

'Sorry,' I said in the same soundless whisper.

I took point, walking a few steps ahead and looking around the crates as we passed. It was slow going. Adam was having problems with the leg he'd damaged in the first attack, and Jesse was too short to be a good crutch when paired with Shawn, who was nearly six feet tall.

I'd heard something, or thought I had, and I stopped. But when the sound didn't repeat, I decided it was still the ringing in my ears, which was coming and going a little. I hadn't taken but three steps when power ran through me like a warm, sweet wind.

'The pack's here,' said Adam.

I'd never felt them like that before, though I suppose I'd never been in a situation where they were all coming together with one purpose. That might have been all it was, or it might have been because I was standing so close to the pack's Alpha.

Adam stopped and closed his eyes, breathing in deeply. I could almost see the strength pouring into him, and he straightened, taking all of his own weight.

Jesse was watching her father, too. Only Shawn kept his mind and his eyes on the job, and it was the widening of his eyes that had me spinning back around.

If the werewolf had been after me, I'd have been dead. But he had picked out the most dangerous of us and brushed by me like a cannonball, knocking me into a crate. The Smith & Wesson flew out of my hand, but didn't go off when it hit the ground. I heard my upper arm crack and felt a wash of pain as the force of his passing continued to spin me until I landed on the floor facing Adam as the wolf jumped on him.

Jesse screamed. Shawn had emptied his gun without slowing down the wolf. He drew a wicked-looking knife and closed in to use it, but the werewolf caught him with one of those quick catlike sideswipes that no canid should have the lateral motion to do. Like me, Shawn hit a crate and collapsed on the floor.

I struggled to my feet and took out Zee's dagger with my left hand. I don't know why I didn't draw my SIG except that the shocking speed of the attack had left me dazed. This week aside, I usually kept the violence in my life controlled and confined to a dojo.

I started forward, and something red rushed past me in a blur of motion. Another werewolf. I had time to believe that we were out of luck, when it grabbed the first wolf by the scruff of the neck and tossed it back down the aisle, away from Adam.

The red wolf didn't pause there, but was on the gray-and-tan animal almost before it landed. Adam was covered in blood, but before I made it to him, the wounds closed in a rush of power that was pack-scented. He rolled to his feet, looking better than I'd seen him since Monday night.

I, rather belatedly, remembered I had another gun, and dropped Zee's knife so I could draw the SIG, waiting for the two wolves to separate enough that I could shoot. With a little perspective I could see that the red animal was taller and leaner than usual, as if he'd been bred for running rather than fighting.

'I don't want them dead if I can help it,' Adam said, though he didn't try to take the gun from me.

'This one needs to die,' I said, because I'd recognized his scent. He was the one who had slapped Jesse's face.

Adam didn't have the chance to argue with me because the gray-and-tan wolf came out on top of the wrestling match and I pulled the trigger three times. It wasn't the .44, but even a 9mm does a lot of damage when it hits the back of a skull at under fifteen feet.

Adam was saying something. I could see his mouth move, but my abused ears were roaring with a sound as big as the seashore. One of the downsides of good hearing is sensitive ears – something the wolves, with their healing abilities, don't have to worry about much.

He must have realized I was having trouble hearing him because he tapped my gun and raised an eyebrow, asking me a question. I looked at the crumpled werewolf, then at Jesse. Adam followed my gaze, and his face grew cold and hard. When he held out his hand, I gave him the SIG.

He stalked to the werewolves, no trace of a limp in his stride. He reached down and grabbed the dead wolf with one hand and hauled him off the other one, who rolled to his feet then stood still, head down, looking dazed. Adam cupped a hand under the red wolf's jaw, checking for damage. Apparently satisfied, he turned to the defeated opponent and emptied the gun into the body.

I saw him snap his fingers, and the red wolf shook his whole body as if he'd just come out of a swimming pool, then came to sit at Adam's heel, just like a well-trained dog. Jesse picked up the dagger and sheathed it for me as Shawn got slowly to his feet. He put a fresh magazine in his gun, then put a hand on my broken arm.

I must have made a noise, but the next thing I remember is being on my knees with my head low and a big, warm hand on the back of my neck. Adam's scent, rich and exotic, was all around me, giving me the strength to calm my queasy stomach. I don't think I lost consciousness completely, but it was a near thing.

When I lifted my head, the red wolf stuck his nose in my face and ran a long tongue over my cheek before Adam cuffed him lightly. I got to my feet with Adam's help, but stood on my own.

Adam reloaded the automatic when I handed him a fresh clip — though he grinned when I took it out of my bra. I think I was glad I couldn't hear well enough to decipher what he said. He put the SIG in my holster, picked up my revolver, and handed it to me. Then he turned his attention to Shawn, who waved away Adam's concern.

The werewolf at our side was more reassuring than the loaded gun I carried as we walked toward the door. It wasn't that he was more effective than the .44, but his presence meant that the pack was near. All we had to do was join them, and we were safe.

I glanced at Adam. He looked healthy, as if he'd never been hurt. I'd heard that the Alpha could take strength from his pack; but I didn't know why it had worked here, when it hadn't had the same effect at Warren's house.

Shawn went through the door first, the red wolf at his heels. It was night, and the waxing moon was high in the sky. Adam held the door open for Jesse and me, then walked out into the field of parked cars like a man walking into his own living room.

At first I could see no one, but then a shadowy form emerged from behind a car, then another one, and another. Silently Adam's pack formed around him. Most of them were in wolf form, but Warren and then Darryl came as humans. They wore dark clothing and both of them were armed.

Warren looked at the red wolf, our rescuer, and raised an eyebrow, but he didn't break the silence. He examined Adam and then touched Jesse's bruised cheek.

'Warren.' Adam spoke in a soft voice that wouldn't carry far. 'Would you take my daughter and Mercedes to safety, please?'

Another time I would have argued with Adam. After all, who had rescued whom? But my arm was throbbing brutally and I'd done my killing for the day. The only good thing was that my ears had quit ringing. Let Adam and his people finish this, I was ready to go home.

'I don't want to leave you,' said Jesse, taking a firm grip on her father's borrowed T-shirt.

'I'll take her to my house,' Warren said, with a reassuring smile at Jesse. 'You can stop and pick her up on the way home.' In a softer voice, he said, 'I'll stay with you until he comes. You'll be safe with me.'

'All right.' Jesse nodded in a quick, jerky motion. I think she'd just figured out that her father wanted her out of the way before he dealt with the people who'd kidnapped her.

'I don't have a car here, though,' Warren told Adam. 'We ran about three miles as the crow flies to get here.'

'Shawn?' I said, trying to keep my voice as quiet as everyone else's had been. 'You told me that there was an old truck around here somewhere that was easy to hot-wire? If you can tell me where to look for it, I can hot-wire it so Warren can get us out of here.'

'On the far side of the warehouse, away from everyone else's cars,' he said.

I started off alone, but Warren and Jesse were soon on my heels. The truck was the only car on the far side of the warehouse. Parked in the center of the pale illumination of one of the warehouse's exterior lights, was a '69 Chevy, painted some dark color that glittered. Someone was going to be very unhappy to see his toy missing – if he survived Adam's wrath.

But that wasn't my problem. My problem was how to hot-wire a car when my right arm was broken. I'd been keeping it tucked against my side, but that wasn't going to be enough for much longer. The pain was steadily getting worse and making me light-headed.

'Do you know how to hot-wire a car?' I asked Warren hopefully, as we approached the truck.

'I'm afraid not.'

'How about you, Jesse?'

She looked up. 'What?'

'Do you know how to hot-wire a car?' I asked again, and she shook her head. She smelled of fear, and I thought of how she had clung to her father.

'That guard tonight,' I said.

She looked puzzled for a minute, then flushed and hunched her shoulders.

'He's not going to bother anyone ever again.'

'He was the dead werewolf?' I couldn't read the expression on her face. 'That's why you killed him?' She frowned suddenly. 'That's why Dad shot him like that. How did he know? He was unconscious – and you didn't say anything to him.'

'I didn't need to,' I answered, and tried to explain that moment of perfect understanding, where a gesture had told Adam everything he needed to know. 'He saw it in my face, I suppose.' I turned to Warren and handed him the .44 so I could do my best with the truck.

Hot-wiring the truck with one hand took me longer than the keys would have, and the awkward position I had to take in order to strip the housing off the steering wheel and touch wires had me bumping my injured arm. But the engine roared to life at last – something bigger than the original power-house rumbled underneath its hood – and I realized my hearing had cleared up completely.

'I've never heard you swear before,' said Jesse, sounding a little better. 'At least not like that.'

'Power words. Without which mechanics the world over would be lost.' Warren's tone was light, but his hands were gentle as they helped me extract myself from the cab. He handed me my gun and, when I fumbled, took it back and made sure it was at half-cock before he handed it to me again.

He opened the passenger door and helped Jesse inside and then held his hand out to me. I took a step toward him, then something attracted my attention.

At first I thought it was a sound, but that was only because I was tired. It was magic. It wasn't wolf magic or fae magic.

And I remembered Elizaveta.

Samuel knew about her, I told myself. But I knew that I couldn't leave. None of the werewolves could feel her magic, not until it was too late, and Samuel might not know how important it was that Adam know that Elizaveta was working with Gerry.

Elizaveta Arkadyevna Vyshnevetskaya was not just any witch. She was the most powerful witch in the Pacific Northwest.

I had to warn Adam.

'Get Jesse to your house,' I told him. 'Feed her, make her drink gallons of orange juice, cover her with a blanket. But I have to stay.'

'Why?'

'Because if Bran brings the wolves out in the open, Adam's witch on retainer loses her income.'

'Elizaveta?'

284

A gun went off, echoed by a second and third crack.

'Get Jesse out of here, I have to warn Adam. Elizaveta's here and she's working on some sort of spell.'

He gave me a grim look. 'How do I turn off the truck?' Bless him. He wasn't going to argue.

'Just pull the wires apart.'

There was gunfire from the other side of the warehouse, four shots. They sounded like they were coming from somewhere near the boarded-up house.

'Be careful,' I told him. He kissed me on the forehead without touching my poor sore body, then hopped in the cab.

I watched him back out, turn on the lights, and drive away. Jesse was safe.

I've always been able to sense magic of all kinds, be it werewolf, witch, or fae – and I know that isn't usual. Charles, when he found out, told me to keep it secret – in light of the vampire's reaction to finding out what I was, I could see that there was more to Charles's advice than I'd thought.

From what Stefan had told me, I was somewhat immune to the vampire's magic, but I wasn't such a fool as to assume the same was true of witchcraft. Once I found her I had no idea what I was going to do with her – but I try not to worry about one impossible task until I've completed the first.

Turning in a slow circle gave me a direction. The pulse of magic felt like a warm wind in my face. I took two steps toward it . . . and the spell drifted away into nothing. All I knew for sure was that Elizaveta was here, and she was somewhere in front of me. The best thing to do was to find Adam and warn him, so I walked back around the warehouse.

Things had changed since I left. Adam, the red wolf still sitting at his feet, had only a handful of wolves with him. Shawn, David's grandsons, and a couple of other humans I didn't know, held guns on a group of men who were stretched out on the ground in a spread eagle.

As I approached them, David and Darryl escorted another man out and sent him sprawling by the other men.

'That's all the humans, Sarge,' David said. 'We left a couple dead in the house. But the wolves have scattered, and I couldn't pick up Gerry's trail, though, not even when I started from the last place I saw him. His scent just fades away.'

'Adam,' I said.

He turned to look at me and the red wolf suddenly leaped into the air as a shot rang out. It wasn't a particularly loud shot; it sounded like a small caliber.

'Get down!' barked David as he dropped to the ground. His men crouched, still holding their guns on their prisoners.

The wolf beside Adam stood for just a moment longer, then collapsed, as if it had listened to David as well – but I could see the dart dangling on his side and knew he'd been hit by one of the tranquilizer guns.

Adam didn't drop. Instead he closed his eyes and canted his face upward. For a moment I wondered what he was doing, then I realized the light on his face came from the moon, which rose above us almost exactly half-full.

Darryl, low to the ground, surged over the distance between Adam and him. He stopped beside the downed wolf, jerked the dart out.

'Ben's okay,' Darryl said, raising his gun so he'd be ready to shoot as he scanned the darkness surrounding us.

Ben was the red wolf. It had been Ben, the psycho-killer from London, who had saved us. Saved Adam twice.

Another shot fired. Adam moved his hand and the dart fell to the ground to roll harmlessly against his feet. His eyes were still closed.

'Sarge, Mercy,' hissed David. 'Get down!'

I realized then that I was still standing, too, leaning a little toward Adam as he called down the moon. I might have knelt then, if only because David told me to, but Adam threw back his head and howled, a wolf's song rising from his human throat.

For a moment the eerie sound rose, echoed, and died away into silence, but not an empty silence. More like the deadly quiet that precedes the start of the hunt. When he howled again, he was answered by every werewolf within hearing distance.

I could feel a song surging into my throat, but like my wild brethren, I knew better than to sing with the wolves.

When Adam called a third time, Darryl and David both dropped their weapons and began to change. The moon's call sang through the trees and I could feel it catch the rest of the wolves and force them into their wolf form. I could hear cries of agony from those who fought it and groans from those who didn't.

Adam stood in the moonlight, which seemed somehow brighter than it had been moments ago. He opened his eyes and looked at the moon's face. This time he used words.

'Come,' he said.

He didn't speak loudly, but somehow his voice, like his song, spread through the abandoned tree-farm like a roll of thunder, powerful and unavoidable. And the wolves came.

They came by ones or twos. Some came with joyful dancing steps, others with feet dragging and tails low. Some were still changing, their bodies stretched and hunched unnaturally.

The warehouse door banged open and a man staggered out, one hand clutched to his chest. It was the guard Shawn had shot. Too weak to change, he still answered the power of Adam's call.

I wasn't immune. I took a step forward without watching the ground and stumbled over a stick. I caught my balance, but the jerky move set off the pain in my arm – and the pain cleared my head like a dose of ammonia. I wiped my watering eyes with the back of my wrist and felt the unmistakable surge of witchcraft.

Heedless of Adam's magic and my arm, I started running, because, in the night air, thick with power, I felt the spell gathering death and it bore Adam's name.

I couldn't take the time to find the witch; the spell was already set in motion. All I could do was throw myself in front of the spell, just as Ben had thrown himself in front of the dart.

I don't know why it worked. Someone told me later that it shouldn't have. Once a spell is given a name, it's sort of like a guided missile rather than a laser beam. It should have moved around me and still hit Adam.

It hit me, brushed through me like a stream of feathers, making me shiver and gasp. Then it paused, and, as if it were a river of molten iron and I a magnet, all the magic flowed back into me. It was death-magic and it whispered to me, *Adam Hauptman*.

It held a voice. Not Elizaveta's voice, but it was someone I knew: a man. The witch wasn't Elizaveta at all – it was her grandson Robert.

My knees bowed under the weight of Robert's voice and under the stress of taking upon myself Adam's name so that the magic stopped with me. My lungs felt as if I were breathing fire and I knew that my interference couldn't last for long.

'Sam,' I whispered. And as if my voice had conjured him from thin air he was suddenly in front of me. I'd expected him to be in wolf form like everyone else, but he wasn't.

He cupped my hot face in his hands. 'What's wrong, Mercy?'

'Witch,' I said and I saw comprehension in his eyes.

'Where is she?'

I shook my head and panted. 'Robert. It's Robert.'

'Where?' he asked again.

I thought I was going to tell him I didn't know, but my arm raised up and pointed at the rooftop of the boarded-up house. 'There.'

Samuel was gone.

As if my gesture had somehow done something, the flow of magic increased fivefold. I collapsed completely, pressing my face against the cold dirt in hopes of keeping the fire burning inside of me from consuming my skin. I closed my eyes and I could see Robert, crouched on the roof.

He'd lost something of his handsomeness, his face twisted with effort and his skin mottled with reddish splotches.

'Mercedes.' He breathed my name to his spell and I could feel it change like a bloodhound given a different handkerchief to sniff. 'Mercedes Thompson.'

*Mercedes*, whispered the spell, satisfied. He'd given death my name.

I screamed as pain rushed through me, making the earlier agony from my arm pale in comparison. Even in the consuming fire, though, I heard a song. I realized there was a rhythm to Robert's spell, and I found myself moving with it, humming the tune softly. The music filled my lungs, then my head, banking the fire for a moment while I waited.

And then Samuel stopped the magic for me.

I think I passed out for a little while because suddenly I was in Samuel's arms.

'They're all here, but for one,' he said.

'Yes.' Adam's voice still held the moon's power.

I struggled and Samuel set me down. I still had to lean against him, but I was on my feet. Samuel, Adam, and I were the only ones on our feet.

There couldn't have been as many as it looked like. The Columbia Basin Pack is not that big, and Gerry's pack was much smaller — but all of them were sitting on the ground like a platoon of Sphinxes awaiting Adam's order.

'Two of the lone wolves, older and more dominant, ran when you first called,' Samuel said. 'The rest answered. They're yours now. All you have to do is call Gerry.'

'He won't come,' Adam said. 'He can't leave. That much I can do. But he's not a lone wolf. He belongs to the Marrok.'

'Will you let me help?'

The moon caught Adam's eyes and, although he was still human, his eyes were all wolf. I could smell his reaction to Samuel's question. A low growl rose over the waiting werewolves as they smelled it, too. Wolves are territorial.

Adam stretched his neck and I heard it pop. 'I would appreciate it,' he said mildly.

Samuel reached out his hand and Adam took it. He straightened and lifted his face to the moon once more. 'Gerry Wallace of the Marrok Pack, I call you to come and face your accusers.'

He must have been very close, because it didn't take him long. Like Samuel, he had stayed in human form. He paused at the edge of the wolves.

'Gerry, old friend,' said Samuel. 'It's time. Come here.'

The gentle words didn't hide their power from me — or from Gerry. He dropped to his hands and knees and crawled through the motionless wolves, his head down submissively. He wasn't fighting anymore.

He stopped when he neared us. I thought he'd be angry — as I would have been if someone had forced me against my will. Or maybe frightened. But I'm not a werewolf. The only emotion I could catch was resignation. He'd lost and he knew it.

Adam crouched until he sat on his heels and put his hand on Gerry's shoulder.

'Why?'

'It was my father,' Gerry said. His face was calm and his voice dreamy, firmly held in the moon's call. 'He was dying. Cancer, they said. I talked and talked. I begged and pleaded. Please, Papa, being a wolf is a wonderful thing. I think he was just tired of me when he agreed. Bran did it – because I couldn't bear it. And at first it was perfect. The cancer went away, and he could run.'

'I heard,' Adam said. 'He couldn't control the wolf.'

'Wouldn't.' It was eerie hearing that peaceful tone while tears slid down Gerry's face. 'Wouldn't. He had been a vegetarian, and suddenly he craved raw meat. He tried to set a bird's wing, and it died of fear of the thing he'd become. Bran said being a werewolf was breaking my father's heart. He couldn't – wouldn't – embrace what he was because he didn't want to be a predator. He didn't want to be like me.'

Adam frowned at him. 'I thought you were trying to keep Bran from exposing us to the humans.'

Gerry wiped his face. 'Bran said if my father was not so dominant, he would not have been able to resist the wolf. But the more he resists, the less control he has. He almost killed my sister.'

'Gerry.' Samuel's voice was firm. 'What does this have to do with Adam?'

Gerry lifted his head. He couldn't meet Samuel's eyes, or Adam's, so he looked at me. 'When you fight,' he said, 'the wolf and the man become one. It would only take once. Just once and my father would be whole.'

'He didn't want Adam to fight Bran,' I said suddenly. 'Did you, Gerry? That's why you weren't concerned with all the silver your men were pumping into him. Did you want to kill him?'

He looked at me with his father's eyes and said, 'Adam had to die.'

'You don't care about Bran's decision to expose the were-wolves, do you?' asked Samuel.

Gerry smiled at him. 'I've been arguing for it ever since the fae came out. But I needed money to set my plan up, and there are a lot of wolves who don't want to come out in public view – and they were willing to pay for it.'

It was suddenly clear. And Samuel was right. Gerry wasn't stupid: he was brilliant.

'Buying new werewolves from Leo in Chicago, the drug experiments, the attack on Adam's house; they were all intended to do two things,' I said. 'To show Bran that you were behind them all, and to prove to your father that you weren't.'

He nodded.

'Adam had to die,' I said, feeling my way. 'But you couldn't kill him. That's why you left him to the mercies of your werewolves when he was still drugged. That's why you stayed away from the warehouse, hoping that your men would pump enough silver into Adam to kill him.'

'Yes. He had to die and not by my hand. I had to be able to look my father in the eye and tell him that I hadn't killed Adam.'

I was shivering because it was cold and my arm, which had been surprisingly quiet for the past few minutes, began to hurt again. 'It wasn't Adam you wanted to fight Bran, it was your father. You were counting on Bran going to your father as soon as he figured out what you were doing.'

'My father called me this afternoon,' Gerry said. 'Bran had asked him about the tranquilizer and told him that I might be behind the attacks on Adam. My father knows I want the wolves to quit hiding. He knows how I feel about animal experimentation and the way some Alphas exploit some of our new wolves. He knows I'd never try to kill Adam.'

'If Adam died, my father would tell yours before he came here to kill you,' Samuel said.

Gerry laughed. 'I don't think so. I think Bran would have come here and killed me for my crimes. I hoped he would. I have killed too many innocents. But when he told my father what I had done, my father wouldn't believe him.'

'Believing the Marrok had you executed for something you didn't do, Carter would challenge him.' Samuel sounded almost admiring. 'And my father couldn't refuse the challenge.'

'What if Bran talked to Dr Wallace first?' I asked.

'It wouldn't have mattered.' Gerry sounded certain. 'Either to protect me or avenge me, my father would challenge Bran. Even before he was wolf, my father was the Marrok's man. He respects him and trusts him. Bran's betrayal, and Dad would see it like that, could have only one answer. Only Bran could unite my father, wolf and man, against him – Dad loves him. If Dad and his wolf face Bran in a fight, they will do it as one being: Bran told me that it would only take that one time for my father to be safe.'

'If Dr Wallace challenged Bran, Bran would kill him,' said Adam.

'Witches are expensive,' whispered Gerry. 'But there are a lot of wolves who want to hide and they gave me money so they could keep their secrets.'

'You were paying Robert, Elizaveta's son. He'd do something to ensure your father's victory.' I'd thought Robert was doing it for money. I just hadn't realized he would be getting it so directly.

'They'd be looking for drugs,' said Gerry. 'But no one except another witch can detect magic.'

'I can,' I told him. 'Robert's been taken care of. If your father challenges Bran, it won't be Bran who dies.'

He sagged a little. 'Then, as a favor to me, Samuel, would you ask Bran to make certain my father never finds out about this? I don't want to cause him any more pain than I already have.'

'Do you have any more questions?' Samuel asked Adam.

Adam shook his head and got to his feet. 'Is he your wolf tonight or mine?'

'Mine,' said Samuel stepping forward.

Gerry looked up at the moon where she hung above us. 'Please,' he said. 'Make it quick.'

Samuel pushed his fingers through Gerry's hair, a gentle, comforting touch. His mouth was tight with sorrow: if a submissive wolf's instinct is to bow to authority, a dominant's is to protect.

Samuel moved so fast that Gerry could not have known what was happening. With a quick jerk, Samuel used his healer's hands to snap Gerry's neck.

I handed Adam my gun so I had a hand free. Then I took out Zee's dagger and I handed it to Samuel.

'It's not silver,' I said, 'but it will do the job.'

I watched as Samuel made certain Gerry stayed dead. It wasn't pleasant, but it was necessary. I wouldn't lessen the moment by looking away.

'I'll call Bran as soon as I have a phone,' he said, cleaning the dagger on his pants leg. 'He'll make sure that Dr Wallace never knows what happened to his son.'

A few hours later, Bran and Carter Wallace took a run in the forest. Bran said the moonlight sparkled on the crystals of the crusted snow that broke beneath their dancing paws.

They crossed a frozen lake bed and surprised a sleeping doe, who flashed her white tail and disappeared into the underbrush as they ran by. He told me that the stars covered the sky, so far from city lights, like a blanket of golden glitter.

Sometime before the sun's first pale rays lit the eastern sky, the wolf who had been Carter Wallace went to sleep, curled up next to his Alpha, and never woke up again.

Samuel hadn't killed Robert, so we turned him over to his grandmother: a fate he did not seem to think was much of an improvement. Elizaveta Arkadyevna was not pleased with him. I wasn't altogether sure that she was unhappy with his betrayal of Adam or with his getting caught.

Samuel decided to stay in the Tri-Cities for a while. He's been spending most of his free time on the paperwork involved in getting his medical license extended to Washington. Until then, he's working at the same Stop And Rob where Warren works – and he seems to like it just fine.

Bran didn't, of course, throw his wolves to the world and abandon them there. He is not one of the Gray Lords to force people out of hiding who don't want to come. So most of the werewolves are still staying hidden, even though Bran found his poster child.

You can't turn on the TV or open the newspaper without seeing a picture of the man who penetrated a terrorist camp to find a missionary and his family who had been kidnapped.

The missionary and his wife had been killed already, but there were three children who were rescued. There's a color photograph that made the cover of one of the news magazines. It shows David Christiansen cuddling the youngest child – a little blond-haired toddler with the bruise of a man's fingers clearly visible on her porcelain skin. Her face is turned into his shoulder, and he is looking at her with an expression of such tenderness that it brings tears to my eyes.

But the best part of the picture is the boy who is standing beside him, his face pale, dirty. When I first saw it, I thought he just looked numb, as if his experiences had been too great to be borne, but then I noticed that his hand is tucked inside of David's and the boy's knuckles are white with the grip he has on the man's big fingers.

# 16

Because there isn't much a mechanic with a broken arm can
do besides get in the way, Zee sent me to the office to work
on my paperwork. I didn't get much done there either, but
at least – as Zee put it – I wasn't whining at him.

He wouldn't tell me anything about his dagger or who
Adelbert was and why he needed smiting – and I hadn't
been able to find it on the Internet, either. When I got
persistent, Zee told me he liked the modern era, with its
steel and electricity, better than the old days because there
was more for a *Metallzauber*, a gremlin, to do than build
swords to kill other folk. Then he exiled me to the office
and went back to fixing cars.

I am right-handed, and it was my right arm that was
broken. I couldn't even use it to hold a piece of paper still
because the doctor at the emergency room insisted I wear
my arm strapped to my side. I even had to type on my
computer using one hand – which made it painstakingly
slow to do any work. So I used the computer to play Vegas-
style solitaire and lost two thousand dollars of imaginary
money, instead.

It was probably not the best moment for Gabriel Sandoval
to show up. I'd forgotten I'd told his mother to send him
over Monday after school.

He had to wait until I typed in their bill, then an hourly
wage that looked fair to me. It would give him twenty hours
to work off, though, and that seemed too much to me. So I
added a couple of dollars an hour, until the time looked
better.

I printed it out and handed it to him. He looked it over and crossed off the salary and replaced it with the original one. 'I'm not worth that yet,' he said. 'But I will be by the end of the first month.'

I reassessed him. He wasn't tall, and he'd never be a big man, but there was something solid about him, as young as he was.

'All right,' I said. 'It's a deal.'

I showed him around the office, which took all of five minutes. Then I sat him down at the computer and ran him through my inventory program and my billing system. When he seemed to have the hang of it, I gave him my stacks of paperwork and left him to it.

I walked back into the shop and tilted my thumb at the office when Zee looked up.

'I think I've found Tad's replacement,' I told him. 'I gave him my paperwork, and he didn't even growl at me.'

Zee raised his eyebrows. 'Tad never growled at you.'

'"Damn it, Mercy, can't you remember to give me the bills the day you get them?"' I quoted in my best crabby-Tad voice.

'You'd think someone raised around werewolves would know the difference between growling and swearing,' Zee observed. He put down his wrench and sighed. 'I'm worried about that boy. You know he got that scholarship so they could have their token fae to tow around and point out.'

'Probably,' I agreed. 'They'll never know what hit them.'

'You think he's all right?'

'I can't imagine a place where Tad wouldn't be all right. Nothing scares him, nothing bothers him, and he's frighteningly competent at whatever he chooses to do.' I patted Zee on the back. I enjoyed watching him play nervous father. This was a conversation we'd been having since Tad left for Harvard. I kept track of them and e-mailed Tad with a count once a week.

I heard the office door open and waved Zee to silence so we could listen to how my new office lackey dealt with customers.

'Can I help you?' he said in a smooth, dark voice that surprised me. I hadn't expected him to flirt.

But then I heard Jesse say, 'I'm here looking for Mercy – she didn't tell me she had someone new working for her.'

There was a short pause, then Gabriel said in a sharp voice, 'Who hit you?'

Jesse laughed and said lightly, 'Don't worry. My dad saw the bruise, and the person who hit me is dead now.'

'Good.' Gabriel sounded as though he wouldn't have minded if it had been the truth. Which it was.

'I have someone waiting for me in the car,' she said. 'I'd better go talk to Mercy.'

She came into the shop with a thoughtful look on her face. 'I like him,' she said.

I nodded. 'Me, too. Nice haircut.'

We'd stopped by Warren's house after cleanup at the tree farm to find Jesse minus the duct tape that had still been stuck to her hair – and also minus most of her hair. Warren had looked . . . well, he ought to have looked ashamed, but there had been amusement in his eyes.

Jesse rolled her eyes at me. 'Who'd have thought a gay man couldn't cut hair.' She ran her fingers through the inch-long strands that had been tipped with a glittery gold color. She looked like a flapper from the 1920s wearing one of those beaded caps.

'He told you he didn't know how to give haircuts,' I said, as she walked over and kissed Zee on the cheek.

'I got it fixed the next day.' She grinned at me, then she

lost her smile. 'Dad called Mom yesterday and told her what happened. Everything that happened.'

I knew her mother. She and Adam had only been divorced four years, and Adam had lived behind me for almost seven. 'What did she say?'

'That he was to fly me back to Eugene on the first flight home and never darken her doorstep again.' She touched her lips. 'She does it on purpose, you know. Tries to make him feel bad, like he's an animal. If that doesn't work, she brings up her four miscarriages as if they didn't hurt him as much as they hurt her. As if everything is his fault. And he buys it every time. I knew what she was going to do, so I made them let me listen in on the extension. I think he was just going to agree with her and send me back, so I said some things that maybe I shouldn't have.'

I didn't ask, just waited. She could tell me if she wanted to. Apparently she did.

'I told Dad about her boyfriend who tried to climb into bed with me when I was twelve. And the time two years ago, when she left for a weekend in Vegas without telling me she was going anywhere. It got pretty ugly.'

'I'm sorry.'

She lifted her chin. 'I'm not. Mom agreed to let me stay here for the rest of the school year, then they'll talk. Anyway, Warren's out waiting for me in the car – Dad said it would be a long time before he could contemplate leaving me alone – at least a week. I have a request for you.'

'What did'ja need?' I asked.

'Dad asked me to stop in and see if you'd come to dinner. Somewhere expensive, 'cause we owe you.'

'I'll close up here so you can go clean up,' Zee said a little eagerly. I hadn't been *that* whiny. Really.

'All right,' I said. 'You can pick me up at—' I started to twist my right wrist, winced and remembered I'd put my

watch on my left wrist that morning. It was almost four.
'Six-thirty.'

'He'll be there,' she said, and waltzed back into the office
to flirt with the help.

'Go,' said Zee.

It wasn't that easy, of course. I introduced Gabriel and
Zee, then puttered around getting things finished until nearly
five. I grabbed my purse out of the safe and started out the
door when my undercover friend pulled up in the parking
lot driving a black and shiny eighties convertible Mustang.

'Tony,' I said.

He was still in his ubermacho guise, I noticed, as he
sprang out of the car, over the door. The opaque black
sunglasses disguising his eyes made him look menacing and
sexy.

'Your engine is missing,' I told him.

'Funny' – he gave his car an implacable look – 'it was
here just a minute ago.'

'Ha-ha,' I said. My arm hurt, and I wasn't in the mood
for stupid jokes. 'Get someone to check your engine.'

'What did you do to your arm?' he asked.

I remembered Jesse's method of telling the whole truth,
and said, 'I got knocked into a bunch of wooden crates by
a werewolf while I was trying to rescue a young girl from
the clutches of an evil witch and a drug lord.'

'Ha-ha,' he said in the exact same tone I'd given his joke.
'Must have been something stupid if you won't tell the truth.'

'Well,' I said, considering it, 'maybe "drug lord" was too
strong a word. And maybe I should have mentioned the girl's
handsome and sexy father. What do you think?'

'Mercy,' he said, taking my good arm and turning me
around so we were walking back into the office. 'We need
to talk.'

'Can't talk,' I said. 'I've got a date.'

'Nice try. But you haven't had a date since I met you.'
He opened the door and escorted me inside.

Gabriel looked up from my . . . *his* paperwork and the
pleasant smile on his face went away.

'What are *you* doing here?' he said, standing up and
coming around the corner. 'Let her go. Now.'

*Great*, I thought. *Just what I need, another macho male in
my life trying to take care of me.*

Tony dropped my arm and collapsed onto one of the
uncomfortable chairs I use to encourage my customers to
find something else to do rather than wait around while I
fix their cars. He buried his face in his hands and either
started laughing or crying. I figured he was laughing.

When he raised his head, he'd done one of those amazing
changes – partially helped, I have to admit, by losing the
sunglasses. But it was body language and facial expression,
as much as anything. He just suddenly looked ten years older
and, except for the earrings, much more respectable.

'Tony?' said Gabriel, obviously stunned.

'I've been working undercover at Kennewick High right
under his nose,' Tony told me. 'He never even noticed. I told
you most people can't recognize me.'

'I've never argued with that,' I said. 'I think you're a good
undercover cop.'

Tony shook his head. 'Hey, Gabriel, would you give us a
minute alone? I have some questions for Mercy.'

'Sure.' Gabriel shook his head and started off. He turned
around once on his way out to the shop, as if to make sure
that Tony was still sitting there.

'I've been giving him a really hard time at school,' Tony
said, once we were alone. 'But he can take care of himself.'

'I really do need to get home,' I told him. 'What did you
need?'

He lifted up one hip and pulled a folded piece of paper

out of his back pocket. 'That kid you had helping you,' he said. 'I've got some more information on him.'

I took the paper and unfolded it. It was a grainy black-and-white picture of Mac with 'MISSING' written across the top in capital letters. It gave his vital statistics – he had been sixteen – but gave no more information.

'Alan MacKenzie Frazier,' I read.

'They traced him here from a phone call he made to his family last week.'

I nodded, handing the paper back and continued to lie to Tony with the truth. 'He asked if he could make a long-distance call the last day he was here – a week ago today. He worked all that day, but I haven't seen him since.'

I'd talked to Bran about Mac. He said he'd see to it that a hiker would find Mac's remains in the spring so that his parents wouldn't have to wait by the phone forever. It wasn't much, but it was the best I could do.

It took some scrambling and a fair bit of help, but I managed to be dressed, clean, and beautiful for dinner with Adam and Jesse. Which turned out to be dinner with just Adam because Jesse told him she wasn't feeling well. He left her home watching a movie with Darryl and Auriele because Warren was out on a date with Kyle.

Under the mellowing influence of good food and good music, Adam relaxed, and I discovered that underneath that overbearing, hot-tempered Alpha disguise he usually wore was a charming, overbearing, hot-tempered man. He seemed to enjoy finding out that I was as stubborn and disrespectful of authority as he'd always suspected.

He ordered dessert without consulting me. I'd have been angrier, but it was something I could never have ordered for myself: chocolate, caramel, nuts, ice cream, real whipped cream, and cake so rich it might as well have been a brownie.

'So,' he said, as I finished the last bit, 'I'm forgiven?'

'You are arrogant and overstep your bounds,' I told him, pointing my cleaned fork at him.

'I try,' he said with false modesty. Then his eyes darkened and he reached across the little table and ran his thumb over my bottom lip. He watched me as he licked the caramel from his skin.

I thumped my hands down on the table and leaned forward. 'That is *not* fair. I'll eat your dessert and like it – but you can't use sex to keep me from getting mad.'

He laughed, one of those soft laughs that start in the belly and rise up through the chest: a relaxed, happy sort of laugh.

To change the subject, because matters were heating up faster than I was comfortable with, I said, 'So, Bran tells me that he ordered you to keep an eye out for me.'

He stopped laughing and raised both his eyebrows. 'Yes. Now ask me if I was watching you for Bran.'

It was a trick question. I could see the amusement in his eyes. I hesitated, but decided I wanted to know anyway. 'Okay, I'll bite. Were you watching me for Bran?'

'Honey,' he drawled, pulling on his Southern roots. 'When a wolf watches a lamb, he's not thinking about the lamb's mommy.'

I grinned. I couldn't help it. The idea of Bran as a lamb's mommy was too funny. 'I'm not much of a lamb,' I said.

He just smiled.

Time to change the subject again, I thought, taking a quick sip of ice water. 'Warren tells me you've accepted our favorite serial rapist as a permanent member of the pack.'

'He wasn't responsible for the rapes in London.'

He sounded certain, which meant that he'd asked Ben for the truth and gotten it. Still, I could hear the irritation in his voice and I couldn't help but push a little bit more. 'They stopped when he left.'

'He came to the rescue twice, and the second time it was only chance that he intercepted a tranquilizer rather than a bullet. Gerry's men carried silver ammunition,' he snapped impatiently.

I smiled at him and he balled up his napkin in disgust. 'Point to you,' he said.

'I bet you wouldn't let him date Jesse,' I told him smugly.

When he drove me home, he got out of the car and walked around to open the door for me. Maybe it was because I couldn't open the door with my broken arm, but I thought it might be the kind of thing that he always did.

He walked me to my front porch and cupped his hands around my face. He stood there for a moment, then glanced over his shoulder and up at the moon, which was nearly full. When he turned back, his eyes had yellow streaks running through the brown.

His lips were soft as they feathered over mine tentatively until I leaned against the pressure of his hands, trying to get closer. Then he laughed, a low, chest-deep sound, and really kissed me.

With my broken arm strapped between us, there was no body language involved, just mouth and hands. He wore cologne. Something rich and subtle that blended with his exotic scent.

When he drew away from me, I left my hand on his cheek, enjoying the faint scratchiness of his beard and the pounding of my heart. Silence grew between us, silence and something tentative and new.

Then the door opened and my new roommate looked out with a grin. 'Hey, guys, are you through yet? I made some hot cocoa because I figured Mercy wasn't wearing much — but I guess you took care of any chill from the weather.'

Samuel had been savage when I came home from the garage and told him that I was going out to dinner with

Adam. I'd had to remind him forcefully that he had no claim on me, not anymore. He was staying with me until he could find an apartment of his own, and that didn't give him the right to dictate who I went to dinner with.

If I'd realized that it was going to be a real date, I'd have been kinder. I knew that Samuel was still interested in me – and part of me still loved him.

When Jesse the Matchmaker called me to tell me that her father was on his way over, and not to worry about her because she was just fine, Samuel'd stalked off to sulk in his room, the bigger of my spare bedrooms. But when I'd started trying to put on my dress, he barged into my room to help. I could have done it myself. I wasn't making pained noises, no matter what he said. But, I had to admit, maneuvering clothes, the myriad of mysterious, but businesslike, Velcro straps that grew off the brace the hospital doctor had given me to keep my arm immobilized, and my broken arm was easier with three hands rather than only one.

He hadn't been happy when I left, but I refused to let guilt decide who I would date. I don't play games with people I care about, and I won't let them play games with me. I promised him that I wouldn't have sex with Adam any more than I'd have sex with Samuel. Not until I knew what I felt and what they felt. But that was as far as I was willing to go.

I'd known that giving him the evening to think about it had been a mistake. I probably should have told Adam that Samuel was still staying with me as soon as I realized he didn't know – but what we'd been experiencing tonight had still been too fragile for that.

So Adam got blindsided by Samuel The Live-in Lover.

'Not kind, Samuel,' I said, then turned to Adam. 'He is staying here until he gets an apartment.' I looked at Samuel. 'It should be really soon now.'

'I thought you had a practice in Montana, Dr Cornick,' said Adam. He'd released me when the door opened, but then he'd put a hand low on my back – one of those staking-claim gestures that guys do around other guys.

Samuel nodded and stepped back, holding the door so that we'd all come inside. As soon as they were both in the enclosed space of my living room, I could smell the power rising from both of them.

'I was working at a clinic in rotation with three other doctors,' he said, leading the way into the kitchen. 'They won't suffer. I left Aspen Creek a while ago, and I've found now that I've returned I can't settle in. So I thought I'd try someplace closer than Texas.'

Adam accepted a steaming cup and blew on it thoughtfully. 'You mean you are petitioning to join my pack?'

Samuel's smile, which hadn't left his face since he opened the door, widened even farther. 'I wouldn't dream of it. I'm going lone wolf – you'll probably get the official letter informing you of that from Bran sometime this week.'

I left them to it. They weren't paying any attention to me anyway. I couldn't get the dress off easily without help, but I pulled a pair of sweats on over the top of it. A loose sweatshirt covered my broken arm, strap-bearing torture device and all. Shoes were harder, but I found an old pair of tennis shoes that I hadn't untied and pulled them on my feet over a pair of ankle socks.

When I went back out to the living room, both men were still involved in one of those pleasant but deadly conversations that usually ended up badly. They stopped speaking when I opened the front door, but as soon as I closed it behind me, I heard them start up again.

I was driving the van, because my Rabbit didn't have power steering. I had to pull over a few miles from home so I could use the cell phone.

'Stefan,' I said. 'Your parts are here. I've got a broken arm, so you'll have to do all the work – but I can talk you through it.'

'How did you break your arm, Mercy?' he asked.

'A werewolf tossed me against a giant packing crate while I was trying to rescue a frightened young girl who'd been kidnapped by an evil witch and a drug lord.'

'It sounds interesting,' Stefan said. 'I'll meet you at your garage.'

See. Some people believe me.

308

# extras

extras

# about the author

**Patricia Briggs** lived a fairly normal life until she learned to read. After that she spent lazy afternoons flying dragonback and looking for magic swords when she wasn't horseback riding in the Rocky Mountains. Once she graduated from Montana State University with degrees in history and German, she spent her time substitute teaching and writing. She and her family live in the Pacific Northwest, and you can visit her website at www.patriciabriggs.com

Find out more about Patricia and other Orbit authors by registering for the free monthly newsletter at: www.orbitbooks.net

# about the author

Patricia Briggs lived a fairly normal life until she learned to read. After that she spent lazy afternoons flying dragonback and looking for magic swords when she wasn't horseback riding in the Rocky Mountains. Once she graduated from Montana State University with degrees in history and German, she spent her time substitute teaching and writing. She and her family live in the Pacific Northwest, and you can visit her website at www.patriciabriggs.com

Find out more about Patricia and other Orbit authors by registering for the free monthly newsletter at www.orbitbooks.net

# interview

**The Mercy Thompson books are fast-paced, enjoyable and varied. Do you have any tips on how to sustain tension and interest to keep readers hooked throughout a series?**
I only know how to keep me interested <grin>. I need characters I care about, which means I have to understand and believe in their motivations so they feel real. That means that the events of a story have to have an impact on the characters, an impact that might carry over from one book to the next. I need a plot that makes sense and one with an outcome that is important to the main characters. I need a world that is consistent and believable.

**How did Mercy Thompson and her world come into being for you?**
When my editor called to ask me to write an urban fantasy (she knew I loved them because we'd been exchanging reading lists for a long time) she told me they wanted the story to focus on vampires and werewolves with a "strong female protagonist who had a complicated love life", a love life that had something to do with vampires and werewolves. So that was set for me as was the convention that these stories would take place in our world as it would be if the things that go bump in the night were real.

Oddly enough, Mercy's name was the first thing that came

to me. The pun (that she was a VW mechanic named Mercedes) was purely unintentional, though I took advantage of it.

I like shifters, always have. And I knew that I wanted an underpowered character because they are more fun to write about. A coyote just seemed the perfect answer to the were-wolves – and since the coyote is a North American native species it was obvious that Mercy had to be at least part Native American. And since by that time I already knew she'd be caught between worlds, human and preternatural, it seemed proper to have her half Native American and half white so she'd straddle those worlds as well.

Once I had Mercy, I played with various locations to put her stories in. I am tolerably familiar with Spokane, Washington; Seattle, Washington; Portland, Oregon; and even Chicago. But then I started thinking about the Tri Cities (where I was living). It just fit the bill. It was someting a little different with lots of interesting people: Hispanic, Indians (both Native Americans and India Indians), Russians, Laotians, Japanese, Chinese and a host of other people. There are some cool places: The Hanford Nuclear Power Plant, Pacific Northwest Laboratories, and a huge winery/beer industry. And it was all in my own back yard (until we moved again <grin>).

**Your book seems to incorporate a number of different mythological traditions (Mercy herself being American-Indian, and the fae Zee being of Germanic origin, to name some strands). Do you have to do much research for your books?**
Absolutely. I grew up with my sister reading fairy tales to me every night: The Brothers Grimm, Lang's colour fairytale collections, Hans Christian Andersen and all the rest, I was the only one in my elementary school class who knew who Dick Whittington was. I bought Katharine Brigg's Encyclopedia of Fairies twenty-five years ago (when my sister took hers with her). So I'm fairly comfortable with

Celtic/British and Northern European fae folk, which gave me a good solid starting place.

I've also read a lot of American Indian folktales. But when I was reading them as a kid, I didn't pay attention to which tribes the stories came from. So when I started the Mercy books, I did a lot of work brushing up my knowledge of Indian folklore. Again, so I'd have a place to start writing from.

When I get to specifics I do more research. I don't use the folklore like a blueprint, but more as a suggestion or jumping off point.

**I noticed that you have taught Greek and Roman mythology, did this develop from your interest in fantasy fiction, or was it a simultaneous/independent development?**
Ah, that sounds so much more . . . sophisticated than what it was – I taught a bunch of eleven and twelve year olds (sixth graders for those of you who know the US school systems). It was a lot of fun, but hardly needed an expert.

My interest in mythology, like many of my interests, started with horses – in this case, Pegasus. Once I read Pegasus I had to figure out who Medusa was and . . . This happened when I was about seven or so. For most of the next three or four years I read horse stories (I still have large portions of Black Beauty memorized), fairytales (including Greek mythology, which I considered part of the same genre), and Robin Hood stories. It was only later I put Greek and Roman mythology together with the actual Greeks and Romans. I did a little more research on them in college, but when I set out to teach what I knew to a bunch of innocent kids who would take what I said (when they were listening) as gospel, I did a lot more reading and studying.

**How do you manage to fit your writing routine around your life? With a busy home-life it must be hard to juggle the unpredictability of family with work. . .**
Sometimes it gets pretty difficult. Right now I have an office

in town, and that helps a lot. I take my youngest to school in the morning and work until she gets out. But I'm a wife and mother first and a writer, second. Sometimes that means I'm writing at two in the morning when everyone is asleep.

**Again on a theme of writing/writers, you have been a published author for over ten years now with a large number of books to your name. Has the craft become any easier over time? Or not?!**

Some things are a lot easier. I know how to write conversations (or at least I think I do!), transitions and room descriptions that don't bog down the story. I can tell when a story takes an odd turn if it is worth following, or if I should haul it back to follow the track I planned on. I can write faster and write better.

What is harder is trying not to rewrite a story I've written before, or develop themes I've already pounded into the ground. Sometimes the most logical path for a plot to take is a repeat of a scene I used in the last book so I have to figure out something different.

**How extensively do you plot your novels before you start writing them? Do you plot the entire trilogy/series before you start writing or do you prefer to let the story roam where it will?**

I don't do a lot of plotting ahead of time. There are two reasons for that. First, I find if I know where the story goes, I don't have any motivation for writing it. I'm ready to find a new story to play with. The second is that when I do sit down and plot out a story, that plot/outline is only good for a few days of writing before the story changes anyway.

The only exception to that was the Raven duology (Raven Shadow and Raven Strike). Those I plotted out. Partially because it was the first time I wrote a real proposal. (Dragon Blood was also written on spec, but I didn't know I was writing a proposal when my editor asked for a synopsis so I just wrote something off the top of my head and sent it to her.) That's when I discovered that books are much more fun to write when I don't know exactly what's going to happen.

So I start with a character in a place and give them a problem to work on. Usually I have some idea where I want the story to end up, but I'm not too unhappy if it doesn't work out that way. Writing like this means that my edits are extensive, especially the first couple when I have to take out parts from the beginning that are no longer important. But I like the way the story turns out better, it's less predictable and more fun for me.

**Your website is great – packed with interesting information about yourself and your books. I feel one matter in need of further investigaton is the name of your cat – any particular reason why he is called Roadkill?!**
Yes. He was a big cat and, once he'd gotten past his kitten phase, lazy. He'd lie around with both front feet stretched in front of him and his head tucked under his chest. He was the old-fashioned Siamese-type (bulky) so he looked liked he'd died and had a few days to bloat.

*And on a more serious note, to find out more about Patricia and her books, (almost!) everything you might want to know can be found at www.hurog.com*

## if you enjoyed
### MOON CALLED

look out for

# BLOOD BOUND

also by

## Patricia Briggs

# 1

Like most people who own their own businesses, I work long hours that start early in the morning. So when someone calls me in the middle of the night, they'd better be dying.

'Hello, Mercy,' said Stefan's amiable voice in my ear. 'I wonder if you could do me a favor.'

Stefan had done his dying a long time ago, so I saw no reason to be nice. 'I answered the phone at' – I peered blearily at the red numbers on my bedside clock – '*three* o'clock in the morning.'

Okay, that's not exactly what I said. I may have added a few of those words a mechanic picks up to use at recalcitrant bolts and alternators that land on her toes.

'I *suppose* you could go for a second favor,' I continued, 'but I'd prefer you hang up and call me back at a more civilized hour.'

He laughed. Maybe he thought I was trying to be funny. 'I have a job to do, and I believe your particular talents would be a great asset in assuring the success of the venture.'

Old creatures, at least in my experience, like to be a little vague when they're asking you to do something. I'm a business-woman, and I believe in getting to the specifics as quickly as possible.

'At three in the morning you need a mechanic?'

'I'm a vampire, Mercedes,' he said gently. 'Three in the morning is still prime time. But I don't need a mechanic, I need you. You owe me a favor.'

He was right, darn him. He'd helped me when the local Alpha werewolf's daughter was kidnapped. He had warned me that he'd be collecting in return.

I yawned and sat up, giving up all hope of going back to sleep. 'All right. What am I doing for you?'

'I'm supposed to be delivering a message to a vampire who is here without my mistress's permission,' he said, getting to the point. 'I need a witness he won't notice.'

He hung up without getting an answer, or even telling me when he was coming to pick me up. It would serve him right if I just went back to sleep.

Muttering to myself, I threw on clothing: jeans, yesterday's T-shirt complete with mustard stain, and two socks with only one hole between them. Once I was more or less dressed, I shuffled off to the kitchen and poured myself a glass of cranberry juice.

It was a full moon, and my roommate, the werewolf, was out running with the local pack, so I didn't have to explain to him why I was going out with Stefan. Which was just as well.

Samuel wasn't a bad roommate as such things go, but he had a tendency to get possessive and dictatorial. Not that I let him get away with it, but arguing with werewolves requires a certain subtlety I was lacking at – I checked my wristwatch – 3:15 in the morning.

For all that I was raised by them, I'm not a werewolf, not a were-anything. I'm not a servant of the moon's phases, and in the coyote shape that is my second form. I look like any other *canis latrans*: I have the buckshot scars on my backside to prove it.

Werewolves cannot be mistaken for wolves: weres are much bigger than their non-preternatural counterparts – and a lot scarier.

What I am is a walker, though I'm sure there once was another name for it – an Indian name lost when the Europeans devoured the New World. Maybe my father could have told me what it was if he hadn't died in a car wreck before he knew my mother was pregnant. So all I know is what the werewolves could tell me, which wasn't much.

The 'walker' comes from the Skinwalkers of the Southwest Indian tribes, but I have less in common with a Skinwalker, at least from what I've read, than I do with the werewolves. I don't do magic, I don't need a coyote skin to change shape – and I'm not evil.

I sipped my juice and looked out of the kitchen window. I couldn't see the moon herself, just her silver light that touched the nighttime landscape. Thoughts of evil seemed somehow appropriate while I waited for the vampire to come for me. If nothing else, it would keep me from falling asleep: fear has that effect on me. I'm afraid of evil.

In our modern world, even the word seems . . . old fashioned. When it comes out of hiding briefly in a Charles Manson or a Jeffrey Dahmer, we try to explain it away with drug abuse, an unhappy childhood, or mental illness.

Americans in particular are oddly innocent in their faith that science holds explanations for everything. When the werewolves finally admitted what they were to the public several months ago, the scientists immediately started looking for a virus or bacteria that could cause the Change – magic being something their laboratories and computers can't explain. Last I'd heard Johns Hopkins had a whole team devoted to the issue. Doubtless they'd find something, too, but I'm betting they'll never be able to explain how a 180-pound man turns into a 250-pound werewolf. Science doesn't allow for magic any more than it allows for evil.

The devout belief that the world is explainable is both a terrible vulnerability and a stout shield. Evil prefers it when people don't believe. Vampires, as a not-random example, seldom go out and kill people in the street. When they go hunting, they find someone who won't be missed and bring them home where they are tended and kept comfortable – like a cow in a feedlot.

Under the rule of science, there are no witch burnings allowed, no water trials or public lynchings. In return, the average law-abiding, solid, citizen has little to worry about from the things that go bump in the night. Sometimes I wish I were an average citizen.

Average citizens don't get visited by vampires.

Nor do they worry about a pack of werewolves – at least not quite the same way as I was.

Coming out in public was a bold step for the werewolves; one that could easily backfire. Staring out at the moonlit night, I fretted about what would happen if people began to be afraid again. Werewolves aren't evil, but they aren't exactly the peaceful, law-abiding heroes that they're trying to represent themselves as either.

Someone tapped on my front door.

Vampires *are* evil. I knew that – but Stefan was more than just a vampire. Sometimes I was pretty sure he was my friend. So I wasn't really afraid until I opened the door and saw what waited on my porch.

The vampire's dark hair was slicked back, leaving his skin very pale in the moon's light. Dressed in black from head to heels, he ought to have looked like a refugee from a bad Dracula movie, but somehow the whole outfit, from black leather duster to silk gloves, looked more authentic on Stefan than his usual bright-colored T-shirt and grubby jeans. As if he'd removed a costume, rather than put one on.

He looked like someone who could kill as easily as I could change a tire, with as little thought or remorse.

Then his mobile brows climbed his forehead – and he was suddenly the same vampire who'd painted his old VW bus to look like Scooby's Mystery Machine.

'You don't look happy to see me,' he said with a quick grin that didn't show his fangs. In the dark, his eyes looked more black than brown – but then so did mine.

'Come in.' I backed away from the door so he could; then,

because he'd scared me I added snappishly, 'If you want welcoming, try stopping by at a decent hour.'

He hesitated on the threshold, smiled at me, and said, 'By your invitation.' Then he stepped inside my house.

'That threshold thing really works?' I asked.

His smile widened again, this time I saw a glint of white. 'Not after you've invited me in.'

He walked past me and into the living room and then turned like a model on a runway. The folds of his duster spread out with his turn in an effect nearly cape-like.

'So how do you like me *à la Nosferatu*?'

I sighed and admitted it. 'Scared me. I thought you eschewed all things gothic.' I'd seldom seen him in anything other than jeans and T-shirts.

His smile widened even more. 'Usually I do. But the Dracula look does have its place. Oddly enough, used sparingly, it scares other vampires almost as well as it does the odd coyote-girl. Don't worry, I have a bit of costuming for you, too.'

He reached under his coat and pulled out a silver-studded leather harness.

I stared at it a moment. 'Going to an S&M strip club are you? I didn't realize there was anything like that around here.' There wasn't, not to my knowledge. Eastern Washington is more prudish than Seattle or Portland.

He laughed. 'Not tonight, sweetheart. This is for your other self.' He shook the straps out so I could see that it was a dog harness.

I took it from him. It was good leather, soft and flexible with so much silver that it looked like jewelry. If I'd been strictly human, no doubt I'd have been taken aback at wearing such a thing. But when you spend a good part of your time running around as a coyote, collars and the like are pretty useful.

The Marrok, the leader of the North American werewolves, insists that all of the wolves wear a collar when they run in the cities, with tags that identify them as someone's pet. He also insists the names on the tags be something innocuous like Fred or Spot, no Killers or Fangs. It's safer that way — both for the werewolves and the law-enforcement people who might encounter them. Needless to say, it's as popular with the werewolves as the helmet law was with the motorcyclists when it first went into effect. Not that any of them would dream of disobeying the Marrok.

Not being a werewolf, I'm exempt from the Marrok's rules. On the other hand, I don't like running unnecessary risks either. I had a collar in my kitchen junk drawer — but it wasn't made of nifty black leather.

'So I'm part of your costume?' I asked.

'Let's just say that I think this vampire might need more intimidation than most,' he answered lightly, though something in his eyes made me think there was something more going on.

Medea wandered out from wherever she'd been sleeping. Probably Samuel's bed. Purring furiously, she wound her small self around Stefan's left leg and then rubbed her face against his boot to mark him as hers.

'Cats and ghosts don't like vampires,' Stefan said staring down at her.

'Medea likes anything that might feed or pet her,' I told him. 'She's not picky.'

He bent down and scooped her up. Being picked up isn't Medea's favorite thing, so she yowled at him several times before going back to purring as she sank her claws into his expensive leather sleeve.

'You aren't cashing in your favor just to appear more intimidating,' I said, looking up from the soft leather harness to meet his eyes. Unwise with vampires, he himself had told me so, but all I saw was opaque darkness. 'You said you wanted a witness. A witness to what?'

'No, I don't need you in order to appear intimidating,' Stefan agreed softly after I'd stared at him for a few seconds. 'But *he'll* think intimidation is why I have a coyote on my leash.' He hesitated, and then shrugged. 'This vampire has been through here before, and I think that he managed to deceive one of our young ones. Because of what you are, you are immune to many vampiric powers, especially if the vampire in question doesn't know what you are. Thinking you a coyote, he's probably not going to waste his magic on you at all. It is unlikely, but he might manage to deceive me as well as he did Daniel. I don't think he'll be able to deceive you.'

I'd just learned that little tidbit about being resistant to vampiric magic. It wasn't particularly useful for me since a vampire is strong enough to break my neck with the same effort I'd put into snapping a piece of celery.

'He won't hurt you,' Stefan said when I was silent for too long. 'I give you my word of honor.'

I didn't know how old Stefan was, but he used that phrase like a man who meant it. Sometimes he made it hard to remember that vampires are evil. It didn't really matter, though. I owed him.

'All right,' I said.

Looking down at the harness I thought about getting my own collar instead. I could change shape while wearing a collar – my neck wasn't any bigger around as a human than as a coyote. The harness, suitable for a thirty-pound coyote, would be too tight for me to regain human form while I wore it. The advantage of the harness though, was that I wouldn't be attached to Stefan by my neck.

My collar was bright purple with pink flowers embroidered on it. Not very *Nosferatu*.

I handed the harness to Stefan. 'You'll have to put it on me after I change,' I told him. 'I'll be right back.'

I changed shape in my bedroom because I had to take off my clothes to do it. I'm not really all that modest, a shapeshifter gets over that pretty fast, but I try not to get naked in front of someone who might misread my casual nudity for casualness in other areas.

Although Stefan had at least three cars that I knew of, he had apparently taken a 'faster way,' as he put it, to my house, so we got in my Rabbit to travel to his meeting.

For a few minutes, I wasn't certain he was going to be able to get it started. The old diesel didn't like getting up this early in the morning any more than I did. Stefan muttered a few Italian oaths under his breath, and at last it caught and we were off.

Never ride in a car with a vampire who is in a hurry. I didn't know my Rabbit could peel out like that. We turned onto the highway with the rpms redlined; the car stayed on all four wheels, but only just.

The Rabbit actually seemed to like the drive better than I did; the engine roughness I'd been trying for years to get rid of smoothed out and it purred. I closed my eyes and hoped the wheels stayed on.

When Stefan took us over the river on the cable bridge that dropped us off in the middle of Pasco he was driving forty miles an hour over the speed limit. Not slowing noticeably, he crossed through the heart of the industrial area to a cluster of hotels that sprang up on the far edge of town near the on-ramp to the highway that headed out toward Spokane and other points north. By some miracle – probably aided by the early hour – we weren't picked up for speeding.

The hotel Stefan took us to was neither the best nor the worst of them. It catered to truckers, though there was only one of the big rigs parked in the lot. Maybe Tuesday nights were slow. Stefan parked the Rabbit next to the only other car in the lot, a black BMW, despite the plethora of empty parking spaces.

I jumped out of the car's open window into the parking lot and was hit with the smell of vampire and blood. My nose is very good, especially when I'm a coyote, but like anyone else, I don't always notice what I'm smelling. Most of the time it's like trying to listen to all of the conversations in a crowded restaurant. But this was impossible to miss.

Maybe it was bad enough to drive off normal humans, and that's why the parking lot was nearly empty.

I looked at Stefan to see if he smelled it, too, but his attention was focused on the car we'd parked beside. As soon as he'd drawn my attention to it, I realized the smell was coming from the BMW. How was it that the car could smell more like a vampire than Stefan the vampire did?

I caught another, more subtle, scent that caused my lips to draw away from my teeth even though I couldn't have said what the bitter-dark odor was. As soon as it touched my nose it wrapped itself around me, clouding all the other scents until it was all I could smell.

Stefan came around the car in a rush, snatched up the leash and tugged it hard to quiet my growl. I jerked back and snapped my teeth at him. I wasn't a damn dog. He could have asked me to be quiet.

'Settle down,' he said, but he wasn't watching me. He was looking at the hotel. I smelled something else then, a shadow of a scent soon overcome by that other smell. But even that brief whiff was enough to identify the familiar smell of fear, Stefan's fear. What could scare a vampire?

'Come,' he said turning toward the hotel and tugged me forward, out of my confusion.

Once I'd quit resisting his pull, he spoke to me in a rapid and quiet voice. 'I don't want you to do anything, Mercy, no matter what you see or hear. You aren't up to a fight with this one. I just need an impartial witness who won't get herself killed. So play coyote with all your might and if I don't make it out of here, go tell the Mistress what I asked you to do for me – and what you saw.'

How did he expect me to escape something that could kill him? He hadn't been talking like this earlier, nor had he been afraid. Maybe he could smell what I was smelling – and he knew what it was. I couldn't ask him though, because a coyote isn't equipped for human speech.

He led the way to a smoked glass door. It was locked, but there was a key-card box with a small, red-blinking, LED light. He tapped a finger on the box and the light turned green, just as if he'd swiped a magnetic card through it.

The door opened without protest and closed behind us with a final sounding click. There was nothing creepy about the hallway, but it bothered me anyway. Probably Stefan's nerves rubbing off on me. *What would scare a vampire?*

Somewhere, someone slammed a door and I jumped.

Either he knew where the vampire was staying, or his nose wasn't hampered by the scent of that otherness like mine was. He took me briskly through the long hallway and stopped about halfway down. He tapped on the door with his knuckles, though I, and so presumably Stefan, could hear that whoever awaited us inside the room had started for the door as soon as we stopped in front of it.

After all the build up, the vampire who opened the door was almost anticlimatic, like expecting to hear Pavarotti sing Wagner and getting Bugs Bunny and Elmer Fudd instead.

The new vampire was clean shaven and his hair was combed and pulled back into a tidy, short, ponytail. His clothes were neat and clean, though a bit wrinkled as if they'd been in a suitcase – but somehow the overall impression I got was disheveled and filthy. He was significantly shorter than Stefan and much less intimidating. First point to Stefan, which was good since he'd put so much effort into his Prince of Darkness garb.

The stranger's long-sleeved, knit shirt hung on him, as if it rested on skeleton rather than flesh. When he moved, one of his sleeves slid up, revealing an arm so emaciated that the hollow between the bones of his forearm was visible. He stood slightly hunched, as if he didn't quite have the energy to straighten up.

I'd met vampires other than Stefan before: scary vampires

with glowing eyes and fangs. This one looked like an addict so far gone there was nothing left of the person he had once been, as if he might fade away at any moment, leaving only his body behind.

Stefan, though, wasn't reassured by the other's apparent frailty – if anything, his tension had increased. Not being able to smell much around that unpleasant, pervasive bitterness was bothering me more than the vampire who didn't look like much of an opponent at all.

'Word of your coming has reached my mistress,' Stefan said, his voice steady, if a little more clipped than usual. 'She is very disappointed that you did not see fit to tell her you would be visiting her territory.'

'Come in, come in,' said the other vampire, stepping back from the door to invite Stefan through. 'No need to stand out in the hallway waking up people who are trying to sleep.'

I couldn't tell if he knew Stefan was afraid or not. I've never been quite sure how well vampires can scent things – though they clearly have better noses than humans do. He didn't seem intimidated by Stefan and his black clothes, though; instead he sounded almost distracted, as if we'd interrupted something important.

The bathroom door was shut as we walked past it. I pricked my ears, but I couldn't hear anything behind the shut door. My nose was useless. Stefan took us all the way to the far side of the room, near the sliding glass doors that were all but hidden by heavy, floor-to-ceiling, curtains. The room was bare and impersonal except for the suitcase, which lay closed on top of the chest of drawers.

Stefan waited until the other vampire had shut the door before he said in a cold voice, 'There is no one trying to sleep tonight in this hotel.'

It seemed an odd remark, but the stranger seemed to know what Stefan meant because he giggled, cupping a hand coyly over his mouth in a manner that seemed more in keeping with a twelve-year-old girl than a man of any age. It was odd enough that it took me a while to assess Stefan's remark.

Surely he hadn't meant it the way it sounded. No sane vampire would have killed everyone in the hotel. Vampires were as ruthless as the werewolves in enforcing their rules about not drawing unwanted attention to themselves – and wholesale slaughter of humans would draw attention. Even if there weren't many guests, there would be employees of the hotel.

The vampire dropped his hand from his face leaving behind a face empty of amusement. It didn't make me feel any better. It was like watching Dr Jekyll and Mr Hyde, the change was so great.

'No one to wake up?' he asked, as if he hadn't reacted in any other way to Stefan's comment. 'You might be right. It is still poor manners to keep someone waiting at the door, isn't it? Which one of her minions are you?' He held up a hand. 'No, wait, don't tell me. Let me guess.'

While Stefan waited, all of his usual animation completely shut down, the stranger walked all the way around him, pausing just behind us. Unconstrained by anything but the leash, I turned to watch.

When he was directly behind Stefan, the other vampire bent down and scratched me behind my ears.

I usually don't mind being touched, but as soon as his fingers brushed against my fur I knew I didn't want him touching me. Involuntarily, I hunched away from his hand and into Stefan's leg. My fur kept his skin away from mine, but that didn't keep his touch from feeling filthy, unclean.

The scent of him lingered on my fur and I realized the unpleasant odor that had been clogging my nose was coming from him.

'Careful,' Stefan told him without looking around. 'She bites.'

'Animals *love* me.' The remark made my flesh crawl it was so inappropriate coming from this . . . creeping monster. He crouched on his heels and rubbed my ears again. I couldn't tell if Stefan wanted me to bite him or not. I chose not, because I didn't want the taste of him on my tongue. I could always bite him later if I wanted to.

Stefan didn't comment, nor did he look anywhere except straight in front of him. I wondered if he would have lost status points if he'd turned. Werewolves play power games, too, but I know the rules for them. A werewolf would never have allowed a strange wolf to walk behind him.

He left off petting me, stood up, and walked around until he faced Stefan again. 'So you are Stefan, Marsilia's little soldier boy. I *have* heard of you – though your reputation is not what it once was, is it? Running away from Italy like that would soil any man's honor. Somehow, still, I expected more. All those stories . . . I expected to find a monster among monsters, a creature of nightmares who frightens even other vampires – and all I see is a dried-up has-been. I suppose that's what happens when you hide yourself in a little backwater town for a few centuries.'

There was a slight pause after the other vampire's last words.

Then Stefan laughed, and said, 'Whereas *you* have no reputation at all.' His voice was lighter than usual, sounding almost rushed, as if what he was saying was of no moment. I took a step away from him without meaning to, somehow frightened by that light, amused voice. He smiled gently at the other vampire and his tone softened further as he said, 'That's what happens when you are newly made and abandoned.'

It must have been some sort of vampire super-insult because the second vampire erupted, reacting as if Stefan's words had been an electric goad. He didn't go after Stefan, though.

Instead, he bent down and grabbed the bottom of the king-sized box spring and jerk-lifted it and everything above it over his head. He swung it toward the hall door and then around so that the ends of the box spring, mattress, and bedding were balanced for an instant.

He shifted his grip and threw them all the way through the wall and into the empty hotel room next door, landing on the floor in a cloud of Sheetrock dust. Two of the wall studs hung splintered, suspended from somewhere inside the wall, giving the hole in the wall the appearance of a jack-o-lantern's smile. The false headboard, permanently mounted into the wall where the bed had been, looked forlorn and stupid hanging a foot or more above the pedestal of the bed.

The vampire's speed and strength didn't surprise me. I'd seen a few werewolves throw temper tantrums, enough to know that if the vampire had been truly angry, he wouldn't have had the control it took to manage the physics of swinging the two unattached mattresses together through the wall. Apparently, as in werewolf fights, battles between vampires have a lot of impressive fireworks before the main show.

In the silence that followed, I heard something, a hoarse mewling noise coming from behind the closed bathroom door – as if whatever made it had already cried out so much it could only make a small noise, but one that held much more terror than a full-throated scream.

I wondered if Stefan knew what was in the bathroom and that was why he'd been afraid when we were in the parking lot – there were things that even a vampire ought to be afraid of. I took a deep breath, but all I could smell was the bitter darkness – and that was getting stronger. I sneezed, trying to clear my nose, but it didn't work. Both vampires stood still until the noise stopped. Then the stranger dusted his hands lightly, a small smile on his face as if there had not been rage just an instant before.

'I am remiss,' he said, but the old fashioned words sounded false coming from him, as if he were pretending to be a vampire the way the old vampires tried to be human. 'You obviously do not know who I am.'

He gave Stefan a shallow bow. It was obvious, even to me, that this vampire had grown up in a time and place where bowing was something done in Kung Fu Theater movies rather than in everyday life. 'I am Asmodeus,' he said grandly, sounding like a child pretending to be a king.

'I said you have no reputation,' Stefan replied, still in that light, careless voice. 'I didn't say I didn't know your name, Cory Littleton. Asmodeus was destroyed centuries ago.'

'Kurfel, then,' said Cory, nothing childlike in his manner at all.

I knew those names, Asmodeus and Kurfel, both, and as soon as I realized where I'd heard them, I knew what I had been smelling. Once the idea occurred to me, I realized the smell could be nothing else. Suddenly Stefan's fear wasn't surprising or startling at all. Demons were enough to scare anyone.

'Demon' is a catchall phrase, like 'fae,' used to describe beings who are unable to manifest themselves in our world in physical form. Instead, they possess their victims and feed upon them until there is nothing left. Kurfel wouldn't be this one's name, any more than Asmodeus was: knowing a demon's name gave you power over them. I'd never heard of a demon-possessed vampire before. I tried to stretch my mind around the concept.

'You are not Kurfel either,' said Stefan. 'Though something akin to him is allowing you some use of his powers when you amuse him well enough.' He looked toward the bathroom door. 'What *have* you been doing to amuse him, sorcerer?'

*Sorcerer.*

I thought those were just stories – I mean, who would be dumb enough to invite a demon into themselves? And why would a demon, who could just possess any corrupt soul (and to offer yourself to a demon sort of presupposes a corrupt soul, doesn't it?) make a deal with anyone? I didn't believe in sorcerers; I certainly didn't believe in vampire sorcerers.

I suppose somone raised by werewolves should have been more open-minded – but I had to draw the line somewhere.

'I don't like you,' Littleton said coolly, and the hair on the back of my neck stood up as magic gathered around him. 'I don't like you at all.'

He reached out and touched Stefan in the middle of the forehead. I waited for Stefan to knock his hand aside, but he did nothing to defend himself, just dropped to his knees, landing with a heavy thud.

'I thought you'd be more interesting, but you're not.' Cory told him, but the diction and tone of his voice was different. 'Not amusing at all. I'll have to fix that.'

He left Stefan kneeling and went to the bathroom door.

I whined at Stefan and stretched up on my hind feet so I could lick his face, but he didn't even look at me. His eyes were vague and unfocused; he wasn't breathing. Vampires didn't need to, of course, but Stefan mostly did.

The sorcerer had bespelled him somehow.

I tugged at the leash, but Stefan's hand was still closed upon it. Vampires are strong, and even when I threw my whole thirty-two pounds into it, his hand didn't move. If I'd had half an hour I could have chewed through the leather, but I didn't want to be caught here when the sorcerer returned.

Panting, I looked across the room at the open bathroom. What new monster was waiting inside? If I got out of this alive, I'd never let anyone put a leash on me again. Werewolves have strength, semiretractable claws, and inch-long fangs – *Samuel* wouldn't have been caught by the stupid leather harness and leash. One bite and it would have been gone. All I had was speed – which the leash effectively limited.

I was prepared for a horrifying sight, something that could destroy Stefan. But what Cory Littleton dragged out of that room left me stunned with an entirely different sort of horror.

The woman wore one of those fifties-style uniforms that hotels give their maids; this one was mint green with a stiff blue apron. Her color scheme matched the drapes and the hallway carpets, but the rope around her wrists, dark with blood, didn't.

Other than her bleeding wrists, she seemed mostly unharmed, though the sounds she was making made me wonder about that. Her chest was heaving with the effort of her screaming, but even without the bathroom door between us she wasn't making much noise, more of a series of grunts.

I jerked against the harness again and when Stefan still didn't move, I bit him, hard, drawing blood. He didn't even flinch.

I couldn't bear to listen to the woman's terror. She was breathing in hoarse gulping pants and she struggled against Littleton's hold, so focused on him that I don't think she saw Stefan or me at all.

I hit the end of the leash again. When that didn't work I snarled and snapped, twisting around so that I could chew on the leather. My own collar was equipped with a safety fastening that I could have broken, but Stefan's leather harness was fastened with old-fashioned metal buckles.

The sorcerer dropped his victim on the floor in front of me, just out of reach – though I'm not sure what I could have done for her even if I could get within touching distance. She didn't see me; she was too busy trying not to see Littleton. But my struggles had drawn the sorcerer's attention and he squatted down so he was closer to my level.

'I wonder what you'd do if I let you go?' he asked me. 'Are you afraid? Would you run? Would you attack me or does the smell of her blood rouse you as it does a vampire?' He looked up at Stefan then. 'I see your fangs, Soldier. The rich scent of blood and terror: it calls to us, doesn't it? They keep us leashed as tightly as you keep your coyote.' He used the Spanish pronunciation, three syllables rather than two. 'They demand we take only a sip from each when our hearts crave so much more. Blood is not really filling without death is it? You are old enough to remember the Before Times, aren't you, Stefan? When vampires ate as we chose and reveled in the terror and the last throes of our prey. When we fed truly.'

Stefan made a noise and I risked a glance at him. His eyes had changed. I don't know why that was the first thing I noticed about him, when so much else was different. Stefan's eyes were usually the shade of oiled walnut, but now they gleamed like blood-rubies. His lips were drawn back, revealing fangs shorter and more delicate than a werewolf's. His hand, which had tightened on my leash, bore curved claws on the ends of his elongated fingers. After a brief glimpse, I had to turn away, almost as frightened of him as I was of the sorcerer.

'Yes, Stefan,' said Littleton, laughing like the villain in an old black and white movie. 'I see you remember the taste of death. Benjamin Franklin once said that those who give up their freedom for safety deserve neither.' He leaned close. 'Do you feel safe, Stefan? Or do you miss what you once had, what you allowed them to steal from all of us.'

Littleton turned to his victim, then.